H·C·P·C·S

Health Care Procedure Coding System

National Level II
Medicare Codes

D1455988

Color Coded

2018

ISBN 978-1-943009-94-7 (Perfect Bound)
ISBN 978-1-943009-93-0 (Spiral Bound)
ISBN 978-1-943009-95-4 (e-book)

Practice Management Information Corporation (PMIC)
4727 Wilshire Boulevard
Los Angeles, California 90010
1-800-MED-SHOP
http://pmiconline.com

Printed in China

Additional copies of this book may be purchased from any medical book store, from PMIC by mail to the above address, by visiting our web site at http://pmiconline.com or by calling 1-800-MED-SHOP.

FOREWORD

The Health Care Procedure Coding System (HCPCS), National Level II, is a listing of codes and descriptive terminology used for reporting the provision of supplies, materials, injections and certain services and procedures to Medicare. HCPCS 2018 is the most recent revision of the HCPCS National Level II codes. The changes that appear in this revision have been prepared by our editorial staff using the HCPCS revisions released by the Center for Medicare and Medicaid Services (CMS), which is overseen by the Department of Health and Human Services (DHHS).

HCPCS 2018 codes must be used to report supplies, materials, injections and some quality measures on your Medicare claims for items and services provided from January 1, 2018 through December 31, 2018. The proper selection and reporting of HCPCS codes can improve your reimbursement and reduce your audit liability.

James B. Davis, President

DISCLAIMER

This publication is designed to offer basic information regarding coding and billing of medical services, supplies and procedures using the HCPCS coding system. The information presented is based upon material obtained from the Center for Medicare and Medicaid Services (CMS), and the experience and interpretations of the editors and publisher. Though all of the information has been carefully researched and checked for accuracy and completeness, the publisher accepts no responsibility or liability with regard to errors, omissions, misuse or misinterpretation.

CONTENTS

INTRODUCTION

HCPCS is an acronym for Health Care Procedure Coding System. This coding system was developed in 1983 by the Health Care Financing Administration (HCFA) for the purpose of standardizing the coding systems used to process Medicare claims. In 2001, HCFA changed its name to the Center for Medicare and Medicaid Services (CMS) to reflect its increased emphasis on improving Medicare and Medicaid beneficiary services and information.

The HCPCS coding system is primarily used to bill Medicare for supplies, materials and injections. It is also used to bill for certain services and procedures which are not defined in CPT. HCPCS codes must be used when billing Medicare carriers, and in some states, Medicaid carriers. Some private insurance carriers also allow or mandate the use of HCPCS codes, mostly those that are processing Medicare claims.

STRUCTURE OF HCPCS

HCPCS is a systematic method for coding supplies, materials, injections and services performed by health care professionals. Each supply, material, injection or service is identified with a five digit alphanumeric code. With the HCPCS coding system, the supplies, materials and injections can be accurately identified and properly reimbursed. There are three levels of codes within the HCPCS coding system.

LEVEL I CPT CODES

The major portion of the HCPCS coding system, referred to as Level I, is CPT. Most of the procedures and services you perform, even for Medicare patients, are billed using CPT codes. However, one of the major deficiencies of CPT is that it has limited code selections to describe supplies, materials and injections.

LEVEL II NATIONAL CODES

HCPCS National Level II codes are alphanumeric codes which start with a letter followed by four numbers. The range of HCPCS National Level II codes is from A0000 through V0000. There are also HCPCS National Level II modifiers. HCPCS National Level II codes are uniform in description throughout the United States. However, due to what is known as "carrier discretion" the processing and reimbursement of HCPCS National Level II codes is not necessarily uniform.

There are over 5,600 HCPCS National Level II codes covering supplies, materials, injections and services. A fundamental understanding of when and how to use HCPCS National Level II or Local Level III codes can have a significant impact on your Medicare reimbursement. The majority of health care professionals use codes from the Medical and Surgical Supplies section and Drugs Administered by Other Than Oral Method, commonly referred to as "A" codes and "J" codes.

HCPCS CODE OVERLAP

As may be expected, there is some overlap among the HCPCS code levels. On occasion you may have a coding situation where a specific code exists at all three levels for the same service or material. When faced with this situation, the general rule is that Local Level II codes have the highest priority, followed by CPT codes. You should consult your local Medicare carrier if you have any questions regarding HCPCS code overlap.

SECTIONS

The main body of HCPCS National Level II codes is divided into sections. The supplies, materials, injections and services are presented in alphanumeric order within each section. The sections of HCPCS National Level II are:

SECTION	CODE SERIES
Transportation Services	A0000-A0999
Medical And Surgical Supplies	A4000-A8999
Miscellaneous And Experimental	A9000-A9999
Enteral And Parenteral Therapy	B0000-B9999
Temporary Hospital Outpatient PPS	C0000-C9999
Durable Medical Equipment (DME)	E0000-E9999
Temporary Procedures & Professional Services	G0000-G9999
Rehabilitative Services	H0000-H9999
Drugs Administered Other Than Oral Method	J0000-J8999
Chemotherapy Drugs	J9000-J9999
Temporary Codes For DMERCS	K0000-K9999
Orthotic Procedures	L0000-L4999
Prosthetic Procedures	L5000-L9999
Medical Services	M0000-M9999
Pathology and Laboratory	P0000-P9999
Temporary Codes	Q0000-Q9999
Diagnostic Radiology Services	R0000-R9999
Private Payer Codes	S0000-S9999
State Medicaid Agency Codes	T0000-T9999
Vision Services	V0000-V2999
Hearing Services	V5000-V5999

INSTRUCTIONS for USE OF HCPCS NATIONAL LEVEL II CODES

A health care professional using the HCPCS National Level II codes selects the name of the material, supply, injection, service or procedure that most accurately identifies the service performed or supply delivered. Most often, HCPCS National Level II codes will be used instead of, or in addition to, CPT codes for visits, evaluation and management services, or other procedures performed at the same time or during the same visit. All services, procedures, supplies, materials and injections should be properly documented in the medical record.

The listing of a supply, material, injection or service and its code number in a specific section of HCPCS does not usually restrict its use to a specific profession or specialty group. However, there are some HCPCS National Level II codes that are by definition, profession or specialty specific.

GUIDELINES

Specific GUIDELINES are presented at the beginning of most of the sections. These GUIDELINES define items that are necessary to appropriately interpret and report the supplies, materials, injections, services and procedures listed in that section.

HCPCS MODIFIERS

A modifier provides the means by which the health care professional can indicate that a service or procedure that has been performed has been altered by some specific circumstance but not changed in its definition or code. HCPCS modifiers may be used to indicate the following:

- A service was supervised by an anesthesiologist

- A service was performed by a specific health care professional, for example, a clinical psychologist, clinical social worker, nurse practitioner, or physician assistant.

- A service was provided as part of a specific government program

- A service was provided to a specific side of the body

- Equipment was purchased or rented

- Single or multiple patients were seen during nursing home visits

It is important to note that HCPCS National Level II modifiers can be combined with CPT codes when reporting services to Medicare.

An example of the use of HCPCS National Level II modifiers is:

E1280-NR   Heavy duty wheelchair; detachable arms (desk or full length) elevating leg rests - new when rented

A listing of modifiers pertinent to each section of HCPCS National Level II are located in the GUIDELINES of each section. A complete listing of HCPCS National Level II modifiers is found in APPENDIX A.

UNLISTED PROCEDURE OR SERVICE

A service or procedure may be provided that is not listed in this edition of HCPCS National Level II. When reporting such a service, the appropriate "unlisted procedure" code may be used to indicate the service, identifying it by "special report" as defined below. HCPCS National Level II terminology is inconsistent in defining unlisted procedures. The procedure definition may include the term(s) "unlisted," "not otherwise classified," "unspecified," "unclassified," "other" and "miscellaneous." Prior to using these codes, try to determine if a Local Level III or CPT code is available. When an unlisted procedure code is used, the supply, material, injection, service or procedure must be described. Each of these unlisted procedure codes relates to a specific section of HCPCS National Level II and is presented in the GUIDELINES of that section.

SPECIAL REPORT

A supply, material, injection, service or procedure that is rarely provided, unusual, variable or new may require a special report for reimbursement purposes. Pertinent information should include an adequate definition or description of the nature, extent, and need for the supply, material, injection, service or procedure.

HCPCS CODE CHANGES

Each year numerous codes are added, changed or deleted. A summary of revisions to HCPCS 2018 is found in APPENDIX B. The following symbols, identical to those used in CPT, are used to indicate additions, changes and deletions in HCPCS National Level II.

ADDITIONS TO HCPCS

New HCPCS National Level II codes are identified with a small black circle placed to the left of the code number. An example of a new code in HCPCS 2018 is:

● **E0953** Wheelchair accessory, lateral thigh or knee support, any type including fixed mounting hardware, each

CHANGES TO HCPCS

Changes in HCPCS National Level II code definitions are identified with a small black triangle placed to the left of the code number. An example of a changed code in HCPCS 2018 is:

▲ **L8618** Transmitter cable for use with cochlear implant device or auditory osseointegrated device, replacement

DELETIONS FROM HCPCS

Deleted HCPCS National Level II codes are enclosed within parentheses, along with an italicized reference to replacement codes when available. An example of a deleted code in HCPCS 2018 is:

(**G0507** Code deleted December 31, 2017). Use 99484

QUALITY REVIEW SYSTEM MIPS INDICATOR

Ⓣ Indicates a Trigger Code included in one or more MIPS measures. The specific measures may be found in Appendix E.

An example of a MIPS flagged Trigger Code in HCPCS 2018 is:

Ⓣ **C9600** Percutaneous transcatheter placement of drug eluting intracoronary stent(s), with coronary angioplasty when performed; single major coronary artery or branch

Ⓟ Indicates HCPCS Post-Trigger Services assigned to the episode group for Durable Medical Equipment, Prosthetics, Orthotics, and Supplies (DME) Service Category
An example of a MIPS flagged Post-Trigger Service in HCPCS 2018 is:

Ⓟ **A4222** Infusion supplies for external drug infusion pump, per cassette or bag (list drugs separately)

SPECIAL COVERAGE SYMBOLS

NOT PAYABLE BY MEDICARE

 There are codes listed in HCPCS which are not payable by Medicare. These codes are identified by a red bar over the HCPCS code. These codes should not be used to report services to Medicare.

NON-COVERED BY MEDICARE

 There are numerous supplies, materials, injections, services and procedures which are not covered by Medicare, either by program definition or by legislative statute. Examples of non-covered services include routine services and appliances, foot care and supportive devices for feet, custodial care, personal comfort items, and cosmetic surgery. These codes are identified by an orange bar over the HCPCS code. These codes should not be used to report services to Medicare; however, in most cases, you may bill the patient directly for non-covered services.

SPECIAL COVERAGE INSTRUCTIONS

 Your local Medicare carrier has specific coverage instructions for processing certain HCPCS codes. These codes are identified by a yellow bar over the HCPCS code. While these codes are covered by the Medicare program, the use of these codes does not guarantee payment. If you have a question about a specific code in this category, review your Medicare provider manual or consult with your local Medicare carrier.

CARRIER JUDGMENT

 Processing and payment for these codes is done at the discretion of each insurance carrier. These codes are identified by a blue bar over the HCPCS code. For codes in this category, you should check with your Medicare carrier for proper billing instructions prior to filing an insurance claim.

DURABLE MEDICAL EQUIPMENT MEDICARE ADMINISTRATIVE CONTRACTORS (DME-MACs)

All Medicare claims for durable medical equipment (DME), prosthetics, orthotics and supplies go to one of four durable medical equipment Medicare administrative contractors, or DME-MACs (formerly known as DMERCs).

MEDICARE SUPPLIER NUMBER

Before submitting claims to DME-MACs, you must apply for a supplier number. You must use this number when submitting claims to all four carriers. To find out more information, go to the Medicare website at http://www.cms.gov.

REGIONALIZATION OF CLAIM PROCESSING

Listed below are the contracted carriers and the states that they serve. The residence of the beneficiary is what determines which regional carrier processes the claim.

REGION A: STATES	REGION A: CONTRACTOR
Connecticut, Delaware, District of Columbia, Maine, Maryland, Massachusetts, New Hampshire, New Jersey, New York - Entire State, Pennsylvania, Rhode Island, Vermont	**Noridian Healthcare Solutions, LLC** PO Box 6727 900 42nd Street South Fargo, ND 58108-6727 https://med.noridianmedicare.com/web/jddme

REGION B: STATES	REGION B: CONTRACTOR
Illinois, Indiana, Kentucky, Michigan, Minnesota, Ohio, Wisconsin	**CGS Administrators, LLC** 2 Vantage Way - Metro Center Nashville, TN 37228- www.cgsmedicare.com/jb

REGION C: STATES	REGION C: CONTRACTOR
Alabama, Arkansas, Colorado, Florida, Georgia, Louisiana, Mississippi, New Mexico, North Carolina, Oklahoma, Puerto Rico, South Carolina, Tennessee, Texas, Virgin Islands, Virginia, West Virginia	**CGS Administrators, LLC** 2 Vantage Way - Metro Center Nashville, TN 37228- www.cgsmedicare.com/jc

REGION D: STATES	REGION D: CONTRACTOR
Alaska, American Samoa, Arizona, California - Entire State, Guam, Hawaii, Idaho, Iowa, Kansas, Missouri - Entire State, Montana, Nebraska, Nevada, North Dakota, Northern Mariana Islands, Oregon, South Dakota, Utah, Washington, Wyoming	**Noridian Healthcare Solutions, LLC** PO Box 6727 900 42nd Street South Fargo, ND 58108-6727 https://med.noridianmedicare.com/web/jddme

CHANGE OF CLAIM JURISDICTION

Prior to October 1, 1993, Medicare carriers processed durable medical equipment (DME), prosthetics, and orthotics claims based on where the transaction for the sale or rental took place. This is called the point of sale. Beginning October 1, 1993 and according to the state by state transfer schedule, regional processing of supplier claims began using beneficiary residence to determine which regional carrier had claim jurisdiction.

ELECTRONIC CLAIM FILING

The Center for Medicare and Medicaid Services is strongly encouraging electronic claims submission to DME-MACs. Suppliers submitting claims electronic must use the designated National Standard Format which meets all Medicare billing requirements and is accepted by other third-party insurance carriers. The regional carriers will assist you in converting to electronic claims submission. You can contact the Electronic Media Coordinator (EMC) at the DME-MACs listed above.

APPENDICES

APPENDIX A: Modifiers: Lists all National Level II modifiers, ambulance service, and PET scan modifiers.

APPENDIX B: Summary of Changes: Includes a summary of official additions, changes, and deletions to the current edition of HCPCS.

APPENDIX C: Table of Drugs: Includes drug names, cross references along with selected dosage, administration route, and HCPCS codes from the official HCPCS Table of Drugs.

APPENDIX D: Medicare References: Includes the complete text from all Medicare Coverage Instruction Manual (CIM) and Medicare Carriers Manual (MCM) citations in the body of the HCPCS book.

APPENDIX E: HCPCS MACR & MIPS Cross-References.

APPENDIX F: HCPCS to NDC Drug Name Cross-Walk

APPENDIX G: NDC Drug Name to HCPCS Cross-Walk

HCPCS 2018 DATA FILES

HCPCS codes are available in a data file format on CD-ROM. The HCPCS data file includes all official HCPCS codes with both short and full descriptions. The data file can be uploaded to your PC for inclusion in billing programs. For more information regarding the HCPCS data file call PMIC at 1-800-MED-SHOP or visit http://pmiconline.com.

Guidelines

In addition to the information presented in the INTRODUCTION, several other items unique to this section are defined or identified here:

1. VEHICLE AND CREW REQUIREMENTS: The ambulance must be designed and equipped for transporting the sick or injured and include patient care equipment, such as a stretcher, clean linens, first aid supplies, oxygen equipment and other safety and lifesaving equipment required by state or local authorities. The ambulance crew must have two members, one of which has medical training equivalent to the standard and advanced Red Cross training. The vehicle and personnel supplier must provide a statement that describes the first-aid, safety and other patient-care items in the vehicle, the extent of first-aid training of the personnel and the supplier's agreement to notify Medicare of any changes that could affect coverage.

2. AIR AMBULANCE SERVICE: Air ambulance services are covered when the point of pick-up is inaccessible by land vehicle; distances or other obstacles are involved in getting the patient to the nearest hospital with appropriate facilities; and, all other conditions of coverage are met.

3. AMBULANCE SERVICE CLAIMS: Reimbursement may be made for expenses incurred for ambulance services when specific conditions have been met and the appropriate medical documentation is provided.

4. MATERIALS SUPPLIED BY AMBULANCE SERVICE: Reusable devices, such as back boards, neck boards and inflatable leg and arm splints, are considered part of general ambulance services and included in the charge for the trip. A separate reasonable charge may be recognized for non-reusable items and disposable supplies, such as oxygen, gauze and dressings, that are required for patient care during the trip.

5. UNLISTED SERVICE OR PROCEDURE: A service or procedure may be provided that is not listed in this edition of HCPCS. When reporting such a service, the appropriate "unlisted procedure" code may be used to indicate the service, identifying it by "special report" as defined below. HCPCS terminology is inconsistent in defining unlisted procedures. The procedure definition may include the term(s) "unlisted", "not otherwise classified", "unspecified", "unclassified", "other" and "miscellaneous". Prior to using these codes, try to determine if a Local Level III code or CPT code is available. The "unlisted procedures" and accompanying codes for TRANSPORTATION SERVICES are as follows:

A0999 Unlisted ambulance service

6. SPECIAL REPORT: A service, material or supply that is rarely provided, unusual, variable or new may require a special report in determining medical appropriateness for reimbursement purposes. Pertinent information should include an adequate definition or description of the nature, extent, and need for the service, material or supply.

7. MODIFIERS: Listed services may be modified under certain circumstances. When appropriate, the modifying circumstance is identified by adding a modifier to the basic procedure code. CPT and HCPCS National Level II modifiers may be used with CPT and HCPCS National Level II procedure

codes. One digit codes are to be used in combination. The first digit should indicate the origin; the second digit should indicate the destination.

The Level II modifiers commonly used with TRANSPORTATION codes are as follows:

-GM   Multiple patients on one ambulance trip

-QM   Ambulance service provided under arrangement by a provider of services

-QN   Ambulance services furnished directly by a provider of services

AMBULANCE SERVICE MODIFIERS

For ambulance service, one-digit modifiers are combined to form a two-digit modifier that identifies the ambulance's place of origin with the first digit, and ambulance's destination with the second digit. They are used in items 12 and 13 on the CMS Form 1491.

One digit ambulance modifiers:

-D   Diagnostic or therapeutic site other than -P or -H when these are used as origin codes

-E   Residential, domiciliary, custodial facility (other than an 1819 facility)

-G   Hospital-based dialysis facility (hospital or hospital related)

-H   Hospital

-I   Site of transfer (for example, airport or helicopter pad) between types of ambulance

-J   Non-hospital-based dialysis facility

-N   Skilled nursing facility (SNF) (1819 facility)

-P   Physician's office (includes HMO non-hospital facility, clinic, etc.)

-R   Residence

-S   Scene of accident or acute event

-X   (Destination code only) Intermediate stop at physician's office on the way to the hospital (includes HMO non-hospital facility, clinic, etc.)

8. CPT CODE CROSS-REFERENCE: Unless specified otherwise, there is no equivalent CPT code for listings in this section.

Transportation Services Including Ambulance

A0021   Ambulance service, outside state per mile, transport (medicaid only) A0030

Ambulance Waiting Time Table			
Units	Time (Hrs)	Units	Time (Hrs)
1	1/2 to 1	6	3 to 3 ½
2	1 to 1 ½	7	3 ½ to 4
3	1 ½ to 2	8	4 to 4 ½
4	2 to 2 ½	9	4 ½ to 5
5	2 to 3	10	5 to 5 ½

A0080 Non-emergency transportation, per mile - vehicle provided by volunteer (individual or organization), with no vested interest

A0090 Non-emergency transportation, per mile - vehicle provided by individual (family member, self, neighbor) with vested interest

A0100 Non-emergency transportation; taxi

A0110 Non-emergency transportation and bus, intra or inter state carrier

A0120 Non-emergency transportation: mini-bus, mountain area transports, or other transportation systems

A0130 Non-emergency transportation: wheelchair van

A0140 Non-emergency transportation and air travel (private or commercial) intra or inter state

A0160 Non-emergency transportation: per mile - case worker or social worker

A0170 Transportation ancillary: parking fees, tolls, other

A0180 Non-emergency transportation: ancillary: lodging-recipient

A0190 Non-emergency transportation: ancillary: meals-recipient

A0200 Non-emergency transportation: ancillary: lodging escort

A0210 Non-emergency transportation: ancillary: meals-escort

A0225 Ambulance service, neonatal transport, base rate, emergency transport, one way

A0380 BLS mileage (per mile) A0425

A0382 BLS routine disposable supplies

A0384 BLS specialized service disposable supplies; defibrillation (used by ALS ambulances and BLS ambulances in jurisdictions where defibrillation is permitted in BLS ambulances)

A0390 ALS mileage (per mile) A0425

A0392 ALS specialized service disposable supplies; defibrillation (to be used only in jurisdictions where defibrillation cannot be performed in BLS ambulances)

A0394 ALS specialized service disposable supplies; iv drug therapy

A0396 ALS specialized service disposable supplies; esophageal intubation

A0398 ALS routine disposable supplies

A0420 Ambulance waiting time (ALS or BLS), one half (1/2) hour increments

A0422 Ambulance (ALS or BLS) oxygen and oxygen supplies, life sustaining situation

A0424 Extra ambulance attendant, ground (ALS or BLS) or air (fixed or rotary winged); (requires medical review)

A0425 Ground mileage, per statute mile

A0426 Ambulance service, advanced life support, non-emergency transport, level 1 (ALS 1)

A0427 Ambulance service, advanced life support, emergency transport, level 1 (ALS 1 - emergency)

A0428 Ambulance service, basic life support, non-emergency transport, (BLS)

A0429 Ambulance service, basic life support, emergency transport (BLS-emergency)

A0430 Ambulance service, conventional air services, transport, one way (fixed wing)

A0431 Ambulance service, conventional air services, transport, one way (rotary wing)

A0432 Paramedic intercept (pi), rural area, transport furnished by a volunteer ambulance company which is prohibited by state law from billing third party payers

A0433 Advanced life support, level 2 (ALS 2)

A0434 Specialty care transport (SCT)

A0435 Fixed wing air mileage, per statute mile

A0436 Rotary wing air mileage, per statute mile

A0888 Noncovered ambulance mileage, per mile (e.g., for miles traveled beyond closest appropriate facility)

MCM: 2125

A0998 Ambulance response and treatment, no transport

A0999 Unlisted ambulance service

MCM: 2120.1, 2125

MEDICAL AND SURGICAL SUPPLIES

Guidelines

In addition to the information presented in the INTRODUCTION, several other items unique to this section are defined or identified here:

1. SUBSECTION INFORMATION: Some of the listed subheadings or subsections have special needs or instructions unique to that section. Where these are indicated, special "notes" will be presented preceding or following the listings. Those subsections within the MEDICAL AND SURGICAL SUPPLIES section that have "notes" are as follows:

Subsection	Code Numbers
External urinary supplies	A4356-A4358
Tracheostomy supplies	A4622-A4626
Supplies for ESRD	A4650-A4927

2. UNLISTED SERVICE OR PROCEDURE: A service or procedure may be provided that is not listed in this edition of HCPCS. When reporting such a service, the appropriate "unlisted procedure" code may be used to indicate the service, identifying it by "special report" as defined below. HCPCS terminology is inconsistent in defining unlisted procedures. The procedure definition may include the term(s) "unlisted", "not otherwise classified", "unspecified", "unclassified", "other" and "miscellaneous". Prior to using these codes, try to determine if a Local Level III code or CPT code is available. The "unlisted procedures" and accompanying codes for MEDICAL AND SURGICAL SUPPLIES are as follows:

   A4335 Incontinence supply; miscellaneous
   A4421 Ostomy supply; miscellaneous
   A4649 Surgical supply; miscellaneous
   A4913 Miscellaneous dialysis supplies, not otherwise specified
   A6261 Wound filler, gel/paste, per fluid ounce, not elsewhere classified
   A6262 Wound filler, dry foam, per gram, not elsewhere classified

3. SPECIAL REPORT: A service, material or supply that is rarely provided, unusual, variable or new may require a special report in determining medical appropriateness for reimbursement purposes. Pertinent information should include an adequate definition or description of the nature, extent, and need for the service, material or supply.

4. MODIFIERS: Listed services may be modified under certain circumstances. When appropriate, the modifying circumstance is identified by adding a modifier to the basic procedure code. CPT and HCPCS National Level II modifiers may be used with CPT and HCPCS National Level II procedure codes. Modifiers commonly used with MEDICAL AND SURGICAL SUPPLIES are as follows:

   -CC Procedure code change (use "CC" when the procedure code submitted was changed either for administrative reasons or because an incorrect code was filed)

   -LT Left side (used to identify procedures performed on the left side of the body)

   -RT Right side (used to identify procedures performed on the right side of the body)

5. CPT CODE CROSS-REFERENCE: Unless specified otherwise, the equivalent CPT code for all listings in this section is 99070.

6. DURABLE MEDICAL EQUIPMENT REGIONAL CARRIERS (DMERCS): Effective October 1, 1993 claims for supplies must be billed to one of four regional carriers depending upon the residence of the beneficiary. The transition dates for DMERC claims is from November 1, 1993 to March 1, 1994, also depending upon the state you practice in. See the Introduction for a complete discussion of DMERCs.

Medical and Surgical Supplies

A4206   Syringe with needle, sterile, 1 cc or less, each

A4207   Syringe with needle, sterile 2 cc, each

A4208   Syringe with needle, sterile 3 cc, each

A4209   Syringe with needle, sterile 5 cc or greater, each

A4210   Needle-free injection device, each

     CIM: 60-9

A4211   Supplies for self-administered injections

     MCM: 2049

A4212   Non-coring needle or stylet with or without catheter

A4213   Syringe, sterile, 20 cc or greater, each

A4215   Needle, sterile, any size, each

A4216   Sterile water, saline and/or dextrose, diluent/flush, 10 ml

     MCM: 2049

A4217   Sterile water/saline, 500 ml

     MCM: 2049

A4218   Sterile saline or water, metered dose dispenser, 10 ml

A4220   Refill kit for implantable infusion pump

     CIM: 60-14

Ⓟ   **A4221**   Supplies for maintenance of non-insulin drug infusion catheter, per week (list drugs separately)

Ⓟ   **A4222**   Infusion supplies for external drug infusion pump, per cassette or bag (list drugs separately)

A4223   Infusion supplies not used with external infusion pump, per cassette or bag (list drugs separately)

A4224   Supplies for maintenance of insulin infusion catheter, per week

A4225   Supplies for external insulin infusion pump, syringe type cartridge, sterile, each

     MCM: 60-14

A4230   Infusion set for external insulin pump, non needle cannula type

CIM: 60-14

A4231   Infusion set for external insulin pump, needle type

CIM: 60-14

A4232   Syringe with needle for external insulin pump, sterile, 3 cc

CIM: 60-14

A4233   Replacement battery, alkaline (other than j cell), for use with medically necessary home blood glucose monitor owned by patient, each

A4234   Replacement battery, alkaline, j cell, for use with medically necessary home blood glucose monitor owned by patient, each

A4235   Replacement battery, lithium, for use with medically necessary home blood glucose monitor owned by patient, each

A4236   Replacement battery, silver oxide, for use with medically necessary home blood glucose monitor owned by patient, each

A4244   Alcohol or peroxide, per pint

A4245   Alcohol wipes, per box

A4246   Betadine or pHisoHex solution, per pint

A4247   Betadine or iodine swabs/wipes, per box

A4248   Chlorhexidine containing antiseptic, 1 ml

A4250   Urine test or reagent strips or tablets (100 tablets or strips)

MCM: 2100

A4252   Blood ketone test or reagent strip, each

Statute: 1861(n)

A4253   Blood glucose test or reagent strips for home blood glucose monitor, per 50 strips

CIM: 60-11

A4255   Platforms for home blood glucose monitor, 50 per box

CIM: 60-11

Ⓟ A4256   Normal, low and high calibrator solution / chips

CIM: 60-11

A4257   Replacement lens shield cartridge for use with laser skin piercing device, each

A4258   Spring-powered device for lancet, each

CIM: 60-11

A4259   Lancets, per box of 100

CIM: 60-11

A4261   Cervical cap for contraceptive use

Statute: 1862a1

A4262   Temporary, absorbable lacrimal duct implant, each

A4263   Permanent, long term, non-dissolvable lacrimal duct implant, each

MCM: 15030

A4264   Permanent implantable contraceptive intratubal occlusion device(s) and delivery system

A4265   Paraffin, per pound

CIM: 60-9

A4266   Diaphragm for contraceptive use

A4267   Contraceptive supply, condom, male, each

A4268   Contraceptive supply, condom, female, each

A4269   Contraceptive supply, spermicide (e.g., foam, gel), each

A4270   Disposable endoscope sheath, each

A4280   Adhesive skin support attachment for use with external breast prosthesis, each

A4281   Tubing for breast pump, replacement

A4282   Adapter for breast pump, replacement

A4283   Cap for breast pump bottle, replacement

A4284   Breast shield and splash protector for use with breast pump, replacement

A4285   Polycarbonate bottle for use with breast pump, replacement

A4286   Locking ring for breast pump, replacement

A4290   Sacral nerve stimulation test lead, each

Vascular Catheters

A4300   Implantable access catheter, (e.g., venous, arterial, epidural subarachnoid, or peritoneal, etc.) external access

MCM: 2130

A4301   Implantable access total catheter, port/reservoir (e.g., venous, arterial, epidural, subarachnoid, peritoneal, etc.)

A4305   Disposable drug delivery system, flow rate of 50 ml or greater per hour

A4306   Disposable drug delivery system, flow rate of less than 50 ml per hour

Incontinence Appliances and Care Supplies

A4310   Insertion tray without drainage bag and without catheter (accessories only)

MCM: 2130

A4311   Insertion tray without drainage bag with indwelling catheter, Foley type, two-way latex with coating (Teflon, silicone, silicone elastomer or hydrophilic, etc.)

MCM: 2130

A4312   Insertion tray without drainage bag with indwelling catheter, Foley type, two-way, all silicone

MCM: 2130

A4313   Insertion tray without drainage bag with indwelling catheter, Foley type, three-way, for continuous irrigation

MCM: 2130

A4314   Insertion tray with drainage bag with indwelling catheter, Foley type, two-way latex with coating (Teflon, silicone, silicone elastomer or hydrophilic, etc.)

MCM: 2130

A4315   Insertion tray with drainage bag with indwelling catheter, Foley type, two-way, all silicone

MCM: 2130

A4316   Insertion tray with drainage bag with indwelling catheter, Foley type, three-way, for continuous irrigation

MCM: 2130

A4320   Irrigation tray with bulb or piston syringe, any purpose

MCM: 2130

A4321   Therapeutic agent for urinary catheter irrigation

MCM: 2130

A4322   Irrigation syringe, bulb or piston, each

MCM: 2130

Ⓟ **A4326**   Male external catheter with integral collection chamber, any type, each

MCM: 2130

A4327   Female external urinary collection device; meatal cup, each

MCM: 2130

A4328   Female external urinary collection device; pouch, each

MCM: 2130

A4330   Perianal fecal collection pouch with adhesive, each

MCM: 2130

A4331   Extension drainage tubing, any type, any length, with connector/adaptor, for use with urinary leg bag or urostomy pouch, each

MCM: 2130

A4332   Lubricant, individual sterile packet, each

MCM: 2130

A4333   Urinary catheter anchoring device, adhesive skin attachment, each

MCM: 2130

A4334   Urinary catheter anchoring device, leg strap, each

MCM: 2130

A4335   Incontinence supply; miscellaneous

MCM: 2130

A4336   Incontinence supply, urethral insert, any type, each

A4337   Incontinence supply, rectal insert, any type, each

MCM: 2130

A4338   Indwelling catheter; Foley type, two-way latex with coating (Teflon, silicone, silicone elastomer, or hydrophilic, etc.), each

MCM: 2130

A4340   Indwelling catheter; specialty type, (e.g., coude, mushroom, wing, etc.), each

MCM: 2130

A4344   Indwelling catheter, Foley type, two-way, all silicone, each

MCM: 2130

A4346   Indwelling catheter; Foley type, three way for continuous irrigation, each

MCM: 2130

Ⓟ **A4349**   Male external catheter, with or without adhesive, disposable, each

MCM: 2130

Ⓟ **A4351**   Intermittent urinary catheter; straight tip, with or without coating (Teflon, silicone, silicone elastomer, or hydrophilic, etc.), each

MCM: 2130

Ⓟ **A4352**   Intermittent urinary catheter; coude (curved) tip, with or without coating (Teflon, silicone, silicone elastomeric, or hydrophilic, etc.), each

MCM: 2130

Ⓟ **A4353**   Intermittent urinary catheter, with insertion supplies

MCM: 2130

A4354   Insertion tray with drainage bag but without catheter

MCM: 2130

A4355   Irrigation tubing set for continuous bladder irrigation through a three-way indwelling Foley catheter, each

MCM: 2130

External Urinary Supplies

A4356   External urethral clamp or compression device (not to be used for catheter clamp), each
MCM: 2130

Ⓟ A4357   Bedside drainage bag, day or night, with or without anti-reflux device, with or without tube, each

MCM: 2130

A4358   Urinary drainage bag, leg or abdomen, vinyl, with or without tube, with straps, each
MCM: 2130

Ostomy Supplies

A4360   Disposable external urethral clamp or compression device, with pad and/or pouch, each

A4361   Ostomy faceplate, each
MCM: 2130

Ⓟ A4362   Skin barrier; solid, 4 x 4 or equivalent; each
MCM: 2130

A4363   Ostomy clamp, any type, replacement only, each

A4364   Adhesive, liquid or equal, any type, per oz
MCM: 2130

A4366   Ostomy vent, any type, each

A4367   Ostomy belt, each
MCM: 2130A

A4368   Ostomy filter, any type, each

A4369   Ostomy skin barrier, liquid (spray, brush, etc.), per oz
MCM: 2130

A4371   Ostomy skin barrier, powder, per oz
MCM: 2130

A4372   Ostomy skin barrier, solid 4 x 4 or equivalent, standard wear, with built-in convexity, each
MCM: 2130

A4373   Ostomy skin barrier, with flange (solid, flexible or accordion), with built-in convexity, any size, each
MCM: 2130

A4375   Ostomy pouch, drainable, with faceplate attached, plastic, each
MCM: 2130

A4376   Ostomy pouch, drainable, with faceplate attached, rubber, each

MCM: 2130

A4377   Ostomy pouch, drainable, for use on faceplate, plastic, each

MCM: 2130

A4378   Ostomy pouch, drainable, for use on faceplate, rubber, each

MCM: 2130

A4379   Ostomy pouch, urinary, with faceplate attached, plastic, each

MCM: 2130

A4380   Ostomy pouch, urinary, with faceplate attached, rubber, each

MCM: 2130

A4381   Ostomy pouch, urinary, for use on faceplate, plastic, each

MCM: 2130

A4382   Ostomy pouch, urinary, for use on faceplate, heavy plastic, each

MCM: 2130

A4383   Ostomy pouch, urinary, for use on faceplate, rubber, each

MCM: 2130

A4384   Ostomy faceplate equivalent, silicone ring, each

MCM: 2130

A4385   Ostomy skin barrier, solid 4 x 4 or equivalent, extended wear, without built-in convexity, each

MCM: 2130

A4387   Ostomy pouch, closed, with barrier attached, with built-in convexity (1 piece), each

MCM: 2130

A4388   Ostomy pouch, drainable, with extended wear barrier attached, (1 piece), each

MCM: 2130

A4389   Ostomy pouch, drainable, with barrier attached, with built-in convexity (1 piece), each

MCM: 2130

A4390   Ostomy pouch, drainable, with extended wear barrier attached, with built-in convexity (1 piece), each

MCM: 2130

A4391   Ostomy pouch, urinary, with extended wear barrier attached (1 piece), each

MCM: 2130

A4392   Ostomy pouch, urinary, with standard wear barrier attached, with built-in convexity (1 piece), each

MCM: 2130

A4393 Ostomy pouch, urinary, with extended wear barrier attached, with built-in convexity (1 piece), each

MCM: 2130

A4394 Ostomy deodorant, with or without lubricant, for use in ostomy pouch, per fluid ounce

MCM: 2130

A4395 Ostomy deodorant for use in ostomy pouch, solid, per tablet

MCM: 2130

A4396 Ostomy belt with peristomal hernia support

MCM: 2130

A4397 Irrigation supply; sleeve, each

MCM: 2130

A4398 Ostomy irrigation supply; bag, each

MCM: 2130

A4399 Ostomy irrigation supply; cone/catheter, with or without brush

MCM: 2130

A4400 Ostomy irrigation set

MCM: 2130

A4402 Lubricant, per ounce

MCM: 2130

A4404 Ostomy ring, each

MCM: 2130

A4405 Ostomy skin barrier, non-pectin based, paste, per ounce

MCM: 2130

A4406 Ostomy skin barrier, pectin-based, paste, per ounce

MCM: 2130

A4407 Ostomy skin barrier, with flange (solid, flexible, or accordion), extended wear, with built-in convexity, 4 x 4 inches or smaller, each

MCM: 2130

A4408 Ostomy skin barrier, with flange (solid, flexible or accordion), extended wear, with built-in convexity, larger than 4 x 4 inches, each

MCM: 2130

A4409 Ostomy skin barrier, with flange (solid, flexible or accordion), extended wear, without built-in convexity, 4 x 4 inches or smaller, each

MCM: 2130

A4410 Ostomy skin barrier, with flange (solid, flexible or accordion), extended wear, without built-in convexity, larger than 4 x 4 inches, each

MCM: 2130

A4411 Ostomy skin barrier, solid 4 x 4 or equivalent, extended wear, with built-in convexity, each

A4412 Ostomy pouch, drainable, high output, for use on a barrier with flange (2 piece system), without filter, each

MCM: 2130

A4413 Ostomy pouch, drainable, high output, for use on a barrier with flange (2 piece system), with filter, each

MCM: 2130

A4414 Ostomy skin barrier, with flange (solid, flexible or accordion), without built-in convexity, 4 x 4 inches or smaller, each

MCM: 2130

A4415 Ostomy skin barrier, with flange (solid, flexible or accordion), without built-in convexity, larger than 4 x 4 inches, each

MCM: 2130

A4416 Ostomy pouch, closed, with barrier attached, with filter (1 piece), each

A4417 Ostomy pouch, closed, with barrier attached, with built-in convexity, with filter (1 piece), each

A4418 Ostomy pouch, closed; without barrier attached, with filter (1 piece), each

A4419 Ostomy pouch, closed; for use on barrier with non-locking flange, with filter (2 piece), each

A4420 Ostomy pouch, closed; for use on barrier with locking flange (2 piece), each

A4421 Ostomy supply; miscellaneous

A4422 Ostomy absorbent material (sheet/pad/crystal packet) for use in ostomy pouch to thicken liquid stomal output, each

MCM: 2130

A4423 Ostomy pouch, closed; for use on barrier with locking flange, with filter (2 piece), each

A4424 Ostomy pouch, drainable, with barrier attached, with filter (1 piece), each

A4425 Ostomy pouch, drainable; for use on barrier with non-locking flange, with filter (2 piece system), each

A4426 Ostomy pouch, drainable; for use on barrier with locking flange (2 piece system), each

A4427 Ostomy pouch, drainable; for use on barrier with locking flange, with filter (2 piece system), each

A4428 Ostomy pouch, urinary, with extended wear barrier attached, with faucet-type tap with valve (1 piece), each

A4429	Ostomy pouch, urinary, with barrier attached, with built-in convexity, with faucet-type tap with valve (1 piece), each
A4430	Ostomy pouch, urinary, with extended wear barrier attached, with built-in convexity, with faucet-type tap with valve (1 piece), each
A4431	Ostomy pouch, urinary; with barrier attached, with faucet-type tap with valve (1 piece), each
A4432	Ostomy pouch, urinary; for use on barrier with non-locking flange, with faucet-type tap with valve (2 piece), each
A4433	Ostomy pouch, urinary; for use on barrier with locking flange (2 piece), each
A4434	Ostomy pouch, urinary; for use on barrier with locking flange, with faucet-type tap with valve (2 piece), each
A4435	Ostomy pouch, drainable, high output, with extended wear barrier (one-piece system), with or without filter, each

Supplies

Ⓟ **A4450** Tape, non-waterproof, per 18 square inches

MCM: 2130

Ⓟ **A4452** Tape, waterproof, per 18 square inches

MCM: 2130

A4455 Adhesive remover or solvent (for tape, cement or other adhesive), per ounce

MCM: 2130

A4456 Adhesive remover, wipes, any type, each

MCM: 2130

A4458 Enema bag with tubing, reusable

A4459 Manual pump-operated enema system, includes balloon, catheter and all accessories, reusable, any type

A4461 Surgical dressing holder, non-reusable, each

A4463 Surgical dressing holder, reusable, each

A4465 Non-elastic binder for extremity

(**A4466** Code deleted December 31, 2016). Use A4467.

A4467 Belt, strap, sleeve, garment, or covering, any type

A4470 Gravlee jet washer

CIM: 50-4

MCM: 2320

A4480 Vabra aspirator

CIM: 50-10

MCM: 2320

A4481 Tracheostoma filter, any type, any size, each

MCM: 2130

A4483 Moisture exchanger, disposable, for use with invasive mechanical ventilation

MCM: 2130

A4490 Surgical stockings above knee length, each

CIM: 60-9

MCM: 2079, 2100

A4495 Surgical stockings thigh length, each

CIM: 60-9

MCM: 2079, 2100

A4500 Surgical stockings below knee length, each

CIM: 60-9

MCM: 2079, 2100

A4510 Surgical stockings full length, each

CIM: 60-9

MCM: 2079, 2100

A4520 Incontinence garment, any type, (e.g., brief, diaper), each

CIM: 60-9

A4550 Surgical trays

MCM: 15030

A4553 Non-disposable underpads, all sizes

A4554 Disposable underpads, all sizes

CIM: 60-9

A4555 Electrode/transducer for use with electrical stimulation device used for cancer treatment, replacement only

A4556 Electrodes, (e.g., apnea monitor), per pair

A4557 Lead wires, (e.g., apnea monitor), per pair

A4558 Conductive gel or paste, for use with electrical device (e.g., tens, NMES), per O

A4559 Coupling gel or paste, for use with ultrasound device, per oz

A4561 Pessary, rubber, any type

A4562 Pessary, non rubber, any type

A4565 Slings

A4566 Shoulder sling or vest design, abduction restrainer, with or without swathe control, prefabricated, includes fitting and adjustment

• New code ▲ Revised code ( ) Deleted code Ⓣ Trigger Ⓟ Post Trigger DME

A4570 Splint

MCM: 2079

A4575 Topical hyperbaric oxygen chamber, disposable

CIM: 35-10

A4580 Cast supplies (e.g., plaster)

MCM: 2079

A4590 Special casting material (e.g., fiberglass)

MCM: 2079

A4595 Electrical stimulator supplies, 2 lead, per month, (e.g., tens, NMES)

CIM: 45-25

Supplies for Oxygen and Related Respiratory Equipment

A4600 Sleeve for intermittent limb compression device, replacement only, each

A4601 Lithium ion battery, rechargeable, for non-prosthetic use, replacement

A4602 Replacement battery for external infusion pump owned by patient, lithium, 1.5 volt, each

Ⓟ **A4604** Tubing with integrated heating element for use with positive airway pressure device

Ⓟ **A4605** Tracheal suction catheter, closed system, each

A4606 Oxygen probe for use with oximeter device, replacement

A4608 Transtracheal oxygen catheter, each

A4611 Battery, heavy duty; replacement for patient owned ventilator

Statute: 1834a3A

A4612 Battery cables; replacement for patient-owned ventilator

Statute: 1834a3A

A4613 Battery charger; replacement for patient-owned ventilator

Statute: 1834a3A

A4614 Peak expiratory flow rate meter, hand held

A4615 Cannula, nasal

CIM: 60-4

MCM: 3312

A4616 Tubing (oxygen), per foot

CIM: 60-4

MCM: 3312

A4617 Mouth piece

CIM: 60-4

MCM: 3312

A4618   Breathing circuits

CIM: 60-4

MCM: 3312

A4619   Face tent

CIM: 60-4

MCM: 3312

A4620   Variable concentration mask

CIM: 60-4

MCM: 3312

Ⓟ A4623   Tracheostomy, inner cannula

CIM: 65-16

MCM: 2130

Ⓟ A4624   Tracheal suction catheter, any type other than closed system, each

A4625   Tracheostomy care kit for new tracheostomy

MCM: 2130

A4626   Tracheostomy cleaning brush, each

MCM: 2130

A4627   Spacer, bag or reservoir, with or without mask, for use with metered dose inhaler

MCM: 2100

A4628   Oropharyngeal suction catheter, each

Ⓟ A4629   Tracheostomy care kit for established tracheostomy

MCM: 2130

Supplies for Other Durable Medical Equipment

A4630   Replacement batteries, medically necessary, transcutaneous electrical stimulator, owned by patient

CIM: 65-8

A4633   Replacement bulb/lamp for ultraviolet light therapy system, each

A4634   Replacement bulb for therapeutic light box, tabletop model

A4635   Underarm pad, crutch, replacement, each

CIM: 60-9

A4636   Replacement, handgrip, cane, crutch, or walker, each

CIM: 60-9

A4637   Replacement, tip, cane, crutch, walker, each.

CIM: 60-9

A4638 Replacement battery for patient-owned ear pulse generator, each

A4639 Replacement pad for infrared heating pad system, each

A4640 Replacement pad for use with medically necessary alternating pressure pad owned by patient

CIM: 60-9

MCM: 4107.6

Supplies for Radiological Procedures

A4641 Radiopharmaceutical, diagnostic, not otherwise classified

A4642 Indium in-111 satumomab pendetide, diagnostic, per study dose, up to 6 millicuries

A4648 Tissue marker, implantable, any type, each

A4649 Surgical supply; miscellaneous

Supplies for ESRD

A4650 Implantable radiation dosimeter, each

A4651 Calibrated microcapillary tube, each

MCM: 4270

A4652 Microcapillary tube sealant

MCM: 4270

A4653 Peritoneal dialysis catheter anchoring device, belt, each

A4657 Syringe, with or without needle, each

MCM: 4270

A4660 Sphygmomanometer/blood pressure apparatus with cuff and stethoscope

MCM: 4270

A4663 Blood pressure cuff only

MCM: 4270

A4670 Automatic blood pressure monitor

CIM: 50-42

MCM: 4270

A4671 Disposable cycler set used with cycler dialysis machine, each

MCM: 4270

A4672 Drainage extension line, sterile, for dialysis, each

MCM: 4270

A4673 Extension line with easy lock connectors, used with dialysis

MCM: 4270

A4674 Chemicals/antiseptics solution used to clean/sterilize dialysis equipment, per 8 oz

MCM: 4270

A4680 Activated carbon filter for hemodialysis, each

CIM: 55-1

MCM: 4270

A4690 Dialyzer (artificial kidneys), all types, all sizes, for hemodialysis, each

MCM: 4270

A4706 Bicarbonate concentrate, solution, for hemodialysis, per gallon

MCM: 4270

A4707 Bicarbonate concentrate, powder, for hemodialysis, per packet

MCM: 4270

A4708 Acetate concentrate solution, for hemodialysis, per gallon

MCM: 4270

A4709 Acid concentrate, solution, for hemodialysis, per gallon

MCM: 4270

A4714 Treated water (deionized, distilled, or reverse osmosis) for peritoneal dialysis, per gallon

CIM: 55-1

MCM: 4270

A4719 "y set" tubing for peritoneal dialysis

MCM: 4270

A4720 Dialysate solution, any concentration of dextrose, fluid volume greater than 249cc, but less than or equal to 999 cc, for peritoneal dialysis

MCM: 4270

A4721 Dialysate solution, any concentration of dextrose, fluid volume greater than 999 cc but less than or equal to 1999 cc, for peritoneal dialysis

MCM: 4270

A4722 Dialysate solution, any concentration of dextrose, fluid volume greater than 1999 cc but less than or equal to 2999 cc, for peritoneal dialysis

MCM: 4270

A4723 Dialysate solution, any concentration of dextrose, fluid volume greater than 2999 cc but less than or equal to 3999 cc, for peritoneal dialysis

MCM: 4270

A4724 Dialysate solution, any concentration of dextrose, fluid volume greater than 3999 cc but less than or equal to 4999 cc, for peritoneal dialysis

MCM: 4270

A4725 Dialysate solution, any concentration of dextrose, fluid volume greater than 4999 cc but less than or equal to 5999 cc, for peritoneal dialysis

MCM: 4270

A4726 Dialysate solution, any concentration of dextrose, fluid volume greater than 5999 cc, for peritoneal dialysis

MCM: 4270

A4728 Dialysate solution, non-dextrose containing, 500 ml

A4730 Fistula cannulation set for hemodialysis, each

MCM: 4270

A4736 Topical anesthetic, for dialysis, per gram

MCM: 4270

A4737 Injectable anesthetic, for dialysis, per 10 ml

MCM: 4270

A4740 Shunt accessory, for hemodialysis, any type, each

MCM: 4270

A4750 Blood tubing, arterial or venous, for hemodialysis, each

MCM: 4270

A4755 Blood tubing, arterial and venous combined, for hemodialysis, each

MCM: 4270

A4760 Dialysate solution test kit, for peritoneal dialysis, any type, each

MCM: 4270

A4765 Dialysate concentrate, powder, additive for peritoneal dialysis, per packet

MCM: 4270

A4766 Dialysate concentrate, solution, additive for peritoneal dialysis, per 10 ml

MCM: 4270

A4770 Blood collection tube, vacuum, for dialysis, per 50

MCM: 4270

A4771 Serum clotting time tube, for dialysis, per 50

MCM: 4270

A4772 Blood glucose test strips, for dialysis, per 50

MCM: 4270

A4773 Occult blood test strips, for dialysis, per 50

MCM: 4270

A4774 Ammonia test strips, for dialysis, per 50

MCM: 4270

A4802   Protamine sulfate, for hemodialysis, per 50 mg

MCM: 4270

A4860   Disposable catheter tips for peritoneal dialysis, per 10

MCM: 4270

A4870   Plumbing and/or electrical work for home hemodialysis equipment

MCM: 4270

A4890   Contracts, repair and maintenance, for hemodialysis equipment

MCM: 2100.4

A4911   Drain bag/bottle, for dialysis, each

A4913   Miscellaneous dialysis supplies, not otherwise specified

A4918   Venous pressure clamp, for hemodialysis, each

A4927   Gloves, non-sterile, per 100

A4928   Surgical mask, per 20

A4929   Tourniquet for dialysis, each

A4930   Gloves, sterile, per pair

A4931   Oral thermometer, reusable, any type, each

A4932   Rectal thermometer, reusable, any type, each

Additional Ostomy Supplies

A5051   Ostomy pouch, closed; with barrier attached (1 piece), each

MCM: 2130

A5052   Ostomy pouch, closed; without barrier attached (1 piece), each

MCM: 2130

A5053   Ostomy pouch, closed; for use on faceplate, each

MCM: 2130

A5054   Ostomy pouch, closed; for use on barrier with flange (2 piece), each

MCM: 2130

A5055   Stoma cap

MCM: 2130

A5056   Ostomy pouch, drainable, with extended wear barrier attached, with filter, (1 piece), each

MCM: 2130

A5057   Ostomy pouch, drainable, with extended wear barrier attached, with built in convexity, with filter, (1 piece), each

MCM: 2130

A5061   Ostomy pouch, drainable; with barrier attached, (1 piece), each

A5062   Ostomy pouch, drainable; without barrier attached (1 piece), each
MCM: 2130

A5063   Ostomy pouch, drainable; for use on barrier with flange (2 piece system), each
MCM: 2130

A5071   Ostomy pouch, urinary; with barrier attached (1 piece), each
MCM: 2130

A5072   Ostomy pouch, urinary; without barrier attached (1 piece), each
MCM: 2130

A5073   Ostomy pouch, urinary; for use on barrier with flange (2 piece), each
MCM: 2130

A5081   Stoma plug or seal, any type
MCM: 2130

A5082   Continent device; catheter for continent stoma
MCM: 2130

A5083   Continent device, stoma absorptive cover for continent stoma

A5093   Ostomy accessory; convex insert
MCM: 2130

Additional Incontinence Appliances/Supplies

A5102   Bedside drainage bottle with or without tubing, rigid or expandable, each
MCM: 2130

A5105   Urinary suspensory with leg bag, with or without tube, each
MCM: 2130

A5112   Urinary drainage bag, leg or abdomen, latex, with or without tube, with straps, each
MCM: 2130

A5113   Leg strap; latex, replacement only, per set
MCM: 2130

A5114   Leg strap; foam or fabric, replacement only, per set
MCM: 2130

Supplies for Either Incontinence or Ostomy Appliances

A5120   Skin barrier, wipes or swabs, each
MCM: 2130

A5121   Skin barrier; solid, 6 x 6 or equivalent, each
MCM: 2130

A5122   Skin barrier; solid, 8 x 8 or equivalent, each

MCM: 2130

A5126   Adhesive or non-adhesive; disk or foam pad

MCM: 2130

A5131   Appliance cleaner, incontinence and ostomy appliances, per 16 oz.

MCM: 2130

A5200   Percutaneous catheter/tube anchoring device, adhesive skin attachment

MCM: 2130

Shoe Supplies for Diabetics

Ⓟ **A5500**   For diabetics only, fitting (including follow-up), custom preparation and supply of off-the-shelf depth-inlay shoe manufactured to accommodate multi-density insert(s), per shoe

MCM: 2134

Ⓟ **A5501**   For diabetics only, fitting (including follow-up), custom preparation and supply of shoe molded from cast(s) of patient's foot (custom molded shoe), per shoe

MCM: 2134

A5503   For diabetics only, modification (including fitting) of off-the-shelf depth-inlay shoe or custom-molded shoe with roller or rigid rocker bottom, per shoe

MCM: 2134

A5504   For diabetics only, modification (including fitting) of off-the-shelf depth-inlay shoe or custom-molded shoe with wedge(s), per shoe

MCM: 2134

A5505   For diabetics only, modification (including fitting) of off-the-shelf depth-inlay shoe or custom-molded shoe with metatarsal bar, per shoe

MCM: 2134

A5506   For diabetics only, modification (including fitting) of off-the-shelf depth-inlay shoe or custom-molded shoe with off-set heel(s), per shoe

MCM: 2134

A5507   For diabetics only, not otherwise specified modification (including fitting) of off-the-shelf depth-inlay shoe or custom-molded shoe, per shoe

MCM: 2134

A5508   For diabetics only, deluxe feature of off-the-shelf depth-inlay shoe or custom-molded shoe, per shoe

MCM: 2134

A5510 For diabetics only, direct formed, compression molded to patient's foot without external heat source, multiple-density insert(s) prefabricated, per shoe

MCM: 2134

Ⓟ A5512 For diabetics only, multiple density insert, direct formed, molded to foot after external heat source of 230 degrees Fahrenheit or higher, total contact with patient's foot, including arch, base layer minimum of 1/4 inch material of shore a 35 durometer or 3/16 inch material of shore a 40 durometer (or higher), prefabricated, each

Ⓟ A5513 For diabetics only, multiple density insert, custom molded from model of patient's foot, total contact with patient's foot, including arch, base layer minimum of 3/16 inch material of shore a 35 durometer or higher), includes arch filler and other shaping material, custom fabricated, each

Wound Dressings

A6000 Non-contact wound warming wound cover for use with the non-contact wound warming device and warming card

MCM: 2303

Ⓟ A6010 Collagen based wound filler, dry form, sterile, per gram of collagen

MCM: 2079

A6011 Collagen based wound filler, gel/paste, per gram of collagen

MCM: 2079

Ⓟ A6021 Collagen dressing, sterile, size 16 sq. in. or less, each

MCM: 2079

Ⓟ A6022 Collagen dressing, sterile, size more than 16 sq. in. but less than or equal to 48 sq. in., each

MCM: 2079

A6023 Collagen dressing, sterile, size more than 48 sq. in., each

MCM: 2079

A6024 Collagen dressing wound filler, sterile, per 6 inches

MCM: 2079

A6025 Gel sheet for dermal or epidermal application, (e.g., silicone, hydrogel, other), each

A6154 Wound pouch, each

MCM: 2079

Ⓟ A6196 Alginate or other fiber gelling dressing, wound cover, sterile, pad size 16 sq. in. or less, each dressing

MCM: 2079

Ⓟ A6197 Alginate or other fiber gelling dressing, wound cover, sterile, pad size more than 16 sq. in. but less than or equal to 48 sq. in., each dressing

MCM: 2079

A6198   Alginate or other fiber gelling dressing, wound cover, sterile, pad size more than 48 sq. in., each dressing

MCM: 2079

Ⓟ   **A6199**   Alginate or other fiber gelling dressing, wound filler, sterile, per 6 inches

MCM: 2079

Ⓟ   **A6203**   Composite dressing, sterile, pad size 16 sq. in. or less, with any size adhesive border, each dressing

MCM: 2079

A6204   Composite dressing, sterile, pad size more than 16 sq. in. but less than or equal to 48 sq. in., with any size adhesive border, each dressing

MCM: 2079

A6205   Composite dressing, sterile, pad size more than 48 sq. in., with any size adhesive border, each dressing

MCM: 2079

A6206   Contact layer, sterile, 16 sq. in. or less, each dressing

MCM: 2079

A6207   Contact layer, sterile, more than 16 sq. in. but less than or equal to 48 sq. in., each dressing

MCM: 2079

A6208   Contact layer, sterile, more than 48 sq. in., each dressing

MCM: 2079

A6209   Foam dressing, wound cover, sterile, pad size 16 sq. in. or less, without adhesive border, each dressing

MCM: 2079

Ⓟ   **A6210**   Foam dressing, wound cover, sterile, pad size more than 16 sq. in. but less than or equal to 48 sq. in., without adhesive border, each dressing

MCM: 2079

Ⓟ   **A6211**   Foam dressing, wound cover, sterile, pad size more than 48 sq. in., without adhesive border, each dressing

MCM: 2079

Ⓟ   **A6212**   Foam dressing, wound cover, sterile, pad size 16 sq. in. or less, with any size adhesive border, each dressing

MCM: 2079

A6213   Foam dressing, wound cover, sterile, pad size more than 16 sq. in. but less than or equal to 48 sq. in., with any size adhesive border, each dressing

MCM: 2079

A6214   Foam dressing, wound cover, sterile, pad size more than 48 sq. in., with any size adhesive border, each dressing

MCM: 2079

A6215   Foam dressing, wound filler, sterile, per gram

MCM: 2079

A6216   Gauze, non-impregnated, non-sterile, pad size 16 sq. in. or less, without adhesive border, each dressing

MCM: 2079

A6217   Gauze, non-impregnated, non-sterile, pad size more than 16 sq. in. but less than or equal to 48 sq. in., without adhesive border, each dressing

MCM: 2079

A6218   Gauze, non-impregnated, non-sterile, pad size more than 48 sq. in., without adhesive border, each dressing

MCM: 2079

A6219   Gauze, non-impregnated, sterile, pad size 16 sq. in. or less, with any size adhesive border, each dressing

MCM: 2079

A6220   Gauze, non-impregnated, sterile, pad size more than 16 sq. in. but less than or equal to 48 sq. in., with any size adhesive border, each dressing

MCM: 2079

A6221   Gauze, non-impregnated, sterile, pad size more than 48 sq. in., with any size adhesive border, each dressing

MCM: 2079

Ⓟ **A6222**   Gauze, impregnated with other than water, normal saline, or hydrogel, sterile, pad size 16 sq. in. or less, without adhesive border, each dressing

MCM: 2079

Ⓟ **A6223**   Gauze, impregnated with other than water, normal saline, or hydrogel, sterile, pad size more than 16 sq. in., but less than or equal to 48 sq. in., without adhesive border, each dressing

MCM: 2079

A6224   Gauze, impregnated with other than water, normal saline, or hydrogel, sterile, pad size more than 48 sq. in., without adhesive border, each dressing

MCM: 2079

A6228   Gauze, impregnated, water or normal saline, sterile, pad size 16 sq. in. or less, without adhesive border, each dressing

MCM: 2079

A6229 Gauze, impregnated, water or normal saline, sterile, pad size more than 16 sq. in. but less than or equal to 48 sq. in., without adhesive border, each dressing

MCM: 2079

A6230 Gauze, impregnated, water or normal saline, sterile, pad size more than 48 sq. in., without adhesive border, each dressing

MCM: 2079

Ⓟ **A6231** Gauze, impregnated, hydrogel, for direct wound contact, sterile, pad size 16 sq. in. or less, each dressing

MCM: 2079

A6232 Gauze, impregnated, hydrogel, for direct wound contact, sterile, pad size greater than 16 sq. in., but less than or equal to 48 sq. in., each dressing

MCM: 2079

A6233 Gauze, impregnated, hydrogel, for direct wound contact, sterile, pad size more than 48 sq. in., each dressing

MCM: 2079

Ⓟ **A6234** Hydrocolloid dressing, wound cover, sterile, pad size 16 sq. in. or less, without adhesive border, each dressing

MCM: 2079

A6235 Hydrocolloid dressing, wound cover, sterile, pad size more than 16 sq. in. but less than or equal to 48 sq. in., without adhesive border, each dressing

MCM: 2079

A6236 Hydrocolloid dressing, wound cover, sterile, pad size more than 48 sq. in., without adhesive border, each dressing

MCM: 2079

A6237 Hydrocolloid dressing, wound cover, sterile, pad size 16 sq. in. or less, with any size adhesive border, each dressing

MCM: 2079

A6238 Hydrocolloid dressing, wound cover, sterile, pad size more than 16 sq. in. but less than or equal to 48 sq. in., with any size adhesive border, each dressing

MCM: 2079

A6239 Hydrocolloid dressing, wound cover, sterile, pad size more than 48 sq. in., with any size adhesive border, each dressing

MCM: 2079

A6240 Hydrocolloid dressing, wound filler, paste, sterile, per ounce

MCM: 2079

A6241 Hydrocolloid dressing, wound filler, dry form, sterile, per gram

MCM: 2079

A6242   Hydrogel dressing, wound cover, sterile, pad size 16 sq. in. or less, without adhesive border, each dressing

MCM: 2079

A6243   Hydrogel dressing, wound cover, sterile, pad size more than 16 sq. in. but less than or equal to 48 sq. in., without adhesive border, each dressing

MCM: 2079

A6244   Hydrogel dressing, wound cover, sterile, pad size more than 48 sq. in., without adhesive border, each dressing

MCM: 2079

A6245   Hydrogel dressing, wound cover, sterile, pad size 16 sq. in. or less, with any size adhesive border, each dressing

MCM: 2079

A6246   Hydrogel dressing, wound cover, sterile, pad size more than 16 sq. in. but less than or equal to 48 sq. in., with any size adhesive border, each dressing

MCM: 2079

A6247   Hydrogel dressing, wound cover, sterile, pad size more than 48 sq. in., with any size adhesive border, each dressing

MCM: 2079

Ⓟ   **A6248**   Hydrogel dressing, wound filler, gel, per fluid ounce

MCM: 2079

A6250   Skin sealants, protectants, moisturizers, ointments, any type, any size

MCM: 2079

A6251   Specialty absorptive dressing, wound cover, sterile, pad size 16 sq. in. or less, without adhesive border, each dressing

MCM: 2079

Ⓟ   **A6252**   Specialty absorptive dressing, wound cover, sterile, pad size more than 16 sq. in. but less than or equal to 48 sq. in., without adhesive border, each dressing

MCM: 2079

Ⓟ   **A6253**   Specialty absorptive dressing, wound cover, sterile, pad size more than 48 sq. in., without adhesive border, each dressing

MCM: 2079

A6254   Specialty absorptive dressing, wound cover, sterile, pad size 16 sq. in. or less, with any size adhesive border, each dressing

MCM: 2079

A6255   Specialty absorptive dressing, wound cover, sterile, pad size more than 16 sq. in. but less than or equal to 48 sq. in., with any size adhesive border, each dressing

MCM: 2079

A6256 Specialty absorptive dressing, wound cover, sterile, pad size more than 48 sq. in., with any size adhesive border, each dressing

MCM: 2079

A6257 Transparent film, sterile, 16 sq. in. or less, each dressing

MCM: 2079

A6258 Transparent film, sterile, more than 16 sq. in. but less than or equal to 48 sq. in., each dressing

MCM: 2079

A6259 Transparent film, sterile, more than 48 sq. in., each dressing

MCM: 2079

A6260 Wound cleansers, any type, any size

MCM: 2079

A6261 Wound filler, gel/paste, per fluid ounce, not otherwise specified

MCM: 2079

A6262 Wound filler, dry form, per gram, not otherwise specified

MCM: 2079

ⓟ **A6266** Gauze, impregnated, other than water, normal saline, or zinc paste, sterile, any width, per linear yard

MCM: 2079

ⓟ **A6402** Gauze, non-impregnated, sterile, pad size 16 sq. in. or less, without adhesive border, each dressing

MCM: 2079

A6403 Gauze, non-impregnated, sterile, pad size more than 16 sq. in. less than or equal to 48 sq. in., without adhesive border, each dressing

MCM: 2079

A6404 Gauze, non-impregnated, sterile, pad size more than 48 sq. in., without adhesive border, each dressing

MCM: 2079

A6407 Packing strips, non-impregnated, sterile, up to 2 inches in width, per linear yard

A6410 Eye pad, sterile, each

MCM: 2079

A6411 Eye pad, non-sterile, each

MCM: 2079

A6412 Eye patch, occlusive, each

A6413 Adhesive bandage, first-aid type, any size, each

Statute: 1861(s)(5)

A6441 Padding bandage, non-elastic, non-woven/non-knitted, width greater than or equal to three inches and less than five inches, per yard

A6442 Conforming bandage, non-elastic, knitted/woven, non-sterile, width less than three inches, per yard

A6443 Conforming bandage, non-elastic, knitted/woven, non-sterile, width greater than or equal to three inches and less than five inches, per yard

A6444 Conforming bandage, non-elastic, knitted/woven, non-sterile, width greater than or equal to 5 inches, per yard

A6445 Conforming bandage, non-elastic, knitted/woven, sterile, width less than three inches, per yard

Ⓟ **A6446** Conforming bandage, non-elastic, knitted/woven, sterile, width greater than or equal to three inches and less than five inches, per yard

A6447 Conforming bandage, non-elastic, knitted/woven, sterile, width greater than or equal to five inches, per yard

A6448 Light compression bandage, elastic, knitted/woven, width less than three inches, per yard

Ⓟ **A6449** Light compression bandage, elastic, knitted/woven, width greater than or equal to three inches and less than five inches, per yard

A6450 Light compression bandage, elastic, knitted/woven, width greater than or equal to five inches, per yard

A6451 Moderate compression bandage, elastic, knitted/woven, load resistance of 1.25 to 1.34 foot pounds at 50% maximum stretch, width greater than or equal to three inches and less than five inches, per yard

A6452 High compression bandage, elastic, knitted/woven, load resistance greater than or equal to 1.35 foot pounds at 50% maximum stretch, width greater than or equal to three inches and less than five inches, per yard

A6453 Self-adherent bandage, elastic, non-knitted/non-woven, width less than three inches, per yard

A6454 Self-adherent bandage, elastic, non-knitted/non-woven, width greater than or equal to three inches and less than five inches, per yard

A6455 Self-adherent bandage, elastic, non-knitted/non-woven, width greater than or equal to five inches, per yard

A6456 Zinc paste impregnated bandage, non-elastic, knitted/woven, width greater than or equal to three inches and less than five inches, per yard

A6457 Tubular dressing with or without elastic, any width, per linear yard

A6501 Compression burn garment, bodysuit (head to foot), custom fabricated

MCM: 2079

A6502 Compression burn garment, chin strap, custom fabricated

MCM: 2079

A6503   Compression burn garment, facial hood, custom fabricated

MCM: 2079

A6504   Compression burn garment, glove to wrist, custom fabricated

MCM: 2079

A6505   Compression burn garment, glove to elbow, custom fabricated

MCM: 2079

A6506   Compression burn garment, glove to axilla, custom fabricated

MCM: 2079

A6507   Compression burn garment, foot to knee length, custom fabricated

MCM: 2079

A6508   Compression burn garment, foot to thigh length, custom fabricated

MCM: 2079

A6509   Compression burn garment, upper trunk to waist including arm openings (vest), custom fabricated

MCM: 2079

A6510   Compression burn garment, trunk, including arms down to leg openings (leotard), custom fabricated

MCM: 2079

A6511   Compression burn garment, lower trunk including leg openings (panty), custom fabricated

MCM: 2079

A6512   Compression burn garment, not otherwise classified

MCM: 2079

A6513   Compression burn mask, face and/or neck, plastic or equal, custom fabricated

A6530   Gradient compression stocking, below knee, 18-30 mmhg, each

CIM: 60-9

A6531   Gradient compression stocking, below knee, 30-40 mmhg, each

MCM: 2079

A6532   Gradient compression stocking, below knee, 40-50 mmhg, each

MCM: 2079

A6533   Gradient compression stocking, thigh length, 18-30 mmhg, each

CIM: 60-9

MCM: 2133

A6534   Gradient compression stocking, thigh length, 30-40 mmhg, each

CIM: 60-9

MCM: 2133

A6535   Gradient compression stocking, thigh length, 40-50 mmhg, each

CIM: 60-9

MCM: 2133

A6536   Gradient compression stocking, full length/chap style, 18-30 mmhg, each

CIM: 60-9

MCM: 2133

A6537   Gradient compression stocking, full length/chap style, 30-40 mmhg, each

CIM: 60-9

MCM: 2133

A6538   Gradient compression stocking, full length/chap style, 40-50 mmhg, each

CIM: 60-9

MCM: 2133

A6539   Gradient compression stocking, waist length, 18-30 mmhg, each

CIM: 60-9

MCM: 2133

A6540   Gradient compression stocking, waist length, 30-40 mmhg, each

CIM: 60-9

MCM: 2133

A6541   Gradient compression stocking, waist length, 40-50 mmhg, each

CIM: 60-9

MCM: 2133

A6544   Gradient compression stocking, garter belt

CIM: 60-9

MCM: 2133

ⓟ **A6545**   Gradient compression wrap, non-elastic, below knee, 30-50 mm hg, each

MCM: 2079

A6549   Gradient compression stocking/sleeve, not otherwise specified

CIM: 60-9

MCM: 2133

ⓟ **A6550**   Wound care set, for negative pressure wound therapy electrical pump, includes all supplies and accessories

ⓟ **A7000**   Canister, disposable, used with suction pump, each

A7001   Canister, non-disposable, used with suction pump, each

A7002   Tubing, used with suction pump, each

ⓟ **A7003**   Administration set, with small volume nonfiltered pneumatic nebulizer, disposable

A7004   Small volume nonfiltered pneumatic nebulizer, disposable

ⓟ **A7005**   Administration set, with small volume nonfiltered pneumatic nebulizer, non-disposable

A7006   Administration set, with small volume filtered pneumatic nebulizer

A7007   Large volume nebulizer, disposable, unfilled, used with aerosol compressor

A7008   Large volume nebulizer, disposable, prefilled, used with aerosol compressor

A7009   Reservoir bottle, non-disposable, used with large volume ultrasonic nebulizer

A7010   Corrugated tubing, disposable, used with large volume nebulizer, 100 feet

A7012   Water collection device, used with large volume nebulizer

A7013   Filter, disposable, used with aerosol compressor or ultrasonic generator

A7014   Filter, nondisposable, used with aerosol compressor or ultrasonic generator

A7015   Aerosol mask, used with DME nebulizer

A7016   Dome and mouthpiece, used with small volume ultrasonic nebulizer

A7017   Nebulizer, durable, glass or autoclavable plastic, bottle type, not used with oxygen

          CIM: 60-9

A7018   Water, distilled, used with large volume nebulizer, 1000 ml

A7020   Interface for cough stimulating device, includes all components, replacement only

A7025   High frequency chest wall oscillation system vest, replacement for use with patient owned equipment, each

A7026   High frequency chest wall oscillation system hose, replacement for use with patient owned equipment, each

A7027   Combination oral/nasal mask, used with continuous positive airway pressure device, each

A7028   Oral cushion for combination oral/nasal mask, replacement only, each

A7029   Nasal pillows for combination oral/nasal mask, replacement only, pair

ⓟ **A7030**   Full face mask used with positive airway pressure device, each

ⓟ **A7031**   Face mask interface, replacement for full face mask, each

ⓟ **A7032**   Cushion for use on nasal mask interface, replacement only, each

ⓟ **A7033**   Pillow for use on nasal cannula type interface, replacement only, pair

ⓟ **A7034**   Nasal interface (mask or cannula type) used with positive airway pressure device, with or without head strap

ⓟ **A7035**   Headgear used with positive airway pressure device

A7036 Chinstrap used with positive airway pressure device

Ⓟ **A7037** Tubing used with positive airway pressure device

Ⓟ **A7038** Filter, disposable, used with positive airway pressure device

A7039 Filter, non disposable, used with positive airway pressure device

A7040 One way chest drain valve

A7041 Water seal drainage container and tubing for use with implanted chest tube

A7044 Oral interface used with positive airway pressure device, each

A7045 Exhalation port with or without swivel used with accessories for positive airway devices, replacement only

CIM: 60-17

Ⓟ **A7046** Water chamber for humidifier, used with positive airway pressure device, replacement, each

CIM: 60-17

A7047 Oral interface used with respiratory suction pump, each

A7048 Vacuum drainage collection unit and tubing kit, including all supplies needed for collection unit change, for use with implanted catheter, each

A7501 Tracheostoma valve, including diaphragm, each

MCM: 2130

A7502 Replacement diaphragm/faceplate for tracheostoma valve, each

MCM: 2130

A7503 Filter holder or filter cap, reusable, for use in a tracheostoma heat and moisture exchange system, each

MCM: 2130

A7504 Filter for use in a tracheostoma heat and moisture exchange system, each

MCM: 2130

A7505 Housing, reusable without adhesive, for use in a heat and moisture exchange system and/or with a tracheostoma valve, each

MCM: 2130

A7506 Adhesive disc for use in a heat and moisture exchange system and/or with tracheostoma valve, any type each

MCM: 2130

A7507 Filter holder and integrated filter without adhesive, for use in a tracheostoma heat and moisture exchange system, each

MCM: 2130

A7508 Housing and integrated adhesive, for use in a tracheostoma heat and moisture exchange system and/or with a tracheostoma valve, each

MCM: 2130

A7509 Filter holder and integrated filter housing, and adhesive, for use as a tracheostoma heat and moisture exchange system, each

MCM: 2130

A7520 Tracheostomy/laryngectomy tube, non-cuffed, polyvinylchloride (pvc), silicone or equal, each

A7521 Tracheostomy/laryngectomy tube, cuffed, polyvinylchloride (pvc), silicone or equal, each

A7522 Tracheostomy/laryngectomy tube, stainless steel or equal (sterilizable and reusable), each

A7523 Tracheostomy shower protector, each

A7524 Tracheostoma stent/stud/button, each

A7525 Tracheostomy mask, each

ⓟ **A7526** Tracheostomy tube collar/holder, each

A7527 Tracheostomy/laryngectomy tube plug/stop, each

A8000 Helmet, protective, soft, prefabricated, includes all components and accessories

A8001 Helmet, protective, hard, prefabricated, includes all components and accessories

A8002 Helmet, protective, soft, custom fabricated, includes all components and accessories

A8003 Helmet, protective, hard, custom fabricated, includes all components and accessories

A8004 Soft interface for helmet, replacement only

ADMINISTRATIVE, MISCELLANEOUS AND INVESTIGATIONAL

NOTE: The following codes do not imply that codes in other sections are necessarily covered.

Guidelines

In addition to the information presented in the INTRODUCTION, several other items unique to this section are defined or identified here:

1. SPECIAL REPORT: A service, material or supply that is rarely provided, unusual, variable or new may require a special report in determining medical appropriateness for reimbursement purposes. Pertinent information should include an adequate definition or description of the nature, extent, and need for the service, material or supply.

2. CPT CODE CROSS-REFERENCE: Unless specified otherwise, there is no equivalent CPT code for listings in this section.

Miscellaneous and Experimental

A9150   Non-prescription drugs

        MCM: 2050.5

A9152   Single vitamin/mineral/trace element, oral, per dose, not otherwise specified

A9153   Multiple vitamins, with or without minerals and trace elements, oral, per dose, not otherwise specified

A9155   Artificial saliva, 30 ml

A9180   Pediculosis (lice infestation) treatment, topical, for administration by patient/caretaker

A9270   Non-covered item or service

        MCM: 2303

A9272   Wound suction, disposable, includes dressing, all accessories and components, any type, each

        Statute: 1861(n)

A9273   Hot water bottle, ice cap or collar, heat and/or cold wrap, any type

A9274   External ambulatory insulin delivery system, disposable, each, includes all supplies and accessories

        Statute: 1861(n)

A9275   Home glucose disposable monitor, includes test strips

A9276   Sensor; invasive (e.g., subcutaneous), disposable, for use with interstitial continuous glucose monitoring system, one unit = 1 day supply

        Statute: 1861(n)

A9277	Transmitter; external, for use with interstitial continuous glucose monitoring system
	Statute: 1861(n)
A9278	Receiver (monitor); external, for use with interstitial continuous glucose monitoring system
	Statute: 1861(n)
A9279	Monitoring feature/device, stand-alone or integrated, any type, includes all accessories, components and electronics, not otherwise classified
	Statute: 1861(n)
A9280	Alert or alarm device, not otherwise classified
	Statute: 1861
A9281	Reaching/grabbing device, any type, any length, each
	Statute: 1862 SSA
A9282	Wig, any type, each
	Statute: 1861SSA
A9283	Foot pressure off loading/supportive device, any type, each
	Statute: 1862a(i)13
A9284	Spirometer, non-electronic, includes all accessories
A9285	Inversion/eversion correction device
A9286	Hygienic item or device, disposable or non-disposable, any type, each
	Statute: 1834
A9300	Exercise equipment
	CIM: 60-9
	MCM: 2100.1
A9500	Technetium tc-99m sestamibi, diagnostic, per study dose
A9501	Technetium tc-99m teboroxime, diagnostic, per study dose
A9502	Technetium tc-99m tetrofosmin, diagnostic, per study dose
A9503	Technetium tc-99m medronate, diagnostic, per study dose, up to 30 millicuries
A9504	Technetium tc-99m apcitide, diagnostic, per study dose, up to 20 millicuries
A9505	Thallium tl-201 thallous chloride, diagnostic, per millicurie
A9507	Indium in-111 capromab pendetide, diagnostic, per study dose, up to 10 millicuries
A9508	Iodine i-131 iobenguane sulfate, diagnostic, per 0.5 millicurie
A9509	Iodine i-123 sodium iodide, diagnostic, per millicurie
A9510	Technetium tc-99m disofenin, diagnostic, per study dose, up to 15 millicuries
A9512	Technetium tc-99m pertechnetate, diagnostic, per millicurie
A9515	Choline c-11, diagnostic, per study dose up to 20 millicuries

A9516	Iodine i-123 sodium iodide, diagnostic, per 100 microcuries, up to 999 microcuries
A9517	Iodine i-131 sodium iodide capsule(s), therapeutic, per millicurie
A9520	Technetium tc-99m tilmanocept, diagnostic, up to 0.5 millicuries
A9521	Technetium tc-99m exametazime, diagnostic, per study dose, up to 25 millicuries
A9524	Iodine i-131 iodinated serum albumin, diagnostic, per 5 microcuries
A9526	Nitrogen n-13 ammonia, diagnostic, per study dose, up to 40 millicuries
A9527	Iodine i-125, sodium iodide solution, therapeutic, per millicurie
A9528	Iodine i-131 sodium iodide capsule(s), diagnostic, per millicurie
A9529	Iodine i-131 sodium iodide solution, diagnostic, per millicurie
A9530	Iodine i-131 sodium iodide solution, therapeutic, per millicurie
A9531	Iodine i-131 sodium iodide, diagnostic, per microcurie (up to 100 microcuries)
A9532	Iodine i-125 serum albumin, diagnostic, per 5 microcuries
A9536	Technetium tc-99m depreotide, diagnostic, per study dose, up to 35 millicuries
A9537	Technetium tc-99m mebrofenin, diagnostic, per study dose, up to 15 millicuries
A9538	Technetium tc-99m pyrophosphate, diagnostic, per study dose, up to 25 millicuries
A9539	Technetium tc-99m pentetate, diagnostic, per study dose, up to 25 millicuries
A9540	Technetium tc-99m macroaggregated albumin, diagnostic, per study dose, up to 10 millicuries
A9541	Technetium tc-99m sulfur colloid, diagnostic, per study dose, up to 20 millicuries
A9542	Indium in-111 ibritumomab tiuxetan, diagnostic, per study dose, up to 5 millicuries
A9543	Yttrium y-90 ibritumomab tiuxetan, therapeutic, per treatment dose, up to 40 millicuries
(**A9544**	Code deleted December 31, 2016).
(**A9545**	Code deleted December 31, 2016).
A9546	Cobalt co-57/58, cyanocobalamin, diagnostic, per study dose, up to 1 microcurie
A9547	Indium in-111 oxyquinoline, diagnostic, per 0.5 millicurie
A9548	Indium in-111 pentetate, diagnostic, per 0.5 millicurie
A9550	Technetium tc-99m sodium gluceptate, diagnostic, per study dose, up to 25 millicurie
A9551	Technetium tc-99m succimer, diagnostic, per study dose, up to 10 millicuries
A9552	Fluorodeoxyglucose f-18 fdg, diagnostic, per study dose, up to 45 millicuries
A9553	Chromium cr-51 sodium chromate, diagnostic, per study dose, up to 250 microcuries
A9554	Iodine i-125 sodium iothalamate, diagnostic, per study dose, up to 10 microcuries
A9555	Rubidium rb-82, diagnostic, per study dose, up to 60 millicuries
A9556	Gallium ga-67 citrate, diagnostic, per millicurie
A9557	Technetium tc-99m bicisate, diagnostic, per study dose, up to 25 millicuries

A9558	Xenon xe-133 gas, diagnostic, per 10 millicuries
A9559	Cobalt co-57 cyanocobalamin, oral, diagnostic, per study dose, up to 1 microcurie
A9560	Technetium tc-99m labeled red blood cells, diagnostic, per study dose, up to 30 millicuries
A9561	Technetium tc-99m oxidronate, diagnostic, per study dose, up to 30 millicuries
A9562	Technetium tc-99m mertiatide, diagnostic, per study dose, up to 15 millicuries
A9563	Sodium phosphate p-32, therapeutic, per millicurie
A9564	Chromic phosphate p-32 suspension, therapeutic, per millicurie
A9566	Technetium tc-99m fanolesomab, diagnostic, per study dose, up to 25 millicuries
A9567	Technetium tc-99m pentetate, diagnostic, aerosol, per study dose, up to 75 millicuries
A9568	Technetium tc-99m arcitumomab, diagnostic, per study dose, up to 45 millicuries
A9569	Technetium tc-99m exametazime labeled autologous white blood cells, diagnostic, per study dose
A9570	Indium in-111 labeled autologous white blood cells, diagnostic, per study dose
A9571	Indium in-111 labeled autologous platelets, diagnostic, per study dose
A9572	Indium in-111 pentetreotide, diagnostic, per study dose, up to 6 millicuries
A9575	Injection, gadoterate meglumine, 0.1 ml
A9576	Injection, gadoteridol, (ProHance multipack), per ml
A9577	Injection, gadobenate dimeglumine (MultiHance), per ml
A9578	Injection, gadobenate dimeglumine (MultiHance multipack), per ml
A9579	Injection, gadolinium-based magnetic resonance contrast agent, not otherwise specified (nos), per ml
A9580	Sodium fluoride f-18, diagnostic, per study dose, up to 30 millicuries
A9581	Injection, gadoxetate disodium, 1 ml
A9582	Iodine i-123 iobenguane, diagnostic, per study dose, up to 15 millicuries
A9583	Injection, gadofosveset trisodium, 1 ml
A9584	Iodine 1-123 ioflupane, diagnostic, per study dose, up to 5 millicuries
A9585	Injection, gadobutrol, 0.1 ml
A9586	Florbetapir f18, diagnostic, per study dose, up to 10 millicuries
A9587	Gallium ga-68, dotatate, diagnostic, 0.1 millicurie
A9588	Fluciclovine f-18, diagnostic, 1 millicurie
A9597	Positron emission tomography radiopharmaceutical, diagnostic, for tumor identification, not otherwise classified
A9598	Positron emission tomography radiopharmaceutical, diagnostic, for non-tumor identification, not otherwise classified

(**A9599** Code deleted December 31, 2017).

A9600 Strontium sr-89 chloride, therapeutic, per millicurie

A9604 Samarium sm-153 lexidronam, therapeutic, per treatment dose, up to 150 millicuries

A9606 Radium ra-223 dichloride, therapeutic, per microcurie

A9698 Non-radioactive contrast imaging material, not otherwise classified, per study

MCM: 15022

A9699 Radiopharmaceutical, therapeutic, not otherwise classified

A9700 Supply of injectable contrast material for use in echocardiography, per study

MCM: 15360

A9900 Miscellaneous DME supply, accessory, and/or service component of another HCPCS code

A9901 DME delivery, set up, and/or dispensing service component of another HCPCS code

A9999 Miscellaneous DME supply or accessory, not otherwise specified

● New code ▲ Revised code ( ) Deleted code Ⓣ Trigger Ⓟ Post Trigger DME

ENTERAL AND PARENTERAL THERAPY

Guidelines

In addition to the information presented in the INTRODUCTION, several other items unique to this section are defined or identified here:

1. SUBSECTION INFORMATION: Some of the listed subheadings or subsections have special needs or instructions unique to that section. Where these are indicated, special "notes" will be presented preceding or following the listings. Those subsections within the ENTERAL AND PARENTERAL THERAPY section that have "notes" are as follows:

SUBSECTION	CODE SERIES
Enteral formulae and enteral medical supplies	B4034-B5200

2. UNLISTED SERVICE OR PROCEDURE: A service or procedure may be provided that is not listed in this edition of HCPCS. When reporting such a service, the appropriate "unlisted procedure" code may be used to indicate the service, identifying it by "special report" as defined below. HCPCS terminology is inconsistent in defining unlisted procedures. The procedure definition may include the term(s) "unlisted", "not otherwise classified", "unspecified", "unclassified", "other" and "miscellaneous". Prior to using these codes, try to determine if a Local Level III code or CPT code is available. The "unlisted procedures" and accompanying codes for ENTERAL AND PARENTERAL THERAPY are as follows:

    B9998   NOC for enteral supplies
    B9999   NOC for parenteral supplies

3. SPECIAL REPORT: A service, material or supply that is rarely provided, unusual, variable or new may require a special report in determining medical appropriateness for reimbursement purposes. Pertinent information should include an adequate definition or description of the nature, extent, and need for the service, material or supply.

4. MODIFIERS: Listed services may be modified under certain circumstances. When appropriate, the modifying circumstance is identified by adding a modifier to the basic procedure code. CPT and HCPCS National Level II modifiers may be used with CPT and HCPCS National Level II procedure codes. Modifiers commonly used with ENTERAL AND PARENTERAL THERAPY are as follows:

    -CC   Procedure code change (used when the procedure code submitted was changed either for administrative reasons or because an incorrect code was filed)

5. CPT CODE CROSS-REFERENCE: Unless specified otherwise, the equivalent CPT code for all listings in this section is 99070.

Enteral Formulae and Enteral Medical Supplies

Ⓟ   **B4034**   Enteral feeding supply kit; syringe fed, per day, includes but not limited to feeding/ flushing syringe, administration set tubing, dressings, tape

---

CIM: 65-10

MCM: 2130, 4450

ⓟ **B4035** Enteral feeding supply kit; pump fed, per day, includes but not limited to feeding/flushing syringe, administration set tubing, dressings, tape

CIM: 65-10

MCM: 2130, 4450

ⓟ **B4036** Enteral feeding supply kit; gravity fed, per day, includes but not limited to feeding/flushing syringe, administration set tubing, dressings, tape

CIM: 65-10

MCM: 2130, 4450

B4081 Nasogastric tubing with stylet

CIM: 65-10

MCM: 2130, 4450

B4082 Nasogastric tubing without stylet

CIM: 65-10

MCM: 2130, 4450

B4083 Stomach tube - Levine type

CIM: 65-10

MCM: 2130, 4450

B4087 Gastrostomy/jejunostomy tube, standard, any material, any type, each

B4088 Gastrostomy/jejunostomy tube, low-profile, any material, any type, each

B4100 Food thickener, administered orally, per ounce

CIM: 60-9

B4102 Enteral formula, for adults, used to replace fluids and electrolytes (e.g., clear liquids), 500 ml = 1 unit

CIM: 65-10

B4103 Enteral formula, for pediatrics, used to replace fluids and electrolytes (e.g., clear liquids), 500 ml = 1 unit

CIM: 65-10

B4104 Additive for enteral formula (e.g., fiber)

CIM: 65-10

B4149 Enteral formula, manufactured blenderized natural foods with intact nutrients, includes proteins, fats, carbohydrates, vitamins and minerals, may include fiber, administered through an enteral feeding tube, 100 calories = 1 unit

CIM: 65-10

MCM: 2130, 4450

ⓟ **B4150**   Enteral formula, nutritionally complete with intact nutrients, includes proteins, fats, carbohydrates, vitamins and minerals, may include fiber, administered through an enteral feeding tube, 100 calories = 1 unit

CIM: 65-10

MCM: 2130, 4450

ⓟ **B4152**   Enteral formula, nutritionally complete, calorically dense (equal to or greater than 1.5 kcal/ml) with intact nutrients, includes proteins, fats, carbohydrates, vitamins and minerals, may include fiber, administered through an enteral feeding tube, 100 calories = 1 unit

CIM: 65-10

MCM: 2130, 4450

ⓟ **B4153**   Enteral formula, nutritionally complete, hydrolyzed proteins (amino acids and peptide chain), includes fats, carbohydrates, vitamins and minerals, may include fiber, administered through an enteral feeding tube, 100 calories = 1 unit

CIM: 65-10

MCM: 2130, 4450

ⓟ **B4154**   Enteral formula, nutritionally complete, for special metabolic needs, excludes inherited disease of metabolism, includes altered composition of proteins, fats, carbohydrates, vitamins and/or minerals, may include fiber, administered through an enteral feeding tube, 100 calories = 1 unit

CIM: 65-10

MCM: 2130, 4450

B4155   Enteral formula, nutritionally incomplete/modular nutrients, includes specific nutrients, carbohydrates (e.g., glucose polymers), proteins/amino acids (e.g., glutamine, arginine), fat (e.g., medium chain triglycerides) or combination, administered through an enteral feeding tube, 100 calories = 1 unit

CIM: 65-10

MCM: 2130, 4450

B4157   Enteral formula, nutritionally complete, for special metabolic needs for inherited disease of metabolism, includes proteins, fats, carbohydrates, vitamins and minerals, may include fiber, administered through an enteral feeding tube, 100 calories = 1 unit

CIM: 65-10

B4158   Enteral formula, for pediatrics, nutritionally complete with intact nutrients, includes proteins, fats, carbohydrates, vitamins and minerals, may include fiber and/or iron, administered through an enteral feeding tube, 100 calories = 1 unit

CIM: 65-10

B4159   Enteral formula, for pediatrics, nutritionally complete soy based with intact nutrients, includes proteins, fats, carbohydrates, vitamins and minerals, may include fiber and/or iron, administered through an enteral feeding tube, 100 calories = 1 unit

CIM: 65-10

B4160 Enteral formula, for pediatrics, nutritionally complete calorically dense (equal to or greater than 0.7 kcal/ml) with intact nutrients, includes proteins, fats, carbohydrates, vitamins and minerals, may include fiber, administered through an enteral feeding tube, 100 calories = 1 unit

CIM: 65-10

B4161 Enteral formula, for pediatrics, hydrolyzed/amino acids and peptide chain proteins, includes fats, carbohydrates, vitamins and minerals, may include fiber, administered through an enteral feeding tube, 100 calories = 1 unit

CIM: 65-10

B4162 Enteral formula, for pediatrics, special metabolic needs for inherited disease of metabolism, includes proteins, fats, carbohydrates, vitamins and minerals, may include fiber, administered through an enteral feeding tube, 100 calories = 1 unit

CIM: 65-10

Parenteral Nutrition

B4164 Parenteral nutrition solution: carbohydrates (dextrose), 50% or less (500 ml = 1 unit) - home mix

CIM: 65-10

MCM: 2130, 4450

B4168 Parenteral nutrition solution; amino acid, 3.5%, (500 ml = 1 unit) - home mix

CIM: 65-10

MCM: 2130, 4450

B4172 Parenteral nutrition solution; amino acid, 5.5% through 7%, (500 ml = 1 unit) - home mix

CIM: 65-10

MCM: 2130, 4450

B4176 Parenteral nutrition solution; amino acid, 7% through 8.5%, (500 ml = 1 unit) - home mix

CIM: 65-10

MCM: 2130, 4450

B4178 Parenteral nutrition solution: amino acid, greater than 8.5% (500 ml = 1 unit) - home mix

CIM: 65-10

MCM: 2130, 4450

B4180 Parenteral nutrition solution; carbohydrates (dextrose), greater than 50% (500 ml = 1 unit) - home mix

CIM: 65-10

MCM: 2130, 4450

Ⓟ **B4185** Parenteral nutrition solution, per 10 grams lipids

Ⓟ **B4189** Parenteral nutrition solution; compounded amino acid and carbohydrates with electrolytes, trace elements, and vitamins, including preparation, any strength, 10 to 51 grams of protein - premix

CIM: 65-10

MCM: 2130, 4450

Ⓟ **B4193** Parenteral nutrition solution; compounded amino acid and carbohydrates with electrolytes, trace elements, and vitamins, including preparation, any strength, 52 to 73 grams of protein - premix

CIM: 65-10

MCM: 2130, 4450

B4197 Parenteral nutrition solution; compounded amino acid and carbohydrates with electrolytes, trace elements and vitamins, including preparation, any strength, 74 to 100 grams of protein - premix

CIM: 65-10

MCM: 2130, 4450

Ⓟ **B4199** Parenteral nutrition solution; compounded amino acid and carbohydrates with electrolytes, trace elements and vitamins, including preparation, any strength, over 100 grams of protein - premix

CIM: 65-10

MCM: 2130, 4450

B4216 Parenteral nutrition; additives (vitamins, trace elements, heparin, electrolytes), home mix, per day

CIM: 65-10

MCM: 2130, 4450

B4220 Parenteral nutrition supply kit; premix, per day

CIM: 65-10

MCM: 2130, 4450

B4222 Parenteral nutrition supply kit; home mix, per day

CIM: 65-10

MCM: 2130, 4450

Ⓟ **B4224** Parenteral nutrition administration kit, per day

CIM: 65-10

MCM: 2130, 4450

B5000 Parenteral nutrition solution compounded amino acid and carbohydrates with electrolytes, trace elements, and vitamins, including preparation, any strength, renal-Aminosyn-rf, NephrAmine, renamine-premix

CIM: 65-10

MCM: 2130, 4450

B5100   Parenteral nutrition solution compounded amino acid and carbohydrates with electrolytes, trace elements, and vitamins, including preparation, any strength, hepatic, HepatAmine-premix

CIM: 65-10

MCM: 2130, 4450

B5200   Parenteral nutrition solution compounded amino acid and carbohydrates with electrolytes, trace elements, and vitamins, including preparation, any strength, stress-branch chain amino acids-FreAmine-HBc-premix

CIM: 65-10

MCM: 2130, 4450

Enteral and Parenteral Pumps

(**B9000**   Code deleted December 31, 2016).

Ⓟ   **B9002**   Enteral nutrition infusion pump, any type

CIM: 65-10

MCM: 2130, 4450

B9004   Parenteral nutrition infusion pump, portable

CIM: 65-10

MCM: 2130, 4450

B9006   Parenteral nutrition infusion pump, stationary

CIM: 65-10

MCM: 2130, 4450

B9998   NOC for enteral supplies

CIM: 65-10

MCM: 2130, 4450

B9999   NOC for parenteral supplies

CIM: 65-10

MCM: 2130, 4450

Guidelines

The "C" codes are unique temporary codes established by CMS for use under the Hospital Outpatient Prospective Payment System (OPPS). Non-OPPS use of these codes for Medicare is not valid.

The purpose of the "C" codes is to provide hospitals with a list of codes and long descriptors for drugs, biologicals and devices eligible for transitional pass-through payments, and for items classified in "new technology" ambulatory payment classifications (APCs) under the new Hospital Outpatient Prospective Payment System (OPPS).

The listing of HCPCS codes in this section does not assure coverage of the specific item or service in a given case. To be eligible for pass-through and new technology payments, the items reported with "C" codes must be considered reasonable and necessary.

All of the "C" codes are used exclusively for services paid under the Hospital Outpatient Prospective Payment System and may not be used to bill for services paid under other Medicare payment systems.

In addition to the information presented above, several other items unique to this section are defined here:

1. SPECIAL REPORT: A service, material or supply that is rarely provided, unusual, variable or new may require a special report in determining medical appropriateness for reimbursement purposes. Pertinent information should include an adequate definition or description of the nature, extent, and need for the service, material or supply.

2. MODIFIERS: Listed services may be modified under certain circumstances. When appropriate, the modifying circumstance is identified by adding a modifier to the basic procedure code. CPT and HCPCS National Level II modifiers may be used with CPT and HCPCS National Level II procedure codes.

Hospital Outpatient PPS Codes

C1713   Anchor/screw for opposing bone-to-bone or soft tissue-to-bone (implantable)

Statute: 1833(T)

C1714   Catheter, transluminal atherectomy, directional

Statute: 1833(T)

C1715   Brachytherapy needle

Statute: 1833(T)

C1716   Brachytherapy source, non-stranded, gold-198, per source

Statute: 1833(T)

C1717   Brachytherapy source, non-stranded, high dose rate iridium-192, per source

Statute: 1833(T)

C1719   Brachytherapy source, non-stranded, non-high dose rate iridium-192, per source

Statute: 1833(T)

C1721   Cardioverter-defibrillator, dual chamber (implantable)

Statute: 1833(T)

C1722   Cardioverter-defibrillator, single chamber (implantable)

Statute: 1833(T)

C1724   Catheter, transluminal atherectomy, rotational

Statute: 1833(T)

C1725   Catheter, transluminal angioplasty, non-laser (may include guidance, infusion/perfusion capability)

Statute: 1833(T)

C1726   Catheter, balloon dilatation, non-vascular

Statute: 1833(T)

C1727   Catheter, balloon tissue dissector, non-vascular (insertable)

Statute: 1833(T)

C1728   Catheter, brachytherapy seed administration

Statute: 1833(T)

C1729   Catheter, drainage

Statute: 1833(T)

C1730   Catheter, electrophysiology, diagnostic, other than 3d mapping (19 or fewer electrodes)

Statute: 1833(T)

C1731   Catheter, electrophysiology, diagnostic, other than 3d mapping (20 or more electrodes)

Statute: 1833(T)

C1732   Catheter, electrophysiology, diagnostic/ablation, 3d or vector mapping

Statute: 1833(T)

C1733   Catheter, electrophysiology, diagnostic/ablation, other than 3d or vector mapping, other than cool-tip

Statute: 1833(T)

C1749   Endoscope, retrograde imaging/illumination colonoscope device (implantable)

Statute: 1833(t)

C1750   Catheter, hemodialysis/peritoneal, long-term

Statute: 1833(T)

C1751   Catheter, infusion, inserted peripherally, centrally or midline (other than hemodialysis)

Statute: 1833(T)

C1752 Catheter, hemodialysis/peritoneal, short-term

Statute: 1833(T)

C1753 Catheter, intravascular ultrasound

Statute: 1833(T)

C1754 Catheter, intradiscal

Statute: 1833(T)

C1755 Catheter, intraspinal

Statute: 1833(T)

C1756 Catheter, pacing, transesophageal

Statute: 1833(T)

C1757 Catheter, thrombectomy/embolectomy

Statute: 1833(T)

C1758 Catheter, ureteral

Statute: 1833(T)

C1759 Catheter, intracardiac echocardiography

Statute: 1833(T)

C1760 Closure device, vascular (implantable/insertable)

Statute: 1833(T)

C1762 Connective tissue, human (includes fascia lata)

Statute: 1833(T)

C1763 Connective tissue, non-human (includes synthetic)

Statute: 1833(T)

C1764 Event recorder, cardiac (implantable)

Statute: 1833(T)

C1765 Adhesion barrier

Statute: 1833(T)

C1766 Introducer/sheath, guiding, intracardiac electrophysiological, steerable, other than peel-away

Statute: 1833(T)

C1767 Generator, neurostimulator (implantable), non-rechargeable

Statute: 1833(T)

C1768 Graft, vascular

Statute: 1833(T)

Not payable
by Medicare   Non-covered
by Medicare   Special coverage
instructions   Carrier
judgement   59

C1769   Guide wire

Statute: 1833(T)

C1770   Imaging coil, magnetic resonance (insertable)

Statute: 1833(T)

C1771   Repair device, urinary, incontinence, with sling graft

Statute: 1833(T)

C1772   Infusion pump, programmable (implantable)

Statute: 1833(T)

C1773   Retrieval device, insertable (used to retrieve fractured medical devices)

Statute: 1833(T)

C1776   Joint device (implantable)

Statute: 1833(T)

C1777   Lead, cardioverter-defibrillator, endocardial single coil (implantable)

Statute: 1833(T)

C1778   Lead, neurostimulator (implantable)

Statute: 1833(T)

C1779   Lead, pacemaker, transvenous VDD single pass

Statute: 1833(T)

C1780   Lens, intraocular (new technology)

Statute: 1833(T)

C1781   Mesh (implantable)

Statute: 1833(T)

C1782   Morcellator

Statute: 1833(T)

C1783   Ocular implant, aqueous drainage assist device

Statute: 1833(T)

C1784   Ocular device, intraoperative, detached retina

Statute: 1833(T)

C1785   Pacemaker, dual chamber, rate-responsive (implantable)

Statute: 1833(T)

C1786   Pacemaker, single chamber, rate-responsive (implantable)

Statute: 1833(T)

C1787   Patient programmer, neurostimulator

Statute: 1833(T)

C1788 Port, indwelling (implantable)

Statute: 1833(T)

C1789 Prosthesis, breast (implantable)

Statute: 1833(T)

C1813 Prosthesis, penile, inflatable

Statute: 1833(T)

C1814 Retinal tamponade device, silicone oil

Statute: 1833t

C1815 Prosthesis, urinary sphincter (implantable)

Statute: 1833(T)

C1816 Receiver and/or transmitter, neurostimulator (implantable)

Statute: 1833(T)

C1817 Septal defect implant system, intracardiac

Statute: 1833(T)

C1818 Integrated keratoprosthesis

Statute: 1833T

C1819 Surgical tissue localization and excision device (implantable)

Statute: 1833T

C1820 Generator, neurostimulator (implantable), non high-frequency with rechargeable battery and charging system

Statute: 1833(T)

C1821 Interspinous process distraction device (implantable)

Statute: 1833(T)

C1822 Generator, neurostimulator (implantable), high frequency, with rechargeable battery and charging system

Statute: 1833(T)

C1830 Powered bone marrow biopsy needle

Statute: 1833(t)

C1840 Lens, intraocular (telescopic)

Statute: 1833(t)

C1841 Retinal prosthesis, includes all internal and external components

Statute: 1833(t)

C1874 Stent, coated/covered, with delivery system

Statute: 1833(T)

C1875   Stent, coated/covered, without delivery system

Statute: 1833(T)

C1876   Stent, non-coated/non-covered, with delivery system

Statute: 1833(T)

C1877   Stent, non-coated/non-covered, without delivery system

Statute: 1833(T)

C1878   Material for vocal cord medialization, synthetic (implantable)

Statute: 1833(T)

C1880   Vena cava filter

Statute: 1833(T)

C1881   Dialysis access system (implantable)

Statute: 1833(T)

C1882   Cardioverter-defibrillator, other than single or dual chamber (implantable)

Statute: 1833(T)

C1883   Adapter/extension, pacing lead or neurostimulator lead (implantable)

Statute: 1833(T)

C1884   Embolization protective system

Statute: 1833T

C1885   Catheter, transluminal angioplasty, laser

Statute: 1833(T)

C1886   Catheter, extravascular tissue ablation, any modality (insertable)

Statute: 1833(t)

C1887   Catheter, guiding (may include infusion/perfusion capability)

Statute: 1833(T)

C1888   Catheter, ablation, non-cardiac, endovascular (implantable)

Statute: 1833(T)

C1889   Implantable/insertable device for device intensive procedure, not otherwise classified

Statute: 1833(T)

C1891   Infusion pump, non-programmable, permanent (implantable)

Statute: 1833(T)

C1892   Introducer/sheath, guiding, intracardiac electrophysiological, fixed-curve, peel-away

Statute: 1833(T)

C1893   Introducer/sheath, guiding, intracardiac electrophysiological, fixed-curve, other than peel-away

Statute: 1833(T)

C1894   Introducer/sheath, other than guiding, other than intracardiac electrophysiological, non-laser

Statute: 1833(T)

C1895   Lead, cardioverter-defibrillator, endocardial dual coil (implantable)

Statute: 1833(T)

C1896   Lead, cardioverter-defibrillator, other than endocardial single or dual coil (implantable)

Statute: 1833(T)

C1897   Lead, neurostimulator test kit (implantable)

Statute: 1833(T)

C1898   Lead, pacemaker, other than transvenous VDD single pass

Statute: 1833(T)

C1899   Lead, pacemaker/cardioverter-defibrillator combination (implantable)

Statute: 1833(T)

C1900   Lead, left ventricular coronary venous system

Statute: 1833(T)

C2613   Lung biopsy plug with delivery system

Statute: 1833(t)

C2614   Probe, percutaneous lumbar discectomy

Statute: 1833(T)

C2615   Sealant, pulmonary, liquid

Statute: 1833(T)

C2616   Brachytherapy source, non-stranded, yttrium-90, per source

Statute: 1833(T)

C2617   Stent, non-coronary, temporary, without delivery system

Statute: 1833(T)

C2618   Probe/needle, cryoablation

Statute: 1833(T)

C2619   Pacemaker, dual chamber, non rate-responsive (implantable)

Statute: 1833(T)

C2620   Pacemaker, single chamber, non rate-responsive (implantable)

Statute: 1833(T)

C2621   Pacemaker, other than single or dual chamber (implantable)

Statute: 1833(T)

C2622 Prosthesis, penile, non-inflatable

Statute: 1833(T)

C2623 Catheter, transluminal angioplasty, drug-coated, non-laser

Statute: 1833(t)

C2624 Implantable wireless pulmonary artery pressure sensor with delivery catheter, including all system components

Statute: 1833(t)

C2625 Stent, non-coronary, temporary, with delivery system

Statute: 1833(T)

C2626 Infusion pump, non-programmable, temporary (implantable)

Statute: 1833(T)

C2627 Catheter, suprapubic/cystoscopic

Statute: 1833(T)

C2628 Catheter, occlusion

Statute: 1833(T)

C2629 Introducer/sheath, other than guiding, other than intracardiac electrophysiological, laser

Statute: 1833(T)

C2630 Catheter, electrophysiology, diagnostic/ablation, other than 3d or vector mapping, cool-tip

Statute: 1833(T)

C2631 Repair device, urinary, incontinence, without sling graft

Statute: 1833(T)

C2634 Brachytherapy source, non-stranded, high activity, iodine-125, greater than 1.01 mCi (nist), per source

Statute: 1833(T)

C2635 Brachytherapy source, non-stranded, high activity, palladium-103, greater than 2.2 mCi (nist), per source

Statute: 1833(T)

C2636 Brachytherapy linear source, non-stranded, palladium-103, per 1 mm

Statute: 1833(T)

C2637 Brachytherapy source, non-stranded, ytterbium-169, per source

Statute: 1833(T)

C2638 Brachytherapy source, stranded, iodine-125, per source

Statute: 1833(t)(2)

C2639   Brachytherapy source, non-stranded, iodine-125, per source

Statute: 1833(t)(2)

C2640   Brachytherapy source, stranded, palladium-103, per source

Statute: 1833(t)(2)

C2641   Brachytherapy source, non-stranded, palladium-103, per source

Statute: 1833(t)(2)

C2642   Brachytherapy source, stranded, cesium-131, per source

Statute: 1833(t)(2)

C2643   Brachytherapy source, non-stranded, cesium-131, per source

Statute: 1833(t)(2)

C2644   Brachytherapy source, cesium-131 chloride solution, per millicurie

Statute: 1833(t)

C2645   Brachytherapy planar source, palladium-103, per square millimeter

Statute: 1833(T)

C2698   Brachytherapy source, stranded, not otherwise specified, per source

Statute: 1833(t)(2)

C2699   Brachytherapy source, non-stranded, not otherwise specified, per source

Statute: 1833(t)(2)

C5271   Application of low cost skin substitute graft to trunk, arms, legs, total wound surface area up to 100 sq cm; first 25 sq cm or less wound surface area

Statute: 1833(t)

C5272   Application of low cost skin substitute graft to trunk, arms, legs, total wound surface area up to 100 sq cm; each additional 25 sq cm wound surface area, or part thereof (list separately in addition to code for primary procedure)

Statute: 1833(t)

C5273   Application of low cost skin substitute graft to trunk, arms, legs, total wound surface area greater than or equal to 100 sq cm; first 100 sq cm wound surface area, or 1% of body area of infants and children

Statute: 1833(t)

C5274   Application of low cost skin substitute graft to trunk, arms, legs, total wound surface area greater than or equal to 100 sq cm; each additional 100 sq cm wound surface area, or part thereof, or each additional 1% of body area of infants and children, or part thereof (list separately in addition to code for primary procedure)

Statute: 1833(t)

C5275   Application of low cost skin substitute graft to face, scalp, eyelids, mouth, neck, ears, orbits, genitalia, hands, feet, and/or multiple digits, total wound surface area up to 100 sq cm; first 25 sq cm or less wound surface area

Statute: 1833(t)

C5276 Application of low cost skin substitute graft to face, scalp, eyelids, mouth, neck, ears, orbits, genitalia, hands, feet, and/or multiple digits, total wound surface area up to 100 sq cm; each additional 25 sq cm wound surface area, or part thereof (list separately in addition to code for primary procedure)

Statute: 1833(t)

C5277 Application of low cost skin substitute graft to face, scalp, eyelids, mouth, neck, ears, orbits, genitalia, hands, feet, and/or multiple digits, total wound surface area greater than or equal to 100 sq cm; first 100 sq cm wound surface area, or 1% of body area of infants and children

Statute: 1833(t)

C5278 Application of low cost skin substitute graft to face, scalp, eyelids, mouth, neck, ears, orbits, genitalia, hands, feet, and/or multiple digits, total wound surface area greater than or equal to 100 sq cm; each additional 100 sq cm wound surface area, or part thereof, or each additional 1% of body area of infants and children, or part thereof (list separately in addition to code for primary procedure)

Statute: 1833(t)

C8900 Magnetic resonance angiography with contrast, abdomen

Statute: 1833(t)(2)

C8901 Magnetic resonance angiography without contrast, abdomen

Statute: 1833(t)(2)

C8902 Magnetic resonance angiography without contrast followed by with contrast, abdomen

Statute: 1833(t)(2)

C8903 Magnetic resonance imaging with contrast, breast; unilateral

Statute: 1833(t)(2)

C8904 Magnetic resonance imaging without contrast, breast; unilateral

Statute: 1833(t)(2)

C8905 Magnetic resonance imaging without contrast followed by with contrast, breast; unilateral

Statute: 1833(t)(2)

C8906 Magnetic resonance imaging with contrast, breast; bilateral

Statute: 1833(t)(2)

C8907 Magnetic resonance imaging without contrast, breast; bilateral

Statute: 1833(t)(2)

C8908 Magnetic resonance imaging without contrast followed by with contrast, breast; bilateral

Statute: 1833(t)(2)

C8909 Magnetic resonance angiography with contrast, chest (excluding myocardium)

Statute: 1833(t)(2)

C8910   Magnetic resonance angiography without contrast, chest (excluding myocardium)

Statute: 1833(t)(2)

C8911   Magnetic resonance angiography without contrast followed by with contrast, chest (excluding myocardium)

Statute: 1833(t)(2)

C8912   Magnetic resonance angiography with contrast, lower extremity

Statute: 1833(t)(2)

C8913   Magnetic resonance angiography without contrast, lower extremity

Statute: 1833(t)(2)

C8914   Magnetic resonance angiography without contrast followed by with contrast, lower extremity

Statute: 1833(t)(2)

C8918   Magnetic resonance angiography with contrast, pelvis

Statute: 430 BIPA

C8919   Magnetic resonance angiography without contrast, pelvis

Statute: 430 BIPA

C8920   Magnetic resonance angiography without contrast followed by with contrast, pelvis

Statute: 430 BIPA

C8921   Transthoracic echocardiography with contrast, or without contrast followed by with contrast, for congenital cardiac anomalies; complete

Statute: 1833(t)(2)

C8922   Transthoracic echocardiography with contrast, or without contrast followed by with contrast, for congenital cardiac anomalies; follow-up or limited study

Statute: 1833(t)(2)

C8923   Transthoracic echocardiography with contrast, or without contrast followed by with contrast, real-time with image documentation (2d), includes m-mode recording, when performed, complete, without spectral or color Doppler echocardiography

Statute: 1833(t)(2)

C8924   Transthoracic echocardiography with contrast, or without contrast followed by with contrast, real-time with image documentation (2d), includes m-mode recording, when performed, follow-up or limited study

Statute: 1833(t)(2)

C8925   Transesophageal echocardiography (tee) with contrast, or without contrast followed by with contrast, real time with image documentation (2d) (with or without m-mode recording); including probe placement, image acquisition, interpretation and report

Statute: 1833(t)(2)

C8926 Transesophageal echocardiography (tee) with contrast, or without contrast followed by with contrast, for congenital cardiac anomalies; including probe placement, image acquisition, interpretation and report

Statute: 1833(t)(2)

C8927 Transesophageal echocardiography (tee) with contrast, or without contrast followed by with contrast, for monitoring purposes, including probe placement, real time 2-dimensional image acquisition and interpretation leading to ongoing (continuous) assessment of (dynamically changing) cardiac pumping function and to therapeutic measures on an immediate time basis

Statute: 1833(t)(2)

C8928 Transthoracic echocardiography with contrast, or without contrast followed by with contrast, real-time with image documentation (2d), includes m-mode recording, when performed, during rest and cardiovascular stress test using treadmill, bicycle exercise and/or pharmacologically induced stress, with interpretation and report

Statute: 1833(t)(2)

C8929 Transthoracic echocardiography with contrast, or without contrast followed by with contrast, real-time with image documentation (2d), includes m-mode recording, when performed, complete, with spectral Doppler echocardiography, and with color flow Doppler echocardiography

Statute: 1833(t)(2)

C8930 Transthoracic echocardiography, with contrast, or without contrast followed by with contrast, real-time with image documentation (2d), includes m-mode recording, when performed, during rest and cardiovascular stress test using treadmill, bicycle exercise and/or pharmacologically induced stress, with interpretation and report; including performance of continuous electrocardiographic monitoring, with physician supervision

Statute: 1833(t)(2)

C8931 Magnetic resonance angiography with contrast, spinal canal and contents

Statute: 1833(t)

C8932 Magnetic resonance angiography without contrast, spinal canal and contents

Statute: 1833(t)

C8933 Magnetic resonance angiography without contrast followed by with contrast, spinal canal and contents

Statute: 1833(t)

C8934 Magnetic resonance angiography with contrast, upper extremity

Statute: 1833(t)

C8935 Magnetic resonance angiography without contrast, upper extremity

Statute: 1833(t)

C8936 Magnetic resonance angiography without contrast followed by with contrast, upper extremity

Statute: 1833(t)

C8957   Intravenous infusion for therapy/diagnosis; initiation of prolonged infusion (more than 8 hours), requiring use of portable or implantable pump

Statute: 1833(t)

• **C9014**   Injection, cerliponase alfa, 1 mg

• **C9015**   Injection, c-1 esterase inhibitor (human), haegarda, 10 units

• **C9016**   Injection, triptorelin extended release, 3.75 mg

• **C9024**   Injection, liposomal, 1 mg daunorubicin and 2.27 mg cytarabine

• **C9028**   Injection, inotuzumab ozogamicin, 0.1 mg

• **C9029**   Injection, guselkumab, 1 mg

C9113   Injection, pantoprazole sodium, per vial

Statute: 1833(T)

(**C9121**   Code deleted December 31, 2016). Use J0883.

C9132   Prothrombin complex concentrate (human), Kcentra, per i.u. of factor ix activity

Statute: 1833(t)

(**C9137**   Code deleted December 31, 2016). Use J7207.

(**C9138**   Code deleted December 31, 2016). Use J7209.

(**C9139**   Code deleted December 31, 2016). Use J7202.

(**C9140**   Code deleted December 31, 2017). Use J7210.

C9248   Injection, clevidipine butyrate, 1 mg

Statute: 1833(t)

C9250   Human plasma fibrin sealant, vapor-heated, solvent-detergent (Artiss), 2 ml

Statute: 621MMA

C9254   Injection, lacosamide, 1 mg

Statute: 621MMA

C9257   Injection, bevacizumab, 0.25 mg

Statute: 1833(t)

C9275   Injection, hexaminolevulinate hydrochloride, 100 mg, per study dose

Statute: 1833(t)

C9285   Lidocaine 70 mg/tetracaine 70 mg, per patch

Statute: 1833(t)

C9290   Injection, bupivacaine liposome, 1 mg

Statute: 1833(t)

C9293   Injection, glucarpidase, 10 units

Statute: 1833(t)

Not payable by Medicare   Non-covered by Medicare   Special coverage instructions   Carrier judgement

(**C9349** Code deleted December 31, 2016). Use Q4172.

C9352 Microporous collagen implantable tube (NeuraGen nerve guide), per centimeter length

Statute: 621MMA

C9353 Microporous collagen implantable slit tube (neurawrap nerve protector), per centimeter length

Statute: 621MMA

C9354 Acellular pericardial tissue matrix of non-human origin (veritas), per square centimeter

Statute: 621MMA

C9355 Collagen nerve cuff (neuromatrix), per 0.5 centimeter length

Statute: 621MMA

C9356 Tendon, porous matrix of cross-linked collagen and glycosaminoglycan matrix (TenoGlide tendon protector sheet), per square centimeter

Statute: 621 MMA

C9358 Dermal substitute, native, non-denatured collagen, fetal bovine origin (Surgimend collagen matrix), per 0.5 square centimeters

Statute: 621 MMA

C9359 Porous purified collagen matrix bone void filler (Integra Mozaik osteoconductive scaffold putty, Integra os osteoconductive scaffold putty), per 0.5 cc

Statute: 1833(T)

C9360 Dermal substitute, native, non-denatured collagen, neonatal bovine origin (Surgimend collagen matrix), per 0.5 square centimeters

Statute: 621MMA

C9361 Collagen matrix nerve wrap (neuromend collagen nerve wrap), per 0.5 centimeter length

Statute: 621MMA

C9362 Porous purified collagen matrix bone void filler (Integra Mozaik osteoconductive scaffold strip), per 0.5 cc

Statute: 621MMA

C9363 Skin substitute, Integra meshed bilayer wound matrix, per square centimeter

Statute: 621MMA

C9364 Porcine implant, Permacol, per square centimeter

Statute: 621MMA

C9399 Unclassified drugs or biologicals

Statute: 621MMA

C9447 Injection, phenylephrine and ketorolac, 4 ml vial

Statute: 1833(t)

(**C9458** Code deleted June 30, 2016.) Use Q9983.

(**C9459** Code deleted June 30, 2016.) Use Q9982.

C9460 Injection, cangrelor, 1 mg

Statute: 1833(t)

(**C9461** Code deleted December 31, 2016). Use A9515.

(**C9461** Code deleted December 31, 2016). Use A9515.

(**C9470** Code deleted December 31, 2016). Use J1942.

(**C9471** Code deleted December 31, 2016). Use J7322.

(**C9472** Code deleted December 31, 2016). Use J9325.

(**C9473** Code deleted December 31, 2016). Use J2182.

(**C9474** Code deleted December 31, 2016). Use J9205.

(**C9475** Code deleted December 31, 2016). Use J9295.

(**C9476** Code deleted December 31, 2016). Use J9145.

(**C9477** Code deleted December 31, 2016). Use J9176.

(**C9478** Code deleted December 31, 2016). Use J2840.

(**C9479** Code deleted December 31, 2016). Use J7342.

(**C9480** Code deleted December 31, 2016). Use J9352.

C9482 Injection, sotalol hydrochloride, 1 mg

Statute: 1833(t)

(**C9483** Code deleted December 31, 2017). Use J9022.

(**C9484** Code deleted December 31, 2017). Use J1428.

(**C9485** Code deleted December 31, 2017). Use J9285.

(**C9486** Code deleted December 31, 2017). Use J1627.

(**C9487** Code deleted July 1, 2017).

• **C9488** Injection, conivaptan hydrochloride, 1 mg

(**C9489** Code deleted December 31, 2017). Use J2326.

(**C9490** Code deleted December 31, 2017). Use J0565.

(**C9491** Code deleted December 31, 2017). Use J9023.

• **C9492** Injection, durvalumab, 10 mg

• **C9493** Injection, edaravone, 1 mg

(**C9494** Code deleted December 31, 2017). Use J2350.

C9497 Loxapine, inhalation powder, 10 mg

Statute: 1833(t)

Ⓣ **C9600** Percutaneous transcatheter placement of drug eluting intracoronary stent(s), with coronary angioplasty when performed; single major coronary artery or branch

Not payable
by Medicare

Non-covered
by Medicare

Special coverage
instructions

Carrier
judgement

71

Statute: 1833(t)

Ⓣ **C9601**   Percutaneous transcatheter placement of drug-eluting intracoronary stent(s), with coronary angioplasty when performed; each additional branch of a major coronary artery (list separately in addition to code for primary procedure)

Statute: 1833(t)

Ⓣ **C9602**   Percutaneous transluminal coronary atherectomy, with drug eluting intracoronary stent, with coronary angioplasty when performed; single major coronary artery or branch

Statute: 1833(t)

Ⓣ **C9603**   Percutaneous transluminal coronary atherectomy, with drug-eluting intracoronary stent, with coronary angioplasty when performed; each additional branch of a major coronary artery (list separately in addition to code for primary procedure)

Statute: 1833(t)

Ⓣ **C9604**   Percutaneous transluminal revascularization of or through coronary artery bypass graft (internal mammary, free arterial, venous), any combination of drug-eluting intracoronary stent, atherectomy and angioplasty, including distal protection when performed; single vessel

Statute: 1833(t)

Ⓣ **C9605**   Percutaneous transluminal revascularization of or through coronary artery bypass graft (internal mammary, free arterial, venous), any combination of drug-eluting intracoronary stent, atherectomy and angioplasty, including distal protection when performed; each additional branch subtended by the bypass graft (list separately in addition to code for primary procedure)

Statute: 1833(t)

Ⓣ **C9606**   Percutaneous transluminal revascularization of acute total/subtotal occlusion during acute myocardial infarction, coronary artery or coronary artery bypass graft, any combination of drug-eluting intracoronary stent, atherectomy and angioplasty, including aspiration thrombectomy when performed, single vessel

Statute: 1833(t)

Ⓣ **C9607**   Percutaneous transluminal revascularization of chronic total occlusion, coronary artery, coronary artery branch, or coronary artery bypass graft, any combination of drug-eluting intracoronary stent, atherectomy and angioplasty; single vessel

Statute: 1833(t)

Ⓣ **C9608**   Percutaneous transluminal revascularization of chronic total occlusion, coronary artery, coronary artery branch, or coronary artery bypass graft, any combination of drug-eluting intracoronary stent, atherectomy and angioplasty; each additional coronary artery, coronary artery branch, or bypass graft (list separately in addition to code for primary procedure)

Statute: 1833(t)

C9726   Placement and removal (if performed) of applicator into breast for intraoperative radiation therapy, add-on to primary breast procedure

Statute: 1833(T)

C9727   Insertion of implants into the soft palate; minimum of three implants

Statute: 1833(T)

C9728   Placement of interstitial device(s) for radiation therapy/surgery guidance (e.g., fiducial markers, dosimeter), for other than the following sites (any approach): abdomen, pelvis, prostate, retroperitoneum, thorax, single or multiple

Statute: 1833(T)

C9733   Non-ophthalmic fluorescent vascular angiography

Statute: 1833(t)

C9734   Focused ultrasound ablation/therapeutic intervention, other than uterine leiomyomata, with magnetic resonance (mr) guidance

Statute: 1833(t)

• **C9738**   Adjunctive blue light cystoscopy with fluorescent imaging agent (list separately in addition to code for primary procedure)

C9739   Cystourethroscopy, with insertion of transprostatic implant; 1 to 3 implants

Statute: 1833(t)

C9740   Cystourethroscopy, with insertion of transprostatic implant; 4 or more implants

Statute: 1833(t)

C9741   Right heart catheterization with implantation of wireless pressure sensor in the pulmonary artery, including any type of measurement, angiography, imaging supervision, interpretation, and report

Statute: 1833(t)

(**C9742**   Code deleted December 31, 2016). Use 31573, 31574.

(**C9743**   Code deleted June 30, 2016). Use 0438T.

C9744   Ultrasound, abdominal, with contrast

Statute: 1833(t)

• **C9745**   Nasal endoscopy, surgical; balloon dilation of eustachian tube

• **C9746**   Transperineal implantation of permanent adjustable balloon continence device, with cystourethroscopy, when performed and/or fluoroscopy, when performed

• **C9747**   Ablation of prostate, transrectal, high intensity focused ultrasound (hifu), including imaging guidance

• **C9748**   Transurethral destruction of prostate tissue; by radiofrequency water vapor (steam) thermal therapy

(**C9800**   Code deleted December 31, 2016). Use G0429.

C9898   Radiolabeled product provided during a hospital inpatient stay

C9899   Implanted prosthetic device, payable only for inpatients who do not have inpatient coverage

● New code ▲ Revised code ( ) Deleted code Ⓣ Trigger Ⓟ Post Trigger DME

DURABLE MEDICAL EQUIPMENT

Guidelines

In addition to the information presented in the INTRODUCTION, several other items unique to this section are defined or identified here:

1. DEFINITION OF DURABLE MEDICAL EQUIPMENT: Durable medical equipment (DME) can withstand repeated use and is used primarily to serve a medical purpose. It generally is not useful in the absence of an illness or injury, and is appropriate for use in the home. Expendable medical supplies, such as incontinent pads, lamb's wool pads, catheters, ace bandages, elastic stockings, surgical face masks, irrigating kits, sheets and bags, are not considered to be DME.

2. REASONABLE AND NECESSARY: DME may not be covered in every instance. The equipment must be reasonable and necessary for the illness or injury being treated or for improving the functioning of a malformed body part. A physician's prescription is normally sufficient to establish that the equipment is necessary. To determine reasonableness, the following conditions must be met: the expense must be proportionate to the therapeutic benefits of using the equipment; the cost must not substantially exceed a medically appropriate care plan; and, the item must not serve the same purpose as equipment already available to the patient. Claims for items that are not reasonable will be denied except when it is determined that no alternative plan of care is available for which payment could be made.

3. SUBSECTION INFORMATION: Some of the listed subheadings or subsections have special needs or instructions unique to that section. Where these are indicated, special "notes" will be presented preceding or following the listings. Those subsections within the DURABLE MEDICAL EQUIPMENT section that have "notes" are as follows:

SUBSECTION	CODE SERIES
Artificial kidney machines and accessories	E1510-E1699

4. UNLISTED SERVICE OR PROCEDURE: A service or procedure may be provided that is not listed in this edition of HCPCS. When reporting such a service, the appropriate "unlisted procedure" code may be used to indicate the service, identifying it by "special report" as defined below. HCPCS terminology is inconsistent in defining unlisted procedures. The procedure definition may include the term(s) "unlisted", "not otherwise classified", "unspecified", "unclassified", "other" and "miscellaneous". Prior to using these codes, try to determine if a Local Level III code or CPT code is available. The "unlisted procedures" and accompanying codes for DURABLE MEDICAL EQUIPMENT are as follows:

    E1399   Durable medical equipment, miscellaneous
    E1699   Dialysis equipment, not otherwise specified

5. SPECIAL REPORT: A service, material or supply that is rarely provided, unusual, variable or new may require a special report in determining medical appropriateness for reimbursement purposes. Pertinent information should include an adequate definition or description of the nature, extent, and need for the service, material or supply.

6. MODIFIERS: Listed services may be modified under certain circumstances. When appropriate, the modifying circumstance is identified by adding a modifier to the basic procedure code. CPT and HCPCS National Level II modifiers may be used with CPT and HCPCS National Level II procedure codes. Modifiers commonly used with DURABLE MEDICAL EQUIPMENT are as follows:

-CC Procedure code change (use "CC" when the procedure code submitted was changed either for administrative reasons or because an incorrect code was filed)

-LL Lease/rental (used the "LL" modifier when DME rental is to be applied against the purchase price)

-LT Left side (used to identify procedures performed on the left side of the body)

-MS Six-month maintenance and servicing fee for reasonable and necessary parts and labor which are not covered under any manufacturer or supplier warranty

-NR New when rented (use the "NR" modifier when DME which was new at the time of rental is subsequently purchased)

-NU New equipment

-QE Prescribed amount of oxygen is less than 1 liter per minute (LPM)

-QF Prescribed amount of oxygen exceeds 4 liters per minute (LPM) and portable oxygen is prescribed

-QG Prescribed amount of oxygen is greater than 4 liters per minute (LPM)

-QH Oxygen conserving device is being used with an oxygen delivery system

-QT Recording and storage on tape by an analog tape recorder

-RP Replacement and repair (may be used to indicate replacement of DME, orthotic and prosthetic devices which have been in use for some time. The claim shows the code for the part, followed by the "RP" modifier and the charge for the part.)

-RR Rental (used when DME is to be rented)

-RT Right side (used to identify procedures performed on the right side of the body)

-TC Technical component. Under certain circumstances, a charge may be made for the technical component alone. Under those circumstances, the technical component charge is identified by adding modifier -TC to the usual procedure code. Technical component charges are institutional charges and are not billed separately by physicians. However, portable x-ray suppliers bill only for technical component and should utilize modifier -TC. The charge data from portable x-ray suppliers will then be used to build customary and prevailing profiles.

-UE Used durable medical equipment

7. CPT CODE CROSS-REFERENCE: Unless otherwise specified, the equivalent CPT code for all listings in this section is 99070.

8. DURABLE MEDICAL EQUIPMENT REGIONAL CARRIERS (DMERCS): Effective October 1, 1993 claims for durable medical equipment (DME) must be billed to one of four regional carriers depending upon the residence of the beneficiary. The transition dates for DMERC claims is from November 1, 1993 to March 1, 1994 depending upon the state you practice in. See the Introduction for a complete discussion of DMERCs.

Durable Medical Equipment Canes

Ⓟ **E0100** Cane, includes canes of all materials, adjustable or fixed, with tip

CIM: 60-3, 60-9

MCM: 2100.1

Ⓟ **E0105** Cane, quad or three prong, includes canes of all materials, adjustable or fixed, with tips

CIM: 60-15, 60-9

MCM: 2100.1

Crutches

Ⓟ **E0110** Crutches, forearm, includes crutches of various materials, adjustable or fixed, pair, complete with tips and handgrips

CIM: 60-9

MCM: 2100.1

E0111 Crutch forearm, includes crutches of various materials, adjustable or fixed, each, with tip and handgrips

CIM: 60-9

MCM: 2100.1

E0112 Crutches underarm, wood, adjustable or fixed, pair, with pads, tips and handgrips

CIM: 60-9

MCM: 2100.1

E0113 Crutch underarm, wood, adjustable or fixed, each, with pad, tip and handgrip

CIM: 60-9

MCM: 2100.1

Ⓟ **E0114** Crutches underarm, other than wood, adjustable or fixed, pair, with pads, tips and handgrips

CIM: 60-9

MCM: 2100.1

E0116 Crutch, underarm, other than wood, adjustable or fixed, with pad, tip, handgrip, with or without shock absorber, each

CIM: 60-9

MCM: 2100.1

	Not payable by Medicare		Non-covered by Medicare		Special coverage instructions		Carrier judgement	

E0117   Crutch, underarm, articulating, spring assisted, each

MCM: 2100.1

E0118   Crutch substitute, lower leg platform, with or without wheels, each

Walkers

E0130   Walker, rigid (pickup), adjustable or fixed height

CIM: 60-9

MCM: 2100.1

Ⓟ E0135   Walker, folding (pickup), adjustable or fixed height

CIM: 60-9

MCM: 2100.1

E0140   Walker, with trunk support, adjustable or fixed height, any type

CIM: 60-9

MCM: 2100.1

Ⓟ E0141   Walker, rigid, wheeled, adjustable or fixed height

CIM: 60-9

MCM: 2100.1

Ⓟ E0143   Walker, folding, wheeled, adjustable or fixed height

CIM: 60-9

MCM: 2100.1

E0144   Walker, enclosed, four sided framed, rigid or folding, wheeled with posterior seat

CIM: 60-9

MCM: 2100.1

E0147   Walker, heavy duty, multiple braking system, variable wheel resistance

CIM: 60-15

MCM: 2100.1

E0148   Walker, heavy duty, without wheels, rigid or folding, any type, each

Ⓟ E0149   Walker, heavy duty, wheeled, rigid or folding, any type

Attachments

E0153   Platform attachment, forearm crutch, each

Ⓟ E0154   Platform attachment, walker, each

E0155   Wheel attachment, rigid pick-up walker, per pair

Ⓟ E0156   Seat attachment, walker

E0157   Crutch attachment, walker, each

E0158   Leg extensions for walker, per set of four (4)

E0159   Brake attachment for wheeled walker, replacement, each

Commodes

E0160   Sitz type bath or equipment, portable, used with or without commode

   CIM: 60-9

E0161   Sitz type bath or equipment, portable, used with or without commode, with faucet attachment/s

   CIM: 60-9

E0162   Sitz bath chair

   CIM: 60-9

Ⓟ   E0163   Commode chair, mobile or stationary, with fixed arms

   CIM: 60-9

   MCM: 2100.1

Ⓟ   E0165   Commode chair, mobile or stationary, with detachable arms

   CIM: 60-9

   MCM: 2100.1

E0167   Pail or pan for use with commode chair, replacement only

   CIM: 60-9

Ⓟ   E0168   Commode chair, extra wide and/or heavy duty, stationary or mobile, with or without arms, any type, each

E0170   Commode chair with integrated seat lift mechanism, electric, any type

E0171   Commode chair with integrated seat lift mechanism, non-electric, any type

E0172   Seat lift mechanism placed over or on top of toilet, any type

   Statute: 1861SSA

E0175   Foot rest, for use with commode chair, each

Decubitus Care Equipment

Ⓟ   E0181   Powered pressure reducing mattress overlay/pad, alternating, with pump, includes heavy duty

   CIM: 60-9

   MCM: 4107.6

E0182   Pump for alternating pressure pad, for replacement only

   CIM: 60-9

MCM: 4107.6

Ⓟ **E0184** Dry pressure mattress

CIM: 60-9

MCM: 4107.6

Ⓟ **E0185** Gel or gel-like pressure pad for mattress, standard mattress length and width

CIM: 60-9

MCM: 4107.6

E0186 Air pressure mattress

CIM: 60-9

E0187 Water pressure mattress

CIM: 60-9

E0188 Synthetic sheepskin pad

CIM: 60-9

MCM: 4107.6

E0189 Lambs wool sheepskin pad, any size

CIM: 60-9

MCM: 4107.6

E0190 Positioning cushion/pillow/wedge, any shape or size, includes all components and accessories

MCM: 2100.1

E0191 Heel or elbow protector, each

E0193 Powered air flotation bed (low air loss therapy)

E0194 Air fluidized bed

CIM: 60-19

E0196 Gel pressure mattress

CIM: 60-9

E0197 Air pressure pad for mattress, standard mattress length and width

CIM: 60-9

E0198 Water pressure pad for mattress, standard mattress length and width

CIM: 60-9

E0199 Dry pressure pad for mattress, standard mattress length and width

CIM: 60-9

Heat/Cold Application

E0200 Heat lamp, without stand (table model), includes bulb, or infrared element

CIM: 60-9

MCM: 2100.1

E0202 Phototherapy (bilirubin) light with photometer

E0203 Therapeutic light box, minimum 10,000 lux, table top model

CIM: 60-9

E0205 Heat lamp, with stand, includes bulb, or infrared element

CIM: 60-9

MCM: 2100.1

E0210 Electric heat pad, standard

CIM: 60-9

E0215 Electric heat pad, moist

CIM: 60-9

E0217 Water circulating heat pad with pump

CIM: 60-9

E0218 Water circulating cold pad with pump

CIM: 60-9

E0221 Infrared heating pad system

E0225 Hydrocollator unit, includes pads

CIM: 60-9

MCM: 2210.3

E0231 Non-contact wound warming device (temperature control unit, ac adapter and power cord) for use with warming card and wound cover

MCM: 2303

E0232 Warming card for use with the non contact wound warming device and non contact wound warming wound cover

MCM: 2303

E0235 Paraffin bath unit, portable (see medical supply code a4265 for paraffin)

CIM: 60-9

MCM: 2210.3

E0236 Pump for water circulating pad

CIM: 60-9

E0239 Hydrocollator unit, portable

CIM: 60-9

MCM: 2210.3

Bath and Toilet Aids

E0240   Bath/shower chair, with or without wheels, any size

CIM: 60-9

E0241   Bath tub wall rail, each

CIM: 60-9

MCM: 2100.1

E0242   Bath tub rail, floor base

CIM: 60-9

MCM: 2100.1

E0243   Toilet rail, each

CIM: 60-9

MCM: 2100.1

E0244   Raised toilet seat

CIM: 60-9

E0245   Tub stool or bench

CIM: 60-9

E0246   Transfer tub rail attachment

E0247   Transfer bench for tub or toilet with or without commode opening

CIM: 60-9

E0248   Transfer bench, heavy duty, for tub or toilet with or without commode opening

CIM: 60-9

E0249   Pad for water circulating heat unit, for replacement only

CIM: 60-9

Hospital Beds and Accessories

Ⓟ   E0250   Hospital bed, fixed height, with any type side rails, with mattress

CIM: 60-18

MCM: 2100.1

E0251   Hospital bed, fixed height, with any type side rails, without mattress

CIM: 60-18

MCM: 2100.1

Ⓟ   E0255   Hospital bed, variable height, hi-lo, with any type side rails, with mattress

CIM: 60-18

MCM: 2100.1

E0256   Hospital bed, variable height, hi-lo, with any type side rails, without mattress

CIM: 60-18

MCM: 2100.1

Ⓟ **E0260**   Hospital bed, semi-electric (head and foot adjustment), with any type side rails, with mattress

CIM: 60-18

MCM: 2100.1

Ⓟ **E0261**   Hospital bed, semi-electric (head and foot adjustment), with any type side rails, without mattress

CIM: 60-18

MCM: 2100.1

E0265   Hospital bed, total electric (head, foot and height adjustments), with any type side rails, with mattress

CIM: 60-18

MCM: 2100.1

E0266   Hospital bed, total electric (head, foot and height adjustments), with any type side rails, without mattress

CIM: 60-18

MCM: 2100.1

E0270   Hospital bed, institutional type includes: oscillating, circulating and Stryker frame, with mattress

CIM: 60-9

Ⓟ **E0271**   Mattress, innerspring

CIM: 60-18, 60-9

E0272   Mattress, foam rubber

CIM: 60-18, 60-9

E0273   Bed board

CIM: 60-9

E0274   Over-bed table

CIM: 60-9

E0275   Bed pan, standard, metal or plastic

CIM: 60-9

E0276   Bed pan, fracture, metal or plastic

CIM: 60-9

Ⓟ **E0277**   Powered pressure-reducing air mattress

CIM: 60-9

E0280 Bed cradle, any type

E0290 Hospital bed, fixed height, without side rails, with mattress

CIM: 60-18

MCM: 2100.1

E0291 Hospital bed, fixed height, without side rails, without mattress

CIM: 60-18

MCM: 2100.1

E0292 Hospital bed, variable height, hi-lo, without side rails, with mattress

CIM: 60-18

MCM: 2100.1

E0293 Hospital bed, variable height, hi-lo, without side rails, without mattress

CIM: 60-18

MCM: 2100.1

E0294 Hospital bed, semi-electric (head and foot adjustment), without side rails, with mattress

CIM: 60-18

MCM: 2100.1

Ⓟ **E0295** Hospital bed, semi-electric (head and foot adjustment), without side rails, without mattress

CIM: 60-18

MCM: 2100.1

E0296 Hospital bed, total electric (head, foot and height adjustments). without side rails, with mattress

CIM: 60-18

MCM: 2100.1

E0297 Hospital bed, total electric (head, foot and height adjustments), without side rails, without mattress

CIM: 60-18

MCM: 2100.1

E0300 Pediatric crib, hospital grade, fully enclosed, with or without top enclosure

E0301 Hospital bed, heavy duty, extra wide, with weight capacity greater than 350 pounds, but less than or equal to 600 pounds, with any type side rails, without mattress

CIM: 60-18

E0302 Hospital bed, extra heavy duty, extra wide, with weight capacity greater than 600 pounds, with any type side rails, without mattress

CIM: 60-18

• New code   ▲ Revised code   ( ) Deleted code   ⓉTrigger   Ⓟ Post Trigger DME

Ⓟ **E0303**   Hospital bed, heavy duty, extra wide, with weight capacity greater than 350 pounds, but less than or equal to 600 pounds, with any type side rails, with mattress

CIM: 60-18

E0304   Hospital bed, extra heavy duty, extra wide, with weight capacity greater than 600 pounds, with any type side rails, with mattress

CIM: 60-18

E0305   Bed side rails, half length

CIM: 60-18

E0310   Bed side rails, full length

CIM: 60-18

E0315   Bed accessory: board, table, or support device, any type

CIM: 60-9

E0316   Safety enclosure frame/canopy for use with hospital bed, any type

E0325   Urinal; male, jug-type, any material

CIM: 60-9

E0326   Urinal; female, jug-type, any material

CIM: 60-9

E0328   Hospital bed, pediatric, manual, 360 degree side enclosures, top of headboard, footboard and side rails up to 24 inches above the spring, includes mattress

E0329   Hospital bed, pediatric, electric or semi-electric, 360 degree side enclosures, top of headboard, footboard and side rails up to 24 inches above the spring, includes mattress

E0350   Control unit for electronic bowel irrigation/evacuation system

E0352   Disposable pack (water reservoir bag, speculum, valving mechanism and collection bag/box) for use with the electronic bowel irrigation/evacuation system

E0370   Air pressure elevator for heel

E0371   Nonpowered advanced pressure reducing overlay for mattress, standard mattress length and width

E0372   Powered air overlay for mattress, standard mattress length and width

E0373   Nonpowered advanced pressure reducing mattress

Oxygen and Related Respiratory Equipment

E0424   Stationary compressed gaseous oxygen system, rental; includes container, contents, regulator, flowmeter, humidifier, nebulizer, cannula or mask, and tubing

CIM: 60-4

MCM: 4107.9

E0425   Stationary compressed gas system, purchase; includes regulator, flowmeter, humidifier, nebulizer, cannula or mask, and tubing

CIM: 60-4

MCM: 4107.9

E0430 Portable gaseous oxygen system, purchase; includes regulator, flowmeter, humidifier, cannula or mask, and tubing

CIM: 60-4

MCM: 4107.9

Ⓟ **E0431** Portable gaseous oxygen system, rental; includes portable container, regulator, flowmeter, humidifier, cannula or mask, and tubing

CIM: 60-4

MCM: 4107.9

E0433 Portable liquid oxygen system, rental; home liquefier used to fill portable liquid oxygen containers, includes portable containers, regulator, flowmeter, humidifier, cannula or mask and tubing, with or without supply reservoir and contents gauge

E0434 Portable liquid oxygen system, rental; includes portable container, supply reservoir, humidifier, flowmeter, refill adaptor, contents gauge, cannula or mask, and tubing

CIM: 60-4

MCM: 4107.9

E0435 Portable liquid oxygen system, purchase; includes portable container, supply reservoir, flowmeter, humidifier, contents gauge, cannula or mask, tubing and refill adaptor

CIM: 60-4

MCM: 4107.9

Ⓟ **E0439** Stationary liquid oxygen system, rental; includes container, contents, regulator, flowmeter, humidifier, nebulizer, cannula or mask, & tubing

CIM: 60-4

MCM: 4107.9

E0440 Stationary liquid oxygen system, purchase; includes use of reservoir, contents indicator, regulator, flowmeter, humidifier, nebulizer, cannula or mask, and tubing

CIM: 60-4

MCM: 4107.9

E0441 Stationary oxygen contents, gaseous, 1 month's supply = 1 unit

CIM: 60-4

MCM: 4107.9

Ⓟ **E0442** Stationary oxygen contents, liquid, 1 month's supply = 1 unit

CIM: 60-4

MCM: 4107.9

Ⓟ **E0443** Portable oxygen contents, gaseous, 1 month's supply = 1 unit

---

CIM: 60-4

MCM: 4107.9

Ⓟ **E0444** Portable oxygen contents, liquid, 1 month's supply = 1 unit

CIM: 60-4

MCM: 4107.9

E0445 Oximeter device for measuring blood oxygen levels non-invasively

E0446 Topical oxygen delivery system, not otherwise specified, includes all supplies and accessories

E0455 Oxygen tent, excluding croup or pediatric tents

CIM: 60-4

MCM: 4107.9

E0457 Chest shell (cuirass)

E0459 Chest wrap

E0462 Rocking bed with or without side rails

Ⓟ **E0465** Home ventilator, any type, used with invasive interface, (e.g., tracheostomy tube)

MCM: 60-9

Ⓟ **E0466** Home ventilator, any type, used with non-invasive interface, (e.g., mask, chest shell)

MCM: 60-9

Ⓟ **E0470** Respiratory assist device, bi-level pressure capability, without backup rate feature, used with noninvasive interface, e.g., nasal or facial mask (intermittent assist device with continuous positive airway pressure device)

CIM: 60-9

Ⓟ **E0471** Respiratory assist device, bi-level pressure capability, with back-up rate feature, used with noninvasive interface, e.g., nasal or facial mask (intermittent assist device with continuous positive airway pressure device)

CIM: 60-9

E0472 Respiratory assist device, bi-level pressure capability, with backup rate feature, used with invasive interface, e.g., tracheostomy tube (intermittent assist device with continuous positive airway pressure device)

CIM: 60-9

E0480 Percussor, electric or pneumatic, home model

CIM: 60-9

E0481 Intrapulmonary percussive ventilation system and related accessories

CIM: 60-21

Ⓟ **E0482** Cough stimulating device, alternating positive and negative airway pressure

Ⓟ **E0483** High frequency chest wall oscillation air-pulse generator system, (includes hoses and vest), each

| E0484 | Oscillatory positive expiratory pressure device, non-electric, any type, each |

| E0485 | Oral device/appliance used to reduce upper airway collapsibility, adjustable or non-adjustable, prefabricated, includes fitting and adjustment |

Ⓟ | E0486 | Oral device/appliance used to reduce upper airway collapsibility, adjustable or non-adjustable, custom fabricated, includes fitting and adjustment |

| E0487 | Spirometer, electronic, includes all accessories |

IPPB Machines

| E0500 | IPPB machine, all types, with built-in nebulization; manual or automatic valves; internal or external power source |

CIM: 60-9

Humidifiers/Nebulizers for Use With Oxygen IPPB Equipment

| E0550 | Humidifier, durable for extensive supplemental humidification during IPPB treatments or oxygen delivery |

CIM: 60-9

| E0555 | Humidifier, durable, glass or autoclavable plastic bottle type, for use with regulator or flowmeter |

CIM: 60-9

MCM: 4107.9

| E0560 | Humidifier, durable for supplemental humidification during IPPB treatment or oxygen delivery |

CIM: 60-9

| E0561 | Humidifier, non-heated, used with positive airway pressure device |

Ⓟ | E0562 | Humidifier, heated, used with positive airway pressure device |

| E0565 | Compressor, air power source for equipment which is not self-contained or cylinder driven |

Ⓟ | E0570 | Nebulizer, with compressor |

CIM: 60-9

MCM: 4107.9

| E0572 | Aerosol compressor, adjustable pressure, light duty for intermittent use |

| E0574 | Ultrasonic/electronic aerosol generator with small volume nebulizer |

| E0575 | Nebulizer, ultrasonic, large volume |

CIM: 60-9

| E0580 | Nebulizer, durable, glass or autoclavable plastic, bottle type, for use with regulator or flowmeter |

CIM: 60-9

MCM: 4107.9

E0585 Nebulizer, with compressor and heater

CIM: 60-9

MCM: 4107.9

Suction Pump/Room Vaporizers

Ⓟ **E0600** Respiratory suction pump, home model, portable or stationary, electric

CIM: 60-9

Ⓟ **E0601** Continuous positive airway pressure (CPAP) device

CIM: 60-17

E0602 Breast pump, manual, any type

E0603 Breast pump, electric (ac and/or dc), any type

E0604 Breast pump, hospital grade, electric (ac and / or dc), any type

E0605 Vaporizer, room type

CIM: 60-9

E0606 Postural drainage board

CIM: 60-9

Monitoring Equipment

E0607 Home blood glucose monitor

CIM: 60-11

Pacemaker Monitor

E0610 Pacemaker monitor, self-contained, (checks battery depletion, includes audible and visible check systems)

CIM: 60-7, 50-1

E0615 Pacemaker monitor, self contained, checks battery depletion and other pacemaker components, includes digital/visible check systems

CIM: 60-7, 50-1

E0616 Implantable cardiac event recorder with memory, activator and programmer

E0617 External defibrillator with integrated electrocardiogram analysis

E0618 Apnea monitor, without recording feature

E0619 Apnea monitor, with recording feature

E0620 Skin piercing device for collection of capillary blood, laser, each

Patient Lifts

E0621 Sling or seat, patient lift, canvas or nylon

CIM: 60-9

E0625 Patient lift, bathroom or toilet, not otherwise classified

CIM: 60-9

ⓟ **E0627** Seat lift mechanism, electric, any type

CIM: 60-8

MCM: 4107.8

(**E0628** Code deleted December 31, 2016). Use Q0078.

E0629 Seat lift mechanism, non-electric, any type

MCM: 4107.8

ⓟ **E0630** Patient lift, hydraulic or mechanical, includes any seat, sling, strap(s) or pad(s)

CIM: 60-9

E0635 Patient lift, electric with seat or sling

CIM: 60-9

E0636 Multipositional patient support system, with integrated lift, patient accessible controls

E0637 Combination sit to stand frame/table system, any size including pediatric, with seat lift feature, with or without wheels

CIM: 60-9

E0638 Standing frame/table system, one position (e.g., upright, supine or prone stander), any size including pediatric, with or without wheels

CIM: 60-9

E0639 Patient lift, moveable from room to room with disassembly and reassembly, includes all components/accessories

E0640 Patient lift, fixed system, includes all components/accessories

E0641 Standing frame/table system, multi-position (e.g., three-way stander), any size including pediatric, with or without wheels

CIM: 60-9

E0642 Standing frame/table system, mobile (dynamic stander), any size including pediatric

CIM: 60-9

Pneumatic Compressor and Appliances (Lymphedema Pump)

E0650 Pneumatic compressor, non-segmental home model

CIM: 60-16

ⓟ **E0651** Pneumatic compressor, segmental home model without calibrated gradient pressure

---

• New code   ▲ Revised code   ( ) Deleted code   ⓣTrigger   ⓟ Post Trigger DME

CIM: 60-16

E0652 Pneumatic compressor, segmental home model with calibrated gradient pressure

CIM: 60-16

E0655 Non-segmental pneumatic appliance for use with pneumatic compressor, half arm

CIM: 60-16

E0656 Segmental pneumatic appliance for use with pneumatic compressor, trunk

E0657 Segmental pneumatic appliance for use with pneumatic compressor, chest

E0660 Non-segmental pneumatic appliance for use with pneumatic compressor, full leg

CIM: 60-16

E0665 Non-segmental pneumatic appliance for use with pneumatic compressor, full arm

CIM: 60-16

E0666 Non-segmental pneumatic appliance for use with pneumatic compressor, half leg

CIM: 60-16

Ⓟ **E0667** Segmental pneumatic appliance for use with pneumatic compressor, full leg

CIM: 60-16

E0668 Segmental pneumatic appliance for use with pneumatic compressor, full arm

CIM: 60-16

E0669 Segmental pneumatic appliance for use with pneumatic compressor, half leg

CIM: 60-16

E0670 Segmental pneumatic appliance for use with pneumatic compressor, integrated, 2 full legs and trunk

CIM: 60-16

E0671 Segmental gradient pressure pneumatic appliance, full leg

CIM: 60-16

E0672 Segmental gradient pressure pneumatic appliance, full arm

CIM: 60-16

E0673 Segmental gradient pressure pneumatic appliance, half leg

CIM: 60-16

E0675 Pneumatic compression device, high pressure, rapid inflation/deflation cycle, for arterial insufficiency (unilateral or bilateral system)

E0676 Intermittent limb compression device (includes all accessories), not otherwise specified

Ultraviolet Cabinet

E0691 Ultraviolet light therapy system, includes bulbs/lamps, timer and eye protection; treatment area 2 square feet or less

E0692 Ultraviolet light therapy system panel, includes bulbs/lamps, timer and eye protection, 4 foot panel

E0693 Ultraviolet light therapy system panel, includes bulbs/lamps, timer and eye protection, 6 foot panel

E0694 Ultraviolet multidirectional light therapy system in 6 foot cabinet, includes bulbs/lamps, timer and eye protection

Safety Equipment

E0700 Safety equipment, device or accessory, any type

Restraints

Ⓟ E0705 Transfer device, any type, each

E0710 Restraints, any type (body, chest, wrist or ankle)

Transcutaneous and/or Neuromuscular Electrical Nerve Stimulators - TENS

E0720 Transcutaneous electrical nerve stimulation (tens) device, two lead, localized stimulation

CIM: 35-20, 35-46

MCM: 4107.6

Ⓟ E0730 Transcutaneous electrical nerve stimulation (tens) device, four or more leads, for multiple nerve stimulation

CIM: 35-20, 35-46

MCM: 4107.6

Ⓟ E0731 Form fitting conductive garment for delivery of tens or NMES (with conductive fibers separated from the patient's skin by layers of fabric)

CIM: 45-25

E0740 Non-implanted pelvic floor electrical stimulator, complete system

CIM: 60.24

E0744 Neuromuscular stimulator for scoliosis

Ⓟ E0745 Neuromuscular stimulator, electronic shock unit

CIM: 35-77

E0746 Electromyography (EMG), biofeedback device

CIM: 35-27

E0747 Osteogenesis stimulator, electrical, non-invasive, other than spinal applications

CIM: 35-48

Ⓟ E0748 Osteogenesis stimulator, electrical, non-invasive, spinal applications

CIM: 35-48

| E0749 | Osteogenesis stimulator, electrical, surgically implanted |
| | *CIM:* 35-48 |

| E0755 | Electronic salivary reflex stimulator (intra-oral/non-invasive) |

Ⓟ | E0760 | Osteogenesis stimulator, low intensity ultrasound, non-invasive |
| | *MCM:* 35-48 |

| E0761 | Non-thermal pulsed high frequency radio waves, high peak power electromagnetic energy treatment device |
| | *CIM:* 35-102 |

| E0762 | Transcutaneous electrical joint stimulation device system, includes all accessories |

| E0764 | Functional neuromuscular stimulation, transcutaneous stimulation of sequential muscle groups of ambulation with computer control, used for walking by spinal cord injured, entire system, after completion of training program |
| | *CIM:* 35-77 |

| E0765 | FDA approved nerve stimulator, with replaceable batteries, for treatment of nausea and vomiting |

| E0766 | Electrical stimulation device used for cancer treatment, includes all accessories, any type |

| E0769 | Electrical stimulation or electromagnetic wound treatment device, not otherwise classified |
| | *CIM:* 35-102 |

| E0770 | Functional electrical stimulator, transcutaneous stimulation of nerve and/or muscle groups, any type, complete system, not otherwise specified |

Infusion Pumps

Ⓟ | E0776 | IV pole |

| E0779 | Ambulatory infusion pump, mechanical, reusable, for infusion 8 hours or greater |

| E0780 | Ambulatory infusion pump, mechanical, reusable, for infusion less than 8 hours |

| E0781 | Ambulatory infusion pump, single or multiple channels, electric or battery operated, with administrative equipment, worn by patient |
| | *CIM:* 60-14 |

| E0782 | Infusion pump, implantable, non-programmable (includes all components, e.g., pump, catheter, connectors, etc.) |
| | *CIM:* 60-14 |

| E0783 | Infusion pump system, implantable, programmable (includes all components, e.g., pump, catheter, connectors, etc.) |
| | *CIM:* 60-14 |

Ⓟ | E0784 | External ambulatory infusion pump, insulin |
| | *CIM:* 60-14 |

E0785   Implantable intraspinal (epidural/intrathecal) catheter used with implantable infusion pump, replacement

MCM: 60-14

E0786   Implantable programmable infusion pump, replacement (excludes implantable intraspinal catheter)

CIM: 60-14

E0791   Parenteral infusion pump, stationary, single or multi-channel

CIM: 65-10

MCM: 2130, 4450

Traction Equipment

E0830   Ambulatory traction device, all types, each

CIM: 60-9

E0840   Traction frame, attached to headboard, cervical traction

CIM: 60-9

E0849   Traction equipment, cervical, free-standing stand/frame, pneumatic, applying traction force to other than mandible

E0850   Traction stand, free standing, cervical traction

CIM: 60-9

E0855   Cervical traction equipment not requiring additional stand or frame

E0856   Cervical traction device, with inflatable air bladder(s)

E0860   Traction equipment, overdoor, cervical

CIM: 60-9

E0870   Traction frame, attached to footboard, extremity traction, (e.g., buck's)

CIM: 60-9

E0880   Traction stand, free standing, extremity traction, (e.g., buck's)

CIM: 60-9

E0890   Traction frame, attached to footboard, pelvic traction

CIM: 60-9

E0900   Traction stand, free standing, pelvic traction, (e.g., buck's)

CIM: 60-9

Trapeze Equipment, Fracture Frame, and Other Orthopedic Devices

E0910   Trapeze bars, a/k/a patient helper, attached to bed, with grab bar

CIM: 60-9

E0911 Trapeze bar, heavy duty, for patient weight capacity greater than 250 pounds, attached to bed, with grab bar

CIM: 60-9

E0912 Trapeze bar, heavy duty, for patient weight capacity greater than 250 pounds, free standing, complete with grab bar

CIM: 60-9

E0920 Fracture frame, attached to bed, includes weights

CIM: 60-9

E0930 Fracture frame, free standing, includes weights

CIM: 60-9

Ⓟ **E0935** Continuous passive motion exercise device for use on knee only

CIM: 60-9

E0936 Continuous passive motion exercise device for use other than knee

E0940 Trapeze bar, free standing, complete with grab bar

CIM: 60-9

E0941 Gravity assisted traction device, any type

CIM: 60-9

E0942 Cervical head harness/halter

E0944 Pelvic belt/harness/boot

E0945 Extremity belt/harness

E0946 Fracture, frame, dual with cross bars, attached to bed, (e.g., Balken, 4 poster)

CIM: 60-9

E0947 Fracture frame, attachments for complex pelvic traction

CIM: 60-9

E0948 Fracture frame, attachments for complex cervical traction

CIM: 60-9

Wheelchair Accessories

Ⓟ **E0950** Wheelchair accessory, tray, each

CIM: 60-9

Ⓟ **E0951** Heel loop/holder, any type, with or without ankle strap, each

E0952 Toe loop/holder, any type, each

CIM: 60-9

• **E0953** Wheelchair accessory, lateral thigh or knee support, any type including fixed mounting hardware, each

● **E0954** Wheelchair accessory, foot box, any type, includes attachment and mounting hardware, each foot

Ⓟ **E0955** Wheelchair accessory, headrest, cushioned, any type, including fixed mounting hardware, each

E0956 Wheelchair accessory, lateral trunk or hip support, any type, including fixed mounting hardware, each

E0957 Wheelchair accessory, medial thigh support, any type, including fixed mounting hardware, each

E0958 Manual wheelchair accessory, one-arm drive attachment, each

CIM: 60-9

E0959 Manual wheelchair accessory, adapter for amputee, each

CIM: 60-9

E0960 Wheelchair accessory, shoulder harness/straps or chest strap, including any type mounting hardware

Ⓟ **E0961** Manual wheelchair accessory, wheel lock brake extension (handle), each

CIM: 60-9

E0966 Manual wheelchair accessory, headrest extension, each

CIM: 60-9

E0967 Manual wheelchair accessory, hand rim with projections, any type, replacement only, each

CIM: 60-9

E0968 Commode seat, wheelchair

CIM: 60-9

E0969 Narrowing device, wheelchair

CIM: 60-9

E0970 No. 2 footplates, except for elevating leg rest

CIM: 60-9

Ⓟ **E0971** Manual wheelchair accessory, anti-tipping device, each

CIM: 60-9 K0021

Ⓟ **E0973** Wheelchair accessory, adjustable height, detachable armrest, complete assembly, each

CIM: 60-9

E0974 Manual wheelchair accessory, anti-rollback device, each

CIM: 60-9

Ⓟ **E0978** Wheelchair accessory, positioning belt/safety belt/pelvic strap, each

E0980 Safety vest, wheelchair

E0981 Wheelchair accessory, seat upholstery, replacement only, each

E0982 Wheelchair accessory, back upholstery, replacement only, each

E0983 Manual wheelchair accessory, power add-on to convert manual wheelchair to motorized wheelchair, joystick control

E0984 Manual wheelchair accessory, power add-on to convert manual wheelchair to motorized wheelchair, tiller control

E0985 Wheelchair accessory, seat lift mechanism

E0986 Manual wheelchair accessory, push-rim activated power assist system

E0988 Manual wheelchair accessory, lever-activated, wheel drive, pair

E0990 Wheelchair accessory, elevating leg rest, complete assembly, each

CIM: 60-9

E0992 Manual wheelchair accessory, solid seat insert

E0994 Arm rest, each

CIM: 60-9

E0995 Wheelchair accessory, calf rest/pad, replacement only, each

CIM: 60-9

Ⓟ **E1002** Wheelchair accessory, power seating system, tilt only

E1003 Wheelchair accessory, power seating system, recline only, without shear reduction

E1004 Wheelchair accessory, power seating system, recline only, with mechanical shear reduction

E1005 Wheelchair accessory, power seating system, recline only, with power shear reduction

E1006 Wheelchair accessory, power seating system, combination tilt and recline, without shear reduction

Ⓟ **E1007** Wheelchair accessory, power seating system, combination tilt and recline, with mechanical shear reduction

Ⓟ **E1008** Wheelchair accessory, power seating system, combination tilt and recline, with power shear reduction

E1009 Wheelchair accessory, addition to power seating system, mechanically linked leg elevation system, including pushrod and leg rest, each

E1010 Wheelchair accessory, addition to power seating system, power leg elevation system, including leg rest, pair

E1011 Modification to pediatric size wheelchair, width adjustment package (not to be dispensed with initial chair)

CIM: 60-9

Ⓟ **E1012** Wheelchair accessory, addition to power seating system, center mount power elevating leg rest/platform, complete system, any type, each

E1014 Reclining back, addition to pediatric size wheelchair

CIM: 60-9

E1015   Shock absorber for manual wheelchair, each

MCM: 60.9

E1016   Shock absorber for power wheelchair, each

MCM: 60.9

E1017   Heavy duty shock absorber for heavy duty or extra heavy duty manual wheelchair, each

MCM: 60.9

E1018   Heavy duty shock absorber for heavy duty or extra heavy duty power wheelchair, each

MCM: 60.9

E1020   Residual limb support system for wheelchair, any type

MCM: 60-6

Ⓟ E1028   Wheelchair accessory, manual Swing-Away, retractable or removable mounting hardware for joystick, other control interface or positioning accessory

E1029   Wheelchair accessory, ventilator tray, fixed

E1030   Wheelchair accessory, ventilator tray, gimbaled

Rollabout Chair

E1031   Rollabout chair, any and all types with casters 5" or greater

CIM: 60-9

E1035   Multi-positional patient transfer system, with integrated seat, operated by care giver, patient weight capacity up to and including 300 lbs

MCM: 2100

E1036   Multi-positional patient transfer system, extra-wide, with integrated seat, operated by caregiver, patient weight capacity greater than 300 lbs

E1037   Transport chair, pediatric size

CIM: 60-9

Ⓟ E1038   Transport chair, adult size, patient weight capacity up to and including 300 pounds

CIM: 60-9

E1039   Transport chair, adult size, heavy duty, patient weight capacity greater than 300 pounds

Wheelchairs; Fully-Reclining, Semi-Reclining, Standard, Amputee, and Special Size

E1050   Fully-reclining wheelchair, fixed full length arms, swing away detachable elevating leg rests

CIM: 60-9

E1060   Fully-reclining wheelchair, detachable arms, desk or full length, swing away detachable elevating leg rests

CIM: 60-9

E1070 Fully-reclining wheelchair, detachable arms (desk or full length) swing away detachable footrest

CIM: 60-9

E1083 Hemi-wheelchair, fixed full length arms, swing away detachable elevating leg rest

CIM: 60-9

E1084 Hemi-wheelchair, detachable arms desk or full length arms, swing away detachable elevating leg rests

CIM: 60-9

E1085 Hemi-wheelchair, fixed full length arms, swing away detachable foot rests

CIM: 60-9 K0002

E1086 Hemi-wheelchair detachable arms desk or full length, swing away detachable footrests

CIM: 60-9 K0002

E1087 High strength lightweight wheelchair, fixed full length arms, swing away detachable elevating leg rests

CIM: 60-9

E1088 High strength lightweight wheelchair, detachable arms desk or full length, swing away detachable elevating leg rests

CIM: 60-9

E1089 High strength lightweight wheelchair, fixed length arms, swing away detachable footrest

CIM: 60-9 K0004

E1090 High strength lightweight wheelchair, detachable arms desk or full length, swing away detachable foot rests

CIM: 60-9 K0004

E1092 Wide heavy duty wheel chair, detachable arms (desk or full length), swing away detachable elevating leg rests

CIM: 60-9

E1093 Wide heavy duty wheelchair, detachable arms desk or full length arms, swing away detachable footrests

CIM: 60-9

E1100 Semi-reclining wheelchair, fixed full length arms, swing away detachable elevating leg rests

CIM: 60-9

E1110 Semi-reclining wheelchair, detachable arms (desk or full length) elevating leg rest

CIM: 60-9

E1130 Standard wheelchair, fixed full length arms, fixed or swing away detachable footrests

Not payable by Medicare	Non-covered by Medicare	Special coverage instructions	Carrier judgement	99

CIM: 60-9 K0001

E1140   Wheelchair, detachable arms, desk or full length, swing away detachable footrests

CIM: 60-9 K0001

E1150   Wheelchair, detachable arms, desk or full length swing away detachable elevating leg rests

CIM: 60-9

E1160   Wheelchair, fixed full length arms, swing away detachable elevating leg rests

CIM: 60-9

Ⓟ **E1161**   Manual adult size wheelchair, includes tilt in space

E1170   Amputee wheelchair, fixed full length arms, swing away detachable elevating leg rests

CIM: 60-9

E1171   Amputee wheelchair, fixed full length arms, without footrests or leg rest

CIM: 60-9

E1172   Amputee wheelchair, detachable arms (desk or full length) without footrests or leg rest

CIM: 60-9

E1180   Amputee wheelchair, detachable arms (desk or full length) swing away detachable footrests

CIM: 60-9

E1190   Amputee wheelchair, detachable arms (desk or full length) swing away detachable elevating leg rests

CIM: 60-9

E1195   Heavy duty wheelchair, fixed full length arms, swing away detachable elevating leg rests

CIM: 60-9

E1200   Amputee wheelchair, fixed full length arms, swing away detachable footrest

CIM: 60-9

E1220   Wheelchair; specially sized or constructed, (indicate brand name, model number, if any) and justification

CIM: 60-6

E1221   Wheelchair with fixed arm, footrests

CIM: 60-6

E1222   Wheelchair with fixed arm, elevating leg rests

CIM: 60-6

E1223   Wheelchair with detachable arms, footrests

CIM: 60-6

E1224   Wheelchair with detachable arms, elevating leg rests

CIM: 60-6

E1225   Wheelchair accessory, manual semi-reclining back, (recline greater than 15 degrees, but less than 80 degrees), each

CIM: 60-6

Ⓟ   **E1226**   Wheelchair accessory, manual fully reclining back, (recline greater than 80 degrees), each

CIM: 60-9

E1227   Special height arms for wheelchair

CIM: 60-6

E1228   Special back height for wheelchair

CIM: 60-6

E1229   Wheelchair, pediatric size, not otherwise specified

Power Operated Vehicle

E1230   Power operated vehicle (three or four wheel non highway) specify brand name and model number

CIM: 60-5

MCM: 4107.6

Wheelchairs; Lightweight and Heavy Duty

E1231   Wheelchair, pediatric size, tilt-in-space, rigid, adjustable, with seating system

CIM: 60-9

E1232   Wheelchair, pediatric size, tilt-in-space, folding, adjustable, with seating system

CIM: 60-9

E1233   Wheelchair, pediatric size, tilt-in-space, rigid, adjustable, without seating system

CIM: 60-9

E1234   Wheelchair, pediatric size, tilt-in-space, folding, adjustable, without seating system

CIM: 60-9

E1235   Wheelchair, pediatric size, rigid, adjustable, with seating system

CIM: 60-9

E1236   Wheelchair, pediatric size, folding, adjustable, with seating system

CIM: 60-9

E1237   Wheelchair, pediatric size, rigid, adjustable, without seating system

CIM: 60-9

E1238   Wheelchair, pediatric size, folding, adjustable, without seating system

CIM: 60-9

E1239   Power wheelchair, pediatric size, not otherwise specified

E1240   Lightweight wheelchair, detachable arms, (desk or full length) swing away detachable, elevating leg rest

CIM: 60-9

E1250   Lightweight wheelchair, fixed full length arms, swing away detachable footrest

CIM: 60-9 K0003

E1260   Lightweight wheelchair, detachable arms (desk or full length) swing away detachable footrest

CIM: 60-9 K0003

E1270   Lightweight wheelchair, fixed full length arms, swing away detachable elevating leg rests

CIM: 60-9

E1280   Heavy duty wheelchair, detachable arms (desk or full length) elevating leg rests

CIM: 60-9

E1285   Heavy duty wheelchair, fixed full length arms, swing away detachable footrest

CIM: 60-9 K0006

E1290   Heavy duty wheelchair, detachable arms (desk or full length) swing away detachable footrest

CIM: 60-9 K0006

E1295   Heavy duty wheelchair, fixed full length arms, elevating leg rest

CIM: 60-9

E1296   Special wheelchair seat height from floor

CIM: 60-6

E1297   Special wheelchair seat depth, by upholstery

CIM: 60-6

E1298   Special wheelchair seat depth and/or width, by construction

CIM: 60-6

Whirlpool Equipment

E1300   Whirlpool, portable (over tub type)

CIM: 60-9

E1310   Whirlpool, non-portable (built-in type)

CIM: 60-9

Additional Oxygen Related Supplies and Equipment

E1352   Oxygen accessory, flow regulator capable of positive inspiratory pressure

E1353 Regulator

CIM: 60-4

MCM: 4107.9

E1354 Oxygen accessory, wheeled cart for portable cylinder or portable concentrator, any type, replacement only, each

E1355 Stand/rack

CIM: 60-4

E1356 Oxygen accessory, battery pack/cartridge for portable concentrator, any type, replacement only, each

E1357 Oxygen accessory, battery charger for portable concentrator, any type, replacement only, each

E1358 Oxygen accessory, dc power adapter for portable concentrator, any type, replacement only, each

E1372 Immersion external heater for nebulizer

CIM: 60-4

Ⓟ **E1390** Oxygen concentrator, single delivery port, capable of delivering 85 percent or greater oxygen concentration at the prescribed flow rate

CIM: 60-4

E1391 Oxygen concentrator, dual delivery port, capable of delivering 85 percent or greater oxygen concentration at the prescribed flow rate, each

CIM: 60-4

Ⓟ **E1392** Portable oxygen concentrator, rental

CIM: 60-4

E1399 Durable medical equipment, miscellaneous

E1405 Oxygen and water vapor enriching system with heated delivery

CIM: 60-4

MCM: 4107

E1406 Oxygen and water vapor enriching system without heated delivery

CIM: 60-4

MCM: 4107

Artificial Kidney Machines and Accessories

E1500 Centrifuge, for dialysis

E1510 Kidney, dialysate delivery syst kidney machine, pump recirculating, air removal syst, flowrate meter, power off, heater and temperature control with alarm, i.v. poles, pressure gauge, concentrate container

E1520 Heparin infusion pump for hemodialysis

E1530 Air bubble detector for hemodialysis, each, replacement

E1540 Pressure alarm for hemodialysis, each, replacement

E1550 Bath conductivity meter for hemodialysis, each

E1560 Blood leak detector for hemodialysis, each, replacement

E1570 Adjustable chair, for ESRD patients

E1575 Transducer protectors/fluid barriers, for hemodialysis, any size, per 10

E1580 Unipuncture control system for hemodialysis

E1590 Hemodialysis machine

E1592 Automatic intermittent peritoneal dialysis system

E1594 Cycler dialysis machine for peritoneal dialysis

E1600 Delivery and/or installation charges for hemodialysis equipment

E1610 Reverse osmosis water purification system, for hemodialysis

CIM: 55-1A

E1615 Deionizer water purification system, for hemodialysis

CIM: 55-1A

E1620 Blood pump for hemodialysis, replacement

E1625 Water softening system, for hemodialysis

CIM: 55-1B

E1630 Reciprocating peritoneal dialysis system

E1632 Wearable artificial kidney, each

E1634 Peritoneal dialysis clamps, each

MCM: 4270

E1635 Compact (portable) travel hemodialyzer system

E1636 Sorbent cartridges, for hemodialysis, per 10

E1637 Hemostats, each

E1639 Scale, each

E1699 Dialysis equipment, not otherwise specified

Extension/Flexion Devices

E1700 Jaw motion rehabilitation system

E1701 Replacement cushions for jaw motion rehabilitation system, pkg. of 6

E1702 Replacement measuring scales for jaw motion rehabilitation system, pkg. of 200

E1800 Dynamic adjustable elbow extension/flexion device, includes soft interface material

E1801 Static progressive stretch elbow device, extension and/or flexion, with or without range of motion adjustment, includes all components and accessories

E1802   Dynamic adjustable forearm pronation/supination device, includes soft interface material

E1805   Dynamic adjustable wrist extension / flexion device, includes soft interface material

E1806   Static progressive stretch wrist device, flexion and/or extension, with or without range of motion adjustment, includes all components and accessories

Ⓟ **E1810**   Dynamic adjustable knee extension / flexion device, includes soft interface material

Ⓟ **E1811**   Static progressive stretch knee device, extension and/or flexion, with or without range of motion adjustment, includes all components and accessories

E1812   Dynamic knee, extension/flexion device with active resistance control

E1815   Dynamic adjustable ankle extension/flexion device, includes soft interface material

E1816   Static progressive stretch ankle device, flexion and/or extension, with or without range of motion adjustment, includes all components and accessories

E1818   Static progressive stretch forearm pronation / supination device, with or without range of motion adjustment, includes all components and accessories

E1820   Replacement soft interface material, dynamic adjustable extension/flexion device

E1821   Replacement soft interface material/cuffs for bi-directional static progressive stretch device

E1825   Dynamic adjustable finger extension/flexion device, includes soft interface material

E1830   Dynamic adjustable toe extension/flexion device, includes soft interface material

E1831   Static progressive stretch toe device, extension and/or flexion, with or without range of motion adjustment, includes all components and accessories

E1840   Dynamic adjustable shoulder flexion / abduction / rotation device, includes soft interface material

E1841   Static progressive stretch shoulder device, with or without range of motion adjustment, includes all components and accessories

E1902   Communication board, non-electronic augmentative or alternative communication device

E2000   Gastric suction pump, home model, portable or stationary, electric

E2100   Blood glucose monitor with integrated voice synthesizer

CIM: 60-11

E2101   Blood glucose monitor with integrated lancing/blood sample

CIM: 60-11

E2120   Pulse generator system for tympanic treatment of inner ear endolymphatic fluid

Manual Wheelchair Accessories

Ⓟ **E2201**   Manual wheelchair accessory, nonstandard seat frame, width greater than or equal to 20 inches and less than 24 inches

E2202   Manual wheelchair accessory, nonstandard seat frame width, 24-27 inches

(P) **E2203** Manual wheelchair accessory, nonstandard seat frame depth, 20 to less than 22 inches

E2204 Manual wheelchair accessory, nonstandard seat frame depth, 22 to 25 inches

E2205 Manual wheelchair accessory, hand rim without projections (includes ergonomic or contoured), any type, replacement only, each

E2206 Manual wheelchair accessory, wheel lock assembly, complete, replacement only, each

E2207 Wheelchair accessory, crutch and cane holder, each

E2208 Wheelchair accessory, cylinder tank carrier, each

(P) **E2209** Accessory, arm trough, with or without hand support, each

E2210 Wheelchair accessory, bearings, any type, replacement only, each

E2211 Manual wheelchair accessory, pneumatic propulsion tire, any size, each

E2212 Manual wheelchair accessory, tube for pneumatic propulsion tire, any size, each

E2213 Manual wheelchair accessory, insert for pneumatic propulsion tire (removable), any type, any size, each

E2214 Manual wheelchair accessory, pneumatic caster tire, any size, each

E2215 Manual wheelchair accessory, tube for pneumatic caster tire, any size, each

E2216 Manual wheelchair accessory, foam filled propulsion tire, any size, each

E2217 Manual wheelchair accessory, foam filled caster tire, any size, each

E2218 Manual wheelchair accessory, foam propulsion tire, any size, each

E2219 Manual wheelchair accessory, foam caster tire, any size, each

E2220 Manual wheelchair accessory, solid (rubber/plastic) propulsion tire, any size, replacement only, each

E2221 Manual wheelchair accessory, solid (rubber/plastic) caster tire (removable), any size, replacement only, each

E2222 Manual wheelchair accessory, solid (rubber/plastic) caster tire with integrated wheel, any size, replacement only, each

E2224 Manual wheelchair accessory, propulsion wheel excludes tire, any size, replacement only, each

E2225 Manual wheelchair accessory, caster wheel excludes tire, any size, replacement only, each

E2226 Manual wheelchair accessory, caster fork, any size, replacement only, each

E2227 Manual wheelchair accessory, gear reduction drive wheel, each

(P) **E2228** Manual wheelchair accessory, wheel braking system and lock, complete, each

E2230 Manual wheelchair accessory, manual standing system

E2231 Manual wheelchair accessory, solid seat support base (replaces sling seat), includes any type mounting hardware

E2291 Back, planar, for pediatric size wheelchair including fixed attaching hardware

E2292 Seat, planar, for pediatric size wheelchair including fixed attaching hardware

E2293 Back, contoured, for pediatric size wheelchair including fixed attaching hardware

E2294 Seat, contoured, for pediatric size wheelchair including fixed attaching hardware

E2295 Manual wheelchair accessory, for pediatric size wheelchair, dynamic seating frame, allows coordinated movement of multiple positioning features

E2300 Wheelchair accessory, power seat elevation system, any type

E2301 Wheelchair accessory, power standing system, any type

Power Wheelchair Accessories

E2310 Power wheelchair accessory, electronic connection between wheelchair controller and one power seating system motor, including all related electronics, indicator feature, mechanical function selection switch, and fixed mounting hardware

ⓟ **E2311** Power wheelchair accessory, electronic connection between wheelchair controller and two or more power seating system motors, including all related electronics, indicator feature, mechanical function selection switch, and fixed mounting hardware

E2312 Power wheelchair accessory, hand or chin control interface, mini-proportional remote joystick, proportional, including fixed mounting hardware

ⓟ **E2313** Power wheelchair accessory, harness for upgrade to expandable controller, including all fasteners, connectors and mounting hardware, each

E2321 Power wheelchair accessory, hand control interface, remote joystick, nonproportional, including all related electronics, mechanical stop switch, and fixed mounting hardware

E2322 Power wheelchair accessory, hand control interface, multiple mechanical switches, nonproportional, including all related electronics, mechanical stop switch, and fixed mounting hardware

E2323 Power wheelchair accessory, specialty joystick handle for hand control interface, prefabricated

E2324 Power wheelchair accessory, chin cup for chin control interface

E2325 Power wheelchair accessory, sip and puff interface, nonproportional, including all related electronics, mechanical stop switch, and manual Swing-Away mounting hardware

E2326 Power wheelchair accessory, breath tube kit for sip and puff interface

E2327 Power wheelchair accessory, head control interface, mechanical, proportional, including all related electronics, mechanical direction change switch, and fixed mounting hardware

E2328 Power wheelchair accessory, head control or extremity control interface, electronic, proportional, including all related electronics and fixed mounting hardware

E2329 Power wheelchair accessory, head control interface, contact switch mechanism, nonproportional, including all related electronics, mechanical stop switch, mechanical direction change switch, head array, and fixed mounting hardware

	E2330	Power wheelchair accessory, head control interface, proximity switch mechanism, nonproportional, including all related electronics, mechanical stop switch, mechanical direction change switch, head array, and fixed mounting hardware
	E2331	Power wheelchair accessory, attendant control, proportional, including all related electronics and fixed mounting hardware
	E2340	Power wheelchair accessory, nonstandard seat frame width, 20-23 inches
	E2341	Power wheelchair accessory, nonstandard seat frame width, 24-27 inches
	E2342	Power wheelchair accessory, nonstandard seat frame depth, 20 or 21 inches
	E2343	Power wheelchair accessory, nonstandard seat frame depth, 22-25 inches
	E2351	Power wheelchair accessory, electronic interface to operate speech generating device using power wheelchair control interface
	E2358	Power wheelchair accessory, group 34 non-sealed lead acid battery, each
	E2359	Power wheelchair accessory, group 34 sealed lead acid battery, each (e.g., gel cell, absorbed glassmat)
	E2360	Power wheelchair accessory, 22nf non-sealed lead acid battery, each
℗	**E2361**	Power wheelchair accessory, 22nf sealed lead acid battery, each, (e.g., gel cell, absorbed glassmat)
	E2362	Power wheelchair accessory, group 24 non-sealed lead acid battery, each
	E2363	Power wheelchair accessory, group 24 sealed lead acid battery, each (e.g., gel cell, absorbed glassmat)
℗	**E2364**	Power wheelchair accessory, u-1 non-sealed lead acid battery, each
	E2365	Power wheelchair accessory, u-1 sealed lead acid battery, each (e.g., gel cell, absorbed glassmat)
	E2366	Power wheelchair accessory, battery charger, single mode, for use with only one battery type, sealed or non-sealed, each
	E2367	Power wheelchair accessory, battery charger, dual mode, for use with either battery type, sealed or non-sealed, each
	E2368	Power wheelchair component, drive wheel motor, replacement only
	E2369	Power wheelchair component, drive wheel gear box, replacement only
℗	**E2370**	Power wheelchair component, integrated drive wheel motor and gear box combination, replacement only
	E2371	Power wheelchair accessory, group 27 sealed lead acid battery, (e.g., gel cell, absorbed glassmat), each
	E2372	Power wheelchair accessory, group 27 non-sealed lead acid battery, each
	E2373	Power wheelchair accessory, hand or chin control interface, compact remote joystick, proportional, including fixed mounting hardware
℗	**E2374**	Power wheelchair accessory, hand or chin control interface, standard remote joystick (not including controller), proportional, including all related electronics and fixed mounting hardware, replacement only

ⓟ **E2375** Power wheelchair accessory, non-expandable controller, including all related electronics and mounting hardware, replacement only

E2376 Power wheelchair accessory, expandable controller, including all related electronics and mounting hardware, replacement only

ⓟ **E2377** Power wheelchair accessory, expandable controller, including all related electronics and mounting hardware, upgrade provided at initial issue

E2378 Power wheelchair component, actuator, replacement only

E2381 Power wheelchair accessory, pneumatic drive wheel tire, any size, replacement only, each

E2382 Power wheelchair accessory, tube for pneumatic drive wheel tire, any size, replacement only, each

E2383 Power wheelchair accessory, insert for pneumatic drive wheel tire (removable), any type, any size, replacement only, each

E2384 Power wheelchair accessory, pneumatic caster tire, any size, replacement only, each

E2385 Power wheelchair accessory, tube for pneumatic caster tire, any size, replacement only, each

E2386 Power wheelchair accessory, foam filled drive wheel tire, any size, replacement only, each

E2387 Power wheelchair accessory, foam filled caster tire, any size, replacement only, each

E2388 Power wheelchair accessory, foam drive wheel tire, any size, replacement only, each

E2389 Power wheelchair accessory, foam caster tire, any size, replacement only, each

E2390 Power wheelchair accessory, solid (rubber/plastic) drive wheel tire, any size, replacement only, each

E2391 Power wheelchair accessory, solid (rubber/plastic) caster tire (removable), any size, replacement only, each

E2392 Power wheelchair accessory, solid (rubber/plastic) caster tire with integrated wheel, any size, replacement only, each

E2394 Power wheelchair accessory, drive wheel excludes tire, any size, replacement only, each

E2395 Power wheelchair accessory, caster wheel excludes tire, any size, replacement only, each

E2396 Power wheelchair accessory, caster fork, any size, replacement only, each

E2397 Power wheelchair accessory, lithium-based battery, each

ⓟ **E2402** Negative pressure wound therapy electrical pump, stationary or portable

Speech Generating Device and Accessories

E2500 Speech generating device, digitized speech, using pre-recorded messages, less than or equal to 8 minutes recording time

CIM: 60-23

E2502 Speech generating device, digitized speech, using pre-recorded messages, greater than 8 minutes but less than or equal to 20 minutes recording time

CIM: 60-23

E2504 Speech generating device, digitized speech, using pre-recorded messages, greater than 20 minutes but less than or equal to 40 minutes recording time

CIM: 60-23

E2506 Speech generating device, digitized speech, using pre-recorded messages, greater than 40 minutes recording time

CIM: 60-23

E2508 Speech generating device, synthesized speech, requiring message formulation by spelling and access by physical contact with the device

CIM: 60-23

Ⓟ **E2510** Speech generating device, synthesized speech, permitting multiple methods of message formulation and multiple methods of device access

CIM: 60-23

E2511 Speech generating software program, for personal computer or personal digital assistant

CIM: 60-23

E2512 Accessory for speech generating device, mounting system

CIM: 60-23

Ⓟ **E2599** Accessory for speech generating device, not otherwise classified

CIM: 60-23

Wheelchair Cushions and Support Devices

Ⓟ **E2601** General use wheelchair seat cushion, width less than 22 inches, any depth

E2602 General use wheelchair seat cushion, width 22 inches or greater, any depth

Ⓟ **E2603** Skin protection wheelchair seat cushion, width less than 22 inches, any depth

E2604 Skin protection wheelchair seat cushion, width 22 inches or greater, any depth

E2605 Positioning wheelchair seat cushion, width less than 22 inches, any depth

E2606 Positioning wheelchair seat cushion, width 22 inches or greater, any depth

Ⓟ **E2607** Skin protection and positioning wheelchair seat cushion, width less than 22 inches, any depth

E2608 Skin protection and positioning wheelchair seat cushion, width 22 inches or greater, any depth

E2609 Custom fabricated wheelchair seat cushion, any size

E2610 Wheelchair seat cushion, powered

Ⓟ **E2611** General use wheelchair back cushion, width less than 22 inches, any height, including any type mounting hardware

E2612 General use wheelchair back cushion, width 22 inches or greater, any height, including any type mounting hardware

⑪ **E2613** Positioning wheelchair back cushion, posterior, width less than 22 inches, any height, including any type mounting hardware

E2614 Positioning wheelchair back cushion, posterior, width 22 inches or greater, any height, including any type mounting hardware

⑪ **E2615** Positioning wheelchair back cushion, posterior-lateral, width less than 22 inches, any height, including any type mounting hardware

E2616 Positioning wheelchair back cushion, posterior-lateral, width 22 inches or greater, any height, including any type mounting hardware

E2617 Custom fabricated wheelchair back cushion, any size, including any type mounting hardware

E2619 Replacement cover for wheelchair seat cushion or back cushion, each

⑪ **E2620** Positioning wheelchair back cushion, planar back with lateral supports, width less than 22 inches, any height, including any type mounting hardware

E2621 Positioning wheelchair back cushion, planar back with lateral supports, width 22 inches or greater, any height, including any type mounting hardware

⑪ **E2622** Skin protection wheelchair seat cushion, adjustable, width less than 22 inches, any depth

E2623 Skin protection wheelchair seat cushion, adjustable, width 22 inches or greater, any depth

E2624 Skin protection and positioning wheelchair seat cushion, adjustable, width less than 22 inches, any depth

E2625 Skin protection and positioning wheelchair seat cushion, adjustable, width 22 inches or greater, any depth

E2626 Wheelchair accessory, shoulder elbow, mobile arm support attached to wheelchair, balanced, adjustable

E2627 Wheelchair accessory, shoulder elbow, mobile arm support attached to wheelchair, balanced, adjustable rancho type

E2628 Wheelchair accessory, shoulder elbow, mobile arm support attached to wheelchair, balanced, reclining

E2629 Wheelchair accessory, shoulder elbow, mobile arm support attached to wheelchair, balanced, friction arm support (friction dampening to proximal and distal joints)

E2630 Wheelchair accessory, shoulder elbow, mobile arm support, monosuspension arm and hand support, overhead elbow forearm hand sling support, yoke type suspension support

E2631 Wheelchair accessory, addition to mobile arm support, elevating proximal arm

E2632 Wheelchair accessory, addition to mobile arm support, offset or lateral rocker arm with elastic balance control

E2633 Wheelchair accessory, addition to mobile arm support, supinator

Gait Trainer

E8000   Gait trainer, pediatric size, posterior support, includes all accessories and components

E8001   Gait trainer, pediatric size, upright support, includes all accessories and components

E8002   Gait trainer, pediatric size, anterior support, includes all accessories and components

PROCEDURES AND PROFESSIONAL SERVICES

Guidelines

In addition to the information presented in the INTRODUCTION, several other items unique to this section are defined or identified here:

1. TEMPORARY CODES: The codes listed in this section are assigned by CMS on a temporary basis to identify procedures/services.

Procedures/Professional Services

	G0008	Administration of influenza virus vaccine
	G0009	Administration of pneumococcal vaccine
	G0010	Administration of hepatitis b vaccine
	G0027	Semen analysis; presence and/or motility of sperm excluding Huhner
	G0101	Cervical or vaginal cancer screening; pelvic and clinical breast examination
	G0102	Prostate cancer screening; digital rectal examination

CIM: 50-55

MCM: 4182

G0103 Prostate cancer screening; prostate specific antigen test (PSA)

CIM: 50-55

MCM: 4182

G0104 Colorectal cancer screening; flexible sigmoidoscopy

Ⓣ **G0105** Colorectal cancer screening; colonoscopy on individual at high risk

G0106 Colorectal cancer screening; alternative to g0104, screening sigmoidoscopy, barium enema

G0108 Diabetes outpatient self-management training services, individual, per 30 minutes

G0109 Diabetes outpatient self-management training services, group session (2 or more), per 30 minutes

G0117 Glaucoma screening for high risk patients furnished by an optometrist or ophthalmologist

G0118 Glaucoma screening for high risk patient furnished under the direct supervision of an optometrist or ophthalmologist

G0120 Colorectal cancer screening; alternative to g0105, screening colonoscopy, barium enema.

Ⓣ **G0121** Colorectal cancer screening; colonoscopy on individual not meeting criteria for high risk

G0122 Colorectal cancer screening; barium enema

G0123 Screening cytopathology, cervical or vaginal (any reporting system), collected in preservative fluid, automated thin layer preparation, screening by cytotechnologist under physician supervision

CIM: 50-20

G0124 Screening cytopathology, cervical or vaginal (any reporting system), collected in preservative fluid, automated thin layer preparation, requiring interpretation by physician

CIM: 50-20

G0127 Trimming of dystrophic nails, any number

MCM: 2323

G0128 Direct (face-to-face with patient) skilled nursing services of a registered nurse provided in a comprehensive outpatient rehabilitation facility, each 10 minutes beyond the first 5 minutes

Statute: 1833(a)

G0129 Occupational therapy services requiring the skills of a qualified occupational therapist, furnished as a component of a partial hospitalization treatment program, per session (45 minutes or more)

G0130 Single energy x-ray absorptiometry (sexa) bone density study, one or more sites; appendicular skeleton (peripheral) (e.g., radius, wrist, heel)

CIM: 50-44

G0141 Screening cytopathology smears, cervical or vaginal, performed by automated system, with manual rescreening, requiring interpretation by physician

G0143 Screening cytopathology, cervical or vaginal (any reporting system), collected in preservative fluid, automated thin layer preparation, with manual screening and rescreening by cytotechnologist under physician supervision

G0144 Screening cytopathology, cervical or vaginal (any reporting system), collected in preservative fluid, automated thin layer preparation, with screening by automated system, under physician supervision

G0145 Screening cytopathology, cervical or vaginal (any reporting system), collected in preservative fluid, automated thin layer preparation, with screening by automated system and manual rescreening under physician supervision

G0147 Screening cytopathology smears, cervical or vaginal, performed by automated system under physician supervision

G0148 Screening cytopathology smears, cervical or vaginal, performed by automated system with manual rescreening

G0151 Services performed by a qualified physical therapist in the home health or hospice setting, each 15 minutes

G0152 Services performed by a qualified occupational therapist in the home health or hospice setting, each 15 minutes

G0153 Services performed by a qualified speech-language pathologist in the home health or hospice setting, each 15 minutes

(**G0154** Code deleted February 29, 2016).

G0155 Services of clinical social worker in home health or hospice settings, each 15 minutes

G0156 Services of home health/hospice aide in home health or hospice settings, each 15 minutes

G0157 Services performed by a qualified physical therapist assistant in the home health or hospice setting, each 15 minutes

G0158 Services performed by a qualified occupational therapist assistant in the home health or hospice setting, each 15 minutes

G0159 Services performed by a qualified physical therapist, in the home health setting, in the establishment or delivery of a safe and effective physical therapy maintenance program, each 15 minutes

G0160 Services performed by a qualified occupational therapist, in the home health setting, in the establishment or delivery of a safe and effective occupational therapy maintenance program, each 15 minutes

G0161 Services performed by a qualified speech-language pathologist, in the home health setting, in the establishment or delivery of a safe and effective speech-language pathology maintenance program, each 15 minutes

G0162 Skilled services by a registered nurse (RN) for management and evaluation of the plan of care; each 15 minutes (the patient's underlying condition or complication requires an RN to ensure that essential non-skilled care achieves its purpose in the home health or hospice setting)

(**G0163** Code deleted December 31, 2016).

(**G0164** Code deleted December 31, 2016).

G0166 External counterpulsation, per treatment session

CIM: 35-74

G0168 Wound closure utilizing tissue adhesive(s) only

G0175 Scheduled interdisciplinary team conference (minimum of three exclusive of patient care nursing staff) with patient present

G0176 Activity therapy, such as music, dance, art or play therapies not for recreation, related to the care and treatment of patient's disabling mental health problems, per session (45 minutes or more)

G0177 Training and educational services related to the care and treatment of patient's disabling mental health problems per session (45 minutes or more)

G0179 Physician re-certification for medicare-covered home health services under a home health plan of care (patient not present), including contacts with home health agency and review of reports of patient status required by physicians to affirm the initial implementation of the plan of care that meets patient's needs, per re-certification period

G0180 Physician certification for medicare-covered home health services under a home health plan of care (patient not present), including contacts with home health agency and

| Not payable by Medicare | Non-covered by Medicare | Special coverage instructions | Carrier judgement | 115 |

review of reports of patient status required by physicians to affirm the initial implementation of the plan of care that meets patient's needs, per certification period

G0181 Physician supervision of a patient receiving medicare-covered services provided by a participating home health agency (patient not present) requiring complex and multidisciplinary care modalities involving regular physician development and/or revision of care plans, review of subsequent reports of patient status, review of laboratory and other studies, communication (including telephone calls) with other health care professionals involved in the patient's care, integration of new information into the medical treatment plan and/or adjustment of medical therapy, within a calendar month, 30 minutes or more

G0182 Physician supervision of a patient under a medicare-approved hospice (patient not present) requiring complex and multidisciplinary care modalities involving regular physician development and/or revision of care plans, review of subsequent reports of patient status, review of laboratory and other studies, communication (including telephone calls) with other health care professionals involved in the patient's care, integration of new information into the medical treatment plan and/or adjustment of medical therapy, within a calendar month, 30 minutes or more

G0186 Destruction of localized lesion of choroid (for example, choroidal neovascularization); photocoagulation, feeder vessel technique (one or more sessions)

(G0202 Code deleted December 31, 2017). Use 77067.

(G0204 Code deleted December 31, 2017). Use 77066.

(G0206 Code deleted December 31, 2017). Use 77065.

G0219 Pet imaging whole body; melanoma for non-covered indications

CIM: 50-36

MCM: 4173

G0235 Pet imaging, any site, not otherwise specified

CIM: 50-36

G0237 Therapeutic procedures to increase strength or endurance of respiratory muscles, face to face, one on one, each 15 minutes (includes monitoring)

G0238 Therapeutic procedures to improve respiratory function, other than described by g0237, one on one, face to face, per 15 minutes (includes monitoring)

G0239 Therapeutic procedures to improve respiratory function or increase strength or endurance of respiratory muscles, two or more individuals (includes monitoring)

G0245 Initial physician evaluation and management of a diabetic patient with diabetic sensory neuropathy resulting in a loss of protective sensation (lops) which must include: (1) the diagnosis of lops, (2) a patient history, (3) a physical examination that consists of at least the following elements: (a) visual inspection of the forefoot, hindfoot and toe web spaces, (b) evaluation of a protective sensation, (c) evaluation of foot structure and biomechanics, (d) evaluation of vascular status and skin integrity, and (e) evaluation and recommendation of footwear and (4) patient education

CIM: 50.81

G0246   Follow-up physician evaluation and management of a diabetic patient with diabetic sensory neuropathy resulting in a loss of protective sensation (lops) to include at least the following: (1) a patient history, (2) a physical examination that includes: (a) visual inspection of the forefoot, hindfoot and toe web spaces, (b) evaluation of protective sensation, (c) evaluation of foot structure and biomechanics, (d) evaluation of vascular status and skin integrity, and (e) evaluation and recommendation of footwear, and (3) patient education

CIM: 50.81

G0247   Routine foot care by a physician of a diabetic patient with diabetic sensory neuropathy resulting in a loss of protective sensation (lops) to include, the local care of superficial wounds (i.e. superficial to muscle and fascia) and at least the following if present: (1) local care of superficial wounds, (2) debridement of corns and calluses, and (3) trimming and debridement of nails

CIM: 50.81

G0248   Demonstration, prior to initiation of home INR monitoring, for patient with either mechanical heart valve(s), chronic atrial fibrillation, or venous thromboembolism who meets Medicare coverage criteria, under the direction of a physician; includes: face-to-face demonstration of use and care of the INR monitor, obtaining at least one blood sample, provision of instructions for reporting home INR test results, and documentation of patient's ability to perform testing and report results

CIM: 50.55

G0249   Provision of test materials and equipment for home INR monitoring of patient with either mechanical heart valve(s), chronic atrial fibrillation, or venous thromboembolism who meets Medicare coverage criteria; includes: provision of materials for use in the home and reporting of test results to physician; testing not occurring more frequently than once a week; testing materials, billing units of service include 4 tests

CIM: 50.55

G0250   Physician review, interpretation, and patient management of home INR testing for patient with either mechanical heart valve(s), chronic atrial fibrillation, or venous thromboembolism who meets Medicare coverage criteria; testing not occurring more frequently than once a week; billing units of service include 4 tests

CIM: 50.55

G0252   Pet imaging, full and partial-ring pet scanners only, for initial diagnosis of breast cancer and/or surgical planning for breast cancer (e.g., initial staging of axillary lymph nodes)

CIM: 50-36

G0255   Current perception threshold/sensory nerve conduction test, (sNCT) per limb, any nerve

CIM: 50-57

G0257   Unscheduled or emergency dialysis treatment for an ESRD patient in a hospital outpatient department that is not certified as an ESRD facility

G0259   Injection procedure for sacroiliac joint; arthrography

G0260 Injection procedure for sacroiliac joint; provision of anesthetic, steroid and/or other therapeutic agent, with or without arthrography

G0268 Removal of impacted cerumen (one or both ears) by physician on same date of service as audiologic function testing

G0269 Placement of occlusive device into either a venous or arterial access site, post surgical or interventional procedure (e.g., Angio-Seal plug, vascular plug)

G0270 Medical nutrition therapy; reassessment and subsequent intervention(s) following second referral in same year for change in diagnosis, medical condition or treatment regimen (including additional hours needed for renal disease), individual, face to face with the patient, each 15 minutes

G0271 Medical nutrition therapy, reassessment and subsequent intervention(s) following second referral in same year for change in diagnosis, medical condition, or treatment regimen (including additional hours needed for renal disease), group (2 or more individuals), each 30 minutes

G0276 Blinded procedure for lumbar stenosis, percutaneous image-guided lumbar decompression (PILD) or placebo-control, performed in an approved coverage with evidence development (CED) clinical trial

G0277 Hyperbaric oxygen under pressure, full body chamber, per 30 minute interval

CIM: 35-10

G0278 Iliac and/or femoral artery angiography, non-selective, bilateral or ipsilateral to catheter insertion, performed at the same time as cardiac catheterization and/or coronary angiography, includes positioning or placement of the catheter in the distal aorta or ipsilateral femoral or iliac artery, injection of dye, production of permanent images, and radiologic supervision and interpretation (list separately in addition to primary procedure)

G0279 Diagnostic digital breast tomosynthesis, unilateral or bilateral (list separately in addition to G0204 or G0206)

G0281 Electrical stimulation, (unattended), to one or more areas, for chronic stage iii and stage iv pressure ulcers, arterial ulcers, diabetic ulcers, and venous stasis ulcers not demonstrating measurable signs of healing after 30 days of conventional care, as part of a therapy plan of care

G0282 Electrical stimulation, (unattended), to one or more areas, for wound care other than described in g0281

MCM: 35-98

G0283 Electrical stimulation (unattended), to one or more areas for indication(s) other than wound care, as part of a therapy plan of care

G0288 Reconstruction, computed tomographic angiography of aorta for surgical planning for vascular surgery

G0289 Arthroscopy, knee, surgical, for removal of loose body, foreign body, debridement/shaving of articular cartilage (chondroplasty) at the time of other surgical knee arthroscopy in a different compartment of the same knee

G0293 Noncovered surgical procedure(s) using conscious sedation, regional, general or spinal anesthesia in a Medicare qualifying clinical trial, per day

G0294 Noncovered procedure(s) using either no anesthesia or local anesthesia only, in a Medicare qualifying clinical trial, per day

G0295 Electromagnetic therapy, to one or more areas, for wound care other than described in G0329 or for other uses

CIM: 35-98

G0296 Counseling visit to discuss need for lung cancer screening (LDCT) using low dose ct scan (service is for eligibility determination and shared decision making)

G0297 Low dose ct scan (LDCT) for lung cancer screening

G0298 HIV antigen/antibody, combination assay, screening

G0299 Direct skilled nursing services of a registered nurse (RN) in the home health or hospice setting, each 15 minutes

G0300 Direct skilled nursing services of a license practical nurse (LPN) in the home health or hospice setting, each 15 minutes

G0302 Pre-operative pulmonary surgery services for preparation for LVRS, complete course of services, to include a minimum of 16 days of services

G0303 Pre-operative pulmonary surgery services for preparation for LVRS, 10 to 15 days of services

G0304 Pre-operative pulmonary surgery services for preparation for LVRS, 1 to 9 days of services

G0305 Post-discharge pulmonary surgery services after LVRS, minimum of 6 days of services

G0306 Complete CBC, automated (hgb, hCT, rbc, wbc, without platelet count) and automated wbc differential count

G0307 Complete (CBC), automated (hgb, hCT, rbc, wbc; without platelet count)

G0328 Colorectal cancer screening; fecal occult blood test, immunoassay, 1-3 simultaneous

G0329 Electromagnetic therapy, to one or more areas for chronic stage iii and stage iv pressure ulcers, arterial ulcers, diabetic ulcers and venous stasis ulcers not demonstrating measurable signs of healing after 30 days of conventional care as part of a therapy plan of care

ⓟ G0333 Pharmacy dispensing fee for inhalation drug(s); initial 30-day supply as a beneficiary

G0337 Hospice evaluation and counseling services, pre-election

G0339 Image-guided robotic linear accelerator-based stereotactic radiosurgery, complete course of therapy in one session or first session of fractionated treatment

G0340 Image-guided robotic linear accelerator-based stereotactic radiosurgery, delivery including collimator changes and custom plugging, fractionated treatment, all lesions, per session, second through fifth sessions, maximum five sessions per course of treatment

G0341 Percutaneous islet cell transplant, includes portal vein catheterization and infusion

CIM: 260.3

G0342   Laparoscopy for islet cell transplant, includes portal vein catheterization and infusion

CIM: 35-82

G0343   Laparotomy for islet cell transplant, includes portal vein catheterization and infusion

CIM: 35-82

(**G0364**   Code deleted December 31, 2017

G0365   Vessel mapping of vessels for hemodialysis access (services for preoperative vessel mapping prior to creation of hemodialysis access using an autogenous hemodialysis conduit, including arterial inflow and venous outflow)

G0372   Physician service required to establish and document the need for a power mobility device

G0378   Hospital observation service, per hour

G0379   Direct admission of patient for hospital observation care

G0380   Level 1 hospital emergency department visit provided in a type b emergency department; (the ed must meet at least one of the following requirements: (1) it is licensed by the state in which it is located under applicable state law as an emergency room or emergency department; (2) it is held out to the public (by name, posted signs, advertising, or other means) as a place that provides care for emergency medical conditions on an urgent basis without requiring a previously scheduled appointment; or (3) during the calendar year immediately preceding the calendar year in which a determination under 42 cfr 489.24 is being made, based on a representative sample of patient visits that occurred during that calendar year, it provides at least one-third of all of its outpatient visits for the treatment of emergency medical conditions on an urgent basis without requiring a previously scheduled appointment)

G0381   Level 2 hospital emergency department visit provided in a type b emergency department; (the ed must meet at least one of the following requirements: (1) it is licensed by the state in which it is located under applicable state law as an emergency room or emergency department; (2) it is held out to the public (by name, posted signs, advertising, or other means) as a place that provides care for emergency medical conditions on an urgent basis without requiring a previously scheduled appointment; or (3) during the calendar year immediately preceding the calendar year in which a determination under 42 cfr 489.24 is being made, based on a representative sample of patient visits that occurred during that calendar year, it provides at least one-third of all of its outpatient visits for the treatment of emergency medical conditions on an urgent basis without requiring a previously scheduled appointment)

G0382   Level 3 hospital emergency department visit provided in a type b emergency department; (the ed must meet at least one of the following requirements: (1) it is licensed by the state in which it is located under applicable state law as an emergency room or emergency department; (2) it is held out to the public (by name, posted signs, advertising, or other means) as a place that provides care for emergency medical conditions on an urgent basis without requiring a previously scheduled appointment; or (3) during the calendar year immediately preceding the calendar year in which a determination under 42 cfr 489.24 is being made, based on a representative sample of patient visits that occurred during that calendar year, it provides at least one-third of all of its outpatient visits for the treatment of emergency medical conditions on an urgent basis without requiring a previously scheduled appointment)

G0383 Level 4 hospital emergency department visit provided in a type b emergency department; (the ed must meet at least one of the following requirements: (1) it is licensed by the state in which it is located under applicable state law as an emergency room or emergency department; (2) it is held out to the public (by name, posted signs, advertising, or other means) as a place that provides care for emergency medical conditions on an urgent basis without requiring a previously scheduled appointment; or (3) during the calendar year immediately preceding the calendar year in which a determination under 42 cfr 489.24 is being made, based on a representative sample of patient visits that occurred during that calendar year, it provides at least one-third of all of its outpatient visits for the treatment of emergency medical conditions on an urgent basis without requiring a previously scheduled appointment)

G0384 Level 5 hospital emergency department visit provided in a type b emergency department; (the ed must meet at least one of the following requirements: (1) it is licensed by the state in which it is located under applicable state law as an emergency room or emergency department; (2) it is held out to the public (by name, posted signs, advertising, or other means) as a place that provides care for emergency medical conditions on an urgent basis without requiring a previously scheduled appointment; or (3) during the calendar year immediately preceding the calendar year in which a determination under 42 cfr 489.24 is being made, based on a representative sample of patient visits that occurred during that calendar year, it provides at least one-third of all of its outpatient visits for the treatment of emergency medical conditions on an urgent basis without requiring a previously scheduled appointment)

(**G0389** Code deleted December 31, 2016).

G0390 Trauma response team associated with hospital critical care service

G0396 Alcohol and/or substance (other than tobacco) abuse structured assessment (e.g., audit, DAST), and brief intervention 15 to 30 minutes

G0397 Alcohol and/or substance (other than tobacco) abuse structured assessment (e.g., audit, DAST), and intervention, greater than 30 minutes

G0398 Home sleep study test (hst) with type ii portable monitor, unattended; minimum of 7 channels: eeg, eog, EMG, ECG/heart rate, airflow, respiratory effort and oxygen saturation

G0399 Home sleep test (hst) with type iii portable monitor, unattended; minimum of 4 channels: 2 respiratory movement/airflow, 1 ECG/heart rate and 1 oxygen saturation

G0400 Home sleep test (hst) with type iv portable monitor, unattended; minimum of 3 channels

G0402 Initial preventive physical examination; face-to-face visit, services limited to new beneficiary during the first 12 months of Medicare enrollment

G0403 Electrocardiogram, routine ECG with 12 leads; performed as a screening for the initial preventive physical examination with interpretation and report

G0404 Electrocardiogram, routine ECG with 12 leads; tracing only, without interpretation and report, performed as a screening for the initial preventive physical examination

G0405 Electrocardiogram, routine ECG with 12 leads; interpretation and report only, performed as a screening for the initial preventive physical examination

G0406 Follow-up inpatient consultation, limited, physicians typically spend 15 minutes communicating with the patient via telehealth

G0407 Follow-up inpatient consultation, intermediate, physicians typically spend 25 minutes communicating with the patient via telehealth

G0408 Follow-up inpatient consultation, complex, physicians typically spend 35 minutes communicating with the patient via telehealth

G0409 Social work and psychological services, directly relating to and/or furthering the patient's rehabilitation goals, each 15 minutes, face-to-face; individual (services provided by a corf-qualified social worker or psychologist in a corf)

G0410 Group psychotherapy other than of a multiple-family group, in a partial hospitalization setting, approximately 45 to 50 minutes

G0411 Interactive group psychotherapy, in a partial hospitalization setting, approximately 45 to 50 minutes

G0412 Open treatment of iliac spine(s), tuberosity avulsion, or iliac wing fracture(s), unilateral or bilateral for pelvic bone fracture patterns which do not disrupt the pelvic ring includes internal fixation, when performed

G0413 Percutaneous skeletal fixation of posterior pelvic bone fracture and/or dislocation, for fracture patterns which disrupt the pelvic ring, unilateral or bilateral, (includes ilium, sacroiliac joint and/or sacrum)

G0414 Open treatment of anterior pelvic bone fracture and/or dislocation for fracture patterns which disrupt the pelvic ring, unilateral or bilateral, includes internal fixation when performed (includes pubic symphysis and/or superior/inferior rami)

G0415 Open treatment of posterior pelvic bone fracture and/or dislocation, for fracture patterns which disrupt the pelvic ring, unilateral or bilateral, includes internal fixation, when performed (includes ilium, sacroiliac joint and/or sacrum)

G0416 Surgical pathology, gross and microscopic examinations, for prostate needle biopsy, any method

G0420 Face-to-face educational services related to the care of chronic kidney disease; individual, per session, per one hour

G0421 Face-to-face educational services related to the care of chronic kidney disease; group, per session, per one hour

G0422 Intensive cardiac rehabilitation; with or without continuous ECG monitoring with exercise, per session

G0423 Intensive cardiac rehabilitation; with or without continuous ECG monitoring; without exercise, per session

G0424 Pulmonary rehabilitation, including exercise (includes monitoring), one hour, per session, up to two sessions per day

G0425 Telehealth consultation, emergency department or initial inpatient, typically 30 minutes communicating with the patient via telehealth

G0426 Telehealth consultation, emergency department or initial inpatient, typically 50 minutes communicating with the patient via telehealth

G0427 Telehealth consultation, emergency department or initial inpatient, typically 70 minutes or more communicating with the patient via telehealth

G0428 Collagen meniscus implant procedure for filling meniscal defects (e.g., CMI, collagen scaffold, menaflex)

G0429 Dermal filler injection(s) for the treatment of facial lipodystrophy syndrome (LDS) (e.g., as a result of highly active antiretroviral therapy)

G0432 Infectious agent antibody detection by enzyme immunoassay (EIA) technique, hiv-1 and/or hiv-2, screening

G0433 Infectious agent antibody detection by enzyme-linked immunosorbent assay (ELISA) technique, hiv-1 and/or hiv-2, screening

G0435 Infectious agent antibody detection by rapid antibody test, hiv-1 and/or hiv-2, screening

(G0436 Code deleted 09/30/16). Use 99406, 99407.

(G0437 Code deleted 09/30/16). Use 99406, 99407.

G0438 Annual wellness visit; includes a personalized prevention plan of service (pps), initial visit

G0439 Annual wellness visit, includes a personalized prevention plan of service (pps), subsequent visit

G0442 Annual alcohol misuse screening, 15 minutes

G0443 Brief face-to-face behavioral counseling for alcohol misuse, 15 minutes

G0444 Annual depression screening, 15 minutes

G0445 High intensity behavioral counseling to prevent sexually transmitted infection; face-to-face, individual, includes: education, skills training and guidance on how to change sexual behavior; performed semi-annually, 30 minutes

G0446 Annual, face-to-face intensive behavioral therapy for cardiovascular disease, individual, 15 minutes

G0447 Face-to-face behavioral counseling for obesity, 15 minutes

G0448 Insertion or replacement of a permanent pacing cardioverter-defibrillator system with transvenous lead(s), single or dual chamber with insertion of pacing electrode, cardiac venous system, for left ventricular pacing

G0451 Development testing, with interpretation and report, per standardized instrument form

G0452 Molecular pathology procedure; physician interpretation and report

G0453 Continuous intraoperative neurophysiology monitoring, from outside the operating room (remote or nearby), per patient, (attention directed exclusively to one patient) each 15 minutes (list in addition to primary procedure)

G0454 Physician documentation of face-to-face visit for durable medical equipment determination performed by nurse practitioner, physician assistant or clinical nurse specialist

G0455 Preparation with instillation of fecal microbiota by any method, including assessment of donor specimen

G0458 Low dose rate (LDR) prostate brachytherapy services, composite rate

G0459 Inpatient telehealth pharmacologic management, including prescription, use, and review of medication with no more than minimal medical psychotherapy

G0460 Autologous platelet rich plasma for chronic wounds/ulcers, including phlebotomy, centrifugation, and all other preparatory procedures, administration and dressings, per treatment

G0463 Hospital outpatient clinic visit for assessment and management of a patient

G0464 Colorectal cancer screening; stool-based DNA and fecal occult hemoglobin (e.g., KRAS, ndrg4 and bmp3)

G0466 Federally qualified health center (fqhc) visit, new patient; a medically-necessary, face-to-face encounter (one-on-one) between a new patient and a fqhc practitioner during which time one or more fqhc services are rendered and includes a typical bundle of medicare-covered services that would be furnished per diem to a patient receiving a fqhc visit

G0467 Federally qualified health center (fqhc) visit, established patient; a medically-necessary, face-to-face encounter (one-on-one) between an established patient and a fqhc practitioner during which time one or more fqhc services are rendered and includes a typical bundle of medicare-covered services that would be furnished per diem to a patient receiving a fqhc visit

G0468 Federally qualified health center (fqhc) visit, IPPE or AWV; a fqhc visit that includes an initial preventive physical examination (IPPE) or annual wellness visit (AWV) and includes a typical bundle of medicare-covered services that would be furnished per diem to a patient receiving an IPPE or AWV

G0469 Federally qualified health center (fqhc) visit, mental health, new patient; a medically-necessary, face-to-face mental health encounter (one-on-one) between a new patient and a fqhc practitioner during which time one or more fqhc services are rendered and includes a typical bundle of medicare-covered services that would be furnished per diem to a patient receiving a mental health visit

G0470 Federally qualified health center (fqhc) visit, mental health, established patient; a medically-necessary, face-to-face mental health encounter (one-on-one) between an established patient and a fqhc practitioner during which time one or more fqhc services are rendered and includes a typical bundle of medicare-covered services that would be furnished per diem to a patient receiving a mental health visit

G0471 Collection of venous blood by venipuncture or urine sample by catheterization from an individual in a skilled nursing facility (snf) or by a laboratory on behalf of a home health agency (HHA)

G0472 Hepatitis c antibody screening, for individual at high risk and other covered indication(s)

Statute: 1861SSA

G0473 Face-to-face behavioral counseling for obesity, group (2-10), 30 minutes

G0475 HIV antigen/antibody, combination assay, screening

G0476 Infectious agent detection by nucleic acid (DNA or rna); human papillomavirus (HPV), high-risk types (eg, 16, 18, 31, 33, 35, 39, 45, 51, 52, 56, 58, 59, 68) for cervical cancer screening, must be performed in addition to pap test

G0490 Face-to-face home health nursing visit by a rural health clinic (RHC) or federally qualified health center (fqhc) in an area with a shortage of home health agencies; (services limited to RN or LPN only)

G0491 Dialysis procedure at a Medicare certified ESRD facility for acute kidney injury without ESRD

G0492 Dialysis procedure with single evaluation by a physician or other qualified health care professional for acute kidney injury without ESRD

G0493 Skilled services of a registered nurse (RN) for the observation and assessment of the patient's condition, each 15 minutes (the change in the patient's condition requires skilled nursing personnel to identify and evaluate the patient's need for possible modification of treatment in the home health or hospice setting)

G0494 Skilled services of a licensed practical nurse (LPN) for the observation and assessment of the patient's condition, each 15 minutes (the change in the patient's condition requires skilled nursing personnel to identify and evaluate the patient's need for possible modification of treatment in the home health or hospice setting)

G0495 Skilled services of a registered nurse (RN), in the training and/or education of a patient or family member, in the home health or hospice setting, each 15 minutes

G0496 Skilled services of a licensed practical nurse (LPN), in the training and/or education of a patient or family member, in the home health or hospice setting, each 15 minutes

G0498 Chemotherapy administration, intravenous infusion technique; initiation of infusion in the office/clinic setting using office/clinic pump/supplies, with continuation of the infusion in the community setting (e.g., home, domiciliary, rest home or assisted living) using a portable pump provided by the office/clinic, includes follow up office/clinic visit at the conclusion of the infusion

G0499 Hepatitis b screening in non-pregnant, high risk individual includes hepatitis b surface antigen (HBsAg) followed by a neutralizing confirmatory test for initially reactive results, and antibodies to HBsAg (anti-HBs) and hepatitis b core antigen (anti-HBc)

G0500 Moderate sedation services provided by the same physician or other qualified health care professional performing a gastrointestinal endoscopic service that sedation supports, requiring the presence of an independent trained observer to assist in the monitoring of the patient's level of consciousness and physiological status; initial 15 minutes of intra-service time; patient age 5 years or older (additional time may be reported with 99153, as appropriate)

G0501 Resource-intensive services for patients for whom the use of specialized mobility-assistive technology (such as adjustable height chairs or tables, patient lift, and adjustable padded leg supports) is medically necessary and used during the provision of an office/outpatient, evaluation and management visit (list separately in addition to primary service)

(**G0502** Code deleted December 31, 2017). Use 99492.

(**G0503** Code deleted December 31, 2017). Use 99493.

(**G0504** Code deleted December 31, 2017). Use 99494.

(**G0505** Code deleted December 31, 2017). Use 99483.

(**G0507** Code deleted December 31, 2017). Use 99484.

G0508 Telehealth consultation, critical care, initial , physicians typically spend 60 minutes communicating with the patient and providers via telehealth

G0509 Telehealth consultation, critical care, subsequent, physicians typically spend 50 minutes communicating with the patient and providers via telehealth

• **G0511** Rural health clinic or federally qualified health center (RHC or fqhc) only, general care management, 20 minutes or more of clinical staff time for chronic care management services or behavioral health integration services directed by an RHC or fqhc practitioner (physician, np, pa, or cnm), per calendar month

• **G0512** Rural health clinic or federally qualified health center (RHC/fqhc) only, psychiatric collaborative care model (psychiatric cocm), 60 minutes or more of clinical staff time for psychiatric cocm services directed by an RHC or fqhc practitioner (physician, np, pa, or cnm) and including services furnished by a behavioral health care manager and consultation with a psychiatric consultant, per calendar month

• **G0513** Prolonged preventive service(s) (beyond the typical service time of the primary procedure), in the office or other outpatient setting requiring direct patient contact beyond the usual service; first 30 minutes (list separately in addition to code for preventive service)

• **G0514** Prolonged preventive service(s) (beyond the typical service time of the primary procedure), in the office or other outpatient setting requiring direct patient contact beyond the usual service; each additional 30 minutes (list separately in addition to code g0513 for additional 30 minutes of preventive service)

• **G0515** Development of cognitive skills to improve attention, memory, problem solving (includes compensatory training), direct (one-on-one) patient contact, each 15 minutes

• **G0516** Insertion of non-biodegradable drug delivery implants, 4 or more (services for subdermal rod implant)

• **G0517** Removal of non-biodegradable drug delivery implants, 4 or more (services for subdermal implants)

• **G0518** Removal with reinsertion, non-biodegradable drug delivery implants, 4 or more (services for subdermal implants)

G0913 Improvement in visual function achieved within 90 days following cataract surgery

G0914 Patient care survey was not completed by patient

G0915 Improvement in visual function not achieved within 90 days following cataract surgery

G0916 Satisfaction with care achieved within 90 days following cataract surgery

G0917 Patient satisfaction survey was not completed by patient

G0918 Satisfaction with care not achieved within 90 days following cataract surgery

(**G3001** Code deleted December 31, 2016).

G6001 Ultrasonic guidance for placement of radiation therapy fields

CIM: 50-7

G6002 Stereoscopic x-ray guidance for localization of target volume for the delivery of radiation therapy

G6003 Radiation treatment delivery, single treatment area, single port or parallel opposed ports, simple blocks or no blocks: up to 5 mev

G6004 Radiation treatment delivery, single treatment area, single port or parallel opposed ports, simple blocks or no blocks: 6-10 mev

G6005 Radiation treatment delivery, single treatment area, single port or parallel opposed ports, simple blocks or no blocks: 11-19 mev

G6006 Radiation treatment delivery, single treatment area, single port or parallel opposed ports, simple blocks or no blocks: 20 mev or greater

G6007 Radiation treatment delivery, 2 separate treatment areas, 3 or more ports on a single treatment area, use of multiple blocks: up to 5 mev

G6008 Radiation treatment delivery, 2 separate treatment areas, 3 or more ports on a single treatment area, use of multiple blocks: 6-10 mev

G6009 Radiation treatment delivery, 2 separate treatment areas, 3 or more ports on a single treatment area, use of multiple blocks: 11-19 mev

G6010 Radiation treatment delivery, 2 separate treatment areas, 3 or more ports on a single treatment area, use of multiple blocks: 20 mev or greater

G6011 Radiation treatment delivery,3 or more separate treatment areas, custom blocking, tangential ports, wedges, rotational beam, compensators, electron beam; up to 5 mev

G6012 Radiation treatment delivery,3 or more separate treatment areas, custom blocking, tangential ports, wedges, rotational beam, compensators, electron beam; 6-10 mev

G6013 Radiation treatment delivery,3 or more separate treatment areas, custom blocking, tangential ports, wedges, rotational beam, compensators, electron beam; 11-19 mev

G6014 Radiation treatment delivery,3 or more separate treatment areas, custom blocking, tangential ports, wedges, rotational beam, compensators, electron beam; 20 mev or greater

G6015 Intensity modulated treatment delivery, single or multiple fields/arcs, via narrow spatially and temporally modulated beams, binary, dynamic mlc, per treatment session

G6016 Compensator-based beam modulation treatment delivery of inverse planned treatment using 3 or more high resolution (milled or cast) compensator, convergent beam modulated fields, per treatment session

G6017 Intra-fraction localization and tracking of target or patient motion during delivery of radiation therapy (eg,3d positional tracking, gating, 3d surface tracking), each fraction of treatment

G6030 Amitriptyline

G6031 Benzodiazepines

G6032 Desipramine

G6034	Doxepin
G6035	Gold
G6036	Assay of imipramine
G6037	Nortriptyline
G6038	Salicylate
G6039	Acetaminophen
G6040	Alcohol (ethanol); any specimen except breath
G6041	Alkaloids, urine, quantitative
G6042	Amphetamine or methamphetamine
G6043	Barbiturates, not elsewhere specified
G6044	Cocaine or metabolite
G6045	Dihydrocodeinone
G6046	Dihydromorphinone
G6047	Dihydrotestosterone
G6048	Dimethadione
G6049	Epiandrosterone
G6050	Ethchlorvynol
G6051	Flurazepam
G6052	Meprobamate
G6053	Methadone
G6054	Methsuximide
G6055	Nicotine
G6056	Opiate(s), drug and metabolites, each procedure
G6057	Phenothiazine
G6058	Drug confirmation, each procedure
G8395	Left ventricular ejection fraction (LVEF) >= 40% or documentation as normal or mildly depressed left ventricular systolic function
G8396	Left ventricular ejection fraction (LVEF) not performed or documented
G8397	Dilated macular or fundus exam performed, including documentation of the presence or absence of macular edema and level of severity of retinopathy
G8398	Dilated macular or fundus exam not performed
G8399	Patient with documented results of a central dual-energy x-ray absorptiometry (DXA) ever being performed
G8400	Patient with central dual-energy x-ray absorptiometry (DXA) results not documented, reason not given

(**G8401** Code deleted December 31, 2016).

G8404 Lower extremity neurological exam performed and documented

G8405 Lower extremity neurological exam not performed

G8410 Footwear evaluation performed and documented

G8415 Footwear evaluation was not performed

G8416 Clinician documented that patient was not an eligible candidate for footwear evaluation measure

G8417 BMI is documented above normal parameters and a follow-up plan is documented

G8418 BMI is documented below normal parameters and a follow-up plan is documented

G8419 BMI documented outside normal parameters, no follow-up plan documented, no reason given

G8420 BMI is documented within normal parameters and no follow-up plan is required

G8421 BMI not documented and no reason is given

G8422 BMI not documented, documentation the patient is not eligible for BMI calculation

G8427 Eligible clinician attests to documenting in the medical record they obtained, updated, or reviewed the patient's current medications

G8428 Current list of medications not documented as obtained, updated, or reviewed by the eligible clinician, reason not given

G8430 Eligible clinician attests to documenting in the medical record the patient is not eligible for a current list of medications being obtained, updated, or reviewed by the eligible clinician

G8431 Screening for depression is documented as being positive and a follow-up plan is documented

G8432 Depression screening not documented, reason not given

G8433 Screening for depression not completed, documented reason

▲ **G8442** Pain assessment not documented as being performed, documentation the patient is not eligible for a pain assessment using a standardized tool at the time of the encounter

G8450 Beta-blocker therapy prescribed

G8451 Beta-blocker therapy for LVEF < 40% not prescribed for reasons documented by the clinician (e.g., low blood pressure, fluid overload, asthma, patients recently treated with an intravenous positive inotropic agent, allergy, intolerance, other medical reasons, patient declined, other patient reasons, or other reasons attributable to the healthcare system)

G8452 Beta-blocker therapy not prescribed

(**G8458** Code deleted December 31, 2016).

(**G8460** Code deleted December 31, 2016).

(**G8461** Code deleted December 31, 2016).

G8465 High or very high risk of recurrence of prostate cancer

G8473 Angiotensin converting enzyme (ace) inhibitor or angiotensin receptor blocker (arb) therapy prescribed

G8474 Angiotensin converting enzyme (ace) inhibitor or angiotensin receptor blocker (arb) therapy not prescribed for reasons documented by the clinician (e.g., allergy, intolerance, pregnancy, renal failure due to ace inhibitor, diseases of the aortic or mitral valve, other medical reasons) or (e.g., patient declined, other patient reasons) or (e.g., lack of drug availability, other reasons attributable to the health care system)

G8475 Angiotensin converting enzyme (ace) inhibitor or angiotensin receptor blocker (arb) therapy not prescribed, reason not given

G8476 Most recent blood pressure has a systolic measurement of < 140 mmhg and a diastolic measurement of < 90 mmhg

G8477 Most recent blood pressure has a systolic measurement of >= 140 mmhg and/or a diastolic measurement of >= 90 mmhg

G8478 Blood pressure measurement not performed or documented, reason not given

G8482 Influenza immunization administered or previously received

G8483 Influenza immunization was not administered for reasons documented by clinician (e.g., patient allergy or other medical reasons, patient declined or other patient reasons, vaccine not available or other system reasons)

G8484 Influenza immunization was not administered, reason not given

(**G8485** Code deleted December 31, 2016).

(**G8486** Code deleted December 31, 2016).

(**G8487** Code deleted December 31, 2016).

(**G8489** Code deleted December 31, 2016).

(**G8490** Code deleted December 31, 2016).

(**G8491** Code deleted December 31, 2016).

(**G8494** Code deleted December 31, 2016).

(**G8495** Code deleted December 31, 2016).

(**G8496** Code deleted December 31, 2016).

(**G8497** Code deleted December 31, 2016).

(**G8498** Code deleted December 31, 2016).

(**G8499** Code deleted December 31, 2016).

(**G8500** Code deleted December 31, 2016).

G8506 Patient receiving angiotensin converting enzyme (ace) inhibitor or angiotensin receptor blocker (arb) therapy

G8509 Pain assessment documented as positive using a standardized tool, follow-up plan not documented, reason not given

G8510 Screening for depression is documented as negative, a follow-up plan is not required

G8511 Screening for depression documented as positive, follow-up plan not documented, reason not given

▲ **G8535** Elder maltreatment screen not documented; documentation that patient is not eligible for the elder maltreatment screen at the time of the encounter

G8536 No documentation of an elder maltreatment screen, reason not given

G8539 Functional outcome assessment documented as positive using a standardized tool and a care plan based on identified deficiencies on the date of functional outcome assessment, is documented

▲ **G8540** Functional outcome assessment not documented as being performed, documentation the patient is not eligible for a functional outcome assessment using a standardized tool at the time of the encounter

G8541 Functional outcome assessment using a standardized tool not documented, reason not given

G8542 Functional outcome assessment using a standardized tool is documented; no functional deficiencies identified, care plan not required

G8543 Documentation of a positive functional outcome assessment using a standardized tool; care plan not documented, reason not given

(**G8544** Code deleted December 31, 2016).

(**G8545** Code deleted December 31, 2016).

(**G8548** Code deleted December 31, 2016).

(**G8549** Code deleted December 31, 2016).

(**G8551** Code deleted December 31, 2016).

G8559 Patient referred to a physician (preferably a physician with training in disorders of the ear) for an otologic evaluation

G8560 Patient has a history of active drainage from the ear within the previous 90 days

G8561 Patient is not eligible for the referral for otologic evaluation for patients with a history of active drainage measure

G8562 Patient does not have a history of active drainage from the ear within the previous 90 days

G8563 Patient not referred to a physician (preferably a physician with training in disorders of the ear) for an otologic evaluation, reason not given

G8564 Patient was referred to a physician (preferably a physician with training in disorders of the ear) for an otologic evaluation, reason not specified)

G8565 Verification and documentation of sudden or rapidly progressive hearing loss

G8566 Patient is not eligible for the "referral for otologic evaluation for sudden or rapidly progressive hearing loss" measure

G8567 Patient does not have verification and documentation of sudden or rapidly progressive hearing loss

G8568 Patient was not referred to a physician (preferably a physician with training in disorders of the ear) for an otologic evaluation, reason not given

G8569 Prolonged postoperative intubation (> 24 hrs) required

G8570 Prolonged postoperative intubation (> 24 hrs) not required

G8571 Development of deep sternal wound infection/mediastinitis within 30 days postoperatively

G8572 No deep sternal wound infection/mediastinitis

G8573 Stroke following isolated CABG surgery

G8574 No stroke following isolated CABG surgery

G8575 Developed postoperative renal failure or required dialysis

G8576 No postoperative renal failure/dialysis not required

G8577 Re-exploration required due to mediastinal bleeding with or without tamponade, graft occlusion, valve dysfunction or other cardiac reason

G8578 Re-exploration not required due to mediastinal bleeding with or without tamponade, graft occlusion, valve dysfunction or other cardiac reason

G8598 Aspirin or another antiplatelet therapy used

G8599 Aspirin or another antiplatelet therapy not used, reason not given

G8600 IV t-pa initiated within three hours (<= 180 minutes) of time last known well

G8601 IV t-pa not initiated within three hours (<= 180 minutes) of time last known well for reasons documented by clinician

G8602 IV t-pa not initiated within three hours (<= 180 minutes) of time last known well, reason not given

G8627 Surgical procedure performed within 30 days following cataract surgery for major complications (e.g., retained nuclear fragments, endophthalmitis, dislocated or wrong power IOL, retinal detachment, or wound dehiscence)

G8628 Surgical procedure not performed within 30 days following cataract surgery for major complications (e.g., retained nuclear fragments, endophthalmitis, dislocated or wrong power IOL, retinal detachment, or wound dehiscence)

G8633 Pharmacologic therapy (other than minerals/vitamins) for osteoporosis prescribed

(**G8634** Code deleted December 31, 2016).

G8635 Pharmacologic therapy for osteoporosis was not prescribed, reason not given

(**G8645** Code deleted December 31, 2016).

(**G8646** Code deleted December 31, 2016).

G8647 Risk-adjusted functional status change residual score for the knee successfully calculated and the score was equal to zero (0) or greater than zero (>0)

G8648 Risk-adjusted functional status change residual score for the knee successfully calculated and the score was less than zero (<0)

G8649 Risk-adjusted functional status change residual scores for the knee not measured because the patient did not complete foto's status survey near discharge, not appropriate

G8650 Risk-adjusted functional status change residual scores for the knee not measured because the patient did not complete foto's functional intake on admission and/or follow up status survey near discharge, reason not given

G8651 Risk-adjusted functional status change residual score for the hip successfully calculated and the score was equal to zero (0) or greater than zero (>0)

G8652 Risk-adjusted functional status change residual score for the hip successfully calculated and the score was less than zero (<0)

G8653 Risk-adjusted functional status change residual scores for the hip not measured because the patient did not complete follow up status survey near discharge, patient not appropriate

G8654 Risk-adjusted functional status change residual scores for the hip not measured because the patient did not complete foto's functional intake on admission and/or follow up status survey near discharge, reason not given

G8655 Risk-adjusted functional status change residual score for the foot or ankle successfully calculated and the score was equal to zero (0) or greater than zero (> 0)

G8656 Risk-adjusted functional status change residual score for the foot or ankle successfully calculated and the score was less than zero (< 0)

G8657 Risk-adjusted functional status change residual scores for the foot or ankle not measured because the patient did not complete foto's status survey near discharge, patient not appropriate

G8658 Risk-adjusted functional status change residual scores for the foot or ankle not measured because the patient did not complete foto's functional intake on admission and/or follow up status survey near discharge, reason not given

G8659 Risk-adjusted functional status change residual score for the lumbar impairment successfully calculated and the score was equal to zero (0) or greater than zero (> 0)

G8660 Risk-adjusted functional status change residual score for the lumbar impairment successfully calculated and the score was less than zero (< 0)

G8661 Risk-adjusted functional status change residual scores for the lumbar impairment not measured because the patient did not complete foto's status survey near discharge, patient not appropriate

G8662 Risk-adjusted functional status change residual scores for the lumbar impairment not measured because the patient did not complete foto's functional intake on admission and/or follow up status survey near discharge, reason not given

G8663 Risk-adjusted functional status change residual score for the shoulder successfully calculated and the score was equal to zero (0) or greater than zero (>0)

G8664 Risk-adjusted functional status change residual score for the shoulder successfully calculated and the score was less than zero (<0)

G8665 Risk-adjusted functional status change residual scores for the shoulder not measured because the patient did not complete foto's functional status survey near discharge, patient not appropriate

G8666 Risk-adjusted functional status change residual scores for the shoulder not measured because the patient did not complete foto's functional intake on admission and/or follow up status survey near discharge, reason not given

G8667 Risk-adjusted functional status change residual score for the elbow, wrist or hand successfully calculated and the score was equal to zero (0) or greater than zero (>0)

G8668 Risk-adjusted functional status change residual score for the elbow, wrist or hand successfully calculated and the score was less than zero (<0)

G8669 Risk-adjusted functional status change residual scores for the elbow, wrist or hand not measured because the patient did not complete foto's functional follow up status survey near discharge, patient not appropriate

G8670 Risk-adjusted functional status change residual scores for the elbow, wrist or hand not measured because the patient did not complete foto's functional intake on admission and/or follow up status survey near discharge, reason not given

G8671 Risk-adjusted functional status change residual score for the neck, cranium, mandible, thoracic spine, ribs, or other general orthopaedic impairment successfully calculated and the score was equal to zero (0) or greater than zero (> 0)

G8672 Risk-adjusted functional status change residual score for the neck, cranium, mandible, thoracic spine, ribs, or other general orthopedic impairment successfully calculated and the score was less than zero (<0)

G8673 Risk-adjusted functional status change residual scores for the neck, cranium, mandible, thoracic spine, ribs, or other general orthopaedic impairment not measured because the patient did not complete foto's functional follow up status survey near discharge, patient not appropriate

G8674 Risk-adjusted functional status change residual scores for the neck, cranium, mandible, thoracic spine, ribs, or other general orthopaedic impairment not measured because the patient did not complete foto's functional intake on admission and/or follow up status survey near discharge, reason not given

G8694 Left ventricular ejection fraction (LVEF) < 40%

(**G8696** Code deleted December 31, 2017).

(**G8697** Code deleted December 31, 2017).

(**G8698** Code deleted December 31, 2017).

G8708 Patient not prescribed or dispensed antibiotic

G8709 Patient prescribed or dispensed antibiotic for documented medical reason(s) (e.g., intestinal infection, pertussis, bacterial infection, lyme disease, otitis media, acute sinusitis, acute pharyngitis, acute tonsillitis, chronic sinusitis, infection of the pharynx/larynx/tonsils/adenoids, prostatitis, cellulitis, mastoiditis, or bone infections, acute lymphadenitis, impetigo, skin staph infections, pneumonia/gonococcal infections, venereal disease (syphilis, chlamydia, inflammatory diseases (female reproductive organs)), infections of the kidney, cystitis or UTI, and acne)

G8710	Patient prescribed or dispensed antibiotic
G8711	Prescribed or dispensed antibiotic
G8712	Antibiotic not prescribed or dispensed
G8721	Pt category (primary tumor), pn category (regional lymph nodes), and histologic grade were documented in pathology report
G8722	Documentation of medical reason(s) for not including the pt category, the pn category or the histologic grade in the pathology report (e.g., re-excision without residual tumor; non-carcinomas anal canal)
G8723	Specimen site is other than anatomic location of primary tumor
G8724	Pt category, pn category and histologic grade were not documented in the pathology report, reason not given
(G8725	Code deleted December 31, 2016).
(G8726	Code deleted December 31, 2016).
(G8728	Code deleted December 31, 2016).
G8730	Pain assessment documented as positive using a standardized tool and a follow-up plan is documented
G8731	Pain assessment using a standardized tool is documented as negative, no follow-up plan required
G8732	No documentation of pain assessment, reason not given
G8733	Elder maltreatment screen documented as positive and a follow-up plan is documented
G8734	Elder maltreatment screen documented as negative, no follow-up required
G8735	Elder maltreatment screen documented as positive, follow-up plan not documented, reason not given
G8749	Absence of signs of melanoma (cough, dyspnea, tenderness, localized neurologic signs such as weakness, jaundice or any other sign suggesting systemic spread) or absence of symptoms of melanoma (pain, paresthesia, or any other symptom suggesting the possibility of systemic spread of melanoma)
G8752	Most recent systolic blood pressure < 140 mmhg
G8753	Most recent systolic blood pressure >= 140 mmhg
G8754	Most recent diastolic blood pressure < 90 mmhg
G8755	Most recent diastolic blood pressure >= 90 mmhg
G8756	No documentation of blood pressure measurement, reason not given
(G8757	Code deleted December 31, 2016).
(G8758	Code deleted December 31, 2016).
(G8759	Code deleted December 31, 2016).
(G8761	Code deleted December 31, 2016).
(G8762	Code deleted December 31, 2016).

(**G8765**   Code deleted December 31, 2016).

G8783   Normal blood pressure reading documented, follow-up not required

(**G8784**   Code deleted December 31, 2016).

G8785   Blood pressure reading not documented, reason not given

G8797   Specimen site other than anatomic location of esophagus

G8798   Specimen site other than anatomic location of prostate

G8806   Performance of trans-abdominal or trans-vaginal ultrasound

G8807   Trans-abdominal or trans-vaginal ultrasound not performed for reasons documented by clinician (e.g., patient has visited the ed multiple times within 72 hours, patient has a documented intrauterine pregnancy [IUP])

▲ **G8808**   Trans-abdominal or trans-vaginal ultrasound not performed, reason not given

G8809   Rh-immunoglobulin (RhoGAM) ordered

G8810   Rh-immunoglobulin (RhoGAM) not ordered for reasons documented by clinician (e.g., patient had prior documented receipt of RhoGAM within 12 weeks, patient refusal)

G8811   Documentation Rh-immunoglobulin (RhoGAM) was not ordered, reason not given

G8815   Documented reason in the medical records for why the statin therapy was not prescribed (i.e., lower extremity bypass was for a patient with non-atherosclerotic disease)

G8816   Statin medication prescribed at discharge

G8817   Statin therapy not prescribed at discharge, reason not given

G8818   Patient discharge to home no later than post-operative day #7

G8825   Patient not discharged to home by post-operative day #7

G8826   Patient discharge to home no later than post-operative day #2 following EVAR

G8833   Patient not discharged to home by post-operative day #2 following EVAR

G8834   Patient discharged to home no later than post-operative day #2 following CEA

G8838   Patient not discharged to home by post-operative day #2 following CEA

G8839   Sleep apnea symptoms assessed, including presence or absence of snoring and daytime sleepiness

G8840   Documentation of reason(s) for not documenting an assessment of sleep symptoms (e.g., patient didn't have initial daytime sleepiness, patient visited between initial testing and initiation of therapy)

G8841   Sleep apnea symptoms not assessed, reason not given

G8842   Apnea hypopnea index (AHI) or respiratory disturbance index (RDI) measured at the time of initial diagnosis

G8843   Documentation of reason(s) for not measuring an apnea hypopnea index (AHI) or a respiratory disturbance index (RDI) at the time of initial diagnosis (e.g., psychiatric disease, dementia, patient declined, financial, insurance coverage, test ordered but not yet completed)

G8844 Apnea hypopnea index (AHI) or respiratory disturbance index (RDI) not measured at the time of initial diagnosis, reason not given

G8845 Positive airway pressure therapy prescribed

G8846 Moderate or severe obstructive sleep apnea (apnea hypopnea index (AHI) or respiratory disturbance index (RDI) of 15 or greater)

(**G8848** Code deleted December 31, 2016).

G8849 Documentation of reason(s) for not prescribing positive airway pressure therapy (e.g., patient unable to tolerate, alternative therapies use, patient declined, financial, insurance coverage)

G8850 Positive airway pressure therapy not prescribed, reason not given

G8851 Objective measurement of adherence to positive airway pressure therapy, documented

G8852 Positive airway pressure therapy prescribed

(**G8853** Code deleted December 31, 2016).

G8854 Documentation of reason(s) for not objectively measuring adherence to positive airway pressure therapy (e.g., patient didn't bring data from continuous positive airway pressure [CPAP], therapy not yet initiated, not available on machine)

G8855 Objective measurement of adherence to positive airway pressure therapy not performed, reason not given

G8856 Referral to a physician for an otologic evaluation performed

G8857 Patient is not eligible for the referral for otologic evaluation measure (e.g., patients who are already under the care of a physician for acute or chronic dizziness)

G8858 Referral to a physician for an otologic evaluation not performed, reason not given

G8861 Within the past 2 years, central dual-energy x-ray absorptiometry (DXA) ordered and documented, review of systems and medication history or pharmacologic therapy (other than minerals/vitamins) for osteoporosis prescribed

G8863 Patients not assessed for risk of bone loss, reason not given

G8864 Pneumococcal vaccine administered or previously received

G8865 Documentation of medical reason(s) for not administering or previously receiving pneumococcal vaccine (e.g., patient allergic reaction, potential adverse drug reaction)

G8866 Documentation of patient reason(s) for not administering or previously receiving pneumococcal vaccine (e.g., patient refusal)

G8867 Pneumococcal vaccine not administered or previously received, reason not given

(**G8868** Code deleted December 31, 2016).

▲ **G8869** Patient has documented immunity to hepatitis b and initiating anti-TNF therapy

G8872 Excised tissue evaluated by imaging intraoperatively to confirm successful inclusion of targeted lesion

G8873 Patients with needle localization specimens which are not amenable to intraoperative imaging such as MRI needle wire localization, or targets which are tentatively identified on mammogram or ultrasound which do not contain a biopsy marker but which can be verified on intraoperative inspection or pathology (e.g., needle biopsy site where the biopsy marker is remote from the actual biopsy site)

G8874 Excised tissue not evaluated by imaging intraoperatively to confirm successful inclusion of targeted lesion

G8875 Clinician diagnosed breast cancer preoperatively by a minimally invasive biopsy method

G8876 Documentation of reason(s) for not performing minimally invasive biopsy to diagnose breast cancer preoperatively (e.g., lesion too close to skin, implant, chest wall, etc., lesion could not be adequately visualized for needle biopsy, patient condition prevents needle biopsy [weight, breast thickness, etc.], duct excision without imaging abnormality, prophylactic mastectomy, reduction mammoplasty, excisional biopsy performed by another physician)

G8877 Clinician did not attempt to achieve the diagnosis of breast cancer preoperatively by a minimally invasive biopsy method, reason not given

G8878 Sentinel lymph node biopsy procedure performed

(**G8879** Code deleted December 31, 2017).

▲ **G8880** Documentation of reason(s) sentinel lymph node biopsy not performed (e.g., reasons could include but not limited to; non-invasive cancer, incidental discovery of breast cancer on prophylactic mastectomy, incidental discovery of breast cancer on reduction mammoplasty, pre-operative biopsy proven lymph node (ln) metastases, inflammatory carcinoma, stage 3 locally advanced cancer, recurrent invasive breast cancer, clinically node positive after neoadjuvant systemic therapy, patient refusal after informed consent)

G8881 Stage of breast cancer is greater than t1n0m0 or t2n0m0

G8882 Sentinel lymph node biopsy procedure not performed, reason not given

G8883 Biopsy results reviewed, communicated, tracked and documented

G8884 Clinician documented reason that patient's biopsy results were not reviewed

G8885 Biopsy results not reviewed, communicated, tracked or documented

(**G8898** Code deleted December 31, 2016).

(**G8899** Code deleted December 31, 2016).

(**G8900** Code deleted December 31, 2016).

(**G8902** Code deleted December 31, 2016).

(**G8903** Code deleted December 31, 2016).

(**G8906** Code deleted December 31, 2016).

G8907 Patient documented not to have experienced any of the following events: a burn prior to discharge; a fall within the facility; wrong site/side/patient/procedure/implant event; or a hospital transfer or hospital admission upon discharge from the facility

G8908 Patient documented to have received a burn prior to discharge

G8909 Patient documented not to have received a burn prior to discharge

G8910 Patient documented to have experienced a fall within asc

G8911 Patient documented not to have experienced a fall within ambulatory surgical center

G8912 Patient documented to have experienced a wrong site, wrong side, wrong patient, wrong procedure or wrong implant event

G8913 Patient documented not to have experienced a wrong site, wrong side, wrong patient, wrong procedure or wrong implant event

G8914 Patient documented to have experienced a hospital transfer or hospital admission upon discharge from asc

G8915 Patient documented not to have experienced a hospital transfer or hospital admission upon discharge from asc

G8916 Patient with preoperative order for iv antibiotic surgical site infection (ssi) prophylaxis, antibiotic initiated on time

G8917 Patient with preoperative order for iv antibiotic surgical site infection (ssi) prophylaxis, antibiotic not initiated on time

G8918 Patient without preoperative order for iv antibiotic surgical site infection (ssi) prophylaxis

G8923 Left ventricular ejection fraction (LVEF) < 40% or documentation of moderately or severely depressed left ventricular systolic function

G8924 Spirometry test results demonstrate fev1/fvc < 70%, fev < 60% predicted and patient has COPD symptoms (e.g., dyspnea, cough/sputum, wheezing)

G8925 Spirometry test results demonstrate fev1 >= 60% fev1/fvc >= 70%, predicted or patient does not have COPD symptoms

G8926 Spirometry test not performed or documented, reason not given

(**G8927** Code deleted December 31, 2016).

(**G8928** Code deleted December 31, 2016).

(**G8929** Code deleted December 31, 2016).

G8934 Left ventricular ejection fraction (LVEF) <40% or documentation of moderately or severely depressed left ventricular systolic function

G8935 Clinician prescribed angiotensin converting enzyme (ace) inhibitor or angiotensin receptor blocker (arb) therapy

G8936 Clinician documented that patient was not an eligible candidate for angiotensin converting enzyme (ace) inhibitor or angiotensin receptor blocker (arb) therapy (eg, allergy, intolerance, pregnancy, renal failure due to ace inhibitor, diseases of the aortic or mitral valve, other medical reasons) or (eg, patient declined, other patient reasons) or (eg, lack of drug availability, other reasons attributable to the health care system)

G8937 Clinician did not prescribe angiotensin converting enzyme (ace) inhibitor or angiotensin receptor blocker (arb) therapy, reason not given

G8938   BMI is documented as being outside of normal limits, follow-up plan is not documented, documentation the patient is not eligible

▲ G8939   Pain assessment documented as positive, follow-up plan not documented, documentation the patient is not eligible at the time of the encounter

(G8940   Code deleted December 31, 2016).

▲ G8941   Elder maltreatment screen documented as positive, follow-up plan not documented, documentation the patient is not eligible for follow-up plan at the time of the encounter

G8942   Functional outcomes assessment using a standardized tool is documented within the previous 30 days and care plan, based on identified deficiencies on the date of the functional outcome assessment, is documented

G8944   AJCC melanoma cancer stage 0 through iic melanoma

G8946   Minimally invasive biopsy method attempted but not diagnostic of breast cancer (e.g., high risk lesion of breast such as atypical ductal hyperplasia, lobular neoplasia, atypical lobular hyperplasia, lobular carcinoma in situ, atypical columnar hyperplastica, flat epithelial atypia, radial scar, complex sclerosing lesion, papillary lesion, or any lesion with spindle cells)

(G8947   Code deleted December 31, 2017).

(G8948   Code deleted December 31, 2016).

G8950   Pre-hypertensive or hypertensive blood pressure reading documented, and the indicated follow-up is documented

G8952   Pre-hypertensive or hypertensive blood pressure reading documented, indicated follow-up not documented, reason not given

(G8953   Code deleted December 31, 2016).

G8955   Most recent assessment of adequacy of volume management documented

G8956   Patient receiving maintenance hemodialysis in an outpatient dialysis facility

G8958   Assessment of adequacy of volume management not documented, reason not given

G8959   Clinician treating major depressive disorder communicates to clinician treating comorbid condition

G8960   Clinician treating major depressive disorder did not communicate to clinician treating comorbid condition, reason not given

G8961   Cardiac stress imaging test primarily performed on low-risk surgery patient for preoperative evaluation within 30 days preceding this surgery

G8962   Cardiac stress imaging test performed on patient for any reason including those who did not have low risk surgery or test that was performed more than 30 days preceding low risk surgery

G8963   Cardiac stress imaging performed primarily for monitoring of asymptomatic patient who had pci within 2 years

	G8964	Cardiac stress imaging test performed primarily for any other reason than monitoring of asymptomatic patient who had pci within 2 years (e.g., symptomatic patient, patient greater than 2 years since pci, initial evaluation, etc)
	G8965	Cardiac stress imaging test primarily performed on low CHD risk patient for initial detection and risk assessment
	G8966	Cardiac stress imaging test performed on symptomatic or higher than low CHD risk patient or for any reason other than initial detection and risk assessment
▲	**G8967**	Warfarin or another FDA approved oral anticoagulant is prescribed
▲	**G8968**	Documentation of medical reason(s) for not prescribing warfarin or another FDA-approved anticoagulant (e.g., atrial appendage device in place)
▲	**G8969**	Documentation of patient reason(s) for not prescribing warfarin or another FDA-approved oral anticoagulant that is FDA approved for the prevention of thromboembolism (e.g., patient choice of having atrial appendage device placed)
(	**G8971**	Code deleted December 31, 2017).
(	**G8972**	Code deleted December 31, 2017).
	G8972	One or more high risk factors for thromboembolism or more than one moderate risk factor for thromboembolism
	G8973	Most recent hemoglobin (hgb) level < 10 g/dl
	G8974	Hemoglobin level measurement not documented, reason not given
	G8975	Documentation of medical reason(s) for patient having a hemoglobin level < 10 g/dl (e.g., patients who have non-renal etiologies of anemia [e.g., sickle cell anemia or other hemoglobinopathies, hypersplenism, primary bone marrow disease, anemia related to chemotherapy for diagnosis of malignancy, postoperative bleeding, active bloodstream or peritoneal infection], other medical reasons)
	G8976	Most recent hemoglobin (hgb) level >= 10 g/dl
(	**G8977**	Code deleted December 31, 2016).
	G8978	Mobility: walking & moving around functional limitation, current status, at therapy episode outset and at reporting intervals
	G8979	Mobility: walking & moving around functional limitation, projected goal status, at therapy episode outset, at reporting intervals, and at discharge or to end reporting
	G8980	Mobility: walking & moving around functional limitation, discharge status, at discharge from therapy or to end reporting
	G8981	Changing & maintaining body position functional limitation, current status, at therapy episode outset and at reporting intervals
	G8982	Changing & maintaining body position functional limitation, projected goal status, at therapy episode outset, at reporting intervals, and at discharge or to end reporting
	G8983	Changing & maintaining body position functional limitation, discharge status, at discharge from therapy or to end reporting
	G8984	Carrying, moving & handling objects functional limitation, current status, at therapy

episode outset and at reporting intervals

G8985 Carrying, moving and handling objects, projected goal status, at therapy episode outset, at reporting intervals, and at discharge or to end reporting

G8986 Carrying, moving & handling objects functional limitation, discharge status, at discharge from therapy or to end reporting

G8987 Self care functional limitation, current status, at therapy episode outset and at reporting intervals

G8988 Self care functional limitation, projected goal status, at therapy episode outset, at reporting intervals, and at discharge or to end reporting

G8989 Self care functional limitation, discharge status, at discharge from therapy or to end reporting

G8990 Other physical or occupational therapy primary functional limitation, current status, at therapy episode outset and at reporting intervals

G8991 Other physical or occupational therapy primary functional limitation, projected goal status, at therapy episode outset, at reporting intervals, and at discharge or to end reporting

G8992 Other physical or occupational therapy primary functional limitation, discharge status, at discharge from therapy or to end reporting

G8993 Other physical or occupational therapy subsequent functional limitation, current status, at therapy episode outset and at reporting intervals

G8994 Other physical or occupational therapy subsequent functional limitation, projected goal status, at therapy episode outset, at reporting intervals, and at discharge or to end reporting

G8995 Other physical or occupational therapy subsequent functional limitation, discharge status, at discharge from therapy or to end reporting

G8996 Swallowing functional limitation, current status at therapy episode outset and at reporting intervals

G8997 Swallowing functional limitation, projected goal status, at therapy episode outset, at reporting intervals, and at discharge or to end reporting

G8998 Swallowing functional limitation, discharge status, at discharge from therapy or to end reporting

G8999 Motor speech functional limitation, current status at therapy episode outset and at reporting intervals

G9001 Coordinated care fee, initial rate

G9002 Coordinated care fee, maintenance rate

G9003 Coordinated care fee, risk adjusted high, initial

G9004 Coordinated care fee, risk adjusted low, initial

G9005 Coordinated care fee, risk adjusted maintenance

G9006 Coordinated care fee, home monitoring

G9007   Coordinated care fee, scheduled team conference

G9008   Coordinated care fee, physician coordinated care oversight services

G9009   Coordinated care fee, risk adjusted maintenance, level 3

G9010   Coordinated care fee, risk adjusted maintenance, level 4

G9011   Coordinated care fee, risk adjusted maintenance, level 5

G9012   Other specified case management service not elsewhere classified

G9013   Esrd demo basic bundle level i

G9014   Esrd demo expanded bundle including venous access and related services

G9016   Smoking cessation counseling, individual, in the absence of or in addition to any other evaluation and management service, per session (6-10 minutes) [demo project code only]

G9017   Amantadine hydrochloride, oral, per 100 mg (for use in a medicare-approved demonstration project)

G9018   Zanamivir, inhalation powder, administered through inhaler, per 10 mg (for use in a medicare-approved demonstration project)

G9019   Oseltamivir phosphate, oral, per 75 mg (for use in a medicare-approved demonstration project)

G9020   Rimantadine hydrochloride, oral, per 100 mg (for use in a medicare-approved demonstration project)

G9033   Amantadine hydrochloride, oral brand, per 100 mg (for use in a medicare-approved demonstration project)

G9034   Zanamivir, inhalation powder, administered through inhaler, brand, per 10 mg (for use in a medicare-approved demonstration project)

G9035   Oseltamivir phosphate, oral, brand, per 75 mg (for use in a medicare-approved demonstration project)

G9036   Rimantadine hydrochloride, oral, brand, per 100 mg (for use in a medicare-approved demonstration project)

G9050   Oncology; primary focus of visit; work-up, evaluation, or staging at the time of cancer diagnosis or recurrence (for use in a medicare-approved demonstration project)

G9051   Oncology; primary focus of visit; treatment decision-making after disease is staged or restaged, discussion of treatment options, supervising/coordinating active cancer directed therapy or managing consequences of cancer directed therapy (for use in a medicare-approved demonstration project)

G9052   Oncology; primary focus of visit; surveillance for disease recurrence for patient who has completed definitive cancer-directed therapy and currently lacks evidence of recurrent disease; cancer directed therapy might be considered in the future (for use in a medicare-approved demonstration project)

G9053   Oncology; primary focus of visit; expectant management of patient with evidence of cancer for whom no cancer directed therapy is being administered or arranged at present; cancer directed therapy might be considered in the future (for use in a medicare-approved demonstration project)

G9054 Oncology; primary focus of visit; supervising, coordinating or managing care of patient with terminal cancer or for whom other medical illness prevents further cancer treatment; includes symptom management, end-of-life care planning, management of palliative therapies (for use in a medicare-approved demonstration project)

G9055 Oncology; primary focus of visit; other, unspecified service not otherwise listed (for use in a medicare-approved demonstration project)

G9056 Oncology; practice guidelines; management adheres to guidelines (for use in a medicare-approved demonstration project)

G9057 Oncology; practice guidelines; management differs from guidelines as a result of patient enrollment in an institutional review board approved clinical trial (for use in a medicare-approved demonstration project)

G9058 Oncology; practice guidelines; management differs from guidelines because the treating physician disagrees with guideline recommendations (for use in a medicare-approved demonstration project)

G9059 Oncology; practice guidelines; management differs from guidelines because the patient, after being offered treatment consistent with guidelines, has opted for alternative treatment or management, including no treatment (for use in a medicare-approved demonstration project)

G9060 Oncology; practice guidelines; management differs from guidelines for reason(s) associated with patient comorbid illness or performance status not factored into guidelines (for use in a medicare-approved demonstration project)

G9061 Oncology; practice guidelines; patient's condition not addressed by available guidelines (for use in a medicare-approved demonstration project)

G9062 Oncology; practice guidelines; management differs from guidelines for other reason(s) not listed (for use in a medicare-approved demonstration project)

G9063 Oncology; disease status; limited to non-small cell lung cancer; extent of disease initially established as stage i (prior to neo-adjuvant therapy, if any) with no evidence of disease progression, recurrence, or metastases (for use in a medicare-approved demonstration project)

G9064 Oncology; disease status; limited to non-small cell lung cancer; extent of disease initially established as stage ii (prior to neo-adjuvant therapy, if any) with no evidence of disease progression, recurrence, or metastases (for use in a medicare-approved demonstration project)

G9065 Oncology; disease status; limited to non-small cell lung cancer; extent of disease initially established as stage iii a (prior to neo-adjuvant therapy, if any) with no evidence of disease progression, recurrence, or metastases (for use in a medicare-approved demonstration project)

G9066 Oncology; disease status; limited to non-small cell lung cancer; stage iii b- iv at diagnosis, metastatic, locally recurrent, or progressive (for use in a medicare-approved demonstration project)

G9067 Oncology; disease status; limited to non-small cell lung cancer; extent of disease unknown, staging in progress, or not listed (for use in a medicare-approved demonstration project)

G9068 Oncology; disease status; limited to small cell and combined small cell/non-small cell; extent of disease initially established as limited with no evidence of disease progression, recurrence, or metastases (for use in a medicare-approved demonstration project)

G9069 Oncology; disease status; small cell lung cancer, limited to small cell and combined small cell/non-small cell; extensive stage at diagnosis, metastatic, locally recurrent, or progressive (for use in a medicare-approved demonstration project)

G9070 Oncology; disease status; small cell lung cancer, limited to small cell and combined small cell/non-small; extent of disease unknown, staging in progress, or not listed (for use in a medicare-approved demonstration project)

G9071 Oncology; disease status; invasive female breast cancer (does not include ductal carcinoma in situ); adenocarcinoma as predominant cell type; stage i or stage iia-iib; or t3, n1, m0; and er and/or pr positive; with no evidence of disease progression, recurrence, or metastases (for use in a medicare-approved demonstration project)

G9072 Oncology; disease status; invasive female breast cancer (does not include ductal carcinoma in situ); adenocarcinoma as predominant cell type; stage i, or stage iia-iib; or t3, n1, m0; and er and pr negative; with no evidence of disease progression, recurrence, or metastases (for use in a medicare-approved demonstration project)

G9073 Oncology; disease status; invasive female breast cancer (does not include ductal carcinoma in situ); adenocarcinoma as predominant cell type; stage IIIa-IIIb; and not t3, n1, m0; and er and/or pr positive; with no evidence of disease progression, recurrence, or metastases (for use in a medicare-approved demonstration project)

G9074 Oncology; disease status; invasive female breast cancer (does not include ductal carcinoma in situ); adenocarcinoma as predominant cell type; stage IIIa-IIIb; and not t3, n1, m0; and er and pr negative; with no evidence of disease progression, recurrence, or metastases (for use in a medicare-approved demonstration project)

G9075 Oncology; disease status; invasive female breast cancer (does not include ductal carcinoma in situ); adenocarcinoma as predominant cell type; m1 at diagnosis, metastatic, locally recurrent, or progressive (for use in a medicare-approved demonstration project)

G9077 Oncology; disease status; prostate cancer, limited to adenocarcinoma as predominant cell type; t1-t2c and Gleason 2-7 and PSA < or equal to 20 at diagnosis with no evidence of disease progression, recurrence, or metastases (for use in a medicare-approved demonstration project)

G9078 Oncology; disease status; prostate cancer, limited to adenocarcinoma as predominant cell type; t2 or t3a Gleason 8-10 or PSA > 20 at diagnosis with no evidence of disease progression, recurrence, or metastases (for use in a medicare-approved demonstration project)

G9079 Oncology; disease status; prostate cancer, limited to adenocarcinoma as predominant cell type; t3b-t4, any n; any t, n1 at diagnosis with no evidence of disease progression, recurrence, or metastases (for use in a medicare-approved demonstration project)

G9080 Oncology; disease status; prostate cancer, limited to adenocarcinoma; after initial treatment with rising PSA or failure of PSA decline (for use in a medicare-approved demonstration project)

G9083 Oncology; disease status; prostate cancer, limited to adenocarcinoma; extent of disease unknown, staging in progress, or not listed (for use in a medicare-approved demonstration project)

G9084 Oncology; disease status; colon cancer, limited to invasive cancer, adenocarcinoma as predominant cell type; extent of disease initially established as t1-3, n0, m0 with no evidence of disease progression, recurrence, or metastases (for use in a medicare-approved demonstration project)

G9085 Oncology; disease status; colon cancer, limited to invasive cancer, adenocarcinoma as predominant cell type; extent of disease initially established as t4, n0, m0 with no evidence of disease progression, recurrence, or metastases (for use in a medicare-approved demonstration project)

G9086 Oncology; disease status; colon cancer, limited to invasive cancer, adenocarcinoma as predominant cell type; extent of disease initially established as t1-4, n1-2, m0 with no evidence of disease progression, recurrence, or metastases (for use in a medicare-approved demonstration project)

G9087 Oncology; disease status; colon cancer, limited to invasive cancer, adenocarcinoma as predominant cell type; m1 at diagnosis, metastatic, locally recurrent, or progressive with current clinical, radiologic, or biochemical evidence of disease (for use in a medicare-approved demonstration project)

G9088 Oncology; disease status; colon cancer, limited to invasive cancer, adenocarcinoma as predominant cell type; m1 at diagnosis, metastatic, locally recurrent, or progressive without current clinical, radiologic, or biochemical evidence of disease (for use in a medicare-approved demonstration project)

G9089 Oncology; disease status; colon cancer, limited to invasive cancer, adenocarcinoma as predominant cell type; extent of disease unknown, staging in progress, or not listed (for use in a medicare-approved demonstration project)

G9090 Oncology; disease status; rectal cancer, limited to invasive cancer, adenocarcinoma as predominant cell type; extent of disease initially established as t1-2, n0, m0 (prior to neo-adjuvant therapy, if any) with no evidence of disease progression, recurrence, or metastases (for use in a medicare-approved demonstration project)

G9091 Oncology; disease status; rectal cancer, limited to invasive cancer, adenocarcinoma as predominant cell type; extent of disease initially established as t3, n0, m0 (prior to neo-adjuvant therapy, if any) with no evidence of disease progression, recurrence, or metastases (for use in a medicare-approved demonstration project)

G9092 Oncology; disease status; rectal cancer, limited to invasive cancer, adenocarcinoma as predominant cell type; extent of disease initially established as t1-3, n1-2, m0 (prior to neo-adjuvant therapy, if any) with no evidence of disease progression, recurrence or metastases (for use in a medicare-approved demonstration project)

G9093 Oncology; disease status; rectal cancer, limited to invasive cancer, adenocarcinoma as predominant cell type; extent of disease initially established as t4, any n, m0 (prior to neo-adjuvant therapy, if any) with no evidence of disease progression, recurrence, or metastases (for use in a medicare-approved demonstration project)

G9094 Oncology; disease status; rectal cancer, limited to invasive cancer, adenocarcinoma as predominant cell type; m1 at diagnosis, metastatic, locally recurrent, or progressive (for use in a medicare-approved demonstration project)

G9095 Oncology; disease status; rectal cancer, limited to invasive cancer, adenocarcinoma as predominant cell type; extent of disease unknown, staging in progress, or not listed (for use in a medicare-approved demonstration project)

G9096 Oncology; disease status; esophageal cancer, limited to adenocarcinoma or squamous cell carcinoma as predominant cell type; extent of disease initially established as t1-t3, n0-n1 or nx (prior to neo-adjuvant therapy, if any) with no evidence of disease progression, recurrence, or metastases (for use in a medicare-approved demonstration project)

G9097 Oncology; disease status; esophageal cancer, limited to adenocarcinoma or squamous cell carcinoma as predominant cell type; extent of disease initially established as t4, any n, m0 (prior to neo-adjuvant therapy, if any) with no evidence of disease progression, recurrence, or metastases (for use in a medicare-approved demonstration project)

G9098 Oncology; disease status; esophageal cancer, limited to adenocarcinoma or squamous cell carcinoma as predominant cell type; m1 at diagnosis, metastatic, locally recurrent, or progressive (for use in a medicare-approved demonstration project)

G9099 Oncology; disease status; esophageal cancer, limited to adenocarcinoma or squamous cell carcinoma as predominant cell type; extent of disease unknown, staging in progress, or not listed (for use in a medicare-approved demonstration project)

G9100 Oncology; disease status; gastric cancer, limited to adenocarcinoma as predominant cell type; post r0 resection (with or without neoadjuvant therapy) with no evidence of disease recurrence, progression, or metastases (for use in a medicare-approved demonstration project)

G9101 Oncology; disease status; gastric cancer, limited to adenocarcinoma as predominant cell type; post r1 or r2 resection (with or without neoadjuvant therapy) with no evidence of disease progression, or metastases (for use in a medicare-approved demonstration project)

G9102 Oncology; disease status; gastric cancer, limited to adenocarcinoma as predominant cell type; clinical or pathologic m0, unresectable with no evidence of disease progression, or metastases (for use in a medicare-approved demonstration project)

G9103 Oncology; disease status; gastric cancer, limited to adenocarcinoma as predominant cell type; clinical or pathologic m1 at diagnosis, metastatic, locally recurrent, or progressive (for use in a medicare-approved demonstration project)

G9104 Oncology; disease status; gastric cancer, limited to adenocarcinoma as predominant cell type; extent of disease unknown, staging in progress, or not listed (for use in a medicare-approved demonstration project)

G9105 Oncology; disease status; pancreatic cancer, limited to adenocarcinoma as predominant cell type; post r0 resection without evidence of disease progression, recurrence, or metastases (for use in a medicare-approved demonstration project)

G9106 Oncology; disease status; pancreatic cancer, limited to adenocarcinoma; post r1 or r2 resection with no evidence of disease progression, or metastases (for use in a medicare-approved demonstration project)

G9107   Oncology; disease status; pancreatic cancer, limited to adenocarcinoma; unresectable at diagnosis, m1 at diagnosis, metastatic, locally recurrent, or progressive (for use in a medicare-approved demonstration project)

G9108   Oncology; disease status; pancreatic cancer, limited to adenocarcinoma; extent of disease unknown, staging in progress, or not listed (for use in a medicare-approved demonstration project)

G9109   Oncology; disease status; head and neck cancer, limited to cancers of oral cavity, pharynx and larynx with squamous cell as predominant cell type; extent of disease initially established as t1-t2 and n0, m0 (prior to neo-adjuvant therapy, if any) with no evidence of disease progression, recurrence, or metastases (for use in a medicare-approved demonstration project)

G9110   Oncology; disease status; head and neck cancer, limited to cancers of oral cavity, pharynx and larynx with squamous cell as predominant cell type; extent of disease initially established as t3-4 and/or n1-3, m0 (prior to neo-adjuvant therapy, if any) with no evidence of disease progression, recurrence, or metastases (for use in a medicare-approved demonstration project)

G9111   Oncology; disease status; head and neck cancer, limited to cancers of oral cavity, pharynx and larynx with squamous cell as predominant cell type; m1 at diagnosis, metastatic, locally recurrent, or progressive (for use in a medicare-approved demonstration project)

G9112   Oncology; disease status; head and neck cancer, limited to cancers of oral cavity, pharynx and larynx with squamous cell as predominant cell type; extent of disease unknown, staging in progress, or not listed (for use in a medicare-approved demonstration project)

G9113   Oncology; disease status; ovarian cancer, limited to epithelial cancer; pathologic stage ia-b (grade 1) without evidence of disease progression, recurrence, or metastases (for use in a medicare-approved demonstration project)

G9114   Oncology; disease status; ovarian cancer, limited to epithelial cancer; pathologic stage ia-b (grade 2-3); or stage ic (all grades); or stage ii; without evidence of disease progression, recurrence, or metastases (for use in a medicare-approved demonstration project)

G9115   Oncology; disease status; ovarian cancer, limited to epithelial cancer; pathologic stage iii-iv; without evidence of progression, recurrence, or metastases (for use in a medicare-approved demonstration project)

G9116   Oncology; disease status; ovarian cancer, limited to epithelial cancer; evidence of disease progression, or recurrence, and/or platinum resistance (for use in a medicare-approved demonstration project)

G9117   Oncology; disease status; ovarian cancer, limited to epithelial cancer; extent of disease unknown, staging in progress, or not listed (for use in a medicare-approved demonstration project)

G9123   Oncology; disease status; chronic myelogenous leukemia, limited to Philadelphia chromosome positive and/or bcr-abl positive; chronic phase not in hematologic, cytogenetic, or molecular remission (for use in a medicare-approved demonstration project)

G9124   Oncology; disease status; chronic myelogenous leukemia, limited to Philadelphia chromosome positive and/or bcr-abl positive; accelerated phase not in hematologic cytogenetic, or molecular remission (for use in a medicare-approved demonstration project)

G9125 Oncology; disease status; chronic myelogenous leukemia, limited to Philadelphia chromosome positive and/or bcr-abl positive; blast phase not in hematologic, cytogenetic, or molecular remission (for use in a medicare-approved demonstration project)

G9126 Oncology; disease status; chronic myelogenous leukemia, limited to Philadelphia chromosome positive and/or bcr-abl positive; in hematologic, cytogenetic, or molecular remission (for use in a medicare-approved demonstration project)

G9128 Oncology; disease status; limited to multiple myeloma, systemic disease; smoldering, stage i (for use in a medicare-approved demonstration project)

G9129 Oncology; disease status; limited to multiple myeloma, systemic disease; stage ii or higher (for use in a medicare-approved demonstration project)

G9130 Oncology; disease status; limited to multiple myeloma, systemic disease; extent of disease unknown, staging in progress, or not listed (for use in a medicare-approved demonstration project)

G9131 Oncology; disease status; invasive female breast cancer (does not include ductal carcinoma in situ); adenocarcinoma as predominant cell type; extent of disease unknown, staging in progress, or not listed (for use in a medicare-approved demonstration project)

G9132 Oncology; disease status; prostate cancer, limited to adenocarcinoma; hormone-refractory/androgen-independent (e.g., rising PSA on anti-androgen therapy or post-orchiectomy); clinical metastases (for use in a medicare-approved demonstration project)

G9133 Oncology; disease status; prostate cancer, limited to adenocarcinoma; hormone-responsive; clinical metastases or m1 at diagnosis (for use in a medicare-approved demonstration project)

G9134 Oncology; disease status; non-Hodgkin's lymphoma, any cellular classification; stage i, ii at diagnosis, not relapsed, not refractory (for use in a medicare-approved demonstration project)

G9135 Oncology; disease status; non-Hodgkin's lymphoma, any cellular classification; stage iii, iv, not relapsed, not refractory (for use in a medicare-approved demonstration project)

G9136 Oncology; disease status; non-Hodgkin's lymphoma, transformed from original cellular diagnosis to a second cellular classification (for use in a medicare-approved demonstration project)

G9137 Oncology; disease status; non-Hodgkin's lymphoma, any cellular classification; relapsed/refractory (for use in a medicare-approved demonstration project)

G9138 Oncology; disease status; non-Hodgkin's lymphoma, any cellular classification; diagnostic evaluation, stage not determined, evaluation of possible relapse or non-response to therapy, or not listed (for use in a medicare-approved demonstration project)

G9139   Oncology; disease status; chronic myelogenous leukemia, limited to Philadelphia chromosome positive and/or bcr-abl positive; extent of disease unknown, staging in progress, not listed (for use in a medicare-approved demonstration project)

G9140   Frontier extended stay clinic demonstration; for a patient stay in a clinic approved for the CMS demonstration project; the following measures should be present: the stay must be equal to or greater than 4 hours; weather or other conditions must prevent transfer or the case falls into a category of monitoring and observation cases that are permitted by the rules of the demonstration; there is a maximum frontier extended stay clinic (FESC) visit of 48 hours, except in the case when weather or other conditions prevent transfer; payment is made on each period up to 4 hours, after the first 4 hours

G9143   Warfarin responsiveness testing by genetic technique using any method, any number of specimen(s)

G9147   Outpatient intravenous insulin treatment (OIVIT) either pulsatile or continuous, by any means, guided by the results of measurements for: respiratory quotient; and/or, urine urea nitrogen (UUN); and/or, arterial, venous or capillary glucose; and/or potassium concentration

G9148   National committee for quality assurance - level 1 medical home

G9149   National committee for quality assurance - level 2 medical home

G9150   National committee for quality assurance - level 3 medical home

G9151   MAPCP demonstration - state provided services

G9152   MAPCP demonstration - community health teams

G9153   MAPCP demonstration - physician incentive pool

G9156   Evaluation for wheelchair requiring face to face visit with physician

G9157   Transesophageal Doppler measurement of cardiac output (including probe placement, image acquisition, and interpretation per course of treatment) for monitoring purposes

G9158   Motor speech functional limitation, discharge status, at discharge from therapy or to end reporting

G9159   Spoken language comprehension functional limitation, current status at therapy episode outset and at reporting intervals

G9160   Spoken language comprehension functional limitation, projected goal status at therapy episode outset, at reporting intervals, and at discharge or to end reporting

G9161   Spoken language comprehension functional limitation, discharge status, at discharge from therapy or to end reporting

G9162   Spoken language expression functional limitation, current status at therapy episode outset and at reporting intervals

G9163   Spoken language expression functional limitation, projected goal status at therapy episode outset, at reporting intervals, and at discharge or to end reporting

G9164   Spoken language expression functional limitation, discharge status at discharge from therapy or to end reporting

G9165   Attention functional limitation, current status at therapy episode outset and at reporting intervals

G9166 Attention functional limitation, projected goal status at therapy episode outset, at reporting intervals, and at discharge or to end reporting

G9167 Attention functional limitation, discharge status at discharge from therapy or to end reporting

G9168 Memory functional limitation, current status at therapy episode outset and at reporting intervals

G9169 Memory functional limitation, projected goal status at therapy episode outset, at reporting intervals, and at discharge or to end reporting

G9170 Memory functional limitation, discharge status at discharge from therapy or to end reporting

G9171 Voice functional limitation, current status at therapy episode outset and at reporting intervals

G9172 Voice functional limitation, projected goal status at therapy episode outset, at reporting intervals, and at discharge or to end reporting

G9173 Voice functional limitation, discharge status at discharge from therapy or to end reporting

G9174 Other speech language pathology functional limitation, current status at therapy episode outset and at reporting intervals

G9175 Other speech language pathology functional limitation, projected goal status at therapy episode outset, at reporting intervals, and at discharge or to end reporting

G9176 Other speech language pathology functional limitation, discharge status at discharge from therapy or to end reporting

G9186 Motor speech functional limitation, projected goal status at therapy episode outset, at reporting intervals, and at discharge or to end reporting

G9187 Bundled payments for care improvement initiative home visit for patient assessment performed by a qualified health care professional for individuals not considered homebound including, but not limited to, assessment of safety, falls, clinical status, fluid status, medication reconciliation/management, patient compliance with orders/plan of care, performance of activities of daily living, appropriateness of care setting; (for use only in the Medicare-approved bundled payments for care improvement initiative); may not be billed for a 30-day period covered by a transitional care management code

G9188 Beta-blocker therapy not prescribed, reason not given

G9189 Beta-blocker therapy prescribed or currently being taken

G9190 Documentation of medical reason(s) for not prescribing beta-blocker therapy (eg, allergy, intolerance, other medical reasons)

G9191 Documentation of patient reason(s) for not prescribing beta-blocker therapy (eg, patient declined, other patient reasons)

G9192 Documentation of system reason(s) for not prescribing beta-blocker therapy (eg, other reasons attributable to the health care system)

G9196   Documentation of medical reason(s) for not ordering a first or second generation cephalosporin for antimicrobial prophylaxis (e.g., patients enrolled in clinical trials, patients with documented infection prior to surgical procedure of interest, patients who were receiving antibiotics more than 24 hours prior to surgery [except colon surgery patients taking oral prophylactic antibiotics], patients who were receiving antibiotics within 24 hours prior to arrival [except colon surgery patients taking oral prophylactic antibiotics], other medical reason(s))

G9197   Documentation of order for first or second generation cephalosporin for antimicrobial prophylaxis

G9198   Order for first or second generation cephalosporin for antimicrobial prophylaxis was not documented, reason not given

(**G9203**   Code deleted December 31, 2016).

(**G9204**   Code deleted December 31, 2016).

(**G9205**   Code deleted December 31, 2016).

(**G9206**   Code deleted December 31, 2016).

(**G9207**   Code deleted December 31, 2016).

(**G9208**   Code deleted December 31, 2016).

(**G9209**   Code deleted December 31, 2016).

(**G9210**   Code deleted December 31, 2016).

(**G9211**   Code deleted December 31, 2016).

G9212   DSM-IV criteria for major depressive disorder documented at the initial evaluation

G9213   DSM-IV-tr criteria for major depressive disorder not documented at the initial evaluation, reason not otherwise specified

(**G9217**   Code deleted December 31, 2016).

(**G9219**   Code deleted December 31, 2016).

(**G9222**   Code deleted December 31, 2016).

G9223   Pneumocystis jiroveci pneumonia prophylaxis prescribed within 3 months of low cd4+ cell count below 500 cells/mm3 or a cd4 percentage below 15%

G9225   Foot exam was not performed, reason not given

G9226   Foot examination performed (includes examination through visual inspection, sensory exam with 10-g monofilament plus testing any one of the following: vibration using 128-hz tuning fork, pinprick sensation, ankle reflexes, or vibration perception threshold, and pulse exam ? report when all of the 3 components are completed)

▲   **G9227**   Functional outcome assessment documented, care plan not documented, documentation the patient is not eligible for a care plan at the time of the encounter

G9228   Chlamydia, gonorrhea and syphilis screening results documented (report when results are present for all of the 3 screenings)

G9229   Chlamydia, gonorrhea, and syphilis screening results not documented (patient refusal is the only allowed exception)

G9230 Chlamydia, gonorrhea, and syphilis not screened, reason not given

G9231 Documentation of end stage renal disease (ESRD), dialysis, renal transplant before or during the measurement period or pregnancy during the measurement period

G9232 Clinician treating major depressive disorder did not communicate to clinician treating comorbid condition for specified patient reason (e.g., patient is unable to communicate the diagnosis of a comorbid condition; the patient is unwilling to communicate the diagnosis of a comorbid condition; or the patient is unaware of the comorbid condition, or any other specified patient reason)

(**G9233** Code deleted December 31, 2016).

(**G9234** Code deleted December 31, 2016).

(**G9235** Code deleted December 31, 2016).

(**G9236** Code deleted December 31, 2016).

(**G9237** Code deleted December 31, 2016).

(**G9238** Code deleted December 31, 2016).

G9239 Documentation of reasons for patient initiating maintenance hemodialysis with a catheter as the mode of vascular access (e.g., patient has a maturing AVF/AVG, time-limited trial of hemodialysis, other medical reasons, patient declined AVF/AVG, other patient reasons, patient followed by reporting nephrologist for fewer than 90 days, other system reasons)

G9240 Patient whose mode of vascular access is a catheter at the time maintenance hemodialysis is initiated

G9241 Patient whose mode of vascular access is not a catheter at the time maintenance hemodialysis is initiated

G9242 Documentation of viral load equal to or greater than 200 copies/ml or viral load not performed

(**G9244** Code deleted December 31, 2016).

(**G9245** Code deleted December 31, 2016).

G9245 Antiretroviral therapy prescribed

G9246 Patient did not have at least one medical visit in each 6 month period of the 24 month measurement period, with a minimum of 60 days between medical visits

G9247 Patient had at least one medical visit in each 6 month period of the 24 month measurement period, with a minimum of 60 days between medical visits

G9250 Documentation of patient pain brought to a comfortable level within 48 hours from initial assessment

G9251 Documentation of patient with pain not brought to a comfortable level within 48 hours from initial assessment

G9254 Documentation of patient discharged to home later than post-operative day 2 following CAS

G9255 Documentation of patient discharged to home no later than post operative day 2 following CAS

G9256	Documentation of patient death following CAS
G9257	Documentation of patient stroke following CAS
G9258	Documentation of patient stroke following CEA
G9259	Documentation of patient survival and absence of stroke following CAS
G9260	Documentation of patient death following CEA
G9261	Documentation of patient survival and absence of stroke following CEA
G9262	Documentation of patient death in the hospital following endovascular aaa repair
▲ **G9263**	Documentation of patient discharged alive following endovascular aaa repair
G9264	Documentation of patient receiving maintenance hemodialysis for greater than or equal to 90 days with a catheter for documented reasons (e.g., other medical reasons, patient declined AVF/AVG, other patient reasons)
G9265	Patient receiving maintenance hemodialysis for greater than or equal to 90 days with a catheter as the mode of vascular access
G9266	Patient receiving maintenance hemodialysis for greater than or equal to 90 days without a catheter as the mode of vascular access
G9267	Documentation of patient with one or more complications or mortality within 30 days
G9268	Documentation of patient with one or more complications within 90 days
G9269	Documentation of patient without one or more complications and without mortality within 30 days
G9270	Documentation of patient without one or more complications within 90 days
G9273	Blood pressure has a systolic value of < 140 and a diastolic value of < 90
G9274	Blood pressure has a systolic value of =140 and a diastolic value of = 90 or systolic value < 140 and diastolic value = 90 or systolic value = 140 and diastolic value < 90
G9275	Documentation that patient is a current non-tobacco user
G9276	Documentation that patient is a current tobacco user
G9277	Documentation that the patient is on daily aspirin or anti-platelet or has documentation of a valid contraindication or exception to aspirin/anti-platelet; contraindications/ exceptions include anti-coagulant use, allergy to aspirin or anti-platelets, history of gastrointestinal bleed and bleeding disorder; additionally, the following exceptions documented by the physician as a reason for not taking daily aspirin or anti-platelet are acceptable (use of non-steroidal anti-inflammatory agents, documented risk for drug interaction, uncontrolled hypertension defined as >180 systolic or >110 diastolic or gastroesophageal reflux)
G9278	Documentation that the patient is not on daily aspirin or anti-platelet regimen
G9279	Pneumococcal screening performed and documentation of vaccination received prior to discharge
G9280	Pneumococcal vaccination not administered prior to discharge, reason not specified
G9281	Screening performed and documentation that vaccination not indicated/patient refusal
G9282	Documentation of medical reason(s) for not reporting the histological type or

NSCLC-nos classification with an explanation (e.g., biopsy taken for other purposes in a patient with a history of non-small cell lung cancer or other documented medical reasons)

G9283 Non small cell lung cancer biopsy and cytology specimen report documents classification into specific histologic type or classified as NSCLC-nos with an explanation

G9284 Non small cell lung cancer biopsy and cytology specimen report does not document classification into specific histologic type or classified as NSCLC-nos with an explanation

G9285 Specimen site other than anatomic location of lung or is not classified as non small cell lung cancer

G9286 Antibiotic regimen prescribed within10 days after onset of symptoms

G9287 Antibiotic regimen not prescribed within 10 days after onset of symptoms

G9288 Documentation of medical reason(s) for not reporting the histological type or NSCLC-nos classification with an explanation (e.g., a solitary fibrous tumor in a person with a history of non-small cell carcinoma or other documented medical reasons)

G9289 Non small cell lung cancer biopsy and cytology specimen report documents classification into specific histologic type or classified as NSCLC-nos with an explanation

G9290 Non small cell lung cancer biopsy and cytology specimen report does not document classification into specific histologic type or classified as NSCLC-nos with an explanation

G9291 Specimen site other than anatomic location of lung, is not classified as non small cell lung cancer or classified as NSCLC-nos

G9292 Documentation of medical reason(s) for not reporting pt category and a statement on thickness and ulceration and for pt1, mitotic rate (e.g., negative skin biopsies in a patient with a history of melanoma or other documented medical reasons)

G9293 Pathology report does not include the pt category and a statement on thickness and ulceration and for pt1, mitotic rate

G9294 Pathology report includes the pt category and a statement on thickness and ulceration and for pt1, mitotic rate

G9295 Specimen site other than anatomic cutaneous location

G9296 Patients with documented shared decision-making including discussion of conservative (non-surgical) therapy (e.g., NSAIDs, analgesics, weight loss, exercise, injections) prior to the procedure

G9297 Shared decision-making including discussion of conservative (non-surgical) therapy (e.g., NSAIDs, analgesics, weight loss, exercise, injections) prior to the procedure, not documented, reason not given

G9298 Patients who are evaluated for venous thromboembolic and cardiovascular risk factors within 30 days prior to the procedure (e.g. history of DVT, pe, mi, arrhythmia and stroke)

G9299 Patients who are not evaluated for venous thromboembolic and cardiovascular risk factors within 30 days prior to the procedure including (e.g., history of DVT, pe, mi, arrhythmia and stroke, reason not given)

G9300 Documentation of medical reason(s) for not completely infusing the prophylactic antibiotic prior to the inflation of the proximal tourniquet (e.g., a tourniquet was not used)

G9301 Patients who had the prophylactic antibiotic completely infused prior to the inflation of the proximal tourniquet

G9302 Prophylactic antibiotic not completely infused prior to the inflation of the proximal tourniquet, reason not given

G9303 Operative report does not identify the prosthetic implant specifications including the prosthetic implant manufacturer, the brand name of the prosthetic implant and the size of each prosthetic implant, reason not given

G9304 Operative report identifies the prosthetic implant specifications including the prosthetic implant manufacturer, the brand name of the prosthetic implant and the size of each prosthetic implant

G9305 Intervention for presence of leak of endoluminal contents through an anastomosis not required

G9306 Intervention for presence of leak of endoluminal contents through an anastomosis required

G9307 No return to the operating room for a surgical procedure, for complications of the principal operative procedure, within 30 days of the principal operative procedure

G9308 Unplanned return to the operating room for a surgical procedure, for complications of the principal operative procedure, within 30 days of the principal operative procedure

G9309 No unplanned hospital readmission within 30 days of principal procedure

G9310 Unplanned hospital readmission within 30 days of principal procedure

G9311 No surgical site infection

G9312 Surgical site infection

▲ **G9313** Amoxicillin, with or without clavulanate, not prescribed as first line antibiotic at the time of diagnosis for documented reason

G9314 Amoxicillin, with or without clavulanate, not prescribed as first line antibiotic at the time of diagnosis, reason not given

G9315 Documentation amoxicillin, with or without clavulanate, prescribed as a first line antibiotic at the time of diagnosis

G9316 Documentation of patient-specific risk assessment with a risk calculator based on multi-institutional clinical data, the specific risk calculator used, and communication of risk assessment from risk calculator with the patient or family

G9317 Documentation of patient-specific risk assessment with a risk calculator based on multi-institutional clinical data, the specific risk calculator used, and communication of risk assessment from risk calculator with the patient or family not completed

G9318 Imaging study named according to standardized nomenclature

G9319 Imaging study not named according to standardized nomenclature, reason not given

G9321 Count of previous ct (any type of ct) and cardiac nuclear medicine (myocardial perfusion) studies documented in the 12-month period prior to the current study

G9322 Count of previous ct and cardiac nuclear medicine (myocardial perfusion) studies not documented in the 12-month period prior to the current study, reason not given

(**G9324** Code deleted December 31, 2016).

G9326 Ct studies performed not reported to a radiation dose index registry that is capable of collecting at a minimum all necessary data elements, reason not given

G9327 Ct studies performed reported to a radiation dose index registry with all necessary data elements

G9329 DICOM format image data available to non-affiliated external healthcare facilities or entities on a secure, media free, reciprocally searchable basis with patient authorization for at least a 12-month period after the study not documented in final report, reason not given

G9340 Final report documented that DICOM format image data available to non-affiliated external healthcare facilities or entities on a secure, media free, reciprocally searchable basis with patient authorization for at least a 12-month period after the study

G9341 Search conducted for prior patient ct studies completed at non-affiliated external healthcare facilities or entities within the past 12-months and are available through a secure, authorized, media-free, shared archive prior to an imaging study being performed

G9342 Search not conducted prior to an imaging study being performed for prior patient ct studies completed at non-affiliated external healthcare facilities or entities within the past 12-months and are available through a secure, authorized, media-free, shared archive, reason not given

G9344 Due to system reasons search not conducted for DICOM format images for prior patient ct imaging studies completed at non-affiliated external healthcare facilities or entities within the past 12 months that are available through a secure, authorized, media-free, shared archive (e.g., non-affiliated external healthcare facilities or entities does not have archival abilities through a shared archival system)

G9345 Follow-up recommendations documented according to recommended guidelines for incidentally detected pulmonary nodules (e.g., follow-up ct imaging studies needed or that no follow-up is needed) based at a minimum on nodule size and patient risk factors

G9347 Follow-up recommendations not documented according to recommended guidelines for incidentally detected pulmonary nodules, reason not given

▲ **G9348** Ct scan of the paranasal sinuses ordered at the time of diagnosis for documented reasons

G9349 Documentation of a ct scan of the paranasal sinuses ordered at the time of diagnosis or received within 28 days after date of diagnosis

G9350 Ct scan of the paranasal sinuses not ordered at the time of diagnosis or received within 28 days after date of diagnosis

G9351 More than one ct scan of the paranasal sinuses ordered or received within 90 days after diagnosis

G9352 More than one ct scan of the paranasal sinuses ordered or received within 90 days after the date of diagnosis, reason not given

G9353 More than one ct scan of the paranasal sinuses ordered or received within 90 days after the date of diagnosis for documented reasons (eg, patients with complications, second ct obtained prior to surgery, other medical reasons)

G9354 One ct scan or no ct scan of the paranasal sinuses ordered within 90 days after the date of diagnosis

G9355 Elective delivery or early induction not performed

G9356 Elective delivery or early induction performed

G9357 Post-partum screenings, evaluations and education performed

G9358 Post-partum screenings, evaluations and education not performed

G9359 Documentation of negative or managed positive tb screen with further evidence that tb is not active within one year of patient visit

G9360 No documentation of negative or managed positive tb screen

G9361 Medical indication for induction [documentation of reason(s) for elective delivery (c-section) or early induction (e.g., hemorrhage and placental complications, hypertension, preeclampsia and eclampsia, rupture of membranes-premature or prolonged, maternal conditions complicating pregnancy/delivery, fetal conditions complicating pregnancy/ delivery, late pregnancy, prior uterine surgery, or participation in clinical trial)]

G9364 Sinusitis caused by, or presumed to be caused by, bacterial infection

G9365 One high-risk medication ordered

G9366 One high-risk medication not ordered

G9367 At least two different high-risk medications ordered

G9368 At least two different high-risk medications not ordered

G9380 Patient offered assistance with end of life issues during the measurement period

(**G9381** Code deleted December 31, 2017).

G9382 Patient not offered assistance with end of life issues during the measurement period

G9383 Patient received screening for HCV infection within the 12 month reporting period

G9384 Documentation of medical reason(s) for not receiving annual screening for HCV infection (e.g., decompensated cirrhosis indicating advanced disease [i.e., ascites, esophageal variceal bleeding, hepatic encephalopathy], hepatocellular carcinoma, waitlist for organ transplant, limited life expectancy, other medical reasons)

G9385 Documentation of patient reason(s) for not receiving annual screening for HCV infection (e.g., patient declined, other patient reasons)

G9386 Screening for HCV infection not received within the 12 month reporting period, reason not given

G9389 Unplanned rupture of the posterior capsule requiring vitrectomy during cataract surgery

G9390 No unplanned rupture of the posterior capsule requiring vitrectomy during cataract surgery

G9393 Patient with an initial phq-9 score greater than nine who achieves remission at twelve months as demonstrated by a twelve month (+/- 30 days) phq-9 score of less than five

G9394 Patient who had a diagnosis of bipolar disorder or personality disorder, death, permanent nursing home resident or receiving hospice or palliative care any time during the measurement or assessment period

G9395 Patient with an initial phq-9 score greater than nine who did not achieve remission at twelve months as demonstrated by a twelve month (+/- 30 days) phq-9 score greater than or equal to five

G9396 Patient with an initial phq-9 score greater than nine who was not assessed for remission at twelve months (+/- 30 days)

G9399 Documentation in the patient record of a discussion between the physician/clinician and the patient that includes all of the following: treatment choices appropriate to genotype, risks and benefits, evidence of effectiveness, and patient preferences toward the outcome of the treatment

G9400 Documentation of medical or patient reason(s) for not discussing treatment options; medical reasons: patient is not a candidate for treatment due to advanced physical or mental health comorbidity (including active substance use); currently receiving antiviral treatment; successful antiviral treatment (with sustained virologic response) prior to reporting period; other documented medical reasons; patient reasons: patient unable or unwilling to participate in the discussion or other patient reasons

G9401 No documentation of a discussion in the patient record of a discussion between the physician or other qualified healthcare professional and the patient that includes all of the following: treatment choices appropriate to genotype, risks and benefits, evidence of effectiveness, and patient preferences toward treatment

G9402 Patient received follow-up on the date of discharge or within 30 days after discharge

G9403 Clinician documented reason patient was not able to complete 30 day follow-up from acute inpatient setting discharge (e.g., patient death prior to follow-up visit, patient non-compliant for visit follow-up)

G9404 Patient did not receive follow-up on the date of discharge or within 30 days after discharge

G9405 Patient received follow-up within 7 days from discharge

G9406 Clinician documented reason patient was not able to complete 7 day follow-up from acute inpatient setting discharge (i.e. patient death prior to follow-up visit, patient non-compliance for visit follow-up)

G9407 Patient did not receive follow-up on or within 7 days after discharge

G9408 Patients with cardiac tamponade and/or pericardiocentesis occurring within 30 days

G9409 Patients without cardiac tamponade and/or pericardiocentesis occurring within 30 days

G9410 Patient admitted within 180 days, status post CIED implantation, replacement, or revision with an infection requiring device removal or surgical revision

G9411 Patient not admitted within 180 days, status post CIED implantation, replacement, or revision with an infection requiring device removal or surgical revision

G9412 Patient admitted within 180 days, status post CIED implantation, replacement, or revision with an infection requiring device removal or surgical revision

G9413 Patient not admitted within 180 days, status post CIED implantation, replacement, or revision with an infection requiring device removal or surgical revision

G9414 Patient had one dose of meningococcal vaccine on or between the patient's 11th and 13th birthdays

G9415 Patient did not have one dose of meningococcal vaccine on or between the patient's 11th and 13th birthdays

G9416 Patient had one tetanus, diphtheria toxoids and acellular pertussis vaccine (Tdap) on or between the patient's 10th and 13th birthdays

G9417 Patient did not have one tetanus, diphtheria toxoids and acellular pertussis vaccine (Tdap) on or between the patient's 10th and 13th birthdays

G9418 Primary non-small cell lung cancer biopsy and cytology specimen report documents classification into specific histologic type or classified as NSCLC-nos with an explanation

G9419 Documentation of medical reason(s) for not including the histological type or NSCLC-nos classification with an explanation (e.g., biopsy taken for other purposes in a patient with a history of primary non-small cell lung cancer or other documented medical reasons)

G9420 Specimen site other than anatomic location of lung or is not classified as primary non-small cell lung cancer

G9421 Primary non-small cell lung cancer biopsy and cytology specimen report does not document classification into specific histologic type or classified as NSCLC-nos with an explanation

G9422 Primary lung carcinoma resection report documents pt category, pn category and for non-small cell lung cancer, histologic type (squamous cell carcinoma, adenocarcinoma and not NSCLC-nos)

G9423 Documentation of medical reason for not including pt category, pn category and histologic type (for patient with appropriate exclusion criteria (e.g. metastatic disease, benign tumors, malignant tumors other than carcinomas, inadequate surgical specimens)

G9424 Specimen site other than anatomic location of lung or classified as NSCLC-nos

G9425 Primary lung carcinoma resection report does not document pt category, pn category and for non-small cell lung cancer, histologic type (squamous cell carcinoma, adenocarcinoma)

● New code ▲ Revised code ( ) Deleted code Ⓣ Trigger Ⓟ Post Trigger DME

G9426 Improvement in median time from ed arrival to initial ed oral or parenteral pain medication administration performed for ed admitted patients

G9427 Improvement in median time from ed arrival to initial ed oral or parenteral pain medication administration not performed for ed admitted patients

G9428 Pathology report includes the pt category and a statement on thickness and ulceration and for pt1, mitotic rate

G9429 Documentation of medical reason(s) for not including pt category and a statement on thickness and ulceration and for pt1, mitotic rate (e.g., negative skin biopsies in a patient with a history of melanoma or other documented medical reasons)

G9430 Specimen site other than anatomic cutaneous location

G9431 Pathology report does not include the pt category and a statement on thickness and ulceration and for pt1, mitotic rate

G9432 Asthma well-controlled based on the act, c-act, acq, or ataq score and results documented

G9434 Asthma not well-controlled based on the act, c-act, acq, or ataq score, or specified asthma control tool not used, reason not given

(**G9435** Code deleted December 31, 2016).

(**G9436** Code deleted December 31, 2016).

(**G9437** Code deleted December 31, 2016).

(**G9438** Code deleted December 31, 2016).

(**G9439** Code deleted December 31, 2016).

(**G9440** Code deleted December 31, 2016).

(**G9441** Code deleted December 31, 2016).

(**G9442** Code deleted December 31, 2016).

(**G9443** Code deleted December 31, 2016).

G9448 Patients who were born in the years 1945-1965

G9449 History of receiving blood transfusions prior to 1992

G9450 History of injection drug use

G9451 Patient received one-time screening for HCV infection

G9452 Documentation of medical reason(s) for not receiving one-time screening for HCV infection (e.g., decompensated cirrhosis indicating advanced disease [ie, ascites, esophageal variceal bleeding, hepatic encephalopathy], hepatocellular carcinoma, waitlist for organ transplant, limited life expectancy, other medical reasons)

G9453 Documentation of patient reason(s) for not receiving one-time screening for HCV infection (e.g., patient declined, other patient reasons)

G9454 One-time screening for HCV infection not received within 12 month reporting period and no documentation of prior screening for HCV infection, reason not given

G9455   Patient underwent abdominal imaging with ultrasound, contrast enhanced ct or contrast MRI for HCC

G9456   Documentation of medical or patient reason(s) for not ordering or performing screening for HCC. medical reason: comorbid medical conditions with expected survival < 5 years, hepatic decompensation and not a candidate for liver transplantation, or other medical reasons; patient reasons: patient declined or other patient reasons (e.g., cost of tests, time related to accessing testing equipment)

G9457   Patient did not undergo abdominal imaging and did not have a documented reason for not undergoing abdominal imaging in the reporting period

G9458   Patient documented as tobacco user and received tobacco cessation intervention (must include at least one of the following: advice given to quit smoking or tobacco use, counseling on the benefits of quitting smoking or tobacco use, assistance with or referral to external smoking or tobacco cessation support programs, or current enrollment in smoking or tobacco use cessation program) if identified as a tobacco user

G9459   Currently a tobacco non-user

G9460   Tobacco assessment or tobacco cessation intervention not performed, reason not given

(G9463   Code deleted December 31, 2016).

(G9464   Code deleted December 31, 2016).

(G9465   Code deleted December 31, 2016).

(G9466   Code deleted December 31, 2016).

(G9467   Code deleted December 31, 2016).

G9468   Patient not receiving corticosteroids greater than or equal to 10 mg/day of prednisone equivalents for 60 or greater consecutive days or a single prescription equating to 600 mg prednisone or greater for all fills

G9469   Patients who have received or are receiving corticosteroids greater than or equal to 10 mg/day of prednisone equivalents for 60 or greater consecutive days or a single prescription equating to 600 mg prednisone or greater for all fills

G9470   Patients not receiving corticosteroids greater than or equal to 10 mg/day of prednisone equivalents for 60 or greater consecutive days or a single prescription equating to 600 mg prednisone or greater for all fills

G9471   Within the past 2 years, central dual-energy x-ray absorptiometry (DXA) not ordered or documented

G9472   Within the past 2 years, central dual-energy x-ray absorptiometry (DXA) not ordered and documented, no review of systems and no medication history or pharmacologic therapy (other than minerals/vitamins) for osteoporosis prescribed

G9473   Services performed by chaplain in the hospice setting, each 15 minutes

G9474   Services performed by dietary counselor in the hospice setting, each 15 minutes

G9475   Services performed by other counselor in the hospice setting, each 15 minutes

G9476 Services performed by volunteer in the hospice setting, each 15 minutes

G9477 Services performed by care coordinator in the hospice setting, each 15 minutes

G9478 Services performed by other qualified therapist in the hospice setting, each 15 minutes

G9479 Services performed by qualified pharmacist in the hospice setting, each 15 minutes

G9480 Admission to Medicare care choice model program (MCCM)

G9481 Remote in-home visit for the evaluation and management of a new patient for use only in the Medicare-approved comprehensive care for joint replacement model, which requires these 3 key components:

- a problem focused history;
- a problem focused examination; and
- straightforward medical decision making, furnished in real time using interactive audio and video technology.

Counseling and coordination of care with other physicians, other qualified health care professionals or agencies are provided consistent with the nature of the problem(s) and the needs of the patient or the family or both. usually, the presenting problem(s) are self limited or minor. Typically, 10 minutes are spent with the patient or family or both via real time, audio and video intercommunications technology

G9482 Remote in-home visit for the evaluation and management of a new patient for use only in the Medicare-approved comprehensive care for joint replacement model, which requires these 3 key components:

- an expanded problem focused history;
- an expanded problem focused examination;
- straightforward medical decision making, furnished in real time using interactive audio and video technology.

Counseling and coordination of care with other physicians, other qualified health care professionals or agencies are provided consistent with the nature of the problem(s) and the needs of the patient or the family or both. usually, the presenting problem(s) are of low to moderate severity. Typically, 20 minutes are spent with the patient or family or both via real time, audio and video intercommunications technology

G9483 Remote in-home visit for the evaluation and management of a new patient for use only in the Medicare-approved comprehensive care for joint replacement model, which requires these 3 key components:

- a detailed history;
- a detailed examination;
- medical decision making of low complexity, furnished in real time using interactive audio and video technology.

Counseling and coordination of care with other physicians, other qualified health care professionals or agencies are provided consistent with the nature of the problem(s) and the needs of the patient or the family or both. usually, the presenting problem(s) are of moderate severity. Typically, 30 minutes are spent with the patient or family or both via real time, audio and video intercommunications technology

G9484 Remote in-home visit for the evaluation and management of a new patient for use only in the Medicare-approved comprehensive care for joint replacement model, which requires these 3 key components:

- a comprehensive history;
- a comprehensive examination;
- medical decision making of moderate complexity, furnished in real time using interactive audio and video technology.

Counseling and coordination of care with other physicians, other qualified health care professionals or agencies are provided consistent with the nature of the problem(s) and the needs of the patient or the family or both. usually, the presenting problem(s) are of moderate to high severity. Typically, 45 minutes are spent with the patient or family or both via real time, audio and video intercommunications technology

G9485 Remote in-home visit for the evaluation and management of a new patient for use only in the Medicare-approved comprehensive care for joint replacement model, which requires these 3 key components:

- a comprehensive history;
- a comprehensive examination;
- medical decision making of high complexity, furnished in real time using interactive audio and video technology.

Counseling and coordination of care with other physicians, other qualified health care professionals or agencies are provided consistent with the nature of the problem(s) and the needs of the patient or the family or both. usually, the presenting problem(s) are of moderate to high severity. Typically, 60 minutes are spent with the patient or family or both via real time, audio and video intercommunications technology

G9486 Remote in-home visit for the evaluation and management of an established patient for use only in the Medicare-approved comprehensive care for joint replacement model, which requires at least 2 of the following 3 key components:

- a problem focused history;
- a problem focused examination;
- straightforward medical decision making, furnished in real time using interactive audio and video technology.

Counseling and coordination of care with other physicians, other qualified health care professionals or agencies are provided consistent with the nature of the problem(s) and the needs of the patient or the family or both. usually, the presenting problem(s) are self limited or minor. Typically, 10 minutes are spent with the patient or family or both via real time, audio and video intercommunications technology

G9487 Remote in-home visit for the evaluation and management of an established patient for use only in the Medicare-approved comprehensive care for joint replacement model, which requires at least 2 of the following 3 key components:

- an expanded problem focused history;
- an expanded problem focused examination;
- medical decision making of low complexity, furnished in real time using interactive audio and video technology.

Counseling and coordination of care with other physicians, other qualified health care professionals or agencies are provided consistent with the nature of the problem(s) and the needs of the patient or the family or both. usually, the presenting problem(s) are of

low to moderate severity. Typically, 15 minutes are spent with the patient or family or both via real time, audio and video intercommunications technology

G9488 Remote in-home visit for the evaluation and management of an established patient for use only in the Medicare-approved comprehensive care for joint replacement model, which requires at least 2 of the following 3 key components:

- a detailed history;
- a detailed examination;
- medical decision making of moderate complexity, furnished in real time using interactive audio and video technology.

Counseling and coordination of care with other physicians, other qualified health care professionals or agencies are provided consistent with the nature of the problem(s) and the needs of the patient or the family or both. usually, the presenting problem(s) are of moderate to high severity. Typically, 25 minutes are spent with the patient or family or both via real time, audio and video intercommunications technology

G9489 Remote in-home visit for the evaluation and management of an established patient for use only in the Medicare-approved comprehensive care for joint replacement model, which requires at least 2 of the following 3 key components:

- a comprehensive history;
- a comprehensive examination;
- medical decision making of high complexity, furnished in real time using interactive audio and video technology.

Counseling and coordination of care with other physicians, other qualified health care professionals or agencies are provided consistent with the nature of the problem(s) and the needs of the patient or the family or both. usually, the presenting problem(s) are of moderate to high severity. Typically, 40 minutes are spent with the patient or family or both via real time, audio and video intercommunications technology

G9490 Comprehensive Care for Joint Replacement model, home visit for patient assessment performed by clinical staff for an individual not considered homebound, including, but not necessarily limited to patient assessment of clinical status, safety/fall prevention, functional status/ambulation, medication reconciliation/management, compliance with orders/plan of care, performance of activities of daily living, and ensuring beneficiary connections to community and other services. (for use only in the Medicare-approved Comprehensive Care for Joint Replacement model); may not be billed for a 30 day period covered by a transitional care management code.

(**G9496** Code deleted December 31, 2017).

G9497 Received instruction from the anesthesiologist or proxy prior to the day of surgery to abstain from smoking on the day of surgery

G9498 Antibiotic regimen prescribed

(**G9499** Code deleted December 31, 2016).

G9500 Radiation exposure indices, or exposure time and number of fluorographic images in final report for procedures using fluoroscopy, documented

G9501 Radiation exposure indices, or exposure time and number of fluorographic images not documented in final report for procedure using fluoroscopy, reason not given

G9502   Documentation of medical reason for not performing foot exam   (i.e., patients who have had either a bilateral amputation above or below the knee, or both a left and right amputation above or below the knee before or during the measurement period)

G9503   Patient taking tamsulosin hydrochloride

▲   G9504   Documented reason for not assessing hepatitis b virus (HBV) status (e.g., patient not initiating anti-TNF therapy, patient declined) prior to initiating anti-TNF therapy

G9505   Antibiotic regimen prescribed within 10 days after onset of symptoms for documented medical reason

G9506   Biologic immune response modifier prescribed

G9507   Documentation that the patient is on a statin medication or has documentation of a valid contraindication or exception to statin medications; contraindications/exceptions that can be defined by diagnosis codes include pregnancy during the measurement period, active liver disease, rhabdomyolysis, end stage renal disease on dialysis and heart failure; provider documented contraindications/exceptions include breastfeeding during the measurement period, woman of child-bearing age not actively taking birth control, allergy to statin, drug interaction (hiv protease inhibitors, nefazodone, cyclosporine, gemfibrozil, and danazol) and intolerance (with supporting documentation of trying a statin at least once within the last 5 years or diagnosis codes for myositis or toxic myopathy related to drugs)

G9508   Documentation that the patient is not on a statin medication

G9509   Remission at twelve months as demonstrated by a twelve month (+/-30 days) phq-9 score of less than 5

G9510   Remission at twelve months not demonstrated by a twelve month (+/-30 days) phq-9 score of less than five; either phq-9 score was not assessed or is greater than or equal to 5

G9511   Index date phq-9 score greater than 9 documented during the twelve month denominator identification period

G9512   Individual had a PDC of 0.8 or greater

G9513   Individual did not have a PDC of 0.8 or greater

G9514   Patient required a return to the operating room within 90 days of surgery

G9515   Patient did not require a return to the operating room within 90 days of surgery

G9516   Patient achieved an improvement in visual acuity, from their preoperative level, within 90 days of surgery

G9517   Patient did not achieve an improvement in visual acuity, from their preoperative level, within 90 days of surgery, reason not given

G9518   Documentation of active injection drug use

G9519   Patient achieves final refraction (spherical equivalent) +/- 0.5 diopters of their planned refraction within 90 days of surgery

G9520   Patient does not achieve final refraction (spherical equivalent) +/- 0.5 diopters of their planned refraction within 90 days of surgery

G9521   Total number of emergency department visits and inpatient hospitalizations less than two in the past 12 months

G9522   Total number of emergency department visits and inpatient hospitalizations equal to or greater than two in the past 12 months or patient not screened, reason not given

G9523   Patient discontinued from hemodialysis or peritoneal dialysis

G9524   Patient was referred to hospice care

G9525   Documentation of patient reason(s) for not referring to hospice care (e.g., patient declined, other patient reasons)

G9526   Patient was not referred to hospice care, reason not given

G9529   Patient with minor blunt head trauma had an appropriate indication(s) for a head ct

G9530   Patient presented within 24 hours of a minor blunt head trauma with a GCS score of 15 and had a head ct ordered for trauma by an emergency care provider

G9531   Patient has documentation of ventricular shunt, brain tumor, multisystem trauma, pregnancy, or is currently taking an antiplatelet medication including: asa/dipyridamole, clopidogrel, prasugrel, ticlopidine, ticagrelor or cilostazol)

G9532   Patient's head injury occurred greater than 24 hours before presentation to the emergency department, or has a GCS score less than 15 or does not have a GCS score documented, or had a head ct for trauma ordered by someone other than an emergency care provider, or was ordered for a reason other than trauma

G9533   Patient with minor blunt head trauma did not have an appropriate indication(s) for a head ct

G9534   Advanced brain imaging (CTA, ct, MRA or MRI) was not ordered

G9535   Patients with a normal neurological examination

G9536   Documentation of medical reason(s) for ordering an advanced brain imaging study (i.e., patient has an abnormal neurological examination; patient has the coexistence of seizures, or both; recent onset of severe headache; change in the type of headache; signs of increased intracranial pressure (e.g., papilledema, absent venous pulsations on funduscopic examination, altered mental status, focal neurologic deficits, signs of meningeal irritation); hiv-positive patients with a new type of headache; immunocompromised patient with unexplained headache symptoms; patient on coagulopathy/anti-coagulation or anti-platelet therapy; very young patients with unexplained headache symptoms)

G9537   Documentation of system reason(s) for ordering an advanced brain imaging study (i.e., needed as part of a clinical trial; other clinician ordered the study)

G9538   Advanced brain imaging (CTA, ct, MRA or MRI) was ordered

G9539   Intent for potential removal at time of placement

G9540   Patient alive 3 months post procedure

G9541   Filter removed within 3 months of placement

G9542   Documented re-assessment for the appropriateness of filter removal within 3 months of placement

G9543 Documentation of at least two attempts to reach the patient to arrange a clinical re-assessment for the appropriateness of filter removal within 3 months of placement

G9544 Patients that do not have the filter removed, documented re-assessment for the appropriateness of filter removal, or documentation of at least two attempts to reach the

patient to arrange a clinical re-assessment for the appropriateness of filter removal within 3 months of placement

G9547 Incidental finding: liver lesion <= 0.5 cm, cystic kidney lesion < 1.0 cm or adrenal lesion <= 1.0 cm

G9548 Final reports for abdominal imaging studies with follow-up imaging recommended

G9549 Documentation of medical reason(s) that follow-up imaging is indicated (e.g., patient has a known malignancy that can metastasize, other medical reason(s) such as fever in an immunocompromised patient)

G9550 Final reports for abdominal imaging studies with follow-up imaging not recommended

G9551 Final reports for abdominal imaging studies without an incidentally found lesion noted: liver lesion <= 0.5 cm, cystic kidney lesion < 1.0 cm or adrenal lesion <= 1.0 cm noted or no lesion found

G9552 Incidental thyroid nodule < 1.0 cm noted in report

G9553 Prior thyroid disease diagnosis

G9554 Final reports for ct, CTA, MRI or MRA of the chest or neck or ultrasound of the neck with follow-up imaging recommended

G9555 Documentation of medical reason(s) for recommending follow up imaging (e.g., patient has multiple endocrine neoplasia, patient has cervical lymphadenopathy, other medical reason(s))

G9556 Final reports for ct, CTA, MRI or MRA of the chest or neck or ultrasound of the neck with follow-up imaging not recommended

G9557 Final reports for ct, CTA, MRI or MRA studies of the chest or neck or ultrasound of the neck without an incidentally found thyroid nodule < 1.0 cm noted or no nodule found

G9558 Patient treated with a beta-lactam antibiotic as definitive therapy

G9559 Documentation of medical reason(s) for not prescribing a beta-lactam antibiotic (e.g., allergy, intolerance to beta -lactam antibiotics)

G9560 Patient not treated with a beta-lactam antibiotic as definitive therapy, reason not given

G9561 Patients prescribed opiates for longer than six weeks

G9562 Patients who had a follow-up evaluation conducted at least every three months during opioid therapy

G9563 Patients who did not have a follow-up evaluation conducted at least every three months during opioid therapy

(**G9572** Code deleted December 31, 2016).

G9573 Remission at six months as demonstrated by a six month (+/-30 days) phq-9 score of less than five

G9574   Remission at six months not demonstrated by a six month (+/-30 days) phq-9 score of less than five. either phq-9 score was not assessed or is greater than or equal to five

G9577   Patients prescribed opiates for longer than six weeks

G9578   Documentation of signed opioid treatment agreement at least once during opioid therapy

G9579   No documentation of signed an opioid treatment agreement at least once during opioid therapy

G9580   Door to puncture time of less than 2 hours

(G9581   Code deleted December 31, 2016).

G9582   Door to puncture time of greater than 2 hours, no reason given

G9583   Patients prescribed opiates for longer than six weeks

G9584   Patient evaluated for risk of misuse of opiates by using a brief validated instrument (e.g., opioid risk tool, soapp-r) or patient interviewed at least once during opioid therapy

G9585   Patient not evaluated for risk of misuse of opiates by using a brief validated instrument (e.g., opioid risk tool, soaap-r) or patient not interviewed at least once during opioid therapy

G9593   Pediatric patient with minor blunt head trauma classified as low risk according to the PECARN prediction rules

G9594   Patient presented within 24 hours of a minor blunt head trauma with a GCS score of 15 and had a head ct ordered for trauma by an emergency care provider

G9595   Patient has documentation of ventricular shunt, brain tumor, coagulopathy, including thrombocytopenia

G9596   Pediatric patient's head injury occurred greater than 24 hours before presentation to the emergency department, or has a GCS score less than 15 or does not have a GCS score documented, or had a head ct for trauma ordered by someone other than an emergency care provider, or was ordered for a reason other than trauma

G9597   Pediatric patient with minor blunt head trauma not classified as low risk according to the PECARN prediction rules

G9598   Aortic aneurysm 5.5 - 5.9 cm maximum diameter on centerline formatted ct or minor diameter on axial formatted ct

G9599   Aortic aneurysm 6.0 cm or greater maximum diameter on centerline formatted ct or minor diameter on axial formatted ct

G9600   Symptomatic AAAS that required urgent/emergent (non-elective) repair

G9601   Patient discharge to home no later than post-operative day #7

G9602   Patient not discharged to home by post-operative day #7

G9603   Patient survey score improved from baseline following treatment

G9604   Patient survey results not available

G9605   Patient survey score did not improve from baseline following treatment

G9606 Intraoperative cystoscopy performed to evaluate for lower tract injury

▲ **G9607** Documented medical reasons for not performing intraoperative cystoscopy (e.g., urethral pathology precluding cystoscopy, any patient who has a congenital or acquired absence of the urethra) or in the case of patient death

G9608 Intraoperative cystoscopy not performed to evaluate for lower tract injury

G9609 Documentation of an order for anti-platelet agents

G9610 Documentation of medical reason(s) in the patient's record for not ordering anti-platelet agents

G9611 Order for anti-platelet agents was not documented in the patient's record, reason not given

G9612 Photodocumentation of one or more cecal landmarks to establish a complete examination

G9613 Documentation of post-surgical anatomy (e.g., right hemicolectomy, ileocecal resection, etc.)

G9614 No photodocumentation of cecal landmarks to establish a complete examination

G9615 Preoperative assessment documented

G9616 Documentation of reason(s) for not documenting a preoperative assessment (e.g., patient with a gynecologic or other pelvic malignancy noted at the time of surgery)

G9617 Preoperative assessment not documented, reason not given

G9618 Documentation of screening for uterine malignancy or those that had an ultrasound and/or endometrial sampling of any kind

(**G9619** Code deleted December 31, 2016).

G9620 Patient not screened for uterine malignancy, or those that have not had an ultrasound and/or endometrial sampling of any kind, reason not given

G9621 Patient identified as an unhealthy alcohol user when screened for unhealthy alcohol use using a systematic screening method and received brief counseling

G9622 Patient not identified as an unhealthy alcohol user when screened for unhealthy alcohol use using a systematic screening method

G9623 Documentation of medical reason(s) for not screening for unhealthy alcohol use (e.g., limited life expectancy, other medical reasons)

▲ **G9624** Patient not screened for unhealthy alcohol use using a systematic screening method or patient did not receive brief counseling if identified as an unhealthy alcohol user, reason not given

G9625 Patient sustained bladder injury at the time of surgery or discovered subsequently up to 1 month post-surgery

G9626 Documented medical reason for not reporting bladder injury (e.g., gynecologic or other pelvic malignancy documented, concurrent surgery involving bladder pathology, injury that occurs during urinary incontinence procedure, patient death from non-medical causes not related to surgery, patient died during procedure without evidence of bladder injury)

G9627 Patient did not sustained bladder injury at the time of surgery or subsequently up to 1 month post-surgery

G9628 Patient sustained bowel injury at the time of surgery or discovered subsequently up to 1 month post-surgery

G9629 Documented medical reasons for not reporting bowel injury (e.g., gynecologic or other pelvic malignancy documented, planned (e.g., not due to an unexpected bowel injury) resection and/or re-anastomosis of bowel, or patient death from non-medical causes not related to surgery, patient died during procedure without evidence of bowel injury)

G9630 Patient did not sustain a bowel injury at the time of surgery nor discovered subsequently up to 1 month post-surgery

G9631 Patient sustained ureter injury at the time of surgery or discovered subsequently up to 1 month post-surgery

G9632 Documented medical reasons for not reporting ureter injury (e.g., gynecologic or other pelvic malignancy documented, concurrent surgery involving bladder pathology, injury that occurs during a urinary incontinence procedure, patient death from non-medical causes not related to surgery, patient died during procedure without evidence of ureter injury)

G9633 Patient did not sustain ureter injury at the time of surgery nor discovered subsequently up to 1 month post-surgery

G9634 Health-related quality of life assessed with tool during at least two visits and quality of life score remained the same or improved

G9635 Health-related quality of life not assessed with tool for documented reason(s) (e.g., patient has a cognitive or neuropsychiatric impairment that impairs his/her ability to complete the HRQOL survey, patient has the inability to read and/or write in order to complete the HRQOL questionnaire)

G9636 Health-related quality of life not assessed with tool during at least two visits or quality of life score declined

▲ G9637 At least two orders for the same high-risk medication

▲ G9638 At least two orders for the same high-risk medication

G9639 Major amputation or open surgical bypass not required within 48 hours of the index endovascular lower extremity revascularization procedure

G9640 Documentation of planned hybrid or staged procedure

G9641 Major amputation or open surgical bypass required within 48 hours of the index endovascular lower extremity revascularization procedure

G9642 Current smokers (e.g., cigarette, cigar, pipe, e-cigarette or marijuana)

G9643 Elective surgery

G9644 Patients who abstained from smoking prior to anesthesia on the day of surgery or procedure

G9645 Patients who did not abstain from smoking prior to anesthesia on the day of surgery or procedure

G9646 Patients with 90 day MRS score of 0 to 2

G9647   Patients in whom MRS score could not be obtained at 90 day follow-up

G9648   Patients with 90 day MRS score greater than 2

G9649   Psoriasis assessment tool documented meeting any one of the specified benchmarks (e.g., (pga; 6-point scale), body surface area (BSA), psoriasis area and severity index (PASI) and/or dermatology life quality index) (DLQI))

(**G9650**   Code deleted December 31, 2016).

G9651   Psoriasis assessment tool documented not meeting any one of the specified benchmarks (e.g., (pga; 6-point scale), body surface area (BSA), psoriasis area and severity index (PASI) and/or dermatology life quality index) (DLQI)) or psoriasis assessment tool not documented

(**G9652**   Code deleted December 31, 2016).

(**G9653**   Code deleted December 31, 2016).

G9654   Monitored anesthesia care (mac)

G9655   A transfer of care protocol or handoff tool/checklist that includes the required key handoff elements is used

▲ **G9656**   Patient transferred directly from anesthetizing location to PACU or other non-ICU location

(**G9657**   Code deleted December 31, 2016).

G9658   A transfer of care protocol or handoff tool/checklist that includes the required key handoff elements is not used

G9659   Patients greater than 85 years of age who did not have a history of colorectal cancer or valid medical reason for the colonoscopy, including: iron deficiency anemia, lower gastrointestinal bleeding, Crohn's disease (i.e., regional enteritis), familial adenomatous polyposis, lynch syndrome (i.e., hereditary non-polyposis colorectal cancer), inflammatory bowel disease, ulcerative colitis, abnormal finding of gastrointestinal tract, or changes in bowel habits

G9660   Documentation of medical reason(s) for a colonoscopy performed on a patient greater than 85 years of age (eg., last colonoscopy incomplete, last colonoscopy had inadequate prep, iron deficiency anemia, lower gastrointestinal bleeding, Crohn's disease (i.e., regional enteritis), familial history of adenomatous polyposis, lynch syndrome (i.e., hereditary non-polyposis colorectal cancer), inflammatory bowel disease, ulcerative colitis, abnormal finding of gastrointestinal tract, or changes in bowel habits)

G9661   Patients greater than 85 years of age who received a routine colonoscopy for a reason other than the following: an assessment of signs/symptoms of GI tract illness, and/or the patient is considered high risk, and/or to follow-up on previously diagnoses advance lesions

G9662   Previously diagnosed or have an active diagnosis of clinical ASCVD

G9663   Any fasting or direct LDL-c laboratory test result = 190 mg/dl

G9664   Patients who are currently statin therapy users or received an order (prescription) for statin therapy

G9665 Patients who are not currently statin therapy users or did not receive an order (prescription) for statin therapy

G9666 The highest fasting or direct LDL-c laboratory test result of 70?189 mg/dl in the measurement period or two years prior to the beginning of the measurement period

(**G9667** Code deleted December 31, 2016).

G9668 Documentation of medical reason (s) for not currently being a statin therapy user or receive an order (prescription) for statin therapy (e.g., patient with adverse effect, allergy or intolerance to statin medication therapy, patients who have an active diagnosis of pregnancy or who are breastfeeding, patients who are receiving palliative care, patients with active liver disease or hepatic disease or insufficiency, patients with end stage renal disease (ESRD), and patients with diabetes who have a fasting or direct LDL-c laboratory test result < 70 mg/dl and are not taking statin therapy)

G9669 I intend to report the multiple chronic conditions measures group

G9670 All quality actions for the applicable measures in the multiple chronic conditions measures group have been performed for this patient

(**G9671** Code deleted December 31, 2016).

(**G9672** Code deleted December 31, 2016).

(**G9673** Code deleted December 31, 2016).

G9674 Patients with clinical ASCVD diagnosis

G9675 Patients who have ever had a fasting or direct laboratory result of LDL-c = 190 mg/dl

G9676 Patients aged 40 to 75 years at the beginning of the measurement period with type 1 or type 2 diabetes and with an LDL-c result of 70?189 mg/dl recorded as the highest fasting or direct laboratory test result in the measurement year or during the two years prior to the beginning of the measurement period

(**G9677** Code deleted December 31, 2016).

G9678 Oncology Care Model (OCM) Monthly Enhanced Oncology Services (MEOS) payment for enhanced care management services for OCM beneficiaries. MEOS covers care management services for Medicare beneficiaries in a 6-month OCM Episode of Care triggered by the administration of chemotherapy. Enhanced care management services include services driven by the OCM practice requirements, including: 24/7 clinician access, use of an ONC-certified Electronic Health Record, utilization of data for quality improvement, patient navigation, documentation of care plans, and use of clinical guidelines. (G9678 may only be billed for OCM beneficiaries by OCM practitioners)

G9679 Onsite acute care treatment of a nursing facility resident with pneumonia. May only be billed once per day per beneficiary. (10/1/2016)

G9680 Onsite acute care treatment of a nursing facility resident with CHF. May only be billed once per day per beneficiary. (10/1/2016)

G9681 Onsite acute care treatment of a resident with COPD or asthma. May only be billed once per day per beneficiary. (10/1/2016)

G9682 Onsite acute care treatment a nursing facility resident with a skin infection. May only be billed once per day per beneficiary (10/1/2016)

G9683 Onsite acute care treatment of a nursing facility resident with fluid or electrolyte disorder or dehydration (similar pattern). May only be billed once per day per beneficiary. (10/1/2016)

G9684 Onsite acute care treatment of a nursing facility resident for a UTI. May only be billed once per day per beneficiary. (10/1/2016)

G9685 Evaluation and management of a beneficiary's acute change in condition in a nursing facility (10/1/2016)

G9686 Onsite nursing facility conference, that is separate and distinct from an evaluation and management visit, including qualified practitioner and at least one member of the nursing facility interdisciplinary care team

G9687 Hospice services provided to patient any time during the measurement period

G9688 Patients using hospice services any time during the measurement period

G9689 Patient admitted for performance of elective carotid intervention

G9690 Patient receiving hospice services any time during the measurement period

G9691 Patient had hospice services any time during the measurement period

G9692 Hospice services received by patient any time during the measurement period

G9693 Patient use of hospice services any time during the measurement period

G9694 Hospice services utilized by patient any time during the measurement period

G9695 Long-acting inhaled bronchodilator prescribed

G9696 Documentation of medical reason(s) for not prescribing a long-acting inhaled bronchodilator

G9697 Documentation of patient reason(s) for not prescribing a long-acting inhaled bronchodilator

G9698 Documentation of system reason(s) for not prescribing a long-acting inhaled bronchodilator

G9699 Long-acting inhaled bronchodilator not prescribed, reason not otherwise specified

G9700 Patients who use hospice services any time during the measurement period

G9701 Children who are taking antibiotics in the 30 days prior to the date of the encounter during which the diagnosis was established

G9702 Patients who use hospice services any time during the measurement period

G9703 Children who are taking antibiotics in the 30 days prior to the diagnosis of pharyngitis

G9704 AJCC breast cancer stage i: t1 mic or t1a documented

G9705 AJCC breast cancer stage i: t1b (tumor > 0.5 cm but <= 1 cm in greatest dimension) documented

G9706 Low (or very low) risk of recurrence, prostate cancer

G9707 Patient received hospice services any time during the measurement period

G9708 Women who had a bilateral mastectomy or who have a history of a bilateral mastectomy or for whom there is evidence of a right and a left unilateral mastectomy

G9709 Hospice services used by patient any time during the measurement period

G9710 Patient was provided hospice services any time during the measurement period

G9711 Patients with a diagnosis or past history of total colectomy or colorectal cancer

G9712 Documentation of medical reason(s) for prescribing or dispensing antibiotic (e.g., intestinal infection, pertussis, bacterial infection, lyme disease, otitis media, acute sinusitis, acute pharyngitis, acute tonsillitis, chronic sinusitis, infection of the pharynx/larynx/tonsils/adenoids, prostatitis, cellulitis/ mastoiditis/bone infections, acute lymphadenitis, impetigo, skin staph infections, pneumonia, gonococcal infections/ venereal disease (syphilis, chlamydia, inflammatory diseases [female reproductive organs]), infections of the kidney, cystitis/UTI, acne, HIV disease/asymptomatic hiv, cystic fibrosis, disorders of the immune system, malignancy neoplasms, chronic bronchitis, emphysema, bronchiectasis, extrinsic allergic alveolitis, chronic airway obstruction, chronic obstructive asthma, pneumoconiosis and other lung disease due to external agents, other diseases of the respiratory system, and tuberculosis

G9713 Patients who use hospice services any time during the measurement period

G9714 Patient is using hospice services any time during the measurement period

G9715 Patients who use hospice services any time during the measurement period

G9716 BMI is documented as being outside of normal limits, follow-up plan is not completed for documented reason

G9717 Documentation stating the patient has an active diagnosis of depression or has a diagnosed bipolar disorder, therefore screening or follow-up not required

G9718 Hospice services for patient provided any time during the measurement period

G9719 Patient is not ambulatory, bed ridden, immobile, confined to chair, wheelchair bound, dependent on helper pushing wheelchair, independent in wheelchair or minimal help in wheelchair

G9720 Hospice services for patient occurred any time during the measurement period

G9721 Patient not ambulatory, bed ridden, immobile, confined to chair, wheelchair bound, dependent on helper pushing wheelchair, independent in wheelchair or minimal help in wheelchair

G9722 Documented history of renal failure or baseline serum creatinine = 4.0 mg/dl; renal transplant recipients are not considered to have preoperative renal failure, unless, since transplantation the cr has been or is 4.0 or higher

G9723 Hospice services for patient received any time during the measurement period

G9724 Patients who had documentation of use of anticoagulant medications overlapping the measurement year

G9725 Patients who use hospice services any time during the measurement period

G9726 Patient refused to participate

G9727 Patient unable to complete the FOTO knee intake prom at admission and discharge due to blindness, illiteracy, severe mental incapacity or language incompatibility and an adequate proxy is not available

G9728   Patient refused to participate

G9729   Patient unable to complete the FOTO hip intake prom at admission and discharge due to blindness, illiteracy, severe mental incapacity or language incompatibility and an adequate proxy is not available

G9730   Patient refused to participate

G9731   Patient unable to complete the FOTO foot or ankle intake prom at admission and discharge due to blindness, illiteracy, severe mental incapacity or language incompatibility and an adequate proxy is not available

G9732   Patient refused to participate

G9733   Patient unable to complete the FOTO lumbar intake prom at admission and discharge due to blindness, illiteracy, severe mental incapacity or language incompatibility and an adequate proxy is not available

G9734   Patient refused to participate

G9735   Patient unable to complete the FOTO shoulder intake prom at admission and discharge due to blindness, illiteracy, severe mental incapacity or language incompatibility and an adequate proxy is not available

G9736   Patient refused to participate

G9737   Patient unable to complete the FOTO elbow, wrist or hand intake prom at admission and discharge due to blindness, illiteracy, severe mental incapacity or language incompatibility and an adequate proxy is not available

G9738   Patient refused to participate

G9739   Patient unable to complete the FOTO general orthopedic intake prom at admission and discharge due to blindness, illiteracy, severe mental incapacity or language incompatibility and an adequate proxy is not available

G9740   Hospice services given to patient any time during the measurement period

G9741   Patients who use hospice services any time during the measurement period

G9742   Psychiatric symptoms assessed

G9743   Psychiatric symptoms not assessed, reason not otherwise specified

G9744   Patient not eligible due to active diagnosis of hypertension

G9745   Documented reason for not screening or recommending a follow-up for high blood pressure

G9746   Patient has mitral stenosis or prosthetic heart valves or patient has transient or reversible cause of af (e.g., pneumonia, hyperthyroidism, pregnancy, cardiac surgery)

G9747   Patient is undergoing palliative dialysis with a catheter

G9748   Patient approved by a qualified transplant program and scheduled to receive a living donor kidney transplant

G9749   Patient is undergoing palliative dialysis with a catheter

G9750   Patient approved by a qualified transplant program and scheduled to receive a living donor kidney transplant

G9751 Patient died at any time during the 24-month measurement period

G9752 Emergency surgery

G9753 Documentation of medical reason for not conducting a search for DICOM format images for prior patient ct imaging studies completed at non-affiliated external healthcare facilities or entities within the past 12 months that are available through a secure,

authorized, media-free, shared archive (e.g., trauma, acute myocardial infarction, stroke, aortic aneurysm where time is of the essence)

G9754 A finding of an incidental pulmonary nodule

G9755 Documentation of medical reason(s) that follow-up imaging is indicated (e.g., patient has a known malignancy that can metastasize, other medical reason(s)

G9756 Surgical procedures that included the use of silicone oil

G9757 Surgical procedures that included the use of silicone oil

▲ **G9758** Patient in hospice at any time during the measurement period

G9759 History of preoperative posterior capsule rupture

G9760 Patients who use hospice services any time during the measurement period

G9761 Patients who use hospice services any time during the measurement period

▲ **G9762** Patient had at least two HPV vaccines (with at least 146 days between the two) or three HPV vaccines on or between the patient's 9th and 13th birthdays

▲ **G9763** Patient did not have at least three HPV vaccines on or between the patient's 9th and 13th birthdays

▲ **G9764** Patient has been treated with an oral systemic or biologic medication for psoriasis vulgaris

▲ **G9765** Documentation that the patient declined therapy change or alternative therapies were unavailable, has documented contraindications, or has not been treated with an oral systemic or biologic for at least six consecutive months (e.g., experienced adverse effects or lack of efficacy with all other therapy options) in order to achieve better disease control as measured by pga, BSA, pasi, or dlqi

G9766 Patients who are transferred from one institution to another with a known diagnosis of CVA for endovascular stroke treatment

G9767 Hospitalized patients with newly diagnosed CVA considered for endovascular stroke treatment

G9768 Patients who utilize hospice services any time during the measurement period

G9769 Patient had a bone mineral density test in the past two years or received osteoporosis medication or therapy in the past 12 months

G9770 Peripheral nerve block (PNB)

G9771 At least 1 body temperature measurement equal to or greater than 35.5 degrees celsius (or 95.9 degrees Fahrenheit) achieved within the 30 minutes immediately before or the 15 minutes immediately after anesthesia end time

G9772 Documentation of one of the following medical reason(s) for not achieving at least 1

body temperature measurement equal to or greater than 35.5 degrees celsius (or 95.9 degrees Fahrenheit) achieved within the 30 minutes immediately before or the 15 minutes immediately after anesthesia end time (e.g., emergency cases, intentional hypothermia, etc.)

G9773 At least 1 body temperature measurement equal to or greater than 35.5 degrees celsius (or 95.9 degrees Fahrenheit) not achieved within the 30 minutes immediately before or the 15 minutes immediately after anesthesia end time

G9774 Patients who have had a hysterectomy

G9775 Patient received at least 2 prophylactic pharmacologic anti-emetic agents of different classes preoperatively and/or intraoperatively

G9776 Documentation of medical reason for not receiving at least 2 prophylactic pharmacologic anti-emetic agents of different classes preoperatively and/or intraoperatively (e.g., intolerance or other medical reason)

G9777 Patient did not receive at least 2 prophylactic pharmacologic anti-emetic agents of different classes preoperatively and/or intraoperatively

G9778 Patients who have a diagnosis of pregnancy

G9779 Patients who are breastfeeding

G9780 Patients who have a diagnosis of rhabdomyolysis

G9781 Documentation of medical reason(s) for not currently being a statin therapy user or receive an order (prescription) for statin therapy (e.g., patient with adverse effect, allergy or intolerance to statin medication therapy, patients who are receiving palliative care, patients with active liver disease or hepatic disease or insufficiency, and patients with end stage renal disease (ESRD))

G9782 History of or active diagnosis of familial or pure hypercholesterolemia

G9783 Documentation of patients with diabetes who have a most recent fasting or direct LDL-c laboratory test result < 70 mg/dl and are not taking statin therapy

G9784 Pathologists/dermatopathologists providing a second opinion on a biopsy

▲ **G9785** Pathology report diagnosing cutaneous basal cell carcinoma or squamous cell carcinoma (to include in situ disease) sent from the pathologist/dermatopathologist to the biopsying clinician for review within 7 days from the time when the tissue specimen was received by the pathologist

▲ **G9786** Pathology report diagnosing cutaneous basal cell carcinoma or squamous cell carcinoma (to include in situ disease) was not sent from the pathologist/dermatopathologist to the biopsying clinician for review within 7 days from the time when the tissue specimen was received by the pathologist

G9787 Patient alive as of the last day of the measurement year

G9788 Most recent bp is less than or equal to 140/90 mm hg

G9789 Blood pressure recorded during inpatient stays, emergency room visits, urgent care visits, and patient self-reported bp's (home and health fair bp results)

G9790 Most recent bp is greater than 140/90 mm hg, or blood pressure not documented

G9791 Most recent tobacco status is tobacco free

G9792	Most recent tobacco status is not tobacco free
G9793	Patient is currently on a daily aspirin or other antiplatelet
▲ G9794	Documentation of medical reason(s) for not on a daily aspirin or other antiplatelet (e.g., history of gastrointestinal bleed, intra-cranial bleed, idiopathic thrombocytopenic purpura (ITP), gastric bypass or documentation of active anticoagulant use during the measurement period)
G9795	Patient is not currently on a daily aspirin or other antiplatelet
G9796	Patient is currently on a statin therapy
G9797	Patient is not on a statin therapy
G9798	Discharge(s) for AMI between July 1 of the year prior measurement year to June 30 of the measurement period
G9799	Patients with a medication dispensing event indicator of a history of asthma any time during the patient's history through the end of the measure period
G9800	Patients who are identified as having an intolerance or allergy to beta-blocker therapy
G9801	Hospitalizations in which the patient was transferred directly to a non-acute care facility for any diagnosis
G9802	Patients who use hospice services any time during the measurement period
G9803	Patient prescribed a 180-day course of treatment with beta-blockers post discharge for AMI
G9804	Patient was not prescribed a 180-day course of treatment with beta-blockers post discharge for AMI
G9805	Patients who use hospice services any time during the measurement period
G9806	Patients who received cervical cytology or an HPV test
G9807	Patients who did not receive cervical cytology or an HPV test
G9808	Any patients who had no asthma controller medications dispensed during the measurement year
G9809	Patients who use hospice services any time during the measurement period
G9810	Patient achieved a PDC of at least 75% for their asthma controller medication
G9811	Patient did not achieve a PDC of at least 75% for their asthma controller medication
G9812	Patient died including all deaths occurring during the hospitalization in which the operation was performed, even if after 30 days, and those deaths occurring after discharge from the hospital, but within 30 days of the procedure
G9813	Patient did not die within 30 days of the procedure or during the index hospitalization
▲ G9814	Death occurring during the index acute care hospitalization
▲ G9815	Death did not occur during the index acute care hospitalization
▲ G9816	Death occurring after discharge from the hospital but within 30 days post procedure
▲ G9817	Death did not occur after discharge from the hospital within 30 days post procedure
G9818	Documentation of sexual activity

G9819	Patients who use hospice services any time during the measurement period
G9820	Documentation of a chlamydia screening test with proper follow-up
G9821	No documentation of a chlamydia screening test with proper follow-up
G9822	Women who had an endometrial ablation procedure during the year prior to the index date (exclusive of the index date)
G9823	Endometrial sampling or hysteroscopy with biopsy and results documented
G9824	Endometrial sampling or hysteroscopy with biopsy and results not documented
G9825	Her-2/neu negative or undocumented/unknown
G9826	Patient transferred to practice after initiation of chemotherapy
G9827	Her2-targeted therapies not administered during the initial course of treatment
G9828	Her2-targeted therapies administered during the initial course of treatment
G9829	Breast adjuvant chemotherapy administered
G9830	Her-2/neu positive
G9831	AJCC stage at breast cancer diagnosis = ii or iii
G9832	AJCC stage at breast cancer diagnosis = i (ia or ib) and t-stage at breast cancer diagnosis does not equal = t1, t1a, t1b
G9833	Patient transfer to practice after initiation of chemotherapy
G9834	Patient has metastatic disease at diagnosis
G9835	Trastuzumab administered within 12 months of diagnosis
G9836	Reason for not administering trastuzumab documented (e.g. patient declined, patient died, patient transferred, contraindication or other clinical exclusion, neoadjuvant chemotherapy or radiation not complete)
G9837	Trastuzumab not administered within 12 months of diagnosis
G9838	Patient has metastatic disease at diagnosis
G9839	Anti-EGFR monoclonal antibody therapy
▲ G9840	Ras (KRAS and NRAS) gene mutation testing performed before initiation of anti-EGFR MoAb
▲ G9841	Ras (KRAS and NRAS) gene mutation testing not performed before initiation of anti-EGFR MoAb
G9842	Patient has metastatic disease at diagnosis
▲ G9843	Ras (KRAS or NRAS) gene mutation
G9844	Patient did not receive anti-EGFR monoclonal antibody therapy
G9845	Patient received anti-EGFR monoclonal antibody therapy
G9846	Patients who died from cancer
G9847	Patient received chemotherapy in the last 14 days of life
G9848	Patient did not receive chemotherapy in the last 14 days of life

G9849   Patients who died from cancer

G9850   Patient had more than one emergency department visit in the last 30 days of life

G9851   Patient had one or less emergency department visits in the last 30 days of life

G9852   Patients who died from cancer

G9853   Patient admitted to the ICU in the last 30 days of life

G9854   Patient was not admitted to the ICU in the last 30 days of life

G9855   Patients who died from cancer

G9856   Patient was not admitted to hospice

G9857   Patient admitted to hospice

G9858   Patient enrolled in hospice

G9859   Patients who died from cancer

G9860   Patient spent less than three days in hospice care

G9861   Patient spent greater than or equal to three days in hospice care

G9862   Documentation of medical reason(s) for not recommending at least a 10 year follow-up interval (e.g., inadequate prep, familial or personal history of colonic polyps, patient had no adenoma and age is = 66 years old, or life expectancy < 10 years old, other medical reasons)

• G9890   Dilated macular exam performed, including documentation of the presence or absence of macular thickening or geographic atrophy or hemorrhage and the level of macular degeneration severity

• G9891   Documentation of medical reason(s) for not performing a dilated macular examination

• G9892   Documentation of patient reason(s) for not performing a dilated macular examination

• G9893   Dilated macular exam was not performed, reason not otherwise specified

• G9894   Androgen deprivation therapy prescribed/administered in combination with external beam radiotherapy to the prostate

• G9895   Documentation of medical reason(s) for not prescribing/administering androgen deprivation therapy in combination with external beam radiotherapy to the prostate (e.g., salvage therapy)

• G9896   Documentation of patient reason(s) for not prescribing/administering androgen deprivation therapy in combination with external beam radiotherapy to the prostate

• G9897   Patients who were not prescribed/administered androgen deprivation therapy in combination with external beam radiotherapy to the prostate, reason not given

• G9898   Patient age 65 or older in institutional special needs plans (snp) or residing in long-term care with pos code 32, 33, 34, 54, or 56 any time during the measurement period

• G9899   Screening, diagnostic, film, digital or digital breast tomosynthesis (3d) mammography results documented and reviewed

- **G9900** Screening, diagnostic, film, digital or digital breast tomosynthesis (3d) mammography results were not documented and reviewed, reason not otherwise specified

- **G9901** Patient age 65 or older in institutional special needs plans (snp) or residing in long-term care with pos code 32, 33, 34, 54, or 56 any time during the measurement period

- **G9902** Patient screened for tobacco use and identified as a tobacco user

- **G9903** Patient screened for tobacco use and identified as a tobacco non-user

- **G9904** Documentation of medical reason(s) for not screening for tobacco use (e.g., limited life expectancy, other medical reason)

- **G9905** Patient not screened for tobacco use, reason not given

- **G9906** Patient identified as a tobacco user received tobacco cessation intervention (counseling and/or pharmacotherapy)

- **G9907** Documentation of medical reason(s) for not providing tobacco cessation intervention (e.g., limited life expectancy, other medical reason)

- **G9908** Patient identified as tobacco user did not receive tobacco cessation intervention (counseling and/or pharmacotherapy), reason not given

- **G9909** Documentation of medical reason(s) for not providing tobacco cessation intervention if identified as a tobacco user (eg, limited life expectancy, other medical reason)

- **G9910** Patients age 65 or older in institutional special needs plans (snp) or residing in long-term care with pos code 32, 33, 34, 54 or 56 anytime during the measurement period

- **G9911** Clinically node negative (t1n0m0 or t2n0m0) invasive breast cancer before or after neoadjuvant systemic therapy

- **G9912** Hepatitis b virus (HBV) status assessed and results interpreted prior to initiating anti-TNF (tumor necrosis factor) therapy

- **G9913** Hepatitis b virus (HBV) status not assessed and results interpreted prior to initiating anti-TNF (tumor necrosis factor) therapy, reason not given

- **G9914** Patient receiving an anti-TNF agent

- **G9915** No record of HBV results documented

- **G9916** Functional status performed once in the last 12 months

- **G9917** Documentation of medical reason(s) for not performing functional status (e.g., patient is severely impaired and caregiver knowledge is limited, other medical reason)

- **G9918** Functional status not performed, reason not otherwise specified

- **G9919** Screening performed and positive and provision of recommendations

- **G9920** Screening performed and negative

- **G9921** No screening performed, partial screening performed or positive screen without recommendations and reason is not given or otherwise specified

- **G9922** Safety concerns screen provided and if positive then documented mitigation recommendations

- **G9923** Safety concerns screen provided and negative

- **G9924** Documentation of medical reason(s) for not providing safety concerns screen or for not providing recommendations, orders or referrals for positive screen (e.g., patient in palliative care, other medical reason)

- **G9925** Safety concerns screening not provided, reason not otherwise specified

- **G9926** Safety concerns screening positive screen is without provision of mitigation recommendations, including but not limited to referral to other resources

- **G9927** Documentation of system reason(s) for not prescribing warfarin or another-approved anticoagulation due to patient being currently enrolled in a clinical trial related to af/atrial flutter treatment

- **G9928** Warfarin or another-approved anticoagulant not prescribed, reason not given

- **G9929** Patient with transient or reversible cause of af (e.g., pneumonia, hyperthyroidism, pregnancy, cardiac surgery)

- **G9930** Patients who are receiving comfort care only

- **G9931** Documentation of cha2ds2-vasc risk score of 0 or 1

- **G9932** Documentation of patient reason(s) for not having records of negative or managed positive tb screen (e.g., patient does not return for Mantoux (PPD) skin test evaluation)

- **G9933** Adenoma(s) or colorectal cancer detected during screening colonoscopy

- **G9934** Documentation that neoplasm detected is only diagnosed as traditional serrated adenoma, sessile serrated polyp, or sessile serrated adenoma

- **G9935** Adenoma(s) or colorectal cancer not detected during screening colonoscopy

- **G9936** Surveillance colonoscopy - personal history of colonic polyps, colon cancer, or other malignant neoplasm of rectum, rectosigmoid junction, and anus

- **G9937** Diagnostic colonoscopy

- **G9938** Patients age 65 or older in institutional special needs plans (snp) or residing in long-term care with pos code 32, 33, 34, 54, or 56 any time during the measurement period

- **G9939** Pathologists/dermatopathologists is the same clinician who performed the biopsy

- **G9940** Documentation of medical reason(s) for not on a statin (e.g., pregnancy, in vitro fertilization, clomiphene rx, esrd, cirrhosis, muscular pain and disease during the measurement period or prior year)

- **G9941** Back pain was measured by the visual analog scale (vas) within three months preoperatively and at three months (6 - 20 weeks) postoperatively

- **G9942** Patient had any additional spine procedures performed on the same date as the lumbar discectomy/laminotomy

- **G9943** Back pain was not measured by the visual analog scale (vas) within three months preoperatively and at three months (6 - 20 weeks) postoperatively

- **G9944** Back pain was measured by the visual analog scale (vas) within three months preoperatively and at one year (9 to 15 months) postoperatively

- **G9945** Patient had cancer, fracture or infection related to the lumbar spine or patient had idiopathic or congenital scoliosis

Not payable
by Medicare

Non-covered
by Medicare

Special coverage
instructions

Carrier
judgement

183

- **G9946** Back pain was not measured by the visual analog scale (vas) within three months preoperatively and at one year (9 to 15 months) postoperatively

- **G9947** Leg pain was measured by the visual analog scale (vas) within three months preoperatively and at three months (6 to 20 weeks) postoperatively

- **G9948** Patient had any additional spine procedures performed on the same date as the lumbar discectomy/laminotomy

- **G9949** Leg pain was not measured by the visual analog scale (vas) within three months preoperatively and at three months (6 to 20 weeks) postoperatively

- **G9954** Patient exhibits 2 or more risk factors for post-operative vomiting

- **G9955** Cases in which an inhalational anesthetic is used only for induction

- **G9956** Patient received combination therapy consisting of at least two prophylactic pharmacologic anti-emetic agents of different classes preoperatively and/or intraoperatively

- **G9957** Documentation of medical reason for not receiving combination therapy consisting of at least two prophylactic pharmacologic anti-emetic agents of different classes preoperatively and/or intraoperatively (e.g., intolerance or other medical reason)

- **G9958** Patient did not receive combination therapy consisting of at least two prophylactic pharmacologic anti-emetic agents of different classes preoperatively and/or intraoperatively

- **G9959** Systemic antimicrobials not prescribed

- **G9960** Documentation of medical reason(s) for prescribing systemic antimicrobials

- **G9961** Systemic antimicrobials prescribed

- **G9962** Embolization endpoints are documented separately for each embolized vessel and ovarian artery angiography or embolization performed in the presence of variant uterine artery anatomy

- **G9963** Embolization endpoints are not documented separately for each embolized vessel or ovarian artery angiography or embolization not performed in the presence of variant uterine artery anatomy

- **G9964** Patient received at least one well-child visit with a pcp during the performance period

- **G9965** Patient did not receive at least one well-child visit with a pcp during the performance period

- **G9966** Children who were screened for risk of developmental, behavioral and social delays using a standardized tool with interpretation and report

- **G9967** Children who were not screened for risk of developmental, behavioral and social delays using a standardized tool with interpretation and report

- **G9968** Patient was referred to another provider or specialist during the performance period

- **G9969** Provider who referred the patient to another provider received a report from the provider to whom the patient was referred

- **G9970** Provider who referred the patient to another provider did not receive a report from the provider to whom the patient was referred

- **G9974** Dilated macular exam performed, including documentation of the presence or absence of macular thickening or geographic atrophy or hemorrhage and the level of macular degeneration severity
- **G9975** Documentation of medical reason(s) for not performing a dilated macular examination
- **G9976** Documentation of patient reason(s) for not performing a dilated macular examination
- **G9977** Dilated macular exam was not performed, reason not otherwise specified

● New code   ▲ Revised code   ( ) Deleted code   Ⓣ Trigger   Ⓟ Post Trigger DME

Rehabilitative Services

H0001 Alcohol and/or drug assessment

H0002 Behavioral health screening to determine eligibility for admission to treatment program

H0003 Alcohol and/or drug screening; laboratory analysis of specimens for presence of alcohol and/or drugs

H0004 Behavioral health counseling and therapy, per 15 minutes

H0005 Alcohol and/or drug services; group counseling by a clinician

H0006 Alcohol and/or drug services; case management

H0007 Alcohol and/or drug services; crisis intervention (outpatient)

H0008 Alcohol and/or drug services; sub-acute detoxification (hospital inpatient)

H0009 Alcohol and/or drug services; acute detoxification (hospital inpatient)

H0010 Alcohol and/or drug services; sub-acute detoxification (residential addiction program inpatient)

H0011 Alcohol and/or drug services; acute detoxification (residential addiction program inpatient)

H0012 Alcohol and/or drug services; sub-acute detoxification (residential addiction program outpatient)

H0013 Alcohol and/or drug services; acute detoxification (residential addiction program outpatient)

H0014 Alcohol and/or drug services; ambulatory detoxification

H0015 Alcohol and/or drug services; intensive outpatient (treatment program that operates at least 3 hours/day and at least 3 days/week and is based on an individualized treatment plan), including assessment, counseling; crisis intervention, and activity therapies or education

H0016 Alcohol and/or drug services; medical/somatic (medical intervention in ambulatory setting)

H0017 Behavioral health; residential (hospital residential treatment program), without room and board, per diem

H0018 Behavioral health; short-term residential (non-hospital residential treatment program), without room and board, per diem

H0019 Behavioral health; long-term residential (non-medical, non-acute care in a residential treatment program where stay is typically longer than 30 days), without room and board, per diem

H0020 Alcohol and/or drug services; methadone administration and/or service (provision of the drug by a licensed program)

H0021	Alcohol and/or drug training service (for staff and personnel not employed by providers)
H0022	Alcohol and/or drug intervention service (planned facilitation)
H0023	Behavioral health outreach service (planned approach to reach a targeted population)
H0024	Behavioral health prevention information dissemination service (one-way direct or non-direct contact with service audiences to affect knowledge and attitude)
H0025	Behavioral health prevention education service (delivery of services with target population to affect knowledge, attitude and/or behavior)
H0026	Alcohol and/or drug prevention process service, community-based (delivery of services to develop skills of impactors)
H0027	Alcohol and/or drug prevention environmental service (broad range of external activities geared toward modifying systems in order to mainstream prevention through policy and law)
H0028	Alcohol and/or drug prevention problem identification and referral service (e.g., student assistance and employee assistance programs), does not include assessment
H0029	Alcohol and/or drug prevention alternatives service (services for populations that exclude alcohol and other drug use e.g., alcohol free social events)
H0030	Behavioral health hotline service
H0031	Mental health assessment, by non-physician
H0032	Mental health service plan development by non-physician
H0033	Oral medication administration, direct observation
H0034	Medication training and support, per 15 minutes
H0035	Mental health partial hospitalization, treatment, less than 24 hours
H0036	Community psychiatric supportive treatment, face-to-face, per 15 minutes
H0037	Community psychiatric supportive treatment program, per diem
H0038	Self-help/peer services, per 15 minutes
H0039	Assertive community treatment, face-to-face, per 15 minutes
H0040	Assertive community treatment program, per diem
H0041	Foster care, child, non-therapeutic, per diem
H0042	Foster care, child, non-therapeutic, per month
H0043	Supported housing, per diem
H0044	Supported housing, per month
H0045	Respite care services, not in the home, per diem
H0046	Mental health services, not otherwise specified
H0047	Alcohol and/or other drug abuse services, not otherwise specified
H0048	Alcohol and/or other drug testing: collection and handling only, specimens other than blood
H0049	Alcohol and/or drug screening

H0050	Alcohol and/or drug services, brief intervention, per 15 minutes
H1000	Prenatal care, at-risk assessment
H1001	Prenatal care, at-risk enhanced service; antepartum management
H1002	Prenatal care, at risk enhanced service; care coordination
H1003	Prenatal care, at-risk enhanced service; education
H1004	Prenatal care, at-risk enhanced service; follow-up home visit
H1005	Prenatal care, at-risk enhanced service package (includes h1001-h1004)
H1010	Non-medical family planning education, per session
H1011	Family assessment by licensed behavioral health professional for state defined purposes
H2000	Comprehensive multidisciplinary evaluation
H2001	Rehabilitation program, per 1/2 day
H2010	Comprehensive medication services, per 15 minutes
H2011	Crisis intervention service, per 15 minutes
H2012	Behavioral health day treatment, per hour
H2013	Psychiatric health facility service, per diem
H2014	Skills training and development, per 15 minutes
H2015	Comprehensive community support services, per 15 minutes
H2016	Comprehensive community support services, per diem
H2017	Psychosocial rehabilitation services, per 15 minutes
H2018	Psychosocial rehabilitation services, per diem
H2019	Therapeutic behavioral services, per 15 minutes
H2020	Therapeutic behavioral services, per diem
H2021	Community-based wrap-around services, per 15 minutes
H2022	Community-based wrap-around services, per diem
H2023	Supported employment, per 15 minutes
H2024	Supported employment, per diem
H2025	Ongoing support to maintain employment, per 15 minutes
H2026	Ongoing support to maintain employment, per diem
H2027	Psychoeducational service, per 15 minutes
H2028	Sexual offender treatment service, per 15 minutes
H2029	Sexual offender treatment service, per diem
H2030	Mental health clubhouse services, per 15 minutes
H2031	Mental health clubhouse services, per diem
H2032	Activity therapy, per 15 minutes

H2033 Multisystemic therapy for juveniles, per 15 minutes

H2034 Alcohol and/or drug abuse halfway house services, per diem

H2035 Alcohol and/or other drug treatment program, per hour

H2036 Alcohol and/or other drug treatment program, per diem

H2037 Developmental delay prevention activities, dependent child of client, per 15 minutes

DRUGS ADMINISTERED OTHER THAN ORAL METHOD

(EXCEPTION: ORAL IMMUNOSUPPRESSIVE DRUGS)

Guidelines

In addition to the information presented in the INTRODUCTION, several other items unique to this section are defined or identified here:

1. EXCEPTION: Oral immunosuppressive drugs are not included in this section.

2. ROUTE OF ADMINISTRATION: Unless otherwise specified, the drugs listed in this section may be injected either subcutaneously, intramuscularly or intravenously.

3. SUBSECTION INFORMATION: Some of the listed subheadings or subsections have special needs or instructions unique to that section. Where these are indicated, special "notes" will be presented preceding or following the listings. Those subsections within the DRUGS ADMINISTERED OTHER THAN ORAL METHOD section that have "notes" are as follows:

Subsection	Code Numbers
Drugs administered other than oral method	J0000-J8999
Immunosuppressive drugs	J7500-J7506
Chemotherapy drugs	J9000-J9999

4. UNLISTED SERVICE OR PROCEDURE: A service or procedure may be provided that is not listed in this edition of HCPCS. When reporting such a service, the appropriate "unlisted procedure" code may be used to indicate the service, identifying it by "special report" as defined below. HCPCS terminology is inconsistent in defining unlisted procedures. The procedure definition may include the term(s) "unlisted", "not otherwise classified", "unspecified", "unclassified", "other" and "miscellaneous". Prior to using these codes, try to determine if a Local Level III code or CPT code is available. The "unlisted procedures" and accompanying codes for DRUGS ADMINISTERED OTHER THAN ORAL METHOD are as follows:

   J3490   Unclassified drugs
   J9999   Not otherwise classified, antineoplastic drugs

5. SPECIAL REPORT: A service, material or supply that is rarely provided, unusual, variable or new may require a special report in determining medical appropriateness for reimbursement purposes. Pertinent information should include an adequate definition or description of the nature, extent, and need for the service, material or supply.

6. MODIFIERS: Listed services may be modified under certain circumstances. When appropriate, the modifying circumstance is identified by adding a modifier to the basic procedure code. CPT and HCPCS National Level II modifiers may be used with CPT and HCPCS National Level II procedure codes. Modifiers commonly used with DRUGS ADMINISTERED OTHER THAN ORAL METHOD are as follows:

   -AA   Anesthesia services performed personally by anesthesiologist

J CODES

-AD   Medical supervision by a physician: more than four concurrent anesthesia procedures.

-CC   Procedure code change (use "CC" when the procedure code submitted was changed either for administrative reasons or because an incorrect code was filed)

-G8   Monitored anesthesia care (MAC) for deep complex, complicated, or markedly invasive surgical procedure

-G9   Monitored anesthesia care (MAC) for patient who has history of severe cardio-pulmonary condition

-TC   Technical component. Under certain circumstances, a charge may be made for the technical component alone. Under those circumstances, the technical component charge is identified by adding modifier -TC to the usual procedure code. Technical component charges are institutional charges and are not billed separately by physicians. However, portable x-ray suppliers bill only for the technical component and should use modifier -TC. The charge data from portable x-ray suppliers will then be used to build customary and prevailing profiles.

7.   CPT CODE CROSS-REFERENCE: Unless otherwise specified, the equivalent CPT codes for all listings in this section fall within the range 90701-90799.

Drugs Administered Other Than Oral Method

The following list of drugs can be injected either subcutaneous, intramuscular, or intravenous. The brand name(s) of the drugs has been included as bold-type in brackets [ ] in some cases.

NOTE: Third party payers may wish to determine a threshold and pay up to a certain dollar limit before developing for the drug. Use procedure code J0110 for processing these cases.

J0120	Injection, tetracycline, up to 250 mg
	MCM: 2049
J0129	Injection, abatacept, 10 mg (code may be used for Medicare when drug administered under the direct supervision of a physician, not for use when drug is self administered)
J0130	Injection abciximab, 10 mg
	MCM: 2049
J0131	Injection, acetaminophen, 10 mg
J0132	Injection, acetylcysteine, 100 mg
J0133	Injection, acyclovir, 5 mg
J0135	Injection, adalimumab, 20 mg
J0153	Injection, adenosine, 1 mg (not to be used to report any adenosine phosphate compounds)
J0171	Injection, adrenalin, epinephrine, 0.1 mg
	MCM: 2049
J0178	Injection, aflibercept, 1 mg

J0180   Injection, agalsidase beta, 1 mg

J0190   Injection, biperiden lactate, per 5 mg

MCM: 2049

J0200   Injection, alatrofloxacin mesylate, 100 mg

MCM: 2049.5

J0202   Injection, alemtuzumab, 1 mg

J0205   Injection, alglucerase, per 10 units

MCM: 2049

J0207   Injection, amifostine, 500 mg

MCM: 2049

J0210   Injection, methyldopate HCL, up to 250 mg

MCM: 2049

J0215   Injection, alefacept, 0.5 mg

J0220   Injection, alglucosidase alfa, 10 mg, not otherwise specified

J0221   Injection, alglucosidase alfa, (lumizyme), 10 mg

J0256   Injection, alpha 1 proteinase inhibitor (human), not otherwise specified, 10 mg

MCM: 2049

J0257   Injection, alpha 1 proteinase inhibitor (human), (glassia), 10 mg

MCM: 2049

J0270   Injection, alprostadil, 1.25 mcg (code may be used for Medicare when drug administered under the direct supervision of a physician, not for use when drug is self administered)

MCM: 2049

J0275   Alprostadil urethral suppository (code may be used for Medicare when drug administered under the direct supervision of a physician, not for use when drug is self administered)

MCM: 2049

J0278   Injection, amikacin sulfate, 100 mg

J0280   Injection, Aminophyllin, up to 250 mg

MCM: 2049

J0282   Injection, amiodarone hydrochloride, 30 mg

MCM: 2049

J0285   Injection, amphotericin b, 50 mg

MCM: 2049

J0287   Injection, amphotericin b lipid complex, 10 mg

MCM: 2049

J0288 Injection, amphotericin b cholesteryl sulfate complex, 10 mg

MCM: 2049

J0289 Injection, amphotericin b liposome, 10 mg

MCM: 2049

J0290 Injection, ampicillin sodium, 500 mg

MCM: 2049

J0295 Injection, ampicillin sodium/sulbactam sodium, per 1.5 gm

MCM: 2049

J0300 Injection, amobarbital, up to 125 mg

MCM: 2049

J0330 Injection, succinylcholine chloride, up to 20 mg

MCM: 2049

J0348 Injection, anidulafungin, 1 mg

J0350 Injection, anistreplase, per 30 units

MCM: 2049

J0360 Injection, hydralazine HCL, up to 20 mg

MCM: 2049

J0364 Injection, apomorphine hydrochloride, 1 mg

J0365 Injection, aprotinin, 10,000 kiu

MCM: 2049

J0380 Injection, metaraminol bitartrate, per 10 mg

MCM: 2049

J0390 Injection, chloroquine hydrochloride, up to 250 mg

MCM: 2049

J0395 Injection, arbutamine HCL, 1 mg

MCM: 2049

J0400 Injection, aripiprazole, intramuscular, 0.25 mg

J0401 Injection, aripiprazole, extended release, 1 mg

J0456 Injection, azithromycin, 500 mg

MCM: 2049.5

J0461 Injection, atropine sulfate, 0.01 mg

MCM: 2049

J0470 Injection, dimercaprol, per 100 mg

MCM: 2049

J0475	Injection, baclofen, 10 mg
	MCM: 2049
J0476	Injection, baclofen, 50 mcg for intrathecal trial
	MCM: 2049
J0480	Injection, basiliximab, 20 mg
	MCM: 2049
J0485	Injection, Belatacept, 1 mg
J0490	Injection, belimumab, 10 mg
J0500	Injection, dicyclomine HCL, up to 20 mg
	MCM: 2049
J0515	Injection, benztropine mesylate, per 1 mg
	MCM: 2049
J0520	Injection, bethanechol chloride, Myotonachol or urecholine, up to 5 mg
	MCM: 2049
J0558	Injection, penicillin g benzathine and penicillin g procaine, 100,000 units
J0561	Injection, penicillin g benzathine, 100,000 units
	MCM: 2049
● J0565	Injection, Bezlotoxumab, 10 mg
J0570	Buprenorphine implant, 74.2 mg
J0571	Buprenorphine/naloxone, oral, less than or equal to 3 mg buprenorphine
J0572	Buprenorphine/naloxone, oral, less than or equal to 3 mg buprenorphine
J0573	Buprenorphine/naloxone, oral, greater than 3 mg, but less than or equal to 6 mg buprenorphine
J0574	Buprenorphine/naloxone, oral, greater than 6 mg, but less than or equal to 10 mg buprenorphine
J0575	Buprenorphine/naloxone, oral, greater than 10 mg buprenorphine
J0583	Injection, bivalirudin, 1 mg
J0585	Injection, onabotulinumtoxinA, 1 unit
	MCM: 2049
J0586	Injection, abobotulinumtoxinA, 5 units
J0587	Injection, rimabotulinumtoxinB, 100 units
	MCM: 2049
J0588	Injection, incobotulinumtoxin a, 1 unit
J0592	Injection, buprenorphine hydrochloride, 0.1 mg
	MCM: 2049

J0594   injection, busulfan, 1 mg

J0595   Injection, butorphanol tartrate, 1 mg

J0596   Injection, c1 esterase inhibitor (recombinant), ruconest, 10 units

J0597   Injection, c-1 esterase inhibitor (human), Berinert, 10 units

J0598   Injection, c-1 esterase inhibitor (human), Cinryze, 10 units

J0600   Injection, edetate calcium disodium, up to 1000 mg

MCM: 2049

● **J0604**   Cinacalcet, oral, 1 mg, (for esrd on dialysis)

● **J0606**   Injection, etelcalcetide, 0.1 mg

J0610   Injection, calcium gluconate, per 10 ml

MCM: 2049

J0620   Injection, calcium glycerophosphate and calcium lactate, per 10 ml

MCM: 2049

J0630   Injection, calcitonin salmon, up to 400 units

MCM: 2049

J0636   Injection, calcitriol, 0.1 mcg

MCM: 2049

J0637   Injection, caspofungin acetate, 5 mg

J0638   Injection, canakinumab, 1 mg

J0640   Injection, leucovorin calcium, per 50 mg

MCM: 2049

J0641   Injection, levoleucovorin calcium, 0.5 mg

J0670   Injection, mepivacaine hydrochloride, per 10 ml

MCM: 2049

J0690   Injection, cefazolin sodium, 500 mg

MCM: 2049

J0692   Injection, cefepime hydrochloride, 500 mg

J0694   Injection, cefoxitin sodium, 1 gm

MCM: 2049,

J0695   Injection, Ceftolozane 50 mg and tazobactam 25 mg

J0696   Injection, ceftriaxone sodium, per 250 mg

MCM: 2049

J0697   Injection, sterile cefuroxime sodium, per 750 mg

MCM: 2049

J0698 Injection, cefotaxime sodium, per gm

MCM: 2049

J0702 Injection, betamethasone acetate 3 mg and betamethasone sodium phosphate 3 mg

MCM: 2049

J0706 Injection, caffeine citrate, 5 mg

J0710 Injection, cephapirin sodium, up to 1 gm

MCM: 2049

J0712 Injection, Ceftaroline fosamil, 10 mg

J0713 Injection, ceftazidime, per 500 mg

MCM: 2049

J0714 Injection, ceftazidime and Avibactam, 0.5 g/0.125 g

J0715 Injection, ceftizoxime sodium, per 500 mg

MCM: 2049

J0716 Injection, Centruroides immune f(ab)2, up to 120 milligrams

J0717 Injection, Certolizumab pegol, 1 mg (code may be used for Medicare when drug administered under the direct supervision of a physician, not for use when drug is self administered)

J0720 Injection, chloramphenicol sodium succinate, up to 1 gm

MCM: 2049

J0725 Injection, chorionic gonadotropin, per 1,000 USP units

MCM: 2049

J0735 Injection, clonidine hydrochloride, 1 mg

MCM: 2049

J0740 Injection, cidofovir, 375 mg

MCM: 2049

J0743 Injection, cilastatin sodium; imipenem, per 250 mg

MCM: 2049

J0744 Injection, ciprofloxacin for intravenous infusion, 200 mg

J0745 Injection, codeine phosphate, per 30 mg

MCM: 2049

(**J0760** Code deleted December 31, 2016).

J0770 Injection, colistimethate sodium, up to 150 mg

MCM: 2049

J0775 Injection, collagenase, clostridium histolyticum, 0.01 mg

J0780 Injection, prochlorperazine, up to 10 mg

MCM: 2049

J0795 Injection, corticorelin ovine triflutate, 1 microgram

MCM: 2049

J0800 Injection, corticotropin, up to 40 units

MCM: 2049

J0833 Injection, cosyntropin, not otherwise specified, 0.25 mg

J0834 Injection, cosyntropin (Cortrosyn), 0.25 mg

J0840 Injection, Crotalidae polyvalent immune Fab (ovine), up to 1 gram

J0850 Injection, cytomegalovirus immune globulin intravenous (human), per vial

MCM: 2049

J0875 Injection, dalbavancin, 5mg

J0878 Injection, daptomycin, 1 mg

J0881 Injection, darbepoetin alfa, 1 microgram (non-ESRD use)

J0882 Injection, darbepoetin alfa, 1 microgram (for ESRD on dialysis)

MCM: 4273.1

J0883 Injection, argatroban, 1 mg (for non-ESRD use)

MCM: 2049, 4273.1

J0884 Injection, argatroban, 1 mg (for ESRD on dialysis)

MCM: 2049, 4273.1

J0885 Injection, epoetin alfa, (for non-ESRD use), 1000 units

MCM: 2049

J0887 Injection, epoetin beta, 1 microgram, (for ESRD on dialysis)

J0888 Injection, epoetin beta, 1 microgram, (for non ESRD use)

J0890 Injection, Peginesatide, 0.1 mg (for ESRD on dialysis)

J0894 Injection, decitabine, 1 mg

J0895 Injection, deferoxamine mesylate, 500 mg

MCM: 2049,

J0897 Injection, denosumab, 1 mg

J0945 Injection, brompheniramine maleate, per 10 mg

MCM: 2049

J1000 Injection, depo-estradiol cypionate, up to 5 mg

MCM: 2049

J1020 Injection, methylprednisolone acetate, 20 mg

MCM: 2049

J1030   Injection, methylprednisolone acetate, 40 mg
MCM: 2049

J1040   Injection, methylprednisolone acetate, 80 mg
MCM: 2049

J1050   Injection, medroxyprogesterone acetate, 1 mg

J1071   Injection, testosterone cypionate, 1 mg

J1094   Injection, dexamethasone acetate, 1 mg
MCM: 2049

J1100   Injection, dexamethasone sodium phosphate, 1 mg
MCM: 2049

J1110   Injection, dihydroergotamine mesylate, per 1 mg
MCM: 2049

J1120   Injection, acetazolamide sodium, up to 500 mg
MCM: 2049

J1130   Injection, diclofenac sodium, 0.5 mg

J1160   Injection, digoxin, up to 0.5 mg
MCM: 2049

J1162   Injection, digoxin immune Fab (ovine), per vial
MCM: 2049

J1165   Injection, phenytoin sodium, per 50 mg
MCM: 2049

J1170   Injection, hydromorphone, up to 4 mg
MCM: 2049

J1180   Injection, dyphylline, up to 500 mg
MCM: 2049

J1190   Injection, dexrazoxane hydrochloride, per 250 mg
MCM: 2049

J1200   Injection, diphenhydramine HCL, up to 50 mg
MCM: 2049

J1205   Injection, chlorothiazide sodium, per 500 mg
MCM: 2049

J1212   Injection, DMSO, dimethyl sulfoxide, 50%, 50 ml
CIM: 45-23
MCM: 2049

J1230 Injection, methadone HCL, up to 10 mg

MCM: 2049

J1240 Injection, dimenhydrinate, up to 50 mg

MCM: 2049

J1245 Injection, dipyridamole, per 10 mg

MCM: 15030, 2049

J1250 Injection, dobutamine hydrochloride, per 250 mg

MCM: 2049

J1260 Injection, dolasetron mesylate, 10 mg

MCM: 2049

J1265 Injection, dopamine HCL, 40 mg

J1267 Injection, doripenem, 10 mg

J1270 Injection, doxercalciferol, 1 mcg

J1290 Injection, ecallantide, 1 mg

J1300 Injection, eculizumab, 10 mg

J1320 Injection, amitriptyline HCL, up to 20 mg

MCM: 2049

J1322 Injection, elosulfase alfa, 1 mg

J1324 Injection, enfuvirtide, 1 mg

J1325 Injection, epoprostenol, 0.5 mg

MCM: 2049

J1327 Injection, eptifibatide, 5 mg

MCM: 2049

J1330 Injection, ergonovine maleate, up to 0.2 mg

MCM: 2049

J1335 Injection, ertapenem sodium, 500 mg

J1364 Injection, erythromycin lactobionate, per 500 mg

MCM: 2049

J1380 Injection, estradiol valerate, up to 10 mg

MCM: 2049

J1410 Injection, estrogen conjugated, per 25 mg

MCM: 2049

• **J1428** Injection, eteplirsen, 10 mg

J1430 Injection, ethanolamine oleate, 100 mg

MCM: 2049

J1435   Injection, estrone, per 1 mg

MCM: 2049

J1436   Injection, etidronate disodium, per 300 mg

MCM: 2049

J1438   Injection, etanercept, 25 mg (code may be used for Medicare when drug administered under the direct supervision of a physician, not for use when drug is self administered)

MCM: 2049

J1439   Injection, ferric Carboxymaltose, 1 mg

J1442   Injection, filgrastim (g-csf), excludes biosimilars, 1 microgram

J1443   Injection, ferric pyrophosphate citrate solution, 0.1 mg of iron

J1447   Injection, tbo-filgrastim, 1 microgram

MCM: 2049.5

J1450   Injection fluconazole, 200 mg

MCM: 2049.5

J1451   Injection, fomepizole, 15 mg

MCM: 2049

J1452   Injection, fomivirsen sodium, intraocular, 1.65 mg

MCM: 2049.3

J1453   Injection, fosaprepitant, 1 mg

J1455   Injection, foscarnet sodium, per 1000 mg

MCM: 2049

J1457   Injection, gallium nitrate, 1 mg

J1458   Injection, galsulfase, 1 mg

J1459   Injection, immune globulin (Privigen), intravenous, non-lyophilized (e.g., liquid), 500 mg

J1460   Injection, gamma globulin, intramuscular, 1 cc

MCM: 2049

•   **J1555**   Injection, immune globulin (cuvitru), 100 mg

J1556   Injection, immune globulin (Bivigam), 500 mg

J1557   Injection, immune globulin, (Gammaplex), intravenous, non-lyophilized (e.g., liquid), 500 mg

J1559   Injection, immune globulin (Hizentra), 100 mg

J1560   Injection, gamma globulin, intramuscular, over 10 cc

MCM: 2049

J1561 Injection, immune globulin, (Gamunex-c/gammaked), non-lyophilized (e.g., liquid), 500 mg

MCM: 2049

J1562 Injection, immune globulin (Vivaglobin), 100 mg

J1566 Injection, immune globulin, intravenous, lyophilized (e.g., powder), not otherwise specified, 500 mg

MCM: 2049

J1568 Injection, immune globulin, (Octagam), intravenous, non-lyophilized (e.g., liquid), 500 mg

J1569 Injection, immune globulin, (Gammagard liquid), non-lyophilized, (e.g., liquid), 500 mg

MCM: 2049

J1570 Injection, ganciclovir sodium, 500 mg

MCM: 2049

J1571 Injection, hepatitis b immune globulin (HepaGam b), intramuscular, 0.5 ml

MCM: 2049

J1572 Injection, immune globulin, (Flebogamma/Flebogamma dif), intravenous, non-lyophilized (e.g., liquid), 500 mg

MCM: 2049

J1573 Injection, hepatitis b immune globulin (HepaGam b), intravenous, 0.5 ml

J1575 Injection, immune globulin/hyaluronidase, (hyqvia), 100 mg immunoglobulin

J1580 Injection, Garamycin, gentamicin, up to 80 mg

MCM: 2049

(**J1590** Code deleted December 31, 2016).

J1595 Injection, glatiramer acetate, 20 mg

MCM: 2049

J1599 Injection, immune globulin, intravenous, non-lyophilized (e.g., liquid), not otherwise specified, 500 mg

J1600 Injection, gold sodium thiomalate, up to 50 mg

MCM: 2049

J1602 Injection, golimumab, 1 mg, for intravenous use

J1610 Injection, glucagon hydrochloride, per 1 mg

MCM: 2049

J1620 Injection, gonadorelin hydrochloride, per 100 mcg

MCM: 2049

J1626 Injection, granisetron hydrochloride, 100 mcg

MCM: 2049

● **J1627**   Injection, granisetron, extended-release, 0.1 mg

J1630   Injection, haloperidol, up to 5 mg

MCM: 2049

J1631   Injection, haloperidol decanoate, per 50 mg

MCM: 2049

J1640   Injection, hemin, 1 mg

MCM: 2049

J1642   Injection, heparin sodium, (heparin lock flush), per 10 units

MCM: 2049

J1644   Injection, heparin sodium, per 1000 units

MCM: 2049

J1645   Injection, dalteparin sodium, per 2500 iu

MCM: 2049

J1650   Injection, enoxaparin sodium, 10 mg

J1652   Injection, fondaparinux sodium, 0.5 mg

MCM: 2049

J1655   Injection, tinzaparin sodium, 1000 iu

J1670   Injection, tetanus immune globulin, human, up to 250 units

MCM: 2049

J1675   Injection, histrelin acetate, 10 micrograms

MCM: 2049

J1700   Injection, hydrocortisone acetate, up to 25 mg

MCM: 2049

J1710   Injection, hydrocortisone sodium phosphate, up to 50 mg

MCM: 2049

J1720   Injection, hydrocortisone sodium succinate, up to 100 mg

MCM: 2049

(**J1725**   Code deleted December 31, 2017).

● **J1726**   Injection, hydroxyprogesterone caproate, (Makena), 10 mg

● **J1729**   Injection, hydroxyprogesterone caproate, not otherwise specified, 10 mg

J1730   Injection, diazoxide, up to 300 mg

MCM: 2049

J1740   Injection, ibandronate sodium, 1 mg

J1741   Injection, ibuprofen, 100 mg

J1742   Injection, ibutilide fumarate, 1 mg

MCM: 2049

J1743   Injection, idursulfase, 1 mg

J1744   Injection, icatibant, 1 mg

J1745   Injection, infliximab, excludes biosimilar, 10 mg

MCM: 2049

J1750   Injection, iron dextran, 50 mg

MCM: 2049.5

J1756   Injection, iron sucrose, 1 mg

J1786   Injection, imiglucerase, 10 units

MCM: 2049

J1790   Injection, droperidol, up to 5 mg

MCM: 2049

J1800   Injection, propranolol HCL, up to 1 mg

MCM: 2049

J1810   Injection, droperidol and fentanyl citrate, up to 2 ml ampule

MCM: 2049

J1815   Injection, insulin, per 5 units

CIM: 60-14

MCM: 2049

J1817   Insulin for administration through DME (i.e., insulin pump) per 50 units

J1826   Injection, interferon beta-1a, 30 mcg

J1830   Injection interferon beta-1b, 0.25 mg (code may be used for Medicare when drug administered under the direct supervision of a physician, not for use when drug is self administered)

MCM: 2049

J1833   Injection, Isavuconazonium, 1 mg

J1835   Injection, itraconazole, 50 mg

J1840   Injection, kanamycin sulfate, up to 500 mg

MCM: 2049

J1850   Injection, kanamycin sulfate, up to 75 mg

MCM: 2049

J1885   Injection, ketorolac tromethamine, per 15 mg

MCM: 2049

J1890   Injection, cephalothin sodium, up to 1 gram

MCM: 2049

J1930   Injection, lanreotide, 1 mg

J1931   Injection, laronidase, 0.1 mg

J1940   Injection, furosemide, up to 20 mg

MCM: 2049

J1942   Injection, aripiprazole lauroxil, 1 mg

J1945   Injection, lepirudin, 50 mg

MCM: 2049

J1950   Injection, leuprolide acetate (for depot suspension), per 3.75 mg

MCM: 2049

J1953   Injection, levetiracetam, 10 mg

J1955   Injection, levocarnitine, per 1 gm

MCM: 2049

J1956   Injection, levofloxacin, 250 mg

MCM: 2049

J1960   Injection, levorphanol tartrate, up to 2 mg

MCM: 2049

J1980   Injection, hyoscyamine sulfate, up to 0.25 mg

MCM: 2049

J1990   Injection, chlordiazepoxide HCL, up to 100 mg

MCM: 2049

J2001   Injection, lidocaine HCL for intravenous infusion, 10 mg

MCM: 2049

J2010   Injection, lincomycin HCL, up to 300 mg

MCM: 2049

J2020   Injection, linezolid, 200 mg

J2060   Injection, lorazepam, 2 mg

MCM: 2049

J2150   Injection, mannitol, 25% in 50 ml

MCM: 2049

J2170   Injection, mecasermin, 1 mg

J2175   Injection, meperidine hydrochloride, per 100 mg

MCM: 2049

J2180   Injection, meperidine and promethazine HCL, up to 50 mg

MCM: 2049

J2182   Injection, mepolizumab, 1 mg

J2185   Injection, meropenem, 100 mg

J2210   Injection, methylergonovine maleate, up to 0.2 mg

MCM: 2049

J2212   Injection, methylnaltrexone, 0.1 mg

J2248   Injection, micafungin sodium, 1 mg

J2250   Injection, midazolam hydrochloride, per 1 mg

MCM: 2049

Ⓟ **J2260**   Injection, milrinone lactate, 5 mg

MCM: 2049

J2265   Injection, minocycline hydrochloride, 1 mg

J2270   Injection, morphine sulfate, up to 10 mg

MCM: 2049

J2274   Injection, morphine sulfate, preservative-free for epidural or intrathecal use, 10 mg

CIM: 60-14

MCM: 2049

J2278   Injection, ziconotide, 1 microgram

J2280   Injection, moxifloxacin, 100 mg

J2300   Injection, nalbuphine hydrochloride, per 10 mg

MCM: 2049

J2310   Injection, naloxone hydrochloride, per 1 mg

MCM: 2049

J2315   Injection, naltrexone, depot form, 1 mg

J2320   Injection, nandrolone decanoate, up to 50 mg

MCM: 2049

J2323   Injection, natalizumab, 1 mg

J2325   Injection, nesiritide, 0.1 mg

MCM: 2049

• **J2326**   Injection, nusinersen, 0.1 mg

• **J2350**   Injection, ocrelizumab, 1 mg

J2353   Injection, octreotide, depot form for intramuscular injection, 1 mg

J2354   Injection, octreotide, non-depot form for subcutaneous or intravenous injection, 25 mcg

J2355   Injection, oprelvekin, 5 mg

MCM: 2049

J2357 Injection, omalizumab, 5 mg

J2358 Injection, olanzapine, long-acting, 1 mg

J2360 Injection, orphenadrine citrate, up to 60 mg

MCM: 2049

J2370 Injection, phenylephrine HCL, up to 1 ml

MCM: 2049

J2400 Injection, chloroprocaine hydrochloride, per 30 ml

MCM: 2049

J2405 Injection, ondansetron hydrochloride, per 1 mg

MCM: 2049

J2407 Injection, oritavancin, 10 mg

MCM: 2049

J2410 Injection, oxymorphone HCL, up to 1 mg

MCM: 2049

J2425 Injection, palifermin, 50 micrograms

J2426 Injection, paliperidone palmitate extended release, 1 mg

J2430 Injection, pamidronate disodium, per 30 mg

MCM: 2049

J2440 Injection, papaverine HCL, up to 60 mg

MCM: 2049

J2460 Injection, oxytetracycline HCL, up to 50 mg

MCM: 2049

J2469 Injection, palonosetron HCL, 25 mcg

J2501 Injection, paricalcitol, 1 mcg

MCM: 2049

J2502 Injection, Pasireotide long acting, 1 mg

J2503 Injection, pegaptanib sodium, 0.3 mg

J2504 Injection, pegademase bovine, 25 iu

MCM: 2049

J2505 Injection, pegfilgrastim, 6 mg

J2507 Injection, pegloticase, 1 mg

J2510 Injection, penicillin g procaine, aqueous, up to 600,000 units

MCM: 2049

Not payable
by Medicare   Non-covered
by Medicare   Special coverage
instructions   Carrier
judgement   207

J2513 Injection, pentastarch, 10% solution, 100 ml

MCM: 2049

J2515 Injection, pentobarbital sodium, per 50 mg

MCM: 2049

J2540 Injection, penicillin g potassium, up to 600,000 units

MCM: 2049

J2543 Injection, piperacillin sodium/tazobactam sodium, 1 gram/0.125 grams (1.125 grams)

MCM: 2049

J2545 Pentamidine isethionate, inhalation solution,-approved final product, non-compounded, administered through DME, unit dose form, per 300 mg

J2547 Injection, peramivir, 1 mg

J2550 Injection, promethazine HCL, up to 50 mg

MCM: 2049

J2560 Injection, phenobarbital sodium, up to 120 mg

MCM: 2049

J2562 Injection, plerixafor, 1 mg

J2590 Injection, oxytocin, up to 10 units

MCM: 2049

J2597 Injection, desmopressin acetate, per 1 mcg

MCM: 2049

J2650 Injection, prednisolone acetate, up to 1 ml

MCM: 2049

J2670 Injection, tolazoline HCL, up to 25 mg

MCM: 2049

J2675 Injection, progesterone, per 50 mg

MCM: 2049

J2680 Injection, fluphenazine decanoate, up to 25 mg

MCM: 2049

J2690 Injection, procainamide HCL, up to 1 gm

MCM: 2049

J2700 Injection, oxacillin sodium, up to 250 mg

MCM: 2049

J2704 Injection, propofol, 10 mg

J2710 Injection, neostigmine methylsulfate, up to 0.5 mg

MCM: 2049

J2720 Injection, protamine sulfate, per 10 mg

MCM: 2049

J2724 Injection, protein c concentrate, intravenous, human, 10 iu

J2725 Injection, protirelin, per 250 mcg

MCM: 2049

J2730 Injection, pralidoxime chloride, up to 1 gm

MCM: 2049

J2760 Injection, phentolamine mesylate, up to 5 mg

MCM: 2049

J2765 Injection, metoclopramide HCL, up to 10 mg

MCM: 2049

J2770 Injection, quinupristin/dalfopristin, 500 mg (150/350)

MCM: 2049

J2778 Injection, ranibizumab, 0.1 mg

J2780 Injection, ranitidine hydrochloride, 25 mg

MCM: 2049

J2783 Injection, rasburicase, 0.5 mg

J2785 Injection, regadenoson, 0.1 mg

J2786 Injection, reslizumab, 1 mg

J2788 Injection, rho d immune globulin, human, minidose, 50 micrograms (250 i.u.)

MCM: 2049

J2790 Injection, rho d immune globulin, human, full dose, 300 micrograms (1500 i.u.)

MCM: 2049

J2791 Injection, rho(d) immune globulin (human), (Rhophylac), intramuscular or intravenous, 100 iu

MCM: 2049

J2792 Injection, rho d immune globulin, intravenous, human, solvent detergent, 100 iu

MCM: 2049

J2793 Injection, rilonacept, 1 mg

MCM: 2049

J2794 Injection, risperidone, long acting, 0.5 mg

J2795 Injection, ropivacaine hydrochloride, 1 mg

J2796 Injection, romiplostim, 10 micrograms

J2800 Injection, methocarbamol, up to 10 ml

MCM: 2049

J2805   Injection, sincalide, 5 micrograms

J2810   Injection, theophylline, per 40 mg

MCM: 2049

J2820   Injection, sargramostim (gm-csf), 50 mcg

MCM: 2049

J2840   Injection, sebelipase alfa, 1 mg

J2850   Injection, secretin, synthetic, human, 1 microgram

MCM: 2049

J2860   Injection, Siltuximab, 10 mg

J2910   Injection, aurothioglucose, up to 50 mg

MCM: 2049

J2916   Injection, sodium ferric gluconate complex in sucrose injection, 12.5 mg

MCM: 2049.2, 2049.4

J2920   Injection, methylprednisolone sodium succinate, up to 40 mg

MCM: 2049

J2930   Injection, methylprednisolone sodium succinate, up to 125 mg

MCM: 2049

J2940   Injection, somatrem, 1 mg

MCM: 2049

Statute: 1861s2b

J2941   Injection, somatropin, 1 mg

MCM: 2049

Statute: 1861s2b

J2950   Injection, promazine HCL, up to 25 mg

MCM: 2049

J2993   Injection, reteplase, 18.1 mg

MCM: 2049

J2995   Injection, streptokinase, per 250,000 iu

MCM: 2049

J2997   Injection, alteplase recombinant, 1 mg

MCM: 2049

J3000   Injection, streptomycin, up to 1 gm

MCM: 2049

J3010   Injection, fentanyl citrate, 0.1 mg

MCM: 2049

J3030   Injection, sumatriptan succinate, 6 mg (code may be used for Medicare when drug administered under the direct supervision of a physician, not for use when drug is self administered)

MCM: 2049

J3060   Injection, taliglucerase alfa, 10 units

J3070   Injection, pentazocine, 30 mg

MCM: 2049

J3090   Injection, Tedizolid phosphate, 1 mg

J3095   Injection, telavancin, 10 mg

J3101   Injection, tenecteplase, 1 mg

J3105   Injection, terbutaline sulfate, up to 1 mg

MCM: 2049

J3110   Injection, teriparatide, 10 mcg

J3121   Injection, testosterone enanthate, 1 mg

J3145   Injection, testosterone undecanoate, 1 mg

J3230   Injection, chlorpromazine HCL, up to 50 mg

MCM: 2049

J3240   Injection, thyrotropin alpha, 0.9 mg, provided in 1.1 mg vial

MCM: 2049

J3243   Injection, tigecycline, 1 mg

J3246   Injection, tirofiban HCL, 0.25 mg

J3250   Injection, trimethobenzamide HCL, up to 200 mg

MCM: 2049

J3260   Injection, tobramycin sulfate, up to 80 mg

MCM: 2049

J3262   Injection, tocilizumab, 1 mg

J3265   Injection, torsemide, 10 mg/ml

MCM: 2049

J3280   Injection, thiethylperazine maleate, up to 10 mg

MCM: 2049

J3285   Injection, treprostinil, 1 mg

J3300   Injection, triamcinolone acetonide, preservative free, 1 mg

J3301   Injection, triamcinolone acetonide, not otherwise specified, 10 mg

MCM: 2049

J3302   Injection, triamcinolone diacetate, per 5mg

MCM: 2049

J3303   Injection, triamcinolone hexacetonide, per 5mg

MCM: 2049

J3305   Injection, trimetrexate glucuronate, per 25 mg

MCM: 2049

J3310   Injection, perphenazine, up to 5 mg

MCM: 2049

J3315   Injection, triptorelin pamoate, 3.75 mg

MCM: 2049

J3320   Injection, spectinomycin dihydrochloride, up to 2 gm

MCM: 2049

J3350   Injection, urea, up to 40 gm

MCM: 2049

J3355   Injection, urofollitropin, 75 iu

MCM: 2049

J3357   Ustekinumab, for subcutaneous injection, 1 mg

• **J3358**   Ustekinumab, for intravenous injection, 1 mg

J3360   Injection, diazepam, up to 5 mg

MCM: 2049

J3364   Injection, urokinase, 5000 iu vial

MCM: 2049

J3365   Injection, iv, urokinase, 250,000 i.u. vial

MCM: 2049,

J3370   Injection, vancomycin HCL, 500 mg

CIM: 60-14

MCM: 2049

J3380   Injection, vedolizumab, 1 mg

J3385   Injection, velaglucerase alfa, 100 units

J3396   Injection, verteporfin, 0.1 mg

MCM: 35-100, 45-30

J3400   Injection, triflupromazine HCL, up to 20 mg

MCM: 2049

J3410   Injection, hydroxyzine HCL, up to 25 mg

MCM: 2049

J3411   Injection, thiamine HCL, 100 mg

J3415   Injection, pyridoxine HCL, 100 mg

J3420   Injection, vitamin b-12 cyanocobalamin, up to 1000 mcg

CIM: 45-4

MCM: 2049

J3430   Injection, phytonadione (vitamin k), per 1 mg

MCM: 2049

J3465   Injection, voriconazole, 10 mg

MCM: 2049

J3470   Injection, hyaluronidase, up to 150 units

MCM: 2049

J3471   Injection, hyaluronidase, ovine, preservative free, per 1 USP unit (up to 999 USP units)

J3472   Injection, hyaluronidase, ovine, preservative free, per 1000 USP units

J3473   Injection, hyaluronidase, recombinant, 1 USP unit

MCM: 2049

J3475   Injection, magnesium sulfate, per 500 mg

MCM: 2049

J3480   Injection, potassium chloride, per 2 mEq

MCM: 2049

J3485   Injection, zidovudine, 10 mg

MCM: 2049

J3486   Injection, ziprasidone mesylate, 10 mg

J3489   Injection, zoledronic acid, 1 mg

J3490   Unclassified drugs

MCM: 2049

J3520   Edetate disodium, per 150 mg

CIM: 35-64, 45-20

J3530   Nasal vaccine inhalation

MCM: 2049

J3535   Drug administered through a metered dose inhaler

MCM: 2050.5

J3570   Laetrile, amygdalin, vitamin b17

CIM: 45-10

J3590   Unclassified biologics

J7030   Infusion, normal saline solution , 1000 cc

MCM: 2049

J7040   Infusion, normal saline solution, sterile (500 ml=1 unit)

MCM: 2049

J7042   5% dextrose/normal saline (500 ml = 1 unit)

MCM: 2049

J7050   Infusion, normal saline solution , 250 cc

MCM: 2049

J7060   5% dextrose/water (500 ml = 1 unit)

MCM: 2049

J7070   Infusion, d5w, 1000 cc

MCM: 2049

J7100   Infusion, dextran 40, 500 ml

MCM: 2049

J7110   Infusion, dextran 75, 500 ml

MCM: 2049

J7120   Ringers lactate infusion, up to 1000 cc

MCM: 2049

J7121   5% dextrose in lactated ringers infusion, up to 1000 cc

MCM: 2049

J7131   Hypertonic saline solution, 1 ml

MCM: 2049

J7175   Injection, factor x, (human), 1 i.u.

J7178   Injection, human fibrinogen concentrate, 1 mg

J7179   Injection, von Willebrand factor (recombinant), (vonvendi), 1 i.u. vwf:rco

J7180   Injection, factor xiii (antihemophilic factor, human), 1 i.u.

J7181   Injection, factor xiii a-subunit, (recombinant), per iu

J7182   Injection, factor viii, (antihemophilic factor, recombinant), (novo eight), per iu

J7183   Injection, von Willebrand factor complex (human), wilate, 1 i.u. vwf:rco

MCM: 2049

J7185   Injection, factor viii (antihemophilic factor, recombinant) (Xyntha), per i.u.

J7186   Injection, antihemophilic factor viii/von Willebrand factor complex (human), per factor viii i.u.

MCM: 2049

J7187 Injection, von Willebrand factor complex (Humate-p), per iu vwf:rco

MCM: 2049

J7188 Injection, factor viii (antihemophilic factor, recombinant), (obizur), per i.u.

MCM: 2049

J7189 Factor VIIa (antihemophilic factor, recombinant), per 1 microgram

MCM: 2049

J7190 Factor viii (antihemophilic factor, human) per i.u.

MCM: 2049

J7191 Factor viii (antihemophilic factor (porcine)), per i.u.

MCM: 2049

J7192 Factor viii (antihemophilic factor, recombinant) per i.u., not otherwise specified

MCM: 2049

J7193 Factor ix (antihemophilic factor, purified, non-recombinant) per i.u.

MCM: 2049

J7194 Factor ix, complex, per i.u.

MCM: 2049

J7195 Injection, factor ix (antihemophilic factor, recombinant) per iu, not otherwise specified

MCM: 2049

J7196 Injection, antithrombin recombinant, 50 i.u.

J7197 Antithrombin iii (human), per i.u.

MCM: 2049

J7198 Anti-inhibitor, per i.u.

CIM: 45-24

MCM: 2049

J7199 Hemophilia clotting factor, not otherwise classified

CIM: 45-24

MCM: 2049

J7200 Injection, factor ix, (antihemophilic factor, recombinant), rixubis, per iu

MCM: 2049

J7201 Injection, factor ix, Fc fusion protein, (recombinant), alprolix, 1 i.u.

MCM: 2049

J7202 Injection, factor ix, albumin fusion protein, (recombinant), idelvion, 1 i.u.

J7205 Injection, factor viii Fc fusion (recombinant), per iu

J7207 Injection, factor viii, (antihemophilic factor, recombinant), pegylated, 1 i.u.

J7209 Injection, factor viii, (antihemophilic factor, recombinant), (nuwiq), 1 i.u.

• **J7210** Injection, factor viii, (antihemophilic factor, recombinant), (afstyla), 1 i.u.

• **J7211** Injection, factor viii, (antihemophilic factor, recombinant), (kovaltry), 1 i.u.

• **J7296** Levonorgestrel-releasing intrauterine contraceptive system, (kyleena), 19.5 mg

J7297 Levonorgestrel-releasing intrauterine contraceptive system (liletta), 52 mg

Statute: 1862(a)(1)

J7298 Levonorgestrel-releasing intrauterine contraceptive system (Mirena), 52 mg

Statute: 1862(a)(1)

J7300 Intrauterine copper contraceptive

Statute: 1862A1

J7301 Levonorgestrel-releasing intrauterine contraceptive system (skyla), 13.5 mg

Statute: 1862(a)(1)

J7303 Contraceptive supply, hormone containing vaginal ring, each

Statute: 1862.1

J7304 Contraceptive supply, hormone containing patch, each

Statute: 1862.1

J7306 Levonorgestrel (contraceptive) implant system, including implants and supplies

J7307 Etonogestrel (contraceptive) implant system, including implant and supplies

J7308 Aminolevulinic acid HCL for topical administration, 20%, single unit dosage form (354 mg)

J7309 Methyl aminolevulinate (mal) for topical administration, 16.8%, 1 gram

J7310 Ganciclovir, 4.5 mg, long-acting implant

MCM: 2049

J7311 Fluocinolone acetonide, intravitreal implant

J7312 Injection, dexamethasone, intravitreal implant, 0.1 mg

J7313 Injection, fluocinolone acetonide, intravitreal implant, 0.01 mg

J7315 Mitomycin, ophthalmic, 0.2 mg

J7316 Injection, Ocriplasmin, 0.125 mg

J7320 Hyaluronan or derivative, genvisc 850, for intra-articular injection, 1 mg

▲ **J7321** Hyaluronan or derivative, Hyalgan, Supartz or visco-3, for intra-articular injection, per dose

J7322 Hyaluronan or derivative, hymovis, for intra-articular injection, 1 mg

J7323 Hyaluronan or derivative, Euflexxa, for intra-articular injection, per dose

J7324 Hyaluronan or derivative, Orthovisc, for intra-articular injection, per dose

J7325 Hyaluronan or derivative, Synvisc or Synvisc-one, for intra-articular injection, 1 mg

J7326   Hyaluronan or derivative, gel-one, for intra-articular injection, per dose

J7327   Hyaluronan or derivative, monovisc, for intra-articular injection, per dose

J7328   Hyaluronan or derivative, gel-syn, for intra-articular injection, 0.1 mg

J7330   Autologous cultured chondrocytes, implant

J7336   Capsaicin 8% patch, per square centimeter

J7340   Carbidopa 5 mg/levodopa 20 mg enteral suspension, 100 ml

J7342   Installation, ciprofloxacin otic suspension, 6 mg

• J7345   Aminolevulinic acid HCl for topical administration, 10% gel, 10 mg

Immunosuppressive Drugs (Includes Non-Injectables)

J7500   Azathioprine, oral, 50 mg

MCM: 2049.5

J7501   Azathioprine, parenteral, 100 mg

MCM: 2049

J7502   Cyclosporine, oral, 100 mg

MCM: 2049.5

J7503   Tacrolimus, extended release, (envarsus XR), oral, 0.25 mg

MCM: 2049.5

J7504   Lymphocyte immune globulin, antithymocyte globulin, equine, parenteral, 250 mg

CIM: 45-22

MCM: 2049

J7505   Muromonab-cd3, parenteral, 5 mg

MCM: 2049

J7507   Tacrolimus, immediate release, oral, 1 mg

MCM: 2049.5

J7508   Tacrolimus, extended release, (Astagraf xl), oral, 0.1 mg

MCM: 2049.5

J7509   Methylprednisolone oral, per 4 mg

MCM: 2049.5

J7510   Prednisolone oral, per 5 mg

MCM: 2049.5

J7511   Lymphocyte immune globulin, antithymocyte globulin, rabbit, parenteral, 25 mg

J7512   Prednisone, immediate release or delayed release, oral, 1 mg

MCM: 2049.5

J7513   Daclizumab, parenteral, 25 mg

MCM: 2049.5

J7515	Cyclosporine, oral, 25 mg
J7516	Cyclosporin, parenteral, 250 mg
J7517	Mycophenolate mofetil, oral, 250 mg
J7518	Mycophenolic acid, oral, 180 mg

MCM: 2050.5, 4471, 5249

J7520   Sirolimus, oral, 1 mg

MCM: 2049.5

J7525   Tacrolimus, parenteral, 5 mg

MCM: 2049.5

J7527   Everolimus, oral, 0.25 mg

MCM: 2049.5

J7599   Immunosuppressive drug, not otherwise classified

MCM: 2049.5

J7604   Acetylcysteine, inhalation solution, compounded product, administered through DME, unit dose form, per gram

Ⓟ **J7605**   Arformoterol, inhalation solution, approved final product, non-compounded, administered through DME, unit dose form, 15 micrograms

Ⓟ **J7606**   Formoterol fumarate, inhalation solution, approved final product, non-compounded, administered through DME, unit dose form, 20 micrograms

J7607   Levalbuterol, inhalation solution, compounded product, administered through DME, concentrated form, 0.5 mg

Ⓟ **J7608**   Acetylcysteine, inhalation solution,-approved final product, non-compounded, administered through DME, unit dose form, per gram

J7609   Albuterol, inhalation solution, compounded product, administered through DME, unit dose, 1 mg

J7610   Albuterol, inhalation solution, compounded product, administered through DME, concentrated form, 1 mg

J7611   Albuterol, inhalation solution,-approved final product, non-compounded, administered through DME, concentrated form, 1 mg

MCM: 2100.5

J7612   Levalbuterol, inhalation solution,-approved final product, non-compounded, administered through DME, concentrated form, 0.5 mg

MCM: 2100.5

Ⓟ **J7613**   Albuterol, inhalation solution,-approved final product, non-compounded, administered through DME, unit dose, 1 mg

MCM: 2100.5

J7614   Levalbuterol, inhalation solution,-approved final product, non-compounded, administered through DME, unit dose, 0.5 mg

MCM: 2100.5

J7615   Levalbuterol, inhalation solution, compounded product, administered through DME, unit dose, 0.5 mg

Ⓟ   **J7620**   Albuterol, up to 2.5 mg and ipratropium bromide, up to 0.5 mg,-approved final product, non-compounded, administered through DME

J7622   Beclomethasone, inhalation solution, compounded product, administered through DME, unit dose form, per milligram

J7624   Betamethasone, inhalation solution, compounded product, administered through DME, unit dose form, per milligram

Ⓟ   **J7626**   Budesonide, inhalation solution,-approved final product, non-compounded, administered through DME, unit dose form, up to 0.5 mg

J7627   Budesonide, inhalation solution, compounded product, administered through DME, unit dose form, up to 0.5 mg

J7628   Bitolterol mesylate, inhalation solution, compounded product, administered through DME, concentrated form, per milligram

J7629   Bitolterol mesylate, inhalation solution, compounded product, administered through DME, unit dose form, per milligram

J7631   Cromolyn sodium, inhalation solution,-approved final product, non-compounded, administered through DME, unit dose form, per 10 milligrams

J7632   Cromolyn sodium, inhalation solution, compounded product, administered through DME, unit dose form, per 10 milligrams

J7633   Budesonide, inhalation solution,-approved final product, non-compounded, administered through DME, concentrated form, per 0.25 milligram

J7634   Budesonide, inhalation solution, compounded product, administered through DME, concentrated form, per 0.25 milligram

J7635   Atropine, inhalation solution, compounded product, administered through DME, concentrated form, per milligram

J7636   Atropine, inhalation solution, compounded product, administered through DME, unit dose form, per milligram

J7637   Dexamethasone, inhalation solution, compounded product, administered through DME, concentrated form, per milligram

J7638   Dexamethasone, inhalation solution, compounded product, administered through DME, unit dose form, per milligram

J7639   Dornase alfa, inhalation solution,-approved final product, non-compounded, administered through DME, unit dose form, per milligram

J7640   Formoterol, inhalation solution, compounded product, administered through DME, unit dose form, 12 micrograms

J7641   Flunisolide, inhalation solution, compounded product, administered through DME, unit dose, per milligram

J7642   Glycopyrrolate, inhalation solution, compounded product, administered through DME, concentrated form, per milligram

J7643   Glycopyrrolate, inhalation solution, compounded product, administered through DME, unit dose form, per milligram

ⓟ   **J7644**   Ipratropium bromide, inhalation solution,-approved final product, non-compounded, administered through DME, unit dose form, per milligram

J7645   Ipratropium bromide, inhalation solution, compounded product, administered through DME, unit dose form, per milligram

J7647   Isoetharine HCL, inhalation solution, compounded product, administered through DME, concentrated form, per milligram

J7648   Isoetharine HCL, inhalation solution,-approved final product, non-compounded, administered through DME, concentrated form, per milligram

J7649   Isoetharine HCL, inhalation solution,-approved final product, non-compounded, administered through DME, unit dose form, per milligram

J7650   Isoetharine HCL, inhalation solution, compounded product, administered through DME, unit dose form, per milligram

J7657   Isoproterenol HCL, inhalation solution, compounded product, administered through DME, concentrated form, per milligram

J7658   Isoproterenol HCL, inhalation solution,-approved final product, non-compounded, administered through DME, concentrated form, per milligram

J7659   Isoproterenol HCL, inhalation solution,-approved final product, non-compounded, administered through DME, unit dose form, per milligram

J7660   Isoproterenol HCL, inhalation solution, compounded product, administered through DME, unit dose form, per milligram

J7665   Mannitol, administered through an inhaler, 5 mg

J7667   Metaproterenol sulfate, inhalation solution, compounded product, concentrated form, per 10 milligrams

J7668   Metaproterenol sulfate, inhalation solution,-approved final product, non-compounded, administered through DME, concentrated form, per 10 milligrams

J7669   Metaproterenol sulfate, inhalation solution,-approved final product, non-compounded, administered through DME, unit dose form, per 10 milligrams

J7670   Metaproterenol sulfate, inhalation solution, compounded product, administered through DME, unit dose form, per 10 milligrams

J7674   Methacholine chloride administered as inhalation solution through a nebulizer, per 1 mg

J7676   Pentamidine isethionate, inhalation solution, compounded product, administered through DME, unit dose form, per 300 mg

J7680   Terbutaline sulfate, inhalation solution, compounded product, administered through DME, concentrated form, per milligram

J7681   Terbutaline sulfate, inhalation solution, compounded product, administered through DME, unit dose form, per milligram

Ⓟ **J7682**   Tobramycin, inhalation solution,-approved final product, non-compounded, unit dose form, administered through DME, per 300 milligrams

J7683   Triamcinolone, inhalation solution, compounded product, administered through DME, concentrated form, per milligram

J7684   Triamcinolone, inhalation solution, compounded product, administered through DME, unit dose form, per milligram

J7685   Tobramycin, inhalation solution, compounded product, administered through DME, unit dose form, per 300 milligrams

Ⓟ **J7686**   Treprostinil, inhalation solution,-approved final product, non-compounded, administered through DME, unit dose form, 1.74 mg

J7699   Noc drugs, inhalation solution administered through DME

J7799   Noc drugs, other than inhalation drugs, administered through DME

MCM: 2100.5

J7999   Compounded drug, not otherwise classified

J8498   Antiemetic drug, rectal/suppository, not otherwise specified

Statute: 1861s2T

J8499   Prescription drug, oral, non chemotherapeutic, nos

MCM: 2049

J8501   Aprepitant, oral, 5 mg

J8510   Busulfan; oral, 2 mg

MCM: 2049.5

J8515   Cabergoline, oral, 0.25 mg

MCM: 2049.5

J8520   Capecitabine, oral, 150 mg

MCM: 2049.5

J8521   Capecitabine, oral, 500 mg

MCM: 2049.5

J8530   Cyclophosphamide; oral, 25 mg

MCM: 2049.5

J8540   Dexamethasone, oral, 0.25 mg

Statute: 1861(s)2T

J8560   Etoposide; oral, 50 mg

MCM: 2049.5

J8562   Fludarabine phosphate, oral, 10 mg

J8565   Gefitinib, oral, 250 mg

J8597   Antiemetic drug, oral, not otherwise specified

Statute: 1861s2T

J8600   Melphalan; oral, 2 mg

MCM: 2049.5

J8610   Methotrexate; oral, 2.5 mg

MCM: 2049.5

J8650   Nabilone, oral, 1 mg

J8655   Netupitant 300 mg and palonosetron 0.5 mg

J8670   Rolapitant, oral, 1 mg

J8700   Temozolomide, oral, 5 mg

MCM: 2049.5C

J8705   Topotecan, oral, 0.25 mg

J8999   Prescription drug, oral, chemotherapeutic, nos

MCM: 2049.5

Guidelines

In addition to the information presented in the INTRODUCTION, several other items unique to this section are defined or identified here:

1. EXCEPTION: Oral immunosuppressive drugs are not included in this section.

2. ROUTE OF ADMINISTRATION: Unless otherwise specified, the drugs listed in this section may be injected either subcutaneously, intramuscularly or intravenously.

3. DRUG COST ONLY: The codes listed in this section include the cost of the chemotherapy drug only and do not include the administration of the drug.

4. SUBSECTION INFORMATION: Some of the listed subheadings or subsections have special needs or instructions unique to that section. Where these are indicated, special "notes" will be presented preceding or following the listings. Those subsections within the CHEMOTHERAPY DRUGS section that have "notes" are as follows:

Subsection	Code Numbers
Chemotherapy drugs	J9000-J9999

5. UNLISTED SERVICE OR PROCEDURE: A service or procedure may be provided that is not listed in this edition of HCPCS. When reporting such a service, the appropriate "unlisted procedure" code may be used to indicate the service, identifying it by "special report" as defined below. HCPCS terminology is inconsistent in defining unlisted procedures. The procedure definition may include the term(s) "unlisted", "not otherwise classified", "unspecified", "unclassified", "other" and "miscellaneous". Prior to using these codes, try to determine if a Local Level III code or CPT code is available. The "unlisted procedures" and accompanying codes for CHEMOTHERAPY DRUGS are as follows:

J9999   Not otherwise classified, antineoplastic drugs

6. SPECIAL REPORT: A service, material or supply that is rarely provided, unusual, variable or new may require a special report in determining medical appropriateness for reimbursement purposes. Pertinent information should include an adequate definition or description of the nature, extent, and need for the service, material or supply.

7. MODIFIERS: Listed services may be modified under certain circumstances. When appropriate, the modifying circumstance is identified by adding a modifier to the basic procedure code. CPT and HCPCS National Level II modifiers may be used with CPT and HCPCS National Level II procedure codes. Modifiers commonly used with CHEMOTHERAPY DRUGS are as follows:

-CC Procedure code change (used when the procedure code submitted was changed either for administrative reasons or because an incorrect code was filed)

-TC Technical component. Under certain circumstances, a charge may be made for the technical component alone. Under these circumstances, the technical component charge is identified by adding the modifier -TC to the usual procedure code. Technical component charges are institutional charges and are not billed separately by physicians. Portable x-ray suppliers bill only for the technical component however, and should use modifier -TC.

8. CPT CODE CROSS-REFERENCE: Unless otherwise specified, the equivalent CPT code for all listings in this section is 96545.

Chemotherapy Drugs

J9000 Injection, doxorubicin hydrochloride, 10 mg
MCM: 2049

J9015 Injection, aldesleukin, per single use vial
MCM: 2049

J9017 Injection, arsenic trioxide, 1 mg

J9019 Injection, asparaginase (Erwinase), 1,000 iu
MCM: 2049

J9020 Injection, asparaginase, not otherwise specified, 10,000 units
MCM: 2049

• **J9022** Injection, atezolizumab, 10 mg

• **J9023** Injection, avelumab, 10 mg

J9025 Injection, azacitidine, 1 mg

J9027 Injection, clofarabine, 1 mg

J9031 BCG (intravesical) per instillation
MCM: 2049

J9032 Injection, Belinostat, 10 mg

J9033 Injection, bendamustine HCL (Treanda), 1 mg

J9034 Injection, bendamustine HCL (bendeka), 1 mg

J9035 Injection, bevacizumab, 10 mg

J9039 Injection, blinatumomab, 1 microgram

J9040 Injection, bleomycin sulfate, 15 units
MCM: 2049

J9041 Injection, bortezomib, 0.1 mg

J9042 Injection, Brentuximab Vedotin, 1 mg

J9043 Injection, cabazitaxel, 1 mg

J9045 Injection, carboplatin, 50 mg
MCM: 2049

J9047   Injection, carfilzomib, 1 mg

J9050   Injection, carmustine, 100 mg

MCM: 2049

J9055   Injection, cetuximab, 10 mg

J9060   Injection, cisplatin, powder or solution, 10 mg

MCM: 2049

J9065   Injection, cladribine, per 1 mg

MCM: 2049

J9070   Cyclophosphamide, 100 mg

MCM: 2049

J9098   Injection, cytarabine liposome, 10 mg

J9100   Injection, cytarabine, 100 mg

MCM: 2049

J9120   Injection, dactinomycin, 0.5 mg

MCM: 2049

J9130   Dacarbazine, 100 mg

MCM: 2049

J9145   Injection, daratumumab, 10 mg

MCM: 2049

J9150   Injection, daunorubicin, 10 mg

MCM: 2049

J9151   Injection, daunorubicin citrate, liposomal formulation, 10 mg

MCM: 2049

J9155   Injection, degarelix, 1 mg

J9160   Injection, denileukin diftitox, 300 micrograms

J9165   Injection, diethylstilbestrol diphosphate, 250 mg

MCM: 2049

J9171   Injection, docetaxel, 1 mg

MCM: 2049

J9175   Injection, Elliotts' b solution, 1 ml

MCM: 2049

J9176   Injection, elotuzumab, 1 mg

J9178   Injection, epirubicin HCL, 2 mg

J9179   Injection, Eribulin mesylate, 0.1 mg

J9181   Injection, etoposide, 10 mg
          MCM: 2049

J9185   Injection, fludarabine phosphate, 50 mg
          MCM: 2049

J9190   Injection, fluorouracil, 500 mg
          MCM: 2049

J9200   Injection, floxuridine, 500 mg
          MCM: 2049

J9201   Injection, gemcitabine hydrochloride, 200 mg
          MCM: 2049

J9202   Goserelin acetate implant, per 3.6 mg
          MCM: 2049

● J9203   Injection, gemtuzumab ozogamicin, 0.1 mg

J9205   Injection, irinotecan liposome, 1 mg
          MCM: 2049

J9206   Injection, irinotecan, 20 mg
          MCM: 2049

J9207   Injection, ixabepilone, 1 mg

J9208   Injection, ifosfamide, 1 gram
          MCM: 2049

J9209   Injection, mesna, 200 mg
          MCM: 2049

J9211   Injection, idarubicin hydrochloride, 5 mg
          MCM: 2049

J9212   Injection, interferon alfacon-1, recombinant, 1 microgram
          MCM: 2049

J9213   Injection, interferon, alfa-2a, recombinant, 3 million units
          MCM: 2049

J9214   Injection, interferon, alfa-2b, recombinant, 1 million units
          MCM: 2049

J9215   Injection, interferon, alfa-n3, (human leukocyte derived), 250,000 iu
          MCM: 2049

J9216   Injection, interferon, gamma 1-b, 3 million units
          MCM: 2049

J9217   Leuprolide acetate (for depot suspension), 7.5 mg

MCM: 2049

J9218   Leuprolide acetate, per 1 mg

MCM: 2049

J9219   Leuprolide acetate implant, 65 mg

MCM: 2049

J9225   Histrelin implant (Vantas), 50 mg

MCM: 2049

J9226   Histrelin implant (Supprelin la), 50 mg

MCM: 2049

J9228   Injection, ipilimumab, 1 mg

J9230   Injection, mechlorethamine hydrochloride, (nitrogen mustard), 10 mg

MCM: 2049

J9245   Injection, melphalan hydrochloride, 50 mg

MCM: 2049

J9250   Methotrexate sodium, 5 mg

MCM: 2049

J9260   Methotrexate sodium, 50 mg

MCM: 2049

J9261   Injection, nelarabine, 50 mg

J9262   Injection, omacetaxine mepesuccinate, 0.01 mg

J9263   Injection, oxaliplatin, 0.5 mg

J9264   Injection, paclitaxel protein-bound particles, 1 mg

J9266   Injection, pegaspargase, per single dose vial

MCM: 2049

J9267   Injection, paclitaxel, 1 mg

J9268   Injection, pentostatin, 10 mg

MCM: 2049

J9270   Injection, plicamycin, 2.5 mg

MCM: 2049

J9271   Injection, Pembrolizumab, 1 mg

J9280   Injection, mitomycin, 5 mg

MCM: 2049

● **J9285**   Injection, olaratumab, 10 mg

J9293   Injection, mitoxantrone hydrochloride, per 5 mg

MCM: 2049

J9295   Injection, necitumumab, 1 mg

J9299   Injection, nivolumab, 1 mg

(**J9300**   Code deleted December 31, 2017).

J9301   Injection, obinutuzumab, 10 mg

J9302   Injection, ofatumumab, 10 mg

J9303   Injection, panitumumab, 10 mg

J9305   Injection, pemetrexed, 10 mg

J9306   Injection, pertuzumab, 1 mg

J9307   Injection, pralatrexate, 1 mg

J9308   Injection, ramucirumab, 5 mg

J9310   Injection, rituximab, 100 mg

MCM: 2049

J9315   Injection, romidepsin, 1 mg

J9320   Injection, streptozocin, 1 gram

MCM: 2049

J9325   Injection, talimogene laherparepvec, per 1 million plaque forming units

J9328   Injection, temozolomide, 1 mg

J9330   Injection, temsirolimus, 1 mg

J9340   Injection, thiotepa, 15 mg

MCM: 2049

J9351   Injection, topotecan, 0.1 mg

J9352   Injection, trabectedin, 0.1 mg

J9354   Injection, ado-trastuzumab Emtansine, 1 mg

J9355   Injection, trastuzumab, 10 mg

J9357   Injection, valrubicin, intravesical, 200 mg

MCM: 2049

J9360   Injection, vinblastine sulfate, 1 mg

MCM: 2049

J9370   Vincristine sulfate, 1 mg

MCM: 2049

J9371   Injection, vincristine sulfate liposome, 1 mg

J9390   Injection, vinorelbine tartrate, 10 mg

MCM: 2049

J9395   Injection, fulvestrant, 25 mg

J9400   Injection, Ziv-aflibercept, 1 mg

J9600   Injection, porfimer sodium, 75 mg

MCM: 2049

J9999   Not otherwise classified, antineoplastic drugs

CIM: 45-16

MCM: 2049

Guidelines

In addition to the information presented in the INTRODUCTION, several other items unique to this section are defined or identified here:

1. EXCLUSIVE USE BY DME-MACs: The codes listed in this section are assigned by CMS on a temporary basis and are for the exclusive use of the Durable Medical Equipment Medicare Administrative Contractors (DME-MACs). These codes are not to be used by providers for reporting purposes unless specifically instructed to do so by the local carrier.

2. UNLISTED SERVICE OR PROCEDURE: A service or procedure may be provided that is not listed in this edition of HCPCS. When reporting such a service, the appropriate "unlisted procedure" code may be used to indicate the service, identifying it by "special report" as defined below. HCPCS terminology is inconsistent in defining unlisted procedures. The procedure definition may include the term(s) "unlisted", "not otherwise classified", "unspecified", "unclassified", "other" and "miscellaneous". Prior to using these codes, try to determine if a Local Level III code or CPT code is available.

3. SPECIAL REPORT: A service, material or supply that is rarely provided, unusual, variable or new may require a special report in determining medical appropriateness for reimbursement purposes. Pertinent information should include an adequate definition or description of the nature, extent, and need for the service, material or supply.

4. CPT CODE CROSS-REFERENCE: Unless otherwise specified, the equivalent CPT code for all listings in this section is 99070.

Temporary Codes for DMERCS

&#9physical; **K0001** Standard wheelchair

Ⓟ **K0001** Standard wheelchair

Ⓟ **K0002** Standard hemi (low seat) wheelchair

Ⓟ **K0003** Lightweight wheelchair

Ⓟ **K0004** High strength, lightweight wheelchair

Ⓟ **K0005** Ultra lightweight wheelchair

Ⓟ **K0006** Heavy duty wheelchair

Ⓟ **K0007** Extra heavy duty wheelchair

K0008 Custom manual wheelchair/base

K0009 Other manual wheelchair/base

K0010 Standard - weight frame motorized/power wheelchair

K0011 Standard - weight frame motorized/power wheelchair with programmable control parameters for speed adjustment, tremor dampening, acceleration control and braking

| | Not payable by Medicare | | Non-covered by Medicare | | Special coverage instructions | | Carrier judgement | 231 |

K0012	Lightweight portable motorized/power wheelchair
K0013	Custom motorized/power wheelchair base
K0014	Other motorized/power wheelchair base
K0015	Detachable, non-adjustable height armrest, each
K0017	Detachable, adjustable height armrest, base, replacement only, each
K0018	Detachable, adjustable height armrest, upper portion, replacement only, each
K0019	Arm pad, replacement only, each
K0020	Fixed, adjustable height armrest, pair
K0037	High mount flip-up footrest, replacement only, each
K0038	Leg strap, each
K0039	Leg strap, h style, each
K0040	Adjustable angle footplate, each
K0041	Large size footplate, each
K0042	Standard size footplate, replacement only, each
K0043	Footrest, lower extension tube, replacement only, each
K0044	Footrest, upper hanger bracket, replacement only, each
K0045	Footrest, complete assembly, replacement only, each
K0046	Elevating leg rest, lower extension tube, replacement only, each
K0047	Elevating leg rest, upper hanger bracket, replacement only, each
K0050	Ratchet assembly, replacement only
K0051	Cam release assembly, footrest or leg rest, replacement only, each
K0052	Swing-Away, detachable footrests, replacement only, each
K0053	Elevating footrests, articulating (telescoping), each
K0056	Seat height less than 17" or equal to or greater than 21" for a high strength, lightweight, or ultra lightweight wheelchair
K0065	Spoke protectors, each
K0069	Rear wheel assembly, complete, with solid tire, spokes or molded, replacement only, each
K0070	Rear wheel assembly, complete, with pneumatic tire, spokes or molded, each
K0071	Front caster assembly, complete, with pneumatic tire, replacement only, each
K0072	Front caster assembly, complete, with semi-pneumatic tire, replacement only, each
K0073	Caster pin lock, each
K0077	Front caster assembly, complete, with solid tire, replacement only, each
K0098	Drive belt for power wheelchair, replacement only
K0105	IV hanger, each

Ⓟ **K0108** Wheelchair component or accessory, not otherwise specified

Ⓟ **K0195** Elevating leg rests, pair (for use with capped rental wheelchair base)

CIM: 60-9

K0455 Infusion pump used for uninterrupted parenteral administration of medication, (e.g., epoprostenol or treprostinil)

CIM: 60-14

Ⓟ **K0462** Temporary replacement for patient owned equipment being repaired, any type

MCM: 5102.3

Ⓟ **K0552** Supplies for external non-insulin drug infusion pump, syringe type cartridge, sterile, each

CIM: 60-14

• **K0553** Supply allowance for therapeutic continuous glucose monitor (cgm), includes all supplies and accessories, 1 month supply = 1 unit of service

• **K0554** Receiver (monitor), dedicated, for use with therapeutic glucose continuous monitor system

K0601 Replacement battery for external infusion pump owned by patient, silver oxide, 1.5 volt, each

K0602 Replacement battery for external infusion pump owned by patient, silver oxide, 3 volt, each

K0603 Replacement battery for external infusion pump owned by patient, alkaline, 1.5 volt, each

K0604 Replacement battery for external infusion pump owned by patient, lithium, 3.6 volt, each

K0605 Replacement battery for external infusion pump owned by patient, lithium, 4.5 volt, each

Ⓟ **K0606** Automatic external defibrillator, with integrated electrocardiogram analysis, garment type

K0607 Replacement battery for automated external defibrillator, garment type only, each

K0608 Replacement garment for use with automated external defibrillator, each

K0609 Replacement electrodes for use with automated external defibrillator, garment type only, each

K0669 Wheelchair accessory, wheelchair seat or back cushion, does not meet specific code criteria or no written coding verification from DME PDAC

K0672 Addition to lower extremity orthosis, removable soft interface, all components, replacement only, each

K0730 Controlled dose inhalation drug delivery system

K0733 Power wheelchair accessory, 12 to 24 amp hour sealed lead acid battery, each (e.g., gel cell, absorbed glassmat)

Ⓟ **K0738** Portable gaseous oxygen system, rental; home compressor used to fill portable oxygen cylinders; includes portable containers, regulator, flowmeter, humidifier, cannula or mask, and tubing

Ⓟ **K0739** Repair or nonroutine service for durable medical equipment other than oxygen equipment requiring the skill of a technician, labor component, per 15 minutes

K0740 Repair or nonroutine service for oxygen equipment requiring the skill of a technician, labor component, per 15 minutes

K0743 Suction pump, home model, portable, for use on wounds

K0744 Absorptive wound dressing for use with suction pump, home model, portable, pad size 16 square inches or less

K0745 Absorptive wound dressing for use with suction pump, home model, portable, pad size more than 16 square inches but less than or equal to 48 square inches

K0746 Absorptive wound dressing for use with suction pump, home model, portable, pad size greater than 48 square inches

Ⓟ **K0800** Power operated vehicle, group 1 standard, patient weight capacity up to and including 300 pounds

K0801 Power operated vehicle, group 1 heavy duty, patient weight capacity 301 to 450 pounds

K0802 Power operated vehicle, group 1 very heavy duty, patient weight capacity 451 to 600 pounds

K0806 Power operated vehicle, group 2 standard, patient weight capacity up to and including 300 pounds

K0807 Power operated vehicle, group 2 heavy duty, patient weight capacity 301 to 450 pounds

K0808 Power operated vehicle, group 2 very heavy duty, patient weight capacity 451 to 600 pounds

K0812 Power operated vehicle, not otherwise classified

K0813 Power wheelchair, group 1 standard, portable, sling/solid seat and back, patient weight capacity up to and including 300 pounds

K0814 Power wheelchair, group 1 standard, portable, captains chair, patient weight capacity up to and including 300 pounds

K0815 Power wheelchair, group 1 standard, sling/solid seat and back, patient weight capacity up to and including 300 pounds

Ⓟ **K0816** Power wheelchair, group 1 standard, captains chair, patient weight capacity up to and including 300 pounds

K0820 Power wheelchair, group 2 standard, portable, sling/solid seat/back, patient weight capacity up to and including 300 pounds

Ⓟ **K0821** Power wheelchair, group 2 standard, portable, captains chair, patient weight capacity up to and including 300 pounds

Ⓟ **K0822** Power wheelchair, group 2 standard, sling/solid seat/back, patient weight capacity up to and including 300 pounds

ⓟ **K0823** Power wheelchair, group 2 standard, captains chair, patient weight capacity up to and including 300 pounds

K0824 Power wheelchair, group 2 heavy duty, sling/solid seat/back, patient weight capacity 301 to 450 pounds

ⓟ **K0825** Power wheelchair, group 2 heavy duty, captains chair, patient weight capacity 301 to 450 pounds

K0826 Power wheelchair, group 2 very heavy duty, sling/solid seat/back, patient weight capacity 451 to 600 pounds

K0827 Power wheelchair, group 2 very heavy duty, captains chair, patient weight capacity 451 to 600 pounds

K0828 Power wheelchair, group 2 extra heavy duty, sling/solid seat/back, patient weight capacity 601 pounds or more

K0829 Power wheelchair, group 2 extra heavy duty, captains chair, patient weight 601 pounds or more

K0830 Power wheelchair, group 2 standard, seat elevator, sling/solid seat/back, patient weight capacity up to and including 300 pounds

K0831 Power wheelchair, group 2 standard, seat elevator, captains chair, patient weight capacity up to and including 300 pounds

ⓟ **K0835** Power wheelchair, group 2 standard, single power option, sling/solid seat/back, patient weight capacity up to and including 300 pounds

K0836 Power wheelchair, group 2 standard, single power option, captains chair, patient weight capacity up to and including 300 pounds

K0837 Power wheelchair, group 2 heavy duty, single power option, sling/solid seat/back, patient weight capacity 301 to 450 pounds

K0838 Power wheelchair, group 2 heavy duty, single power option, captains chair, patient weight capacity 301 to 450 pounds

K0839 Power wheelchair, group 2 very heavy duty, single power option, sling/solid seat/back, patient weight capacity 451 to 600 pounds

K0840 Power wheelchair, group 2 extra heavy duty, single power option, sling/solid seat/back, patient weight capacity 601 pounds or more

K0841 Power wheelchair, group 2 standard, multiple power option, sling/solid seat/back, patient weight capacity up to and including 300 pounds

K0842 Power wheelchair, group 2 standard, multiple power option, captains chair, patient weight capacity up to and including 300 pounds

K0843 Power wheelchair, group 2 heavy duty, multiple power option, sling/solid seat/back, patient weight capacity 301 to 450 pounds

ⓟ **K0848** Power wheelchair, group 3 standard, sling/solid seat/back, patient weight capacity up to and including 300 pounds

ⓟ **K0849** Power wheelchair, group 3 standard, captains chair, patient weight capacity up to and including 300 pounds

K0850	Power wheelchair, group 3 heavy duty, sling/solid seat/back, patient weight capacity 301 to 450 pounds
K0851	Power wheelchair, group 3 heavy duty, captains chair, patient weight capacity 301 to 450 pounds
K0852	Power wheelchair, group 3 very heavy duty, sling/solid seat/back, patient weight capacity 451 to 600 pounds
K0853	Power wheelchair, group 3 very heavy duty, captains chair, patient weight capacity 451 to 600 pounds
K0854	Power wheelchair, group 3 extra heavy duty, sling/solid seat/back, patient weight capacity 601 pounds or more
K0855	Power wheelchair, group 3 extra heavy duty, captains chair, patient weight capacity 601 pounds or more
ⓟ K0856	Power wheelchair, group 3 standard, single power option, sling/solid seat/back, patient weight capacity up to and including 300 pounds
K0857	Power wheelchair, group 3 standard, single power option, captains chair, patient weight capacity up to and including 300 pounds
ⓟ K0858	Power wheelchair, group 3 heavy duty, single power option, sling/solid seat/back, patient weight 301 to 450 pounds
K0859	Power wheelchair, group 3 heavy duty, single power option, captains chair, patient weight capacity 301 to 450 pounds
K0860	Power wheelchair, group 3 very heavy duty, single power option, sling/solid seat/back, patient weight capacity 451 to 600 pounds
ⓟ K0861	Power wheelchair, group 3 standard, multiple power option, sling/solid seat/back, patient weight capacity up to and including 300 pounds
ⓟ K0862	Power wheelchair, group 3 heavy duty, multiple power option, sling/solid seat/back, patient weight capacity 301 to 450 pounds
K0863	Power wheelchair, group 3 very heavy duty, multiple power option, sling/solid seat/back, patient weight capacity 451 to 600 pounds
K0864	Power wheelchair, group 3 extra heavy duty, multiple power option, sling/solid seat/back, patient weight capacity 601 pounds or more
K0868	Power wheelchair, group 4 standard, sling/solid seat/back, patient weight capacity up to and including 300 pounds
K0869	Power wheelchair, group 4 standard, captains chair, patient weight capacity up to and including 300 pounds
K0870	Power wheelchair, group 4 heavy duty, sling/solid seat/back, patient weight capacity 301 to 450 pounds
K0871	Power wheelchair, group 4 very heavy duty, sling/solid seat/back, patient weight capacity 451 to 600 pounds
K0877	Power wheelchair, group 4 standard, single power option, sling/solid seat/back, patient weight capacity up to and including 300 pounds

K0878   Power wheelchair, group 4 standard, single power option, captains chair, patient weight capacity up to and including 300 pounds

K0879   Power wheelchair, group 4 heavy duty, single power option, sling/solid seat/back, patient weight capacity 301 to 450 pounds

K0880   Power wheelchair, group 4 very heavy duty, single power option, sling/solid seat/back, patient weight 451 to 600 pounds

K0884   Power wheelchair, group 4 standard, multiple power option, sling/solid seat/back, patient weight capacity up to and including 300 pounds

K0885   Power wheelchair, group 4 standard, multiple power option, captains chair, patient weight capacity up to and including 300 pounds

K0886   Power wheelchair, group 4 heavy duty, multiple power option, sling/solid seat/back, patient weight capacity 301 to 450 pounds

K0890   Power wheelchair, group 5 pediatric, single power option, sling/solid seat/back, patient weight capacity up to and including 125 pounds

K0891   Power wheelchair, group 5 pediatric, multiple power option, sling/solid seat/back, patient weight capacity up to and including 125 pounds

K0898   Power wheelchair, not otherwise classified

K0899   Power mobility device, not coded by DME PDAC or does not meet criteria

K0900   Customized durable medical equipment, other than wheelchair

(**K0901**   Code deleted December 31, 2016). Use L1851.

(**K0902**   Code deleted December 31, 2016). Use L1852

ORTHOTIC PROCEDURES

Guidelines

In addition to the information presented in the INTRODUCTION, several other items unique to this section are defined or identified here:

1. SUBSECTION INFORMATION: Some of the listed subheadings or subsections have special needs or instructions unique to that section. Where these are indicated, special "notes" will be presented preceding or following the listings. Those subsections within the ORTHOTIC PROCEDURES section that have "notes" are as follows:

Subsection	Code Numbers
Scoliosis procedures	L1000-L1499
Orthotic devices-lower limb	L1600-L2999
Lower limb-hip-knee-angle-foot (or any combination)	L2000-L2199
Orthotic devices-upper limb	L3650-L3999

2. UNLISTED SERVICE OR PROCEDURE: A service or procedure may be provided that is not listed in this edition of HCPCS. When reporting such a service, the appropriate "unlisted procedure" code may be used to indicate the service, identifying it by "special report" as defined below. HCPCS terminology is inconsistent in defining unlisted procedures. The procedure definition may include the term(s) "unlisted", "not otherwise classified", "unspecified", "unclassified", "other" and "miscellaneous". Prior to using these codes, try to determine if a Local Level III code or CPT code is available. The "unlisted procedures" and accompanying codes for ORTHOTIC PROCEDURES are as follows:

L0999   Addition to spinal orthosis, not otherwise specified
L1499   Spinal orthosis, not otherwise specified
L2999   Lower extremity orthosis, not otherwise specified
L3649   Orthopedic shoe, modification, addition or transfer, not otherwise specified
L3999   Upper limb orthosis, not otherwise specified

3. SPECIAL REPORT: A service, material or supply that is rarely provided, unusual, variable or new may require a special report in determining medical appropriateness for reimbursement purposes. Pertinent information should include an adequate definition or description of the nature, extent, and need for the service, material or supply.

4. MODIFIERS: Listed services may be modified under certain circumstances. When appropriate, the modifying circumstance is identified by adding a modifier to the basic procedure code. CPT and HCPCS National Level II modifiers may be used with CPT and HCPCS National Level II procedure codes. Modifiers commonly used with ORTHOTIC PROCEDURES are as follows:

-CC   Procedure code change (use "CC" when the procedure code submitted was changed either for administrative reasons or because an incorrect code was filed)

-LT   Left side (used to identify procedures performed on the left side of the body)

-RT   Right side (used to identify procedures performed on the right side of the body)

-TC Technical component. Under certain circumstances, a charge may be made for the technical component alone. Under those circumstances, the technical component charge is identified by adding modifier -TC to the usual procedure number. Technical component charges are institutional charges and are not billed separately by physicians. However, portable x-ray suppliers bill only for the technical component and should use modifier -TC. The change data from portable x-ray suppliers will then be used to build customary and prevailing profiles.

5. CPT CODE CROSS-REFERENCE: Unless otherwise specified, the equivalent CPT code for all listings in this section is 99070.

6. DURABLE MEDICAL EQUIPMENT REGIONAL CARRIERS (DMERCS): Effective October 1, 1993, claims orthotics must be billed to one of four regional carriers depending upon the residence of the beneficiary. The transition dates for DMERC claims is from November 1, 1993 to March 1, 1994, depending upon the state you practice in. See the Introduction for a complete discussion of DMERCs.

Orthotic Devices Spinal – Cervical

L0112 Cranial cervical orthosis, congenital torticollis type, with or without soft interface material, adjustable range of motion joint, custom fabricated

L0113 Cranial cervical orthosis, torticollis type, with or without joint, with or without soft interface material, prefabricated, includes fitting and adjustment

L0120 Cervical, flexible, non-adjustable, prefabricated, off-the-shelf (foam collar)

L0130 Cervical, flexible, thermoplastic collar, molded to patient

L0140 Cervical, semi-rigid, adjustable (plastic collar)

L0150 Cervical, semi-rigid, adjustable molded chin cup (plastic collar with mandibular/occipital piece)

L0160 Cervical, semi-rigid, wire frame occipital/mandibular support, prefabricated, off-the-shelf

L0170 Cervical, collar, molded to patient model

L0172 Cervical, collar, semi-rigid thermoplastic foam, two-piece, prefabricated, off-the-shelf

L0174 Cervical, collar, semi-rigid, thermoplastic foam, two piece with thoracic extension, prefabricated, off-the-shelf

L0180 Cervical, multiple post collar, occipital/mandibular supports, adjustable

L0190 Cervical, multiple post collar, occipital/mandibular supports, adjustable cervical bars (SOMI, Guilford, Taylor types)

L0200 Cervical, multiple post collar, occipital/mandibular supports, adjustable cervical bars, and thoracic extension

Spinal - Thoracic-Lumbar-Sacral

L0220 Thoracic, rib belt, custom fabricated

L0450 TLSO, flexible, provides trunk support, upper thoracic region, produces intracavitary pressure to reduce load on the intervertebral disks with rigid stays or panel(s), includes shoulder straps and closures, prefabricated, off-the-shelf

L0452 TLSO, flexible, provides trunk support, upper thoracic region, produces intracavitary pressure to reduce load on the intervertebral disks with rigid stays or panel(s), includes shoulder straps and closures, custom fabricated

L0454 TLSO flexible, provides trunk support, extends from sacrococcygeal junction to above t-9 vertebra, restricts gross trunk motion in the sagittal plane, produces intracavitary pressure to reduce load on the intervertebral disks with rigid stays or panel(s), includes shoulder straps and closures, prefabricated item that has been trimmed, bent, molded, assembled, or otherwise customized to fit a specific patient by an individual with expertise

L0455 TLSO, flexible, provides trunk support, extends from sacrococcygeal junction to above t-9 vertebra, restricts gross trunk motion in the sagittal plane, produces intracavitary pressure to reduce load on the intervertebral disks with rigid stays or panel(s), includes shoulder straps and closures, prefabricated, off-the-shelf

L0456 TLSO, flexible, provides trunk support, thoracic region, rigid posterior panel and soft anterior apron, extends from the sacrococcygeal junction and terminates just inferior to the scapular spine, restricts gross trunk motion in the sagittal plane, produces intracavitary pressure to reduce load on the intervertebral disks, includes straps and closures, prefabricated item that has been trimmed, bent, molded, assembled, or otherwise customized to fit a specific patient by an individual with expertise

L0457 TLSO, flexible, provides trunk support, thoracic region, rigid posterior panel and soft anterior apron, extends from the sacrococcygeal junction and terminates just inferior to the scapular spine, restricts gross trunk motion in the sagittal plane, produces intracavitary pressure to reduce load on the intervertebral disks, includes straps and closures, prefabricated, off-the-shelf

L0458 TLSO, triplanar control, modular segmented spinal system, two rigid plastic shells, posterior extends from the sacrococcygeal junction and terminates just inferior to the scapular spine, anterior extends from the symphysis pubis to the xiphoid, soft liner, restricts gross trunk motion in the sagittal, coronal, and transverse planes, lateral strength is provided by overlapping plastic and stabilizing closures, includes straps and closures, prefabricated, includes fitting and adjustment

L0460 TLSO, triplanar control, modular segmented spinal system, two rigid plastic shells, posterior extends from the sacrococcygeal junction and terminates just inferior to the scapular spine, anterior extends from the symphysis pubis to the sternal notch, soft liner, restricts gross trunk motion in the sagittal, coronal, and transverse planes, lateral strength is provided by overlapping plastic and stabilizing closures, includes straps and closures, prefabricated item that has been trimmed, bent, molded, assembled, or otherwise customized to fit a specific patient by an individual with expertise

L0462 TLSO, triplanar control, modular segmented spinal system, three rigid plastic shells, posterior extends from the sacrococcygeal junction and terminates just inferior to the scapular spine, anterior extends from the symphysis pubis to the sternal notch, soft liner, restricts gross trunk motion in the sagittal, coronal, and transverse planes, lateral strength is provided by overlapping plastic and stabilizing closures, includes straps and closures, prefabricated, includes fitting and adjustment

L0464 TLSO, triplanar control, modular segmented spinal system, four rigid plastic shells, posterior extends from sacrococcygeal junction and terminates just inferior to scapular spine, anterior extends from symphysis pubis to the sternal notch, soft liner, restricts gross trunk motion in sagittal, coronal, and transverse planes, lateral strength is provided by overlapping plastic and stabilizing closures, includes straps and closures, prefabricated, includes fitting and adjustment

L0466 TLSO, sagittal control, rigid posterior frame and flexible soft anterior apron with straps, closures and padding, restricts gross trunk motion in sagittal plane, produces intracavitary pressure to reduce load on intervertebral disks, prefabricated item that has been trimmed, bent, molded, assembled, or otherwise customized to fit a specific patient by an individual with expertise

L0467 TLSO, sagittal control, rigid posterior frame and flexible soft anterior apron with straps, closures and padding, restricts gross trunk motion in sagittal plane, produces intracavitary pressure to reduce load on intervertebral disks, prefabricated, off-the-shelf

L0468 TLSO, sagittal-coronal control, rigid posterior frame and flexible soft anterior apron with straps, closures and padding, extends from sacrococcygeal junction over scapulae, lateral strength provided by pelvic, thoracic, and lateral frame pieces, restricts gross trunk motion in sagittal, and coronal planes, produces intracavitary pressure to reduce load on intervertebral disks, prefabricated item that has been trimmed, bent, molded, assembled, or otherwise customized to fit a specific patient by an individual with expertise

L0469 TLSO, sagittal-coronal control, rigid posterior frame and flexible soft anterior apron with straps, closures and padding, extends from sacrococcygeal junction over scapulae, lateral strength provided by pelvic, thoracic, and lateral frame pieces, restricts gross trunk motion in sagittal and coronal planes, produces intracavitary pressure to reduce load on intervertebral disks, prefabricated, off-the-shelf

L0470 TLSO, triplanar control, rigid posterior frame and flexible soft anterior apron with straps, closures and padding, extends from sacrococcygeal junction to scapula, lateral strength provided by pelvic, thoracic, and lateral frame pieces, rotational strength provided by subclavicular extensions, restricts gross trunk motion in sagittal, coronal, and transverse planes, provides intracavitary pressure to reduce load on the intervertebral disks, includes fitting and shaping the frame, prefabricated, includes fitting and adjustment

L0472 TLSO, triplanar control, hyperextension, rigid anterior and lateral frame extends from symphysis pubis to sternal notch with two anterior components (one pubic and one sternal), posterior and lateral pads with straps and closures, limits spinal flexion, restricts gross trunk motion in sagittal, coronal, and transverse planes, includes fitting and shaping the frame, prefabricated, includes fitting and adjustment

L0480 TLSO, triplanar control, one piece rigid plastic shell without interface liner, with multiple straps and closures, posterior extends from sacrococcygeal junction and terminates just inferior to scapular spine, anterior extends from symphysis pubis to sternal notch, anterior or posterior opening, restricts gross trunk motion in sagittal, coronal, and transverse planes, includes a carved plaster or cad-cam model, custom fabricated

L0482 TLSO, triplanar control, one piece rigid plastic shell with interface liner, multiple straps and closures, posterior extends from sacrococcygeal junction and terminates just inferior to scapular spine, anterior extends from symphysis pubis to sternal notch, anterior or posterior opening, restricts gross trunk motion in sagittal, coronal, and transverse planes, includes a carved plaster or cad-cam model, custom fabricated

L0484   TLSO, triplanar control, two piece rigid plastic shell without interface liner, with multiple straps and closures, posterior extends from sacrococcygeal junction and terminates just inferior to scapular spine, anterior extends from symphysis pubis to sternal notch, lateral strength is enhanced by overlapping plastic, restricts gross trunk motion in the sagittal, coronal, and transverse planes, includes a carved plaster or cad-cam model, custom fabricated

L0486   TLSO, triplanar control, two piece rigid plastic shell with interface liner, multiple straps and closures, posterior extends from sacrococcygeal junction and terminates just inferior to scapular spine, anterior extends from symphysis pubis to sternal notch, lateral strength is enhanced by overlapping plastic, restricts gross trunk motion in the sagittal, coronal, and transverse planes, includes a carved plaster or cad-cam model, custom fabricated

L0488   TLSO, triplanar control, one piece rigid plastic shell with interface liner, multiple straps and closures, posterior extends from sacrococcygeal junction and terminates just inferior to scapular spine, anterior extends from symphysis pubis to sternal notch, anterior or posterior opening, restricts gross trunk motion in sagittal, coronal, and transverse planes, prefabricated, includes fitting and adjustment

L0490   TLSO, sagittal-coronal control, one piece rigid plastic shell, with overlapping reinforced anterior, with multiple straps and closures, posterior extends from sacrococcygeal junction and terminates at or before the t-9 vertebra, anterior extends from symphysis pubis to xiphoid, anterior opening, restricts gross trunk motion in sagittal and coronal planes, prefabricated, includes fitting and adjustment

L0491   TLSO, sagittal-coronal control, modular segmented spinal system, two rigid plastic shells, posterior extends from the sacrococcygeal junction and terminates just inferior to the scapular spine, anterior extends from the symphysis pubis to the xiphoid, soft liner, restricts gross trunk motion in the sagittal and coronal planes, lateral strength is provided by overlapping plastic and stabilizing closures, includes straps and closures, prefabricated, includes fitting and adjustment

L0492   TLSO, sagittal-coronal control, modular segmented spinal system, three rigid plastic shells, posterior extends from the sacrococcygeal junction and terminates just inferior to the scapular spine, anterior extends from the symphysis pubis to the xiphoid, soft liner, restricts gross trunk motion in the sagittal and coronal planes, lateral strength is provided by overlapping plastic and stabilizing closures, includes straps and closures, prefabricated, includes fitting and adjustment

Spinal - Sacroiliac Semi-Rigid

L0621   Sacroiliac orthosis, flexible, provides pelvic-sacral support, reduces motion about the sacroiliac joint, includes straps, closures, may include pendulous abdomen design, prefabricated, off-the-shelf

L0622   Sacroiliac orthosis, flexible, provides pelvic-sacral support, reduces motion about the sacroiliac joint, includes straps, closures, may include pendulous abdomen design, custom fabricated

L0623   Sacroiliac orthosis, provides pelvic-sacral support, with rigid or semi-rigid panels over the sacrum and abdomen, reduces motion about the sacroiliac joint, includes straps, closures, may include pendulous abdomen design, prefabricated, off-the-shelf

Not payable by Medicare	Non-covered by Medicare	Special coverage instructions	Carrier judgement	243

L0624 Sacroiliac orthosis, provides pelvic-sacral support, with rigid or semi-rigid panels placed over the sacrum and abdomen, reduces motion about the sacroiliac joint, includes straps, closures, may include pendulous abdomen design, custom fabricated

L0625 Lumbar orthosis, flexible, provides lumbar support, posterior extends from l-1 to below l-5 vertebra, produces intracavitary pressure to reduce load on the intervertebral discs, includes straps, closures, may include pendulous abdomen design, shoulder straps, stays, prefabricated, off-the-shelf

L0626 Lumbar orthosis, sagittal control, with rigid posterior panel(s), posterior extends from l-1 to below l-5 vertebra, produces intracavitary pressure to reduce load on the intervertebral discs, includes straps, closures, may include padding, stays, shoulder straps, pendulous abdomen design, prefabricated item that has been trimmed, bent, molded, assembled, or otherwise customized to fit a specific patient by an individual with expertise

L0627 Lumbar orthosis, sagittal control, with rigid anterior and posterior panels, posterior extends from l-1 to below l-5 vertebra, produces intracavitary pressure to reduce load on the intervertebral discs, includes straps, closures, may include padding, shoulder straps, pendulous abdomen design, prefabricated item that has been trimmed, bent, molded, assembled, or otherwise customized to fit a specific patient by an individual with expertise

L0628 Lumbar-sacral orthosis, flexible, provides lumbo-sacral support, posterior extends from sacrococcygeal junction to t-9 vertebra, produces intracavitary pressure to reduce load on the intervertebral discs, includes straps, closures, may include stays, shoulder straps, pendulous abdomen design, prefabricated, off-the-shelf

L0629 Lumbar-sacral orthosis, flexible, provides lumbo-sacral support, posterior extends from sacrococcygeal junction to t-9 vertebra, produces intracavitary pressure to reduce load on the intervertebral discs, includes straps, closures, may include stays, shoulder straps, pendulous abdomen design, custom fabricated

L0630 Lumbar-sacral orthosis, sagittal control, with rigid posterior panel(s), posterior extends from sacrococcygeal junction to t-9 vertebra, produces intracavitary pressure to reduce load on the intervertebral discs, includes straps, closures, may include padding, stays, shoulder straps, pendulous abdomen design, prefabricated item that has been trimmed, bent, molded, assembled, or otherwise customized to fit a specific patient by an individual with expertise

L0631 Lumbar-sacral orthosis, sagittal control, with rigid anterior and posterior panels, posterior extends from sacrococcygeal junction to t-9 vertebra, produces intracavitary pressure to reduce load on the intervertebral discs, includes straps, closures, may include padding, shoulder straps, pendulous abdomen design, prefabricated item that has been trimmed, bent, molded, assembled, or otherwise customized to fit a specific patient by an individual with expertise

L0632 Lumbar-sacral orthosis, sagittal control, with rigid anterior and posterior panels, posterior extends from sacrococcygeal junction to t-9 vertebra, produces intracavitary pressure to reduce load on the intervertebral discs, includes straps, closures, may include padding, shoulder straps, pendulous abdomen design, custom fabricated

L0633 Lumbar-sacral orthosis, sagittal-coronal control, with rigid posterior frame/panel(s), posterior extends from sacrococcygeal junction to t-9 vertebra, lateral strength provided by rigid lateral frame/panels, produces intracavitary pressure to reduce load on intervertebral discs, includes straps, closures, may include padding, stays, shoulder straps, pendulous abdomen design, prefabricated item that has been trimmed, bent, molded, assembled, or otherwise customized to fit a specific patient by an individual with expertise

L0634   Lumbar-sacral orthosis, sagittal-coronal control, with rigid posterior frame/panel(s), posterior extends from sacrococcygeal junction to t-9 vertebra, lateral strength provided by rigid lateral frame/panel(s), produces intracavitary pressure to reduce load on intervertebral discs, includes straps, closures, may include padding, stays, shoulder straps, pendulous abdomen design, custom fabricated

L0635   Lumbar-sacral orthosis, sagittal-coronal control, lumbar flexion, rigid posterior frame/panel(s), lateral articulating design to flex the lumbar spine, posterior extends from sacrococcygeal junction to t-9 vertebra, lateral strength provided by rigid lateral frame/panel(s), produces intracavitary pressure to reduce load on intervertebral discs, includes straps, closures, may include padding, anterior panel, pendulous abdomen design, prefabricated, includes fitting and adjustment

L0636   Lumbar sacral orthosis, sagittal-coronal control, lumbar flexion, rigid posterior frame/panels, lateral articulating design to flex the lumbar spine, posterior extends from sacrococcygeal junction to t-9 vertebra, lateral strength provided by rigid lateral frame/panels, produces intracavitary pressure to reduce load on intervertebral discs, includes straps, closures, may include padding, anterior panel, pendulous abdomen design, custom fabricated

L0637   Lumbar-sacral orthosis, sagittal-coronal control, with rigid anterior and posterior frame/panels, posterior extends from sacrococcygeal junction to t-9 vertebra, lateral strength provided by rigid lateral frame/panels, produces intracavitary pressure to reduce load on intervertebral discs, includes straps, closures, may include padding, shoulder straps, pendulous abdomen design, prefabricated item that has been trimmed, bent, molded, assembled, or otherwise customized to fit a specific patient by an individual with expertise

L0638   Lumbar-sacral orthosis, sagittal-coronal control, with rigid anterior and posterior frame/panels, posterior extends from sacrococcygeal junction to t-9 vertebra, lateral strength provided by rigid lateral frame/panels, produces intracavitary pressure to reduce load on intervertebral discs, includes straps, closures, may include padding, shoulder straps, pendulous abdomen design, custom fabricated

L0639   Lumbar-sacral orthosis, sagittal-coronal control, rigid shell(s)/panel(s), posterior extends from sacrococcygeal junction to t-9 vertebra, anterior extends from symphysis pubis to xyphoid, produces intracavitary pressure to reduce load on the intervertebral discs, overall strength is provided by overlapping rigid material and stabilizing closures, includes straps, closures, may include soft interface, pendulous abdomen design, prefabricated item that has been trimmed, bent, molded, assembled, or otherwise customized to fit a specific patient by an individual with expertise

L0640   Lumbar-sacral orthosis, sagittal-coronal control, rigid shell(s)/panel(s), posterior extends from sacrococcygeal junction to t-9 vertebra, anterior extends from symphysis pubis to xyphoid, produces intracavitary pressure to reduce load on the intervertebral discs, overall strength is provided by overlapping rigid material and stabilizing closures, includes straps, closures, may include soft interface, pendulous abdomen design, custom fabricated

L0641 Lumbar orthosis, sagittal control, with rigid posterior panel(s), posterior extends from l-1 to below l-5 vertebra, produces intracavitary pressure to reduce load on the intervertebral discs, includes straps, closures, may include padding, stays, shoulder straps, pendulous abdomen design, prefabricated, off-the-shelf

L0642 Lumbar orthosis, sagittal control, with rigid anterior and posterior panels, posterior extends from l-1 to below l-5 vertebra, produces intracavitary pressure to reduce load on the intervertebral discs, includes straps, closures, may include padding, shoulder straps, pendulous abdomen design, prefabricated, off-the-shelf

L0643 Lumbar-sacral orthosis, sagittal control, with rigid posterior panel(s), posterior extends from sacrococcygeal junction to t-9 vertebra, produces intracavitary pressure to reduce load on the intervertebral discs, includes straps, closures, may include padding, stays, shoulder straps, pendulous abdomen design, prefabricated, off-the-shelf

L0648 Lumbar-sacral orthosis, sagittal control, with rigid anterior and posterior panels, posterior extends from sacrococcygeal junction to t-9 vertebra, produces intracavitary pressure to reduce load on the intervertebral discs, includes straps, closures, may include padding, shoulder straps, pendulous abdomen design, prefabricated, off-the-shelf

L0649 Lumbar-sacral orthosis, sagittal-coronal control, with rigid posterior frame/panel(s), posterior extends from sacrococcygeal junction to t-9 vertebra, lateral strength provided by rigid lateral frame/panels, produces intracavitary pressure to reduce load on intervertebral discs, includes straps, closures, may include padding, stays, shoulder straps, pendulous abdomen design, prefabricated, off-the-shelf

L0650 Lumbar-sacral orthosis, sagittal-coronal control, with rigid anterior and posterior frame/panel(s), posterior extends from sacrococcygeal junction to t-9 vertebra, lateral strength provided by rigid lateral frame/panel(s), produces intracavitary pressure to reduce load on intervertebral discs, includes straps, closures, may include padding, shoulder straps, pendulous abdomen design, prefabricated, off-the-shelf

L0651 Lumbar-sacral orthosis, sagittal-coronal control, rigid shell(s)/panel(s), posterior extends from sacrococcygeal junction to t-9 vertebra, anterior extends from symphysis pubis to xyphoid, produces intracavitary pressure to reduce load on the intervertebral discs, overall strength is provided by overlapping rigid material and stabilizing closures, includes straps, closures, may include soft interface, pendulous abdomen design, prefabricated, off-the-shelf

Spinal - Cervical-Thoracic-Lumbar-Sacral – Halo Procedure

L0700 Cervical-thoracic-lumbar-sacral-orthoses (CTLSO), anterior-posterior-lateral control, molded to patient model, (Minerva type)

L0710 CTLSO, anterior-posterior-lateral-control, molded to patient model, with interface material, (Minerva type)

L0810 Halo procedure, cervical halo incorporated into jacket vest

L0820 Halo procedure, cervical halo incorporated into plaster body jacket

L0830 Halo procedure, cervical halo incorporated into Milwaukee type orthosis

Additions to Spinal Orthoses

L0859   Addition to halo procedure, magnetic resonance image compatible systems, rings and pins, any material

L0861   Addition to halo procedure, replacement liner/interface material

L0970   TLSO, corset front

L0972   LSO, corset front

L0974   TLSO, full corset

L0976   LSO, full corset

L0978   Axillary crutch extension

L0980   Peroneal straps, prefabricated, off-the-shelf, pair

L0982   Stocking supporter grips, prefabricated, off-the-shelf, set of four (4)

L0984   Protective body sock, prefabricated, off-the-shelf, each

L0999   Addition to spinal orthosis, not otherwise specified

Orthotic Devices - Scoliosis Procedures

NOTE: The orthotic care of scoliosis differs from other orthotic care in that the treatment is more dynamic in nature and utilizes ongoing, continual modification of the orthosis to the patient's changing condition. This coding structure uses the proper names or eponyms of the procedures because they have historic and universal acceptance in the profession. It should be recognized that variations to the basic procedures described by the founders/developers are accepted in various medical and orthotic practices throughout the country. All procedures include model of patient when indicated.

L1000   Cervical-thoracic-lumbar-sacral orthosis (CTLSO) (Milwaukee), inclusive of furnishing initial orthosis, including model

L1001   Cervical thoracic lumbar sacral orthosis, immobilizer, infant size, prefabricated, includes fitting and adjustment

L1005   Tension based scoliosis orthosis and accessory pads, includes fitting and adjustment

L1010   Addition to cervical-thoracic-lumbar-sacral orthosis (CTLSO) or scoliosis orthosis, axilla sling

L1020   Addition to CTLSO or scoliosis orthosis, kyphosis pad

L1025   Addition to CTLSO or scoliosis orthosis, kyphosis pad, floating

L1030   Addition to CTLSO or scoliosis orthosis, lumbar bolster pad

L1040   Addition to CTLSO or scoliosis orthosis, lumbar or lumbar rib pad

L1050   Addition to CTLSO or scoliosis orthosis, sternal pad

L1060   Addition to CTLSO or scoliosis orthosis, thoracic pad

L1070   Addition to CTLSO or scoliosis orthosis, trapezius sling

L1080   Addition to CTLSO or scoliosis orthosis, outrigger

L1085   Addition to CTLSO or scoliosis orthosis, outrigger, bilateral with vertical extensions

L1090   Addition to CTLSO or scoliosis orthosis, lumbar sling

L1100   Addition to CTLSO or scoliosis orthosis, ring flange, plastic or leather

L1110   Addition to CTLSO or scoliosis orthosis, ring flange, plastic or leather, molded to patient model

L1120   Addition to CTLSO, scoliosis orthosis, cover for upright, each

L1200   Thoracic-lumbar-sacral-orthosis (TLSO), inclusive of furnishing initial orthosis only

L1210   Addition to TLSO, (low profile), lateral thoracic extension

L1220   Addition to TLSO, (low profile), anterior thoracic extension

L1230   Addition to TLSO, (low profile), Milwaukee type superstructure

L1240   Addition to TLSO, (low profile), lumbar derotation pad

L1250   Addition to TLSO, (low profile), anterior ASIS pad

L1260   Addition to TLSO, (low profile), anterior thoracic derotation pad

L1270   Addition to TLSO, (low profile), abdominal pad

L1280   Addition to TLSO, (low profile), rib gusset (elastic), each

L1290   Addition to TLSO, (low profile), lateral trochanteric pad

L1300   Other scoliosis procedure, body jacket molded to patient model

L1310   Other scoliosis procedure, post-operative body jacket

L1499   Spinal orthosis, not otherwise specified

Orthotic Devices - Lower Limb

NOTE: The procedures L1600-L2999 are considered as "base" or the "basic procedures" and may be modified by listing other procedures from the "additions" (L2200-L2999) section and adding them to the base procedure.

L1600   Hip orthosis, abduction control of hip joints, flexible, Frejka type with cover, prefabricated item that has been trimmed, bent, molded, assembled, or otherwise customized to fit a specific patient by an individual with expertise

L1610   Hip orthosis, abduction control of hip joints, flexible, (Frejka cover only), prefabricated item that has been trimmed, bent, molded, assembled, or otherwise customized to fit a specific patient by an individual with expertise

L1620   Hip orthosis, abduction control of hip joints, flexible, (Pavlik harness), prefabricated item that has been trimmed, bent, molded, assembled, or otherwise customized to fit a specific patient by an individual with expertise

L1630   Hip orthosis, abduction control of hip joints, semi-flexible (von Rosen type), custom fabricated

L1640   Hip orthosis, abduction control of hip joints, static, pelvic band or spreader bar, thigh cuffs, custom fabricated

L1650   Hip orthosis, abduction control of hip joints, static, adjustable, (Ilfeld type), prefabricated, includes fitting and adjustment

L1652 Hip orthosis, bilateral thigh cuffs with adjustable abductor spreader bar, adult size, prefabricated, includes fitting and adjustment, any type

L1660 Hip orthosis, abduction control of hip joints, static, plastic, prefabricated, includes fitting and adjustment

L1680 Hip orthosis, abduction control of hip joints, dynamic, pelvic control, adjustable hip motion control, thigh cuffs (rancho hip action type), custom fabricated

L1685 Hip orthosis, abduction control of hip joint, postoperative hip abduction type, custom fabricated

L1686 Hip orthosis, abduction control of hip joint, postoperative hip abduction type, prefabricated, includes fitting and adjustment

L1690 Combination, bilateral, lumbo-sacral, hip, femur orthosis providing adduction and internal rotation control, prefabricated, includes fitting and adjustment

L1700 Legg Perthes orthosis, (Toronto type), custom fabricated

L1710 Legg Perthes orthosis, (newington type), custom fabricated

L1720 Legg Perthes orthosis, trilateral, (Tachdjian type), custom fabricated

L1730 Legg Perthes orthosis, (Scottish rite type), custom fabricated

L1755 Legg Perthes orthosis, (patten bottom type), custom fabricated

(P) **L1810** Knee orthosis, elastic with joints, prefabricated item that has been trimmed, bent, molded, assembled, or otherwise customized to fit a specific patient by an individual with expertise

(P) **L1812** Knee orthosis, elastic with joints, prefabricated, off-the-shelf

(P) **L1820** Knee orthosis, elastic with condylar pads and joints, with or without patellar control, prefabricated, includes fitting and adjustment

(P) **L1830** Knee orthosis, immobilizer, canvas longitudinal, prefabricated, off-the-shelf

L1831 Knee orthosis, locking knee joint(s), positional orthosis, prefabricated, includes fitting and adjustment

(P) **L1832** Knee orthosis, adjustable knee joints (unicentric or polycentric), positional orthosis, rigid support, prefabricated item that has been trimmed, bent, molded, assembled, or otherwise customized to fit a specific patient by an individual with expertise

(P) **L1833** Knee orthosis, adjustable knee joints (unicentric or polycentric), positional orthosis, rigid support, prefabricated, off-the shelf

L1834 Knee orthosis, without knee joint, rigid, custom fabricated

L1836 Knee orthosis, rigid, without joint(s), includes soft interface material, prefabricated, off-the-shelf

L1840 Knee orthosis, derotation, medial-lateral, anterior cruciate ligament, custom fabricated

(P) **L1843** Knee orthosis, single upright, thigh and calf, with adjustable flexion and extension joint (unicentric or polycentric), medial-lateral and rotation control, with or without varus/valgus adjustment, prefabricated item that has been trimmed, bent, molded, assembled, or otherwise customized to fit a specific patient by an individual with expertise

L1844 Knee orthosis, single upright, thigh and calf, with adjustable flexion and extension joint (unicentric or polycentric), medial-lateral and rotation control, with or without varus/valgus adjustment, custom fabricated

Ⓟ **L1845** Knee orthosis, double upright, thigh and calf, with adjustable flexion and extension joint (unicentric or polycentric), medial-lateral and rotation control, with or without varus/valgus adjustment, prefabricated item that has been trimmed, bent, molded, assembled, or otherwise customized to fit a specific patient by an individual with expertise

L1846 Knee orthosis, double upright, thigh and calf, with adjustable flexion and extension joint (unicentric or polycentric), medial-lateral and rotation control, with or without varus/valgus adjustment, custom fabricated

L1847 Knee orthosis, double upright with adjustable joint, with inflatable air support chamber(s), prefabricated item that has been trimmed, bent, molded, assembled, or otherwise customized to fit a specific patient by an individual with expertise

L1848 Knee orthosis, double upright with adjustable joint, with inflatable air support chamber(s), prefabricated, off-the-shelf

L1850 Knee orthosis, Swedish type, prefabricated, off-the-shelf

L1851 Knee orthosis (KO), single upright, thigh and calf, with adjustable flexion and extension joint (unicentric or polycentric), medial-lateral and rotation control, with or without varus/valgus adjustment, prefabricated, off-the-shelf

L1852 Knee orthosis (KO), double upright, thigh and calf, with adjustable flexion and extension joint (unicentric or polycentric), medial-lateral and rotation control, with or without varus/valgus adjustment, prefabricated, off-the-shelf

L1860 Knee orthosis, modification of supracondylar prosthetic socket, custom fabricated (sk)

L1900 Ankle foot orthosis, spring wire, dorsiflexion assist calf band, custom fabricated

L1902 Ankle orthosis, ankle gauntlet or similar, with or without joints, prefabricated, off-the-shelf

L1904 Ankle foot orthosis, multiligamentous ankle support, prefabricated, off-the-shelf

L1906 Ankle foot orthosis, multiligamentous ankle support, prefabricated, off-the-shelf

L1907 Ankle orthosis, supramalleolar with straps, with or without interface/pads, custom fabricated

L1910 Ankle foot orthosis, posterior, single bar, clasp attachment to shoe counter, prefabricated, includes fitting and adjustment

L1920 Ankle foot orthosis, single upright with static or adjustable stop (Phelps or Perlstein type), custom fabricated

Ⓟ **L1930** Ankle foot orthosis, plastic or other material, prefabricated, includes fitting and adjustment

Ⓟ **L1932** AFO, rigid anterior tibial section, total carbon fiber or equal material, prefabricated, includes fitting and adjustment

Ⓟ **L1940** Ankle foot orthosis, plastic or other material, custom fabricated

---

Ⓟ **L1945** Ankle foot orthosis, plastic, rigid anterior tibial section (floor reaction), custom fabricated

Ⓟ **L1950** Ankle foot orthosis, spiral, (institute of rehabilitative medicine type), plastic, custom fabricated

Ⓟ **L1951** Ankle foot orthosis, spiral, (institute of rehabilitative medicine type), plastic or other material, prefabricated, includes fitting and adjustment

Ⓟ **L1960** Ankle foot orthosis, posterior solid ankle, plastic, custom fabricated

Ⓟ **L1970** Ankle foot orthosis, plastic with ankle joint, custom fabricated

L1971 Ankle foot orthosis, plastic or other material with ankle joint, prefabricated, includes fitting and adjustment

Ⓟ **L1980** Ankle foot orthosis, single upright free plantar dorsiflexion, solid stirrup, calf band/cuff (single bar 'BK' orthosis), custom fabricated

Ⓟ **L1990** Ankle foot orthosis, double upright free plantar dorsiflexion, solid stirrup, calf band/cuff (double bar 'BK' orthosis), custom fabricated

L2000 Knee ankle foot orthosis, single upright, free knee, free ankle, solid stirrup, thigh and calf bands/cuffs (single bar 'AK' orthosis), custom fabricated

Ⓟ **L2005** Knee ankle foot orthosis, any material, single or double upright, stance control, automatic lock and swing phase release, any type activation, includes ankle joint, any type, custom fabricated

L2010 Knee ankle foot orthosis, single upright, free ankle, solid stirrup, thigh and calf bands/cuffs (single bar 'AK' orthosis), without knee joint, custom fabricated

Ⓟ **L2020** Knee ankle foot orthosis, double upright, free ankle, solid stirrup, thigh and calf bands/cuffs (double bar 'AK' orthosis), custom fabricated

L2030 Knee ankle foot orthosis, double upright, free ankle, solid stirrup, thigh and calf bands/cuffs, (double bar 'AK' orthosis), without knee joint, custom fabricated

L2034 Knee ankle foot orthosis, full plastic, single upright, with or without free motion knee, medial lateral rotation control, with or without free motion ankle, custom fabricated

L2035 Knee ankle foot orthosis, full plastic, static (pediatric size), without free motion ankle, prefabricated, includes fitting and adjustment

Ⓟ **L2036** Knee ankle foot orthosis, full plastic, double upright, with or without free motion knee, with or without free motion ankle, custom fabricated

L2037 Knee ankle foot orthosis, full plastic, single upright, with or without free motion knee, with or without free motion ankle, custom fabricated

L2038 Knee ankle foot orthosis, full plastic, with or without free motion knee, multi-axis ankle, custom fabricated

Torsion Control

L2040 Hip knee ankle foot orthosis, torsion control, bilateral rotation straps, pelvic band/belt, custom fabricated

L2050	Hip knee ankle foot orthosis, torsion control, bilateral torsion cables, hip joint, pelvic band/belt, custom fabricated
L2060	Hip knee ankle foot orthosis, torsion control, bilateral torsion cables, ball bearing hip joint, pelvic band/ belt, custom fabricated
L2070	Hip knee ankle foot orthosis, torsion control, unilateral rotation straps, pelvic band/belt, custom fabricated
L2080	Hip knee ankle foot orthosis, torsion control, unilateral torsion cable, hip joint, pelvic band/belt, custom fabricated
L2090	Hip knee ankle foot orthosis, torsion control, unilateral torsion cable, ball bearing hip joint, pelvic band/ belt, custom fabricated

Fracture Orthoses and Additions

L2106	Ankle foot orthosis, fracture orthosis, tibial fracture cast orthosis, thermoplastic type casting material, custom fabricated
L2108	Ankle foot orthosis, fracture orthosis, tibial fracture cast orthosis, custom fabricated
L2112	Ankle foot orthosis, fracture orthosis, tibial fracture orthosis, soft, prefabricated, includes fitting and adjustment
L2114	Ankle foot orthosis, fracture orthosis, tibial fracture orthosis, semi-rigid, prefabricated, includes fitting and adjustment
L2116	Ankle foot orthosis, fracture orthosis, tibial fracture orthosis, rigid, prefabricated, includes fitting and adjustment
L2126	Knee ankle foot orthosis, fracture orthosis, femoral fracture cast orthosis, thermoplastic type casting material, custom fabricated
L2128	Knee ankle foot orthosis, fracture orthosis, femoral fracture cast orthosis, custom fabricated
L2132	KAFO, fracture orthosis, femoral fracture cast orthosis, soft, prefabricated, includes fitting and adjustment
L2134	KAFO, fracture orthosis, femoral fracture cast orthosis, semi-rigid, prefabricated, includes fitting and adjustment
L2136	KAFO, fracture orthosis, femoral fracture cast orthosis, rigid, prefabricated, includes fitting and adjustment
L2180	Addition to lower extremity fracture orthosis, plastic shoe insert with ankle joints
L2182	Addition to lower extremity fracture orthosis, drop lock knee joint
L2184	Addition to lower extremity fracture orthosis, limited motion knee joint
L2186	Addition to lower extremity fracture orthosis, adjustable motion knee joint, Lerman type
L2188	Addition to lower extremity fracture orthosis, quadrilateral brim
L2190	Addition to lower extremity fracture orthosis, waist belt

L2192   Addition to lower extremity fracture orthosis, hip joint, pelvic band, thigh flange, and pelvic belt

Additions To Lower Extremity Orthosis

Ⓟ **L2200**   Addition to lower extremity, limited ankle motion, each joint

Ⓟ **L2210**   Addition to lower extremity, dorsiflexion assist (plantar flexion resist), each joint

Ⓟ **L2220**   Addition to lower extremity, dorsiflexion and plantar flexion assist/resist, each joint

L2230   Addition to lower extremity, split flat caliper stirrups and plate attachment

L2232   Addition to lower extremity orthosis, rocker bottom for total contact ankle foot orthosis, for custom fabricated orthosis only

L2240   Addition to lower extremity, round caliper and plate attachment

L2250   Addition to lower extremity, foot plate, molded to patient model, stirrup attachment

L2260   Addition to lower extremity, reinforced solid stirrup (Scott-Craig type)

L2265   Addition to lower extremity, long tongue stirrup

L2270   Addition to lower extremity, varus/valgus correction ('t') strap, padded/lined or malleolus pad

Ⓟ **L2275**   Addition to lower extremity, varus/valgus correction, plastic modification, padded/lined

Ⓟ **L2280**   Addition to lower extremity, molded inner boot

L2300   Addition to lower extremity, abduction bar (bilateral hip involvement), jointed, adjustable

L2310   Addition to lower extremity, abduction bar-straight

L2320   Addition to lower extremity, non-molded lacer, for custom fabricated orthosis only

Ⓟ **L2330**   Addition to lower extremity, lacer molded to patient model, for custom fabricated orthosis only

L2335   Addition to lower extremity, anterior swing band

Ⓟ **L2340**   Addition to lower extremity, pre-tibial shell, molded to patient model

L2350   Addition to lower extremity, prosthetic type, (BK) socket, molded to patient model, (used for 'ptb' 'AFO' orthoses)

L2360   Addition to lower extremity, extended steel shank

L2370   Addition to lower extremity, patten bottom

L2375   Addition to lower extremity, torsion control, ankle joint and half solid stirrup

L2380   Addition to lower extremity, torsion control, straight knee joint, each joint

L2385   Addition to lower extremity, straight knee joint, heavy duty, each joint

L2387   Addition to lower extremity, polycentric knee joint, for custom fabricated knee ankle foot orthosis, each joint

L2390   Addition to lower extremity, offset knee joint, each joint

L2395   Addition to lower extremity, offset knee joint, heavy duty, each joint

| | Not payable by Medicare | | Non-covered by Medicare | | Special coverage instructions | | Carrier judgement | 253 |

℗   **L2397**   Addition to lower extremity orthosis, suspension sleeve

Additions to Knee Joints

L2405   Addition to knee joint, drop lock, each

L2415   Addition to knee lock with integrated release mechanism (bail, cable, or equal), any material, each joint

L2425   Addition to knee joint, disc or dial lock for adjustable knee flexion, each joint

L2430   Addition to knee joint, ratchet lock for active and progressive knee extension, each joint

L2492   Addition to knee joint, lift loop for drop lock ring

Addition to Lower Extremity

L2500   Addition to lower extremity, thigh/weight bearing, gluteal/ ischial weight bearing, ring

L2510   Addition to lower extremity, thigh/weight bearing, quadri- lateral brim, molded to patient model

L2520   Addition to lower extremity, thigh/weight bearing, quadri- lateral brim, custom fitted

L2525   Addition to lower extremity, thigh/weight bearing, ischial containment/narrow m-l brim molded to patient model

L2526   Addition to lower extremity, thigh/weight bearing, ischial containment/narrow m-l brim, custom fitted

L2530   Addition to lower extremity, thigh-weight bearing, lacer, non-molded

L2540   Addition to lower extremity, thigh/weight bearing, lacer, molded to patient model

L2550   Addition to lower extremity, thigh/weight bearing, high roll cuff

L2570   Addition to lower extremity, pelvic control, hip joint, clevis type two position joint, each

L2580   Addition to lower extremity, pelvic control, pelvic sling

L2600   Addition to lower extremity, pelvic control, hip joint, clevis type, or thrust bearing, free, each

L2610   Addition to lower extremity, pelvic control, hip joint, clevis or thrust bearing, lock, each

L2620   Addition to lower extremity, pelvic control, hip joint, heavy duty, each

L2622   Addition to lower extremity, pelvic control, hip joint, adjustable flexion, each

L2624   Addition to lower extremity, pelvic control, hip joint, adjustable flexion, extension, abduction control, each

L2627   Addition to lower extremity, pelvic control, plastic, molded to patient model, reciprocating hip joint and cables

L2628   Addition to lower extremity, pelvic control, metal frame, reciprocating hip joint and cables

L2630   Addition to lower extremity, pelvic control, band and belt, unilateral

L2640   Addition to lower extremity, pelvic control, band and belt, bilateral

L2650   Addition to lower extremity, pelvic and thoracic control, gluteal pad, each

L2660   Addition to lower extremity, thoracic control, thoracic band

L2670   Addition to lower extremity, thoracic control, paraspinal uprights

L2680   Addition to lower extremity, thoracic control, lateral support uprights

L2750   Addition to lower extremity orthosis, plating chrome or nickel, per bar

L2755   Addition to lower extremity orthosis, high strength, lightweight material, all hybrid lamination/prepreg composite, per segment, for custom fabricated orthosis only

L2760   Addition to lower extremity orthosis, extension, per extension, per bar (for lineal adjustment for growth)

L2768   Orthotic side bar disconnect device, per bar

Ⓟ **L2780**   Addition to lower extremity orthosis, non-corrosive finish, per bar

L2785   Addition to lower extremity orthosis, drop lock retainer, each

L2795   Addition to lower extremity orthosis, knee control, full kneecap

L2800   Addition to lower extremity orthosis, knee control, knee cap, medial or lateral pull, for use with custom fabricated orthosis only

L2810   Addition to lower extremity orthosis, knee control, condylar pad

Ⓟ **L2820**   Addition to lower extremity orthosis, soft interface for molded plastic, below knee section

L2830   Addition to lower extremity orthosis, soft interface for molded plastic, above knee section

L2840   Addition to lower extremity orthosis, tibial length sock, fracture or equal, each

L2850   Addition to lower extremity orthosis, femoral length sock, fracture or equal, each

L2861   Addition to lower extremity joint, knee or ankle, concentric adjustable torsion style mechanism for custom fabricated orthotics only, each

L2999   Lower extremity orthoses, not otherwise specified

Foot- Insert and Arch Support

L3000   Foot, insert, removable, molded to patient model, 'UCB' type, Berkeley shell, each

   MCM: 2323

L3001   Foot, insert, removable, molded to patient model, Spenco, each

   MCM: 2323

L3002   Foot, insert, removable, molded to patient model, Plastazote or equal, each

   MCM: 2323

L3003   Foot, insert, removable, molded to patient model, silicone gel, each

   MCM: 2323

| | Not payable by Medicare | | Non-covered by Medicare | | Special coverage instructions | | Carrier judgement | 255 |

L3010 Foot, insert, removable, molded to patient model, longitudinal arch support, each
MCM: 2323

L3020 Foot, insert, removable, molded to patient model, longitudinal/ metatarsal support, each
MCM: 2323

L3030 Foot, insert, removable, formed to patient foot, each
MCM: 2323

L3031 Foot, insert/plate, removable, addition to lower extremity orthosis, high strength, lightweight material, all hybrid lamination/prepreg composite, each

L3040 Foot, arch support, removable, premolded, longitudinal, each
MCM: 2323

L3050 Foot, arch support, removable, premolded, metatarsal, each
MCM: 2323

L3060 Foot, arch support, removable, premolded, longitudinal/ metatarsal, each
MCM: 2323

L3070 Foot, arch support, non-removable attached to shoe, longitudinal, each
MCM: 2323

L3080 Foot, arch support, non-removable attached to shoe, metatarsal, each
MCM: 2323

L3090 Foot, arch support, non-removable attached to shoe, longitudinal/metatarsal, each
MCM: 2323

L3100 Hallus-valgus night dynamic splint, prefabricated, off-the-shelf
MCM: 2323

L3140 Foot, abduction rotation bar, including shoes
MCM: 2323

L3150 Foot, abduction rotatation bar, without shoes
MCM: 2323

L3160 Foot, adjustable shoe-styled positioning device

L3170 Foot, plastic, silicone or equal, heel stabilizer, prefabricated, off-the-shelf, each
MCM: 2323

Orthopedic Footwear

L3201 Orthopedic shoe, oxford with supinator or pronator, infant
MCM: 2323

L3202 Orthopedic shoe, oxford with supinator or pronator, child
MCM: 2323

L3203   Orthopedic shoe, oxford with supinator or pronator, junior

MCM: 2323

L3204   Orthopedic shoe, Hightop with supinator or pronator, infant

MCM: 2323

L3206   Orthopedic shoe, Hightop with supinator or pronator, child

MCM: 2323

L3207   Orthopedic shoe, Hightop with supinator or pronator, junior

MCM: 2323

L3208   Surgical boot, each, infant

MCM: 2079

L3209   Surgical boot, each, child

MCM: 2079

L3211   Surgical boot, each, junior

MCM: 2079

L3212   Benesch boot, pair, infant

MCM: 2079

L3213   Benesch boot, pair, child

MCM: 2079

L3214   Benesch boot, pair, junior

MCM: 2079

L3215   Orthopedic footwear, ladies shoe, oxford, each

Statute: 1862A8

L3216   Orthopedic footwear, ladies shoe, depth inlay, each

Statute: 1862A8

L3217   Orthopedic footwear, ladies shoe, Hightop, depth inlay, each

Statute: 1862A8

L3219   Orthopedic footwear, mens shoe, oxford, each

Statute: 1862A8

L3221   Orthopedic footwear, mens shoe, depth inlay, each

Statute: 1862A8

L3222   Orthopedic footwear, mens shoe, Hightop, depth inlay, each

Statute: 1862A8

L3224   Orthopedic footwear, woman's shoe, oxford, used as an integral part of a brace (orthosis)

Not payable
by Medicare   Non-covered
by Medicare   Special coverage
instructions   Carrier
judgement   257

MCM: 2323D

L3225   Orthopedic footwear, man's shoe, oxford, used as an integral part of a brace (orthosis)

MCM: 2323D

L3230   Orthopedic footwear, custom shoe, depth inlay, each

MCM: 2323

L3250   Orthopedic footwear, custom molded shoe, removable inner mold, prosthetic shoe, each

MCM: 2323

L3251   Foot, shoe molded to patient model, silicone shoe, each

MCM: 2323

L3252   Foot, shoe molded to patient model, Plastazote (or similar), custom fabricated, each

MCM: 2323

L3253   Foot, molded shoe Plastazote (or similar) custom fitted, each

MCM: 2323

L3254   Non-standard size or width

MCM: 2323

L3255   Non-standard size or length

MCM: 2323

L3257   Orthopedic footwear, additional charge for split size

MCM: 2323

L3260   Surgical boot/shoe, each

MCM: 2079

L3265   Plastazote sandal, each

Shoe Modification Lifts

L3300   Lift, elevation, heel, tapered to metatarsals, per inch
MCM: 2323

L3310   Lift, elevation, heel and sole, neoprene, per inch
MCM: 2323

L3320   Lift, elevation, heel and sole, cork, per inch
MCM: 2323

L3330   Lift, elevation, metal extension (skate)
MCM: 2323

L3332   Lift, elevation, inside shoe, tapered, up to one-half inch
MCM: 2323

L3334   Lift, elevation, heel, per inch

MCM: 2323

Wedges

L3340   Heel wedge, SACH

MCM: 2323

L3350   Heel wedge

MCM: 2323

L3360   Sole wedge, outside sole

MCM: 2323

L3370   Sole wedge, between sole

MCM: 2323

L3380   Clubfoot wedge

MCM: 2323

L3390   Outflare wedge

MCM: 2323

L3400   Metatarsal bar wedge, rocker

MCM: 2323

L3410   Metatarsal bar wedge, between sole

MCM: 2323

L3420   Full sole and heel wedge, between sole

MCM: 2323

Heels

L3430   Heel, counter, plastic reinforced

MCM: 2323

L3440   Heel, counter, leather reinforced

MCM: 2323

L3450   Heel, SACH cushion type

MCM: 2323

L3455   Heel, new leather, standard

MCM: 2323

L3460   Heel, new rubber, standard

MCM: 2323

L3465   Heel, Thomas with wedge

MCM: 2323

Not payable
by Medicare   Non-covered
by Medicare   Special coverage
instructions   Carrier
judgement   259

L3470 Heel, Thomas extended to ball

MCM: 2323

L3480 Heel, pad and depression for spur

MCM: 2323

L3485 Heel, pad, removable for spur

MCM: 2323

Orthopedic Shoe Additions

L3500 Orthopedic shoe addition, insole, leather

MCM: 2323

L3510 Orthopedic shoe addition, insole, rubber

MCM: 2323

L3520 Orthopedic shoe addition, insole, felt covered with leather

MCM: 2323

L3530 Orthopedic shoe addition, sole, half

MCM: 2323

L3540 Orthopedic shoe addition, sole, full

MCM: 2323

L3550 Orthopedic shoe addition, toe tap standard

MCM: 2323

L3560 Orthopedic shoe addition, toe tap, horseshoe

MCM: 2323

L3570 Orthopedic shoe addition, special extension to instep (leather with eyelets)

MCM: 2323

L3580 Orthopedic shoe addition, convert instep to Velcro closure

MCM: 2323

L3590 Orthopedic shoe addition, convert firm shoe counter to soft counter

MCM: 2323

L3595 Orthopedic shoe addition, march bar

MCM: 2323

Transfer or Replacement

L3600 Transfer of an orthosis from one shoe to another, caliper plate, existing

MCM: 2323

L3610 Transfer of an orthosis from one shoe to another, caliper plate, new

MCM: 2323

L3620   Transfer of an orthosis from one shoe to another, solid stirrup, existing

MCM: 2323

L3630   Transfer of an orthosis from one shoe to another, solid stirrup, new

MCM: 2323

L3640   Transfer of an orthosis from one shoe to another, Dennis Browne splint (Riveton), both shoes

MCM: 2323

L3649   Orthopedic shoe, modification, addition or transfer, not otherwise specified

MCM: 2323

Orthotic Devices – Upper Limb

L3650   Shoulder orthosis, figure of eight design abduction restrainer, prefabricated, off-the-shelf

L3660   Shoulder orthosis, figure of eight design abduction restrainer, canvas and webbing, prefabricated, off-the-shelf

Ⓟ   **L3670**   Shoulder orthosis, acromio/clavicular (canvas and webbing type), prefabricated, off-the-shelf

L3671   Shoulder orthosis, shoulder joint design, without joints, may include soft interface, straps, custom fabricated, includes fitting and adjustment

L3674   Shoulder orthosis, abduction positioning (airplane design), thoracic component and support bar, with or without nontorsion joint/turnbuckle, may include soft interface, straps, custom fabricated, includes fitting and adjustment

L3675   Shoulder orthosis, vest type abduction restrainer, canvas webbing type or equal, prefabricated, off-the-shelf

L3677   Shoulder orthosis, shoulder joint design, without joints, may include soft interface, straps, prefabricated item that has been trimmed, bent, molded, assembled, or otherwise customized to fit a specific patient by an individual with expertise

MCM: 2130

L3678   Shoulder orthosis, shoulder joint design, without joints, may include soft interface, straps, prefabricated, off-the-shelf

L3702   Elbow orthosis, without joints, may include soft interface, straps, custom fabricated, includes fitting and adjustment

L3710   Elbow orthosis, elastic with metal joints, prefabricated, off-the-shelf

L3720   Elbow orthosis, double upright with forearm/arm cuffs, free motion, custom fabricated

L3730   Elbow orthosis, double upright with forearm/arm cuffs, extension/ flexion assist, custom fabricated

L3740   Elbow orthosis, double upright with forearm/arm cuffs, adjustable position lock with active control, custom fabricated

▲Ⓟ **L3760** Elbow orthosis (EO), with adjustable position locking joint(s), prefabricated, item that has been trimmed, bent, molded, assembled, or otherwise customized to fit a specific patient by an individual with expertise

• **L3761** Elbow orthosis (EO), with adjustable position locking joint(s), prefabricated, off-the-shelf

L3762 Elbow orthosis, rigid, without joints, includes soft interface material, prefabricated, off-the-shelf

L3763 Elbow wrist hand orthosis, rigid, without joints, may include soft interface, straps, custom fabricated, includes fitting and adjustment

L3764 Elbow wrist hand orthosis, includes one or more nontorsion joints, elastic bands, turnbuckles, may include soft interface, straps, custom fabricated, includes fitting and adjustment

L3765 Elbow wrist hand finger orthosis, rigid, without joints, may include soft interface, straps, custom fabricated, includes fitting and adjustment

L3766 Elbow wrist hand finger orthosis, includes one or more nontorsion joints, elastic bands, turnbuckles, may include soft interface, straps, custom fabricated, includes fitting and adjustment

L3806 Wrist hand finger orthosis, includes one or more nontorsion joint(s), turnbuckles, elastic bands/springs, may include soft interface material, straps, custom fabricated, includes fitting and adjustment

L3807 Wrist hand finger orthosis, without joint(s), prefabricated item that has been trimmed, bent, molded, assembled, or otherwise customized to fit a specific patient by an individual with expertise

Ⓟ **L3808** Wrist hand finger orthosis, rigid without joints, may include soft interface material; straps, custom fabricated, includes fitting and adjustment

Ⓟ **L3809** Wrist hand finger orthosis, without joint(s), prefabricated, off-the-shelf, any type

L3891 Addition to upper extremity joint, wrist or elbow, concentric adjustable torsion style mechanism for custom fabricated orthotics only, each

Wrist-Hand-Finger Orthoses

L3900 Wrist hand finger orthosis, dynamic flexor hinge, reciprocal wrist extension/ flexion, finger flexion/extension, wrist or finger driven, custom fabricated

L3901 Wrist hand finger orthosis, dynamic flexor hinge, reciprocal wrist extension/ flexion, finger flexion/extension, cable driven, custom fabricated

L3904 Wrist hand finger orthosis, external powered, electric, custom fabricated

L3905 Wrist hand orthosis, includes one or more nontorsion joints, elastic bands, turnbuckles, may include soft interface, straps, custom fabricated, includes fitting and adjustment

L3906 Wrist hand orthosis, without joints, may include soft interface, straps, custom fabricated, includes fitting and adjustment

Ⓟ **L3908** Wrist hand orthosis, wrist extension control cock-up, non molded, prefabricated, off-the-shelf

L3912 Hand finger orthosis (HFO), flexion glove with elastic finger control, prefabricated, off-the-shelf

L3913 Hand finger orthosis, without joints, may include soft interface, straps, custom fabricated, includes fitting and adjustment

L3915 Wrist hand orthosis, includes one or more nontorsion joint(s), elastic bands, turnbuckles, may include soft interface, straps, prefabricated item that has been trimmed, bent, molded, assembled, or otherwise customized to fit a specific patient by an individual with expertise

L3916 Wrist hand orthosis, includes one or more nontorsion joint(s), elastic bands, turnbuckles, may include soft interface, straps, prefabricated, off-the-shelf

L3917 Hand orthosis, metacarpal fracture orthosis, prefabricated item that has been trimmed, bent, molded, assembled, or otherwise customized to fit a specific patient by an individual with expertise

L3918 Hand orthosis, metacarpal fracture orthosis, prefabricated, off-the-shelf

L3919 Hand orthosis, without joints, may include soft interface, straps, custom fabricated, includes fitting and adjustment

L3921 Hand finger orthosis, includes one or more nontorsion joints, elastic bands, turnbuckles, may include soft interface, straps, custom fabricated, includes fitting and adjustment

L3923 Hand finger orthosis, without joints, may include soft interface, straps, prefabricated item that has been trimmed, bent, molded, assembled, or otherwise customized to fit a specific patient by an individual with expertise

L3924 Hand finger orthosis, without joints, may include soft interface, straps, prefabricated, off-the-shelf

L3925 Finger orthosis, proximal interphalangeal (pip)/distal interphalangeal (dip), non torsion joint/spring, extension/flexion, may include soft interface material, prefabricated, off-the-shelf

L3927 Finger orthosis, proximal interphalangeal (pip)/distal interphalangeal (dip), without joint/spring, extension/flexion (e.g., static or ring type), may include soft interface material, prefabricated, off-the-shelf

L3929 Hand finger orthosis, includes one or more nontorsion joint(s), turnbuckles, elastic bands/springs, may include soft interface material, straps, prefabricated item that has been trimmed, bent, molded, assembled, or otherwise customized to fit a specific patient by an individual with expertise

L3930 Hand finger orthosis, includes one or more nontorsion joint(s), turnbuckles, elastic bands/springs, may include soft interface material, straps, prefabricated, off-the-shelf

L3931 Wrist hand finger orthosis, includes one or more nontorsion joint(s), turnbuckles, elastic bands/springs, may include soft interface material, straps, prefabricated, includes fitting and adjustment

L3933 Finger orthosis, without joints, may include soft interface, custom fabricated, includes fitting and adjustment

L3935 Finger orthosis, nontorsion joint, may include soft interface, custom fabricated, includes fitting and adjustment

L3956   Addition of joint to upper extremity orthosis, any material; per joint

Shoulder-Elbow-Wrist-Hand Orthoses (SEWHO)

L3960   Shoulder elbow wrist hand orthosis, abduction positioning, airplane design, prefabricated, includes fitting and adjustment

L3961   Shoulder elbow wrist hand orthosis, shoulder cap design, without joints, may include soft interface, straps, custom fabricated, includes fitting and adjustment

L3962   Shoulder elbow wrist hand orthosis, abduction positioning, Erb's palsy design, prefabricated, includes fitting and adjustment

L3967   Shoulder elbow wrist hand orthosis, abduction positioning (airplane design), thoracic component and support bar, without joints, may include soft interface, straps, custom fabricated, includes fitting and adjustment

L3971   Shoulder elbow wrist hand orthosis, shoulder cap design, includes one or more nontorsion joints, elastic bands, turnbuckles, may include soft interface, straps, custom fabricated, includes fitting and adjustment

L3973   Shoulder elbow wrist hand orthosis, abduction positioning (airplane design), thoracic component and support bar, includes one or more nontorsion joints, elastic bands, turnbuckles, may include soft interface, straps, custom fabricated, includes fitting and adjustment

L3975   Shoulder elbow wrist hand finger orthosis, shoulder cap design, without joints, may include soft interface, straps, custom fabricated, includes fitting and adjustment

L3976   Shoulder elbow wrist hand finger orthosis, abduction positioning (airplane design), thoracic component and support bar, without joints, may include soft interface, straps, custom fabricated, includes fitting and adjustment

L3977   Shoulder elbow wrist hand finger orthosis, shoulder cap design, includes one or more nontorsion joints, elastic bands, turnbuckles, may include soft interface, straps, custom fabricated, includes fitting and adjustment

L3978   Shoulder elbow wrist hand finger orthosis, abduction positioning (airplane design), thoracic component and support bar, includes one or more nontorsion joints, elastic bands, turnbuckles, may include soft interface, straps, custom fabricated, includes fitting and adjustment

Upper Limb – Fracture Orthoses

L3980   Upper extremity fracture orthosis, humeral, prefabricated, includes fitting and adjustment

L3981   Upper extremity fracture orthosis, humeral, prefabricated, includes shoulder cap design, with or without joints, forearm section, may include soft interface, straps, includes fitting and adjustments

L3982   Upper extremity fracture orthosis, radius/ulnar, prefabricated, includes fitting and adjustment

L3984   Upper extremity fracture orthosis, wrist, prefabricated, includes fitting and adjustment

L3995   Addition to upper extremity orthosis, sock, fracture or equal, each

L3999   Upper limb orthosis, not otherwise specified

Specific Repair

L4000   Replace girdle for spinal orthosis (CTLSO or so)

L4002   Replacement strap, any orthosis, includes all components, any length, any type

L4010   Replace trilateral socket brim

L4020   Replace quadrilateral socket brim, molded to patient model

L4030   Replace quadrilateral socket brim, custom fitted

L4040   Replace molded thigh lacer, for custom fabricated orthosis only

L4045   Replace non-molded thigh lacer, for custom fabricated orthosis only

L4050   Replace molded calf lacer, for custom fabricated orthosis only

L4055   Replace non-molded calf lacer, for custom fabricated orthosis only

L4060   Replace high roll cuff

L4070   Replace proximal and distal upright for KAFO

L4080   Replace metal bands KAFO, proximal thigh

L4090   Replace metal bands KAFO-AFO, calf or distal thigh

L4100   Replace leather cuff KAFO, proximal thigh

L4110   Replace leather cuff KAFO-AFO, calf or distal thigh

L4130   Replace pretibial shell

L4205   Repair of orthotic device, labor component, per 15 minutes

MCM: 2100.4

L4210   Repair of orthotic device, repair or replace minor parts

MCM: 2133, 2100.4, 2130D

Ancillary Orthotic Services

L4350   Ankle control orthosis, stirrup style, rigid, includes any type interface (e.g., pneumatic, gel), prefabricated, off-the-shelf

(P)   L4360   Walking boot, pneumatic and/or vacuum, with or without joints, with or without interface material, prefabricated item that has been trimmed, bent, molded, assembled, or otherwise customized to fit a specific patient by an individual with expertise

(P)   L4361   Walking boot, pneumatic and/or vacuum, with or without joints, with or without interface material, prefabricated, off-the-shelf

L4370   Pneumatic full leg splint, prefabricated, off-the-shelf

L4386   Walking boot, non-pneumatic, with or without joints, with or without interface material, prefabricated item that has been trimmed, bent, molded, assembled, or otherwise customized to fit a specific patient by an individual with expertise

L4387 Walking boot, non-pneumatic, with or without joints, with or without interface material, prefabricated, off-the-shelf

L4392 Replacement, soft interface material, static AFO

L4394 Replace soft interface material, foot drop splint

L4396 Static or dynamic ankle foot orthosis, including soft interface material, adjustable for fit, for positioning, may be used for minimal ambulation, prefabricated item that has been trimmed, bent, molded, assembled, or otherwise customized to fit a specific patient by an individual with expertise

L4397 Static or dynamic ankle foot orthosis, including soft interface material, adjustable for fit, for positioning, may be used for minimal ambulation, prefabricated, off-the-shelf

L4398 Foot drop splint, recumbent positioning device, prefabricated, off-the-shelf

℗ **L4631** Ankle foot orthosis, walking boot type, varus/valgus correction, rocker bottom, anterior tibial shell, soft interface, custom arch support, plastic or other material, includes straps and closures, custom fabricated

---

• New code   ▲ Revised code   ( ) Deleted code   ⊤Trigger   ℗ Post Trigger DME

PROSTHETIC PROCEDURES

Guidelines

In addition to the information presented in the INTRODUCTION, several other items unique to this section are defined or identified here:

1. PROSTHETIC DEVICES: Prosthetic devices (other than dental) which replace all or part of an internal body organ (including contiguous tissue), or replace all or part of the function of a permanently inoperative or malfunctioning internal body organ, are covered when furnished upon a physician's order. This does not require a determination that there is no possibility that the patient's condition may improve in the future. If the medical record and the judgement of the attending physician indicate that the condition is of long and indefinite duration, the test of permanence is met. The device(s) may also be covered as a supply item when furnished incident to a physician's service.

2. SUBSECTION INFORMATION: Some of the listed subheadings or subsections have special needs or instructions unique to that section. Where these are indicated, special "notes" will be presented preceding or following the listings. Those subsections within the PROSTHETIC PROCEDURES section that have "notes" are as follows:

Subsection	Code Numbers
Prosthetic procedures-lower limb	L5000-L5999
Upper limb	L6000-L6590
Additions-upper limb	L6600-L6999

3. UNLISTED SERVICE OR PROCEDURE: A service or procedure may be provided that is not listed in this edition of HCPCS. When reporting such a service, the appropriate "unlisted procedure" code may be used to indicate the service, identifying it by "special report" as defined below. HCPCS terminology is inconsistent in defining unlisted procedures. The procedure definition may include the term(s) "unlisted", "not otherwise classified", "unspecified", "unclassified", "other" and "miscellaneous". Prior to using these codes, try to determine if a Local Level III code or CPT code is available. The "unlisted procedures" and accompanying codes for PROSTHETIC PROCEDURES are as follows:

L5999   Lower extremity prosthesis, not otherwise specified
L7499   Upper extremity prosthesis, not otherwise specified
L8039   Breast prosthesis, not otherwise specified
L8239   Gradient compression stocking, not otherwise specified
L8499   Unlisted procedure for miscellaneous prosthetic services
L8699   Prosthetic implant, not otherwise specified

4. SPECIAL REPORT: A service, material or supply that is rarely provided, unusual, variable or new may require a special report in determining medical appropriateness for reimbursement purposes. Pertinent information should include an adequate definition or description of the nature, extent, and need for the service, material or supply.

5. MODIFIERS: Listed services may be modified under certain circumstances. When appropriate, the modifying circumstance is identified by adding a modifier to the basic procedure code. CPT and HCPCS National Level II modifiers may be used with CPT and HCPCS National Level II procedure codes. Modifiers commonly used with PROSTHETIC PROCEDURES are as follows:

-CC   Procedure code change (use "CC" when the procedure code submitted was changed either for administrative reasons or because an incorrect code was filed)

-LT   Left side (used to identify procedures performed on the left side of the body)

-RT   Right side (used to identify procedures performed on the right side of the body)

-TC   Technical component. Under certain circumstances, a charge may be made for the technical component alone. Under those circumstances, the technical component charge is identified by adding modifier -TC to the usual procedure number. Technical component charges are institutional charges and are not billed separately by physicians. However, portable x-ray suppliers bill only for the technical component and should use modifier -TC. The charge data from portable x-ray suppliers will then be used to build customary and prevailing profiles.

6.   CPT CODE CROSS-REFERENCE: Unless otherwise specified, the equivalent CPT code for all listings in this section is 99070.

7.   DURABLE MEDICAL EQUIPMENT REGIONAL CARRIERS (DMERCS): Effective October 1, 1993 claims for prosthetics must be billed to one of four regional carriers depending upon the residence of the beneficiary. The transition dates for DMERC claims is from November 1, 1993 to March 1, 1994, depending upon the state you practice in. See the Introduction for a complete discussion of DMERCs.

Lower Limb

NOTE: The procedures in this section are considered as "base" or "basic" procedures, and they may be modified by listing items, procedures or special materials from the "additions" section, and adding them to the base procedure.

L5000	Partial foot, shoe insert with longitudinal arch, toe filler
	MCM: 2323
L5010	Partial foot, molded socket, ankle height, with toe filler
	MCM: 2323
L5020	Partial foot, molded socket, tibial tubercle height, with toe filler
	MCM: 2323
L5050	Ankle, Symes, molded socket, SACH foot
L5060	Ankle, Symes, metal frame, molded leather socket, articulated ankle/foot
L5100	Below knee, molded socket, shin, SACH foot
L5105	Below knee, plastic socket, joints and thigh lacer, SACH foot
L5150	Knee disarticulation (or through knee), molded socket, external knee joints, shin, SACH foot
L5160	Knee disarticulation (or through knee), molded socket, bent knee configuration, external knee joints, shin, SACH foot
L5200	Above knee, molded socket, single axis constant friction knee, shin, SACH foot

ⓟ **L5210** Above knee, short prosthesis, no knee joint ('stubbies'), with foot blocks, no ankle joints, each

L5220 Above knee, short prosthesis, no knee joint ('stubbies'), with articulated ankle/foot, dynamically aligned, each

L5230 Above knee, for proximal femoral focal deficiency, constant friction knee, shin, SACH foot

L5250 Hip disarticulation, Canadian type; molded socket, hip joint, single axis constant friction knee, shin, SACH foot

L5270 Hip disarticulation, tilt table type; molded socket, locking hip joint, single axis constant friction knee, shin, SACH foot

L5280 Hemipelvectomy, Canadian type; molded socket, hip joint, single axis constant friction knee, shin, SACH foot

ⓟ **L5301** Below knee, molded socket, shin, SACH foot, endoskeletal system

L5312 Knee disarticulation (or through knee), molded socket, single axis knee, pylon, SACH foot, endoskeletal system

ⓟ **L5321** Above knee, molded socket, open end, SACH foot, endoskeletal system, single axis knee

L5331 Hip disarticulation, Canadian type, molded socket, endoskeletal system, hip joint, single axis knee, SACH foot

L5341 Hemipelvectomy, Canadian type, molded socket, endoskeletal system, hip joint, single axis knee, SACH foot

Immediate Post Surgical or Early Fitting Procedures

L5400 Immediate post surgical or early fitting, application of initial rigid dressing, including fitting, alignment, suspension, and one cast change, below knee

L5410 Immediate post surgical or early fitting, application of initial rigid dressing, including fitting, alignment and suspension, below knee, each additional cast change and realignment

L5420 Immediate post surgical or early fitting, application of initial rigid dressing, including fitting, alignment and suspension and one cast change 'AK' or knee disarticulation

L5430 Immediate post surgical or early fitting, application of initial rigid dressing, incl. fitting, alignment and suspension, 'AK' or knee disarticulation, each additional cast change and realignment

ⓟ **L5450** Immediate post surgical or early fitting, application of non-weight bearing rigid dressing, below knee

L5460 Immediate post surgical or early fitting, application of non-weight bearing rigid dressing, above knee

Initial Prosthesis

L5500 Initial, below knee 'ptb' type socket, non-alignable system, pylon, no cover, SACH foot, plaster socket, direct formed

L5505 Initial, above knee - knee disarticulation, ischial level socket, non-alignable system, pylon, no cover, SACH foot, plaster socket, direct formed

Preparatory Prosthesis

L5510 Preparatory, below knee 'ptb' type socket, non-alignable system, pylon, no cover, SACH foot, plaster socket, molded to model

L5520 Preparatory, below knee 'ptb' type socket, non-alignable system, pylon, no cover, SACH foot, thermoplastic or equal, direct formed

Ⓟ **L5530** Preparatory, below knee 'ptb' type socket, non-alignable system, pylon, no cover, SACH foot, thermoplastic or equal, molded to model

L5535 Preparatory, below knee 'ptb' type socket, non-alignable system, no cover, SACH foot, prefabricated, adjustable open end socket

Ⓟ **L5540** Preparatory, below knee 'ptb' type socket, non-alignable system, pylon, no cover, SACH foot, laminated socket, molded to model

L5560 Preparatory, above knee- knee disarticulation, ischial level socket, non-alignable system, pylon, no cover, SACH foot, plaster socket, molded to model

L5570 Preparatory, above knee - knee disarticulation, ischial level socket, non-alignable system, pylon, no cover, SACH foot, thermoplastic or equal, direct formed

Ⓟ **L5580** Preparatory, above knee - knee disarticulation ischial level socket, non-alignable system, pylon, no cover, SACH foot, thermoplastic or equal, molded to model

L5585 Preparatory, above knee - knee disarticulation, ischial level socket, non-alignable system, pylon, no cover, SACH foot, prefabricated adjustable open end socket

Ⓟ **L5590** Preparatory, above knee - knee disarticulation ischial level socket, non-alignable system, pylon no cover, SACH foot, laminated socket, molded to model

L5595 Preparatory, hip disarticulation-hemipelvectomy, pylon, no cover, SACH foot, thermoplastic or equal, molded to patient model

L5600 Preparatory, hip disarticulation-hemipelvectomy, pylon, no cover, SACH foot, laminated socket, molded to patient model

Additions To Lower Extremity

L5610 Addition to lower extremity, endoskeletal system, above knee, Hydra-Cadence system

Ⓟ **L5611** Addition to lower extremity, endoskeletal system, above knee - knee disarticulation, 4 bar linkage, with friction swing phase control

L5613 Addition to lower extremity, endoskeletal system, above knee-knee disarticulation, 4 bar linkage, with hydraulic swing phase control

L5614 Addition to lower extremity, exoskeletal system, above knee-knee disarticulation, 4 bar linkage, with pneumatic swing phase control

L5616 Addition to lower extremity, endoskeletal system, above knee, universal multiplex system, friction swing phase control

L5617 Addition to lower extremity, quick change self-aligning unit, above knee or below knee, each

Additions - Test Sockets and Socket Variations

L5618 Addition to lower extremity, test socket, Symes

Ⓟ **L5620** Addition to lower extremity, test socket, below knee

L5622 Addition to lower extremity, test socket, knee disarticulation

Ⓟ **L5624** Addition to lower extremity, test socket, above knee

L5626 Addition to lower extremity, test socket, hip disarticulation

L5628 Addition to lower extremity, test socket, hemipelvectomy

Ⓟ **L5629** Addition to lower extremity, below knee, acrylic socket

L5630 Addition to lower extremity, Symes type, expandable wall socket

Ⓟ **L5631** Addition to lower extremity, above knee or knee disarticulation, acrylic socket

L5632 Addition to lower extremity, Symes type, 'ptb' brim design socket

L5634 Addition to lower extremity, Symes type, posterior opening (Canadian) socket

L5636 Addition to lower extremity, Symes type, medial opening socket

Ⓟ **L5637** Addition to lower extremity, below knee, total contact

L5638 Addition to lower extremity, below knee, leather socket

L5639 Addition to lower extremity, below knee, wood socket

L5640 Addition to lower extremity, knee disarticulation, leather socket

L5642 Addition to lower extremity, above knee, leather socket

L5643 Addition to lower extremity, hip disarticulation, flexible inner socket, external frame

L5644 Addition to lower extremity, above knee, wood socket

Ⓟ **L5645** Addition to lower extremity, below knee, flexible inner socket, external frame

L5646 Addition to lower extremity, below knee, air, fluid, gel or equal, cushion socket

Ⓟ **L5647** Addition to lower extremity, below knee suction socket

L5648 Addition to lower extremity, above knee, air, fluid, gel or equal, cushion socket

Ⓟ **L5649** Addition to lower extremity, ischial containment/narrow m-l socket

Ⓟ **L5650** Additions to lower extremity, total contact, above knee or knee disarticulation socket

Ⓟ **L5651** Addition to lower extremity, above knee, flexible inner socket, external frame

Ⓟ **L5652** Addition to lower extremity, suction suspension, above knee or knee disarticulation socket

L5653 Addition to lower extremity, knee disarticulation, expandable wall socket

Additions - Socket Insert and Suspension

L5654 Addition to lower extremity, socket insert, Symes, (Kemblo, Pelite, Aliplast, Plastazote or equal)

L5655 Addition to lower extremity, socket insert, below knee (Kemblo, Pelite, Aliplast, Plastazote or equal)

L5656 Addition to lower extremity, socket insert, knee disarticulation (Kemblo, Pelite, Aliplast, Plastazote or equal)

L5658 Addition to lower extremity, socket insert, above knee (Kemblo, Pelite, Aliplast, Plastazote or equal)

L5661 Addition to lower extremity, socket insert, multi-durometer Symes

L5665 Addition to lower extremity, socket insert, multi-durometer, below knee

L5666 Addition to lower extremity, below knee, cuff suspension

L5668 Addition to lower extremity, below knee, molded distal cushion

L5670 Addition to lower extremity, below knee, molded supracondylar suspension ('pts' or similar)

ⓟ **L5671** Addition to lower extremity, below knee / above knee suspension locking mechanism (shuttle, lanyard or equal), excludes socket insert

L5672 Addition to lower extremity, below knee, removable medial brim suspension

ⓟ **L5673** Addition to lower extremity, below knee/above knee, custom fabricated from existing mold or prefabricated, socket insert, silicone gel, elastomeric or equal, for use with locking mechanism

L5676 Additions to lower extremity, below knee, knee joints, single axis, pair

L5677 Additions to lower extremity, below knee, knee joints, polycentric, pair

L5678 Additions to lower extremity, below knee, joint covers, pair

ⓟ **L5679** Addition to lower extremity, below knee/above knee, custom fabricated from existing mold or prefabricated, socket insert, silicone gel, elastomeric or equal, not for use with locking mechanism

L5680 Addition to lower extremity, below knee, thigh lacer, non-molded

L5681 Addition to lower extremity, below knee/above knee, custom fabricated socket insert for congenital or atypical traumatic amputee, silicone gel, elastomeric or equal, for use with or without locking mechanism, initial only (for other than initial, use code l5673 or l5679)

L5682 Addition to lower extremity, below knee, thigh lacer, gluteal/ischial, molded

ⓟ **L5683** Addition to lower extremity, below knee/above knee, custom fabricated socket insert for other than congenital or atypical traumatic amputee, silicone gel, elastomeric or equal, for use with or without locking mechanism, initial only (for other than initial, use code l5673 or l5679)

L5684 Addition to lower extremity, below knee, fork strap

ⓟ **L5685** Addition to lower extremity prosthesis, below knee, suspension/sealing sleeve, with or without valve, any material, each

	L5686	Addition to lower extremity, below knee, back check (extension control)
	L5688	Addition to lower extremity, below knee, waist belt, webbing
	L5690	Addition to lower extremity, below knee, waist belt, padded and lined
	L5692	Addition to lower extremity, above knee, pelvic control belt, light
	L5694	Addition to lower extremity, above knee, pelvic control belt, padded and lined
	L5695	Addition to lower extremity, above knee, pelvic control, sleeve suspension, neoprene or equal, each
	L5696	Addition to lower extremity, above knee or knee disarticulation, pelvic joint
	L5697	Addition to lower extremity, above knee or knee disarticulation, pelvic band
	L5698	Addition to lower extremity, above knee or knee disarticulation, Silesian bandage
	L5699	All lower extremity prostheses, shoulder harness
Ⓟ	L5700	Replacement, socket, below knee, molded to patient model
Ⓟ	L5701	Replacement, socket, above knee/knee disarticulation, including attachment plate, molded to patient model
	L5702	Replacement, socket, hip disarticulation, including hip joint, molded to patient model
	L5703	Ankle, Symes, molded to patient model, socket without solid ankle cushion heel (SACH) foot, replacement only
Ⓟ	L5704	Custom shaped protective cover, below knee
Ⓟ	L5705	Custom shaped protective cover, above knee
	L5706	Custom shaped protective cover, knee disarticulation
	L5707	Custom shaped protective cover, hip disarticulation

Additions - Knee-Shin System Exoskeletal

	L5710	Addition, exoskeletal knee-shin system, single axis, manual lock
	L5711	Additions exoskeletal knee-shin system, single axis, manual lock, ultra-light material
	L5712	Addition, exoskeletal knee-shin system, single axis, friction swing and stance phase control (safety knee)
	L5714	Addition, exoskeletal knee-shin system, single axis, variable friction swing phase control
	L5716	Addition, exoskeletal knee-shin system, polycentric, mechanical stance phase lock
	L5718	Addition, exoskeletal knee-shin system, polycentric, friction swing and stance phase control
	L5722	Addition, exoskeletal knee-shin system, single axis, pneumatic swing, friction stance phase control
	L5724	Addition, exoskeletal knee-shin system, single axis, fluid swing phase control
	L5726	Addition, exoskeletal knee-shin system, single axis, external joints fluid swing phase control

L5728 | Addition, exoskeletal knee-shin system, single axis, fluid swing and stance phase control

L5780 | Addition, exoskeletal knee-shin system, single axis, pneumatic/hydra pneumatic swing phase control

Ⓟ L5781 | Addition to lower limb prosthesis, vacuum pump, residual limb volume management and moisture evacuation system

L5782 | Addition to lower limb prosthesis, vacuum pump, residual limb volume management and moisture evacuation system, heavy duty

L5785 | Addition, exoskeletal system, below knee, ultra-light material (titanium, carbon fiber or equal)

L5790 | Addition, exoskeletal system, above knee, ultra-light material (titanium, carbon fiber or equal)

L5795 | Addition, exoskeletal system, hip disarticulation, ultra-light material (titanium, carbon fiber or equal)

Endoskeletal

L5810 | Addition, endoskeletal knee-shin system, single axis, manual lock

L5811 | Addition, endoskeletal knee-shin system, single axis, manual lock, ultra-light material

Ⓟ L5812 | Addition, endoskeletal knee-shin system, single axis, friction swing and stance phase control (safety knee)

L5814 | Addition, endoskeletal knee-shin system, polycentric, hydraulic swing phase control, mechanical stance phase lock

L5816 | Addition, endoskeletal knee-shin system, polycentric, mechanical stance phase lock

L5818 | Addition, endoskeletal knee-shin system, polycentric, friction swing, and stance phase control

L5822 | Addition, endoskeletal knee-shin system, single axis, pneumatic swing, friction stance phase control

L5824 | Addition, endoskeletal knee-shin system, single axis, fluid swing phase control

L5826 | Addition, endoskeletal knee-shin system, single axis, hydraulic swing phase control, with miniature high activity frame

Ⓟ L5828 | Addition, endoskeletal knee-shin system, single axis, fluid swing and stance phase control

L5830 | Addition, endoskeletal knee-shin system, single axis, pneumatic/ swing phase control

L5840 | Addition, endoskeletal knee/shin system, 4-bar linkage or multiaxial, pneumatic swing phase control

Ⓟ L5845 | Addition, endoskeletal, knee-shin system, stance flexion feature, adjustable

Ⓟ L5848 | Addition to endoskeletal knee-shin system, fluid stance extension, dampening feature, with or without adjustability

Ⓟ L5850 | Addition, endoskeletal system, above knee or hip disarticulation, knee extension assist

L5855 | Addition, endoskeletal system, hip disarticulation, mechanical hip extension assist

ⓟ **L5856** Addition to lower extremity prosthesis, endoskeletal knee-shin system, microprocessor control feature, swing and stance phase, includes electronic sensor(s), any type

L5857 Addition to lower extremity prosthesis, endoskeletal knee-shin system, microprocessor control feature, swing phase only, includes electronic sensor(s), any type

ⓟ **L5858** Addition to lower extremity prosthesis, endoskeletal knee shin system, microprocessor control feature, stance phase only, includes electronic sensor(s), any type

ⓟ **L5859** Addition to lower extremity prosthesis, endoskeletal knee-shin system, powered and programmable flexion/extension assist control, includes any type motor(s)

ⓟ **L5910** Addition, endoskeletal system, below knee, alignable system

ⓟ **L5920** Addition, endoskeletal system, above knee or hip disarticulation, alignable system

ⓟ **L5925** Addition, endoskeletal system, above knee, knee disarticulation or hip disarticulation, manual lock

L5930 Addition, endoskeletal system, high activity knee control frame

ⓟ **L5940** Addition, endoskeletal system, below knee, ultra-light material (titanium, carbon fiber or equal)

ⓟ **L5950** Addition, endoskeletal system, above knee, ultra-light material (titanium, carbon fiber or equal)

L5960 Addition, endoskeletal system, hip disarticulation, ultra-light material (titanium, carbon fiber or equal)

L5961 Addition, endoskeletal system, polycentric hip joint, pneumatic or hydraulic control, rotation control, with or without flexion and/or extension control

ⓟ **L5962** Addition, endoskeletal system, below knee, flexible protective outer surface covering system

ⓟ **L5964** Addition, endoskeletal system, above knee, flexible protective outer surface covering system

L5966 Addition, endoskeletal system, hip disarticulation, flexible protective outer surface covering system

ⓟ **L5968** Addition to lower limb prosthesis, multiaxial ankle with swing phase active dorsiflexion feature

L5969 Addition, endoskeletal ankle-foot or ankle system, power assist, includes any type motor(s)

L5970 All lower extremity prostheses, foot, external keel, SACH foot

L5971 All lower extremity prosthesis, solid ankle cushion heel (SACH) foot, replacement only

ⓟ **L5972** All lower extremity prostheses, foot, flexible keel

ⓟ **L5973** Endoskeletal ankle foot system, microprocessor controlled feature, dorsiflexion and/or plantar flexion control, includes power source

L5974 All lower extremity prostheses, foot, single axis ankle/foot

L5975 All lower extremity prosthesis, combination single axis ankle and flexible keel foot

L5976 All lower extremity prostheses, energy storing foot (Seattle carbon copy ii or equal)

	L5978	All lower extremity prostheses, foot, multiaxial ankle/foot
	L5979	All lower extremity prosthesis, multi-axial ankle, dynamic response foot, one piece system
Ⓟ	L5980	All lower extremity prostheses, flex foot system
Ⓟ	L5981	All lower extremity prostheses, flex-walk system or equal
	L5982	All exoskeletal lower extremity prostheses, axial rotation unit
	L5984	All endoskeletal lower extremity prosthesis, axial rotation unit, with or without adjustability
	L5985	All endoskeletal lower extremity prostheses, dynamic prosthetic pylon
Ⓟ	L5986	All lower extremity prostheses, multi-axial rotation unit ('MCP' or equal)
Ⓟ	L5987	All lower extremity prosthesis, shank foot system with vertical loading pylon
	L5988	Addition to lower limb prosthesis, vertical shock reducing pylon feature
	L5990	Addition to lower extremity prosthesis, user adjustable heel height
	L5999	Lower extremity prosthesis, not otherwise specified

Upper Limb

NOTE: The procedures in L6000-L6599 are considered as "base" or "basic" procedures and may be modified by listing procedures from the "additions" sections. The base procedures include only standard friction wrist and control cable system unless otherwise specified.

L6000	Partial hand, thumb remaining
L6010	Partial hand, little and/or ring finger remaining
L6020	Partial hand, no finger remaining
L6026	Transcarpal/metacarpal or partial hand disarticulation prosthesis, external power, self-suspended, inner socket with removable forearm section, electrodes and cables, two batteries, charger, myoelectric control of terminal device, excludes terminal device(s)
L6050	Wrist disarticulation, molded socket, flexible elbow hinges, triceps pad
L6055	Wrist disarticulation, molded socket with expandable interface, flexible elbow hinges, triceps pad
L6100	Below elbow, molded socket, flexible elbow hinge, triceps pad
L6110	Below elbow, molded socket, (muenster or northwestern suspension types)
L6120	Below elbow, molded double wall split socket, step-up hinges, half cuff
L6130	Below elbow, molded double wall split socket, stump activated locking hinge, half cuff
L6200	Elbow disarticulation, molded socket, outside locking hinge, forearm
L6205	Elbow disarticulation, molded socket with expandable interface, outside locking hinges, forearm
L6250	Above elbow, molded double wall socket, internal locking elbow, forearm

L6300 Shoulder disarticulation, molded socket, shoulder bulkhead, humeral section, internal locking elbow, forearm

L6310 Shoulder disarticulation, passive restoration (complete prosthesis)

L6320 Shoulder disarticulation, passive restoration (shoulder cap only)

L6350 Interscapular thoracic, molded socket, shoulder bulkhead, humeral section, internal locking elbow, forearm

L6360 Interscapular thoracic, passive restoration (complete prosthesis)

L6370 Interscapular thoracic, passive restoration (shoulder cap only)

L6380 Immediate post surgical or early fitting, application of initial rigid dressing, including fitting alignment and suspension of components, and one cast change, wrist disarticulation or below elbow

L6382 Immediate post surgical or early fitting, application of initial rigid dressing including fitting alignment and suspension of components, and one cast change, elbow disarticulation or above elbow

L6384 Immediate post surgical or early fitting, application of initial rigid dressing including fitting alignment and suspension of components, and one cast change, shoulder disarticulation or interscapular thoracic

L6386 Immediate post surgical or early fitting, each additional cast change and realignment

L6388 Immediate post surgical or early fitting, application of rigid dressing only

L6400 Below elbow, molded socket, endoskeletal system, including soft prosthetic tissue shaping

L6450 Elbow disarticulation, molded socket, endoskeletal system, including soft prosthetic tissue shaping

L6500 Above elbow, molded socket, endoskeletal system, including soft prosthetic tissue shaping

L6550 Shoulder disarticulation, molded socket, endoskeletal system, including soft prosthetic tissue shaping

L6570 Interscapular thoracic, molded socket, endoskeletal system, including soft prosthetic tissue shaping

L6580 Preparatory, wrist disarticulation or below elbow, single wall plastic socket, friction wrist, flexible elbow hinges, figure of eight harness, humeral cuff, Bowden cable control, USMC or equal pylon, no cover, molded to patient model

L6582 Preparatory, wrist disarticulation or below elbow, single wall socket, friction wrist, flexible elbow hinges, figure of eight harness, humeral cuff, Bowden cable control, USMC or equal pylon, no cover, direct formed

L6584 Preparatory, elbow disarticulation or above elbow, single wall plastic socket, friction wrist, locking elbow, figure of eight harness, fair lead cable control, USMC or equal pylon, no cover, molded to patient model

L6586 Preparatory, elbow disarticulation or above elbow, single wall socket, friction wrist, locking elbow, figure of eight harness, fair lead cable control, USMC or equal pylon, no cover, direct formed

| | Not payable by Medicare | | Non-covered by Medicare | | Special coverage instructions | | Carrier judgement | 277 |

L6588   Preparatory, shoulder disarticulation or interscapular thoracic, single wall plastic socket, shoulder joint, locking elbow, friction wrist, chest strap, fair lead cable control, USMC or equal pylon, no cover, molded to patient model

L6590   Preparatory, shoulder disarticulation or interscapular thoracic, single wall socket, shoulder joint, locking elbow, friction wrist, chest strap, fair lead cable control, USMC or equal pylon, no cover, direct formed

Additions - Upper Limb

NOTE: The following procedures, modifications and/or components may be added to other base procedures. The items in this section should reflect the additional complexity of each modification procedure, in addition to base procedure, at the time of the original order.

L6600   Upper extremity additions, polycentric hinge, pair

L6605   Upper extremity additions, single pivot hinge, pair

L6610   Upper extremity additions, flexible metal hinge, pair

L6611   Addition to upper extremity prosthesis, external powered, additional switch, any type

L6615   Upper extremity addition, disconnect locking wrist unit

L6616   Upper extremity addition, additional disconnect insert for locking wrist unit, each

L6620   Upper extremity addition, flexion/extension wrist unit, with or without friction

L6621   Upper extremity prosthesis addition, flexion/extension wrist with or without friction, for use with external powered terminal device

L6623   Upper extremity addition, spring assisted rotational wrist unit with latch release

L6624   Upper extremity addition, flexion/extension and rotation wrist unit

L6625   Upper extremity addition, rotation wrist unit with cable lock

L6628   Upper extremity addition, quick disconnect hook adapter, otto bock or equal

L6629   Upper extremity addition, quick disconnect lamination collar with coupling piece, otto bock or equal

L6630   Upper extremity addition, stainless steel, any wrist

L6632   Upper extremity addition, latex suspension sleeve, each

L6635   Upper extremity addition, lift assist for elbow

L6637   Upper extremity addition, nudge control elbow lock

L6638   Upper extremity addition to prosthesis, electric locking feature, only for use with manually powered elbow

L6640   Upper extremity additions, shoulder abduction joint, pair

L6641   Upper extremity addition, excursion amplifier, pulley type

L6642   Upper extremity addition, excursion amplifier, lever type

L6645   Upper extremity addition, shoulder flexion-abduction joint, each

L6646   Upper extremity addition, shoulder joint, multipositional locking, flexion, adjustable abduction friction control, for use with body powered or external powered system

L6647 Upper extremity addition, shoulder lock mechanism, body powered actuator

L6648 Upper extremity addition, shoulder lock mechanism, external powered actuator

L6650 Upper extremity addition, shoulder universal joint, each

L6655 Upper extremity addition, standard control cable, extra

L6660 Upper extremity addition, heavy duty control cable

L6665 Upper extremity addition, Teflon, or equal, cable lining

L6670 Upper extremity addition, hook to hand, cable adapter

L6672 Upper extremity addition, harness, chest or shoulder, saddle type

L6675 Upper extremity addition, harness, (e.g., figure of eight type), single cable design

L6676 Upper extremity addition, harness, (e.g., figure of eight type), dual cable design

L6677 Upper extremity addition, harness, triple control, simultaneous operation of terminal device and elbow

L6680 Upper extremity addition, test socket, wrist disarticulation or below elbow

L6682 Upper extremity addition, test socket, elbow disarticulation or above elbow

L6684 Upper extremity addition, test socket, shoulder disarticulation or interscapular thoracic

L6686 Upper extremity addition, suction socket

L6687 Upper extremity addition, frame type socket, below elbow or wrist disarticulation

L6688 Upper extremity addition, frame type socket, above elbow or elbow disarticulation

L6689 Upper extremity addition, frame type socket, shoulder disarticulation

L6690 Upper extremity addition, frame type socket, interscapular-thoracic

L6691 Upper extremity addition, removable insert, each

L6692 Upper extremity addition, silicone gel insert or equal, each

L6693 Upper extremity addition, locking elbow, forearm counterbalance

L6694 Addition to upper extremity prosthesis, below elbow/above elbow, custom fabricated from existing mold or prefabricated, socket insert, silicone gel, elastomeric or equal, for use with locking mechanism

L6695 Addition to upper extremity prosthesis, below elbow/above elbow, custom fabricated from existing mold or prefabricated, socket insert, silicone gel, elastomeric or equal, not for use with locking mechanism

L6696 Addition to upper extremity prosthesis, below elbow/above elbow, custom fabricated socket insert for congenital or atypical traumatic amputee, silicone gel, elastomeric or equal, for use with or without locking mechanism, initial only (for other than initial, use code l6694 or l6695)

L6697 Addition to upper extremity prosthesis, below elbow/above elbow, custom fabricated socket insert for other than congenital or atypical traumatic amputee, silicone gel, elastomeric or equal, for use with or without locking mechanism, initial only (for other than initial, use code l6694 or l6695)

L6698 Addition to upper extremity prosthesis, below elbow/above elbow, lock mechanism, excludes socket insert

Terminal Devices Hooks

L6703 Terminal device, passive hand/mitt, any material, any size

L6704 Terminal device, sport/recreational/work attachment, any material, any size

L6706 Terminal device, hook, mechanical, voluntary opening, any material, any size, lined or unlined

L6707 Terminal device, hook, mechanical, voluntary closing, any material, any size, lined or unlined

L6708 Terminal device, hand, mechanical, voluntary opening, any material, any size

L6709 Terminal device, hand, mechanical, voluntary closing, any material, any size

L6711 Terminal device, hook, mechanical, voluntary opening, any material, any size, lined or unlined, pediatric

L6712 Terminal device, hook, mechanical, voluntary closing, any material, any size, lined or unlined, pediatric

L6713 Terminal device, hand, mechanical, voluntary opening, any material, any size, pediatric

L6714 Terminal device, hand, mechanical, voluntary closing, any material, any size, pediatric

L6715 Terminal device, multiple articulating digit, includes motor(s), initial issue or replacement

L6721 Terminal device, hook or hand, heavy duty, mechanical, voluntary opening, any material, any size, lined or unlined

L6722 Terminal device, hook or hand, heavy duty, mechanical, voluntary closing, any material, any size, lined or unlined

L6805 Addition to terminal device, modifier wrist unit

MCM: 2133

L6810 Addition to terminal device, precision pinch device

MCM: 2133

Hands, Gloves and Restoration

L6880 Electric hand, switch or myoelectric controlled, independently articulating digits, any grasp pattern or combination of grasp patterns, includes motor(s)

L6881 Automatic grasp feature, addition to upper limb electric prosthetic terminal device

L6882 Microprocessor control feature, addition to upper limb prosthetic terminal device

MCM: 2133

L6883 Replacement socket, below elbow/wrist disarticulation, molded to patient model, for use with or without external power

L6884 Replacement socket, above elbow/elbow disarticulation, molded to patient model, for use with or without external power

L6885 Replacement socket, shoulder disarticulation/interscapular thoracic, molded to patient model, for use with or without external power

L6890 Addition to upper extremity prosthesis, glove for terminal device, any material, prefabricated, includes fitting and adjustment

L6895 Addition to upper extremity prosthesis, glove for terminal device, any material, custom fabricated

L6900 Hand restoration (casts, shading and measurements included), partial hand, with glove, thumb or one finger remaining

L6905 Hand restoration (casts, shading and measurements included), partial hand, with glove, multiple fingers remaining

L6910 Hand restoration (casts, shading and measurements included), partial hand, with glove, no fingers remaining

L6915 Hand restoration (shading, and measurements included), replacement glove for above

External Power Devices and Batteries

L6920 Wrist disarticulation, external power, self-suspended inner socket, removable forearm shell, otto bock or equal, switch, cables, two batteries and one charger, switch control of terminal device

L6925 Wrist disarticulation, external power, self-suspended inner socket, removable forearm shell, otto bock or equal electrodes, cables, two batteries and one charger, myoelectronic control of terminal device

L6930 Below elbow, external power, self-suspended inner socket, removable forearm shell, otto bock or equal switch, cables, two batteries and one charger, switch control of terminal device

Ⓟ **L6935** Below elbow, external power, self-suspended inner socket, removable forearm shell, otto bock or equal electrodes, cables, two batteries and one charger, myoelectronic control of terminal device

L6940 Elbow disarticulation, external power, molded inner socket, removable humeral shell, outside locking hinges, forearm, otto bock or equal switch, cables, two batteries and one charger, switch control of terminal device

L6945 Elbow disarticulation, external power, molded inner socket, removable humeral shell, outside locking hinges, forearm, otto bock or equal electrodes, cables, two batteries and one charger, myoelectronic control of terminal device

L6950 Above elbow, external power, molded inner socket, removable humeral shell, internal locking elbow, forearm, otto bock or equal switch, cables, two batteries and one charger, switch control of terminal device

L6955 Above elbow, external power, molded inner socket, removable humeral shell, internal locking elbow, forearm, otto bock or equal electrodes, cables, two batteries and one charger, myoelectronic control of terminal device

L6960 Shoulder disarticulation, external power, molded inner socket, removable shoulder shell, shoulder bulkhead, humeral section, mechanical elbow, forearm, otto bock or equal switch, cables, two batteries and one charger, switch control of terminal device

L6965 Shoulder disarticulation, external power, molded inner socket, removable shoulder shell, shoulder bulkhead, humeral section, mechanical elbow, forearm, otto bock or equal electrodes, cables, two batteries and one charger, myoelectronic control of terminal device

L6970 Interscapular-thoracic, external power, molded inner socket, removable shoulder shell, shoulder bulkhead, humeral section, mechanical elbow, forearm, otto bock or equal switch, cables, two batteries and one charger, switch control of terminal device

L6975 Interscapular-thoracic, external power, molded inner socket, removable shoulder shell, shoulder bulkhead, humeral section, mechanical elbow, forearm, otto bock or equal electrodes, cables, two batteries and one charger, myoelectronic control of terminal device

L7007 Electric hand, switch or myoelectric controlled, adult

L7008 Electric hand, switch or myoelectric, controlled, pediatric

L7009 Electric hook, switch or myoelectric controlled, adult

L7040 Prehensile actuator, switch controlled

L7045 Electric hook, switch or myoelectric controlled, pediatric

L7170 Electronic elbow, Hosmer or equal, switch controlled

L7180 Electronic elbow, microprocessor sequential control of elbow and terminal device

L7181 Electronic elbow, microprocessor simultaneous control of elbow and terminal device

L7185 Electronic elbow, adolescent, variety village or equal, switch controlled

L7186 Electronic elbow, child, variety village or equal, switch controlled

L7190 Electronic elbow, adolescent, variety village or equal, myoelectronically controlled

L7191 Electronic elbow, child, variety village or equal, myoelectronically controlled

L7259 Electronic wrist rotator, any type

L7360 Six volt battery, each

L7362 Battery charger, six volt, each

L7364 Twelve volt battery, each

L7366 Battery charger, twelve volt, each

L7367 Lithium ion battery, rechargeable, replacement

L7368 Lithium ion battery charger, replacement only

L7400 Addition to upper extremity prosthesis, below elbow/wrist disarticulation, ultralight material (titanium, carbon fiber or equal)

L7401 Addition to upper extremity prosthesis, above elbow disarticulation, ultralight material (titanium, carbon fiber or equal)

L7402 Addition to upper extremity prosthesis, shoulder disarticulation/interscapular thoracic, ultralight material (titanium, carbon fiber or equal)

L7403 Addition to upper extremity prosthesis, below elbow/wrist disarticulation, acrylic material

• New code   ▲ Revised code   ( ) Deleted code   ⓉTrigger   ⓅPost Trigger DME

L7404   Addition to upper extremity prosthesis, above elbow disarticulation, acrylic material

L7405   Addition to upper extremity prosthesis, shoulder disarticulation/interscapular thoracic, acrylic material

L7499   Upper extremity prosthesis, not otherwise specified

Repairs

L7510   Repair of prosthetic device, repair or replace minor parts

MCM: 2100.4, 2130D, 2133

L7520   Repair prosthetic device, labor component, per 15 minutes

L7600   Prosthetic donning sleeve, any material, each

Statute: 1862(1)(a)

● **L7700**   Gasket or seal, for use with prosthetic socket insert, any type, each

L7900   Male vacuum erection system

Statute: 1834a

L7902   Tension ring, for vacuum erection device, any type, replacement only, each

Statute: 1834a

General - Breast Prostheses

L8000   Breast prosthesis, mastectomy bra, without integrated breast prosthesis form, any size, any type

MCM: 2130A

L8001   Breast prosthesis, mastectomy bra, with integrated breast prosthesis form, unilateral, any size, any type

MCM: 2130A

L8002   Breast prosthesis, mastectomy bra, with integrated breast prosthesis form, bilateral, any size, any type

MCM: 2130A

L8010   Breast prosthesis, mastectomy sleeve

MCM: 2130A

L8015   External breast prosthesis garment, with mastectomy form, post mastectomy

MCM: 2130

L8020   Breast prosthesis, mastectomy form

MCM: 2130A

L8030   Breast prosthesis, silicone or equal, without integral adhesive

MCM: 2130A

L8031   Breast prosthesis, silicone or equal, with integral adhesive

MCM: 2130A

L8032 Nipple prosthesis, reusable, any type, each

L8035 Custom breast prosthesis, post mastectomy, molded to patient model

MCM: 2130

L8039 Breast prosthesis, not otherwise specified

General – Facial Prosthesis

L8040 Nasal prosthesis, provided by a non-physician

L8041 Midfacial prosthesis, provided by a non-physician

L8042 Orbital prosthesis, provided by a non-physician

L8043 Upper facial prosthesis, provided by a non-physician

L8044 Hemi-facial prosthesis, provided by a non-physician

L8045 Auricular prosthesis, provided by a non-physician

L8046 Partial facial prosthesis, provided by a non-physician

L8047 Nasal septal prosthesis, provided by a non-physician

L8048 Unspecified maxillofacial prosthesis, by report, provided by a non-physician

L8049 Repair or modification of maxillofacial prosthesis, labor component, 15 minute increments, provided by a non-physician

General - Trusses

L8300 Truss, single with standard pad

CIM: 70-1, 70-2

MCM: 2133

L8310 Truss, double with standard pads

CIM: 70-170-1, 70-2

MCM: 2133

L8320 Truss, addition to standard pad, water pad

CIM: 70-170-1, 70-2

MCM: 2133

L8330 Truss, addition to standard pad, scrotal pad

CIM: 70-170-1, 70-2

MCM: 2133

Prosthetic Socks

Ⓟ **L8400** Prosthetic sheath, below knee, each

MCM: 2133

L8410 Prosthetic sheath, above knee, each

MCM: 2133

L8415   Prosthetic sheath, upper limb, each

MCM: 2133

L8417   Prosthetic sheath/sock, including a gel cushion layer, below knee or above knee, each

Ⓟ **L8420**   Prosthetic sock, multiple ply, below knee, each

MCM: 2133

Ⓟ **L8430**   Prosthetic sock, multiple ply, above knee, each

MCM: 2133

L8435   Prosthetic sock, multiple ply, upper limb, each

MCM: 2133

Ⓟ **L8440**   Prosthetic shrinker, below knee, each

MCM: 2133

Ⓟ **L8460**   Prosthetic shrinker, above knee, each

MCM: 2133

L8465   Prosthetic shrinker, upper limb, each

MCM: 2133

Ⓟ **L8470**   Prosthetic sock, single ply, fitting, below knee, each

MCM: 2133

L8480   Prosthetic sock, single ply, fitting, above knee, each

MCM: 2133

L8485   Prosthetic sock, single ply, fitting, upper limb, each

MCM: 2133

L8499   Unlisted procedure for miscellaneous prosthetic services

Prosthetic Implants

L8500   Artificial larynx, any type

CIM: 65-5

MCM: 2130,

L8501   Tracheostomy speaking valve

CIM: 65-16

L8505   Artificial larynx replacement battery / accessory, any type

L8507   Tracheo-esophageal voice prosthesis, patient inserted, any type, each

L8509   Tracheo-esophageal voice prosthesis, inserted by a licensed health care provider, any type

L8510   Voice amplifier

CIM: 65-5

L8511 Insert for indwelling tracheoesophageal prosthesis, with or without valve, replacement only, each

L8512 Gelatin capsules or equivalent, for use with tracheoesophageal voice prosthesis, replacement only, per 10

L8513 Cleaning device used with tracheoesophageal voice prosthesis, pipet, brush, or equal, replacement only, each

L8514 Tracheoesophageal puncture dilator, replacement only, each

L8515 Gelatin capsule, application device for use with tracheoesophageal voice prosthesis, each

Integumentary System

L8600 Implantable breast prosthesis, silicone or equal

CIM: 35-47

MCM: 2130,

L8603 Injectable bulking agent, collagen implant, urinary tract, 2.5 ml syringe, includes shipping and necessary supplies

CIM: 65.9

L8604 Injectable bulking agent, dextranomer/hyaluronic acid copolymer implant, urinary tract, 1 ml, includes shipping and necessary supplies

L8605 Injectable bulking agent, dextranomer/hyaluronic acid copolymer implant, anal canal, 1 ml, includes shipping and necessary supplies

L8606 Injectable bulking agent, synthetic implant, urinary tract, 1 ml syringe, includes shipping and necessary supplies

CIM: 65.9

L8607 Injectable bulking agent for vocal cord medialization, 0.1 ml, includes shipping and necessary supplies

MCM: 65.9

Head (Skull, Facial Bones, and Temporomandibular Joint)

L8609 Artificial cornea

L8610 Ocular implant

MCM: 2130

L8612 Aqueous shunt

MCM: 2130

L8613 Ossicula implant

MCM: 2130

L8614 Cochlear device, includes all internal and external components

CIM: 65-14

MCM: 2130,

L8615   Headset/headpiece for use with cochlear implant device, replacement

CIM: 65-14

L8616   Microphone for use with cochlear implant device, replacement

CIM: 65-14

L8617   Transmitting coil for use with cochlear implant device, replacement

CIM: 65-14

▲ **L8618**   Transmitter cable for use with cochlear implant device or auditory osseointegrated device, replacement

CIM: 65-14

L8619   Cochlear implant, external speech processor and controller, integrated system, replacement

CIM: 65-14

L8621   Zinc air battery for use with cochlear implant device and auditory osseointegrated sound processors, replacement, each

L8622   Alkaline battery for use with cochlear implant device, any size, replacement, each

L8623   Lithium ion battery for use with cochlear implant device speech processor, other than ear level, replacement, each

▲ **L8624**   Lithium ion battery for use with cochlear implant or auditory osseointegrated device speech processor, ear level, replacement, each

• **L8625**   External recharging system for battery for use with cochlear implant or auditory osseointegrated device, replacement only, each

CIM: 65-14

L8627   Cochlear implant, external speech processor, component, replacement

CIM: 65-14

L8628   Cochlear implant, external controller component, replacement

CIM: 65-14

L8629   Transmitting coil and cable, integrated, for use with cochlear implant device, replacement

CIM: 65-14

Upper Extremity

L8630   Metacarpophalangeal joint implant

MCM: 2130

L8631   Metacarpal phalangeal joint replacement, two or more pieces, metal (e.g., stainless steel or cobalt chrome), ceramic-like material (e.g., pyrocarbon), for surgical implantation (all sizes, includes entire system)

MCM: 2130

Lower Extremity (Joint: Knee, Ankle, Toe)

L8641   Metatarsal joint implant

MCM: 2130

L8642   Hallux implant

MCM: 2130

Miscellaneous Muscular - Skeletal

L8658   Interphalangeal joint spacer, silicone or equal, each

MCM: 2130

L8659   Interphalangeal finger joint replacement, 2 or more pieces, metal (e.g., stainless steel or cobalt chrome), ceramic-like material (e.g., pyrocarbon) for surgical implantation, any size

MCM: 2130

Cardiovascular System

L8670   Vascular graft material, synthetic, implant

MCM: 2130

L8679   Implantable neurostimulator, pulse generator, any type

CIM: 65-8

L8680   Implantable neurostimulator electrode, each

L8681   Patient programmer (external) for use with implantable programmable neurostimulator pulse generator, replacement only

CIM: 65-8

L8682   Implantable neurostimulator radiofrequency receiver

CIM: 65-8

L8683   Radiofrequency transmitter (external) for use with implantable neurostimulator radiofrequency receiver

CIM: 65-8

L8684   Radiofrequency transmitter (external) for use with implantable sacral root neurostimulator receiver for bowel and bladder management, replacement

CIM: 65-8

L8685   Implantable neurostimulator pulse generator, single array, rechargeable, includes extension

L8686   Implantable neurostimulator pulse generator, single array, non-rechargeable, includes extension

L8687   Implantable neurostimulator pulse generator, dual array, rechargeable, includes extension

L8688   Implantable neurostimulator pulse generator, dual array, non-rechargeable, includes extension

L8689   External recharging system for battery (internal) for use with implantable neurostimulator, replacement only

CIM: 65-8

L8690   Auditory osseointegrated device, includes all internal and external components

▲ L8691   Auditory osseointegrated device, external sound processor, excludes transducer/actuator, replacement only, each

L8692   Auditory osseointegrated device, external sound processor, used without osseointegration, body worn, includes headband or other means of external attachment

Statute: 1862(a)(7)

L8693   Auditory osseointegrated device abutment, any length, replacement only

• L8694   Auditory osseointegrated device, transducer/actuator, replacement only, each

L8695   External recharging system for battery (external) for use with implantable neurostimulator, replacement only

CIM: 65-8

L8696   Antenna (external) for use with implantable diaphragmatic/phrenic nerve stimulation device, replacement, each

Other

L8699   Prosthetic implant, not otherwise specified

L9900   Orthotic and prosthetic supply, accessory, and/or service component of another HCPCS "l" code

Guidelines

In addition to the information presented in the INTRODUCTION, several other items unique to this section are defined or identified here:

1. SUBSECTION INFORMATION: Some of the listed subheadings or subsections have special needs or instructions unique to that section. Where these are indicated, special "notes" will be presented preceding or following the listings. Those subsections within the MEDICAL SERVICES section that have "notes" are as follows:

Subsection	Code Numbers
Office services	M0000-M0009
End-stage renal disease services	M0900-M0999

2. SPECIAL REPORT: A service, material or supply that is rarely provided, unusual, variable or new may require a special report in determining medical appropriateness for reimbursement purposes. Pertinent information should include an adequate definition or description of the nature, extent, and need for the service, material or supply.

3. MODIFIERS: Listed services may be modified under certain circumstances. When appropriate, the modifying circumstance is identified by adding a modifier to the basic procedure code. CPT and HCPCS National Level II modifiers may be used with CPT and HCPCS National Level II procedure codes. Modifiers commonly used with MEDICAL SERVICES are as follows:

-AH   Clinical psychologist

-AJ   Clinical social worker

-CC   Procedure code change (use "CC" when the procedure code submitted was changed either for administrative reasons or because an incorrect code was filed)

-EJ   Subsequent claims for a defined course of therapy (eg., EPO, sodium hyaluronate, infliximab)

-EM   Emergency reserve supply (for ESRD benefit only)

-EP   Service provided as part of Medicaid early periodic screening diagnosis and treatment (EPSDT) program

-FP   Service provided as part of Medicaid family planning program

-Q5   Service furnished by a substitute physician under a reciprocal billing arrangement

-Q6   Service furnished by a locum tenens physician

-QC   Single channel monitoring

-QD   Recording and storage in solid state memory by a digital recorder

-QT   Recording and storage on tape by an analog tape recorder

---

-SF   Second opinion ordered by a professional review organization (PRO) per section 9401, P.L. 99-272 (100 percent reimbursement; no Medicare deductible or coinsurance)

-TC   Technical component. Under certain circumstances, a charge may be made for the technical component alone. Under those circumstances, the technical component charge is identified by adding modifier -TC to the usual procedure number. Technical component charges are institutional charges and are not billed separately by physicians. However, portable x-ray suppliers bill only for the technical component and should use modifier -TC. The charge data from portable x-ray suppliers will then be used to build customary and prevailing profiles.

4. CPT CODE CROSS-REFERENCE: See sections for equivalent CPT code(s) for listings in this section.

Other Medical Services

M0075 Cellular therapy

CIM: 35-5

M0076 Prolotherapy

CIM: 35-13

M0100 Intragastric hypothermia using gastric freezing

CIM: 35-65

M0300 IV chelation therapy (chemical endarterectomy)

CIM: 35-64

M0301 Fabric wrapping of abdominal aneurysm

CIM: 35-34

PATHOLOGY AND LABORATORY

Guidelines

In addition to the information presented in the INTRODUCTION, several other items unique to this section are defined or identified here:

1. SPECIAL REPORT: A service, material or supply that is rarely provided, unusual, variable or new may require a special report in determining medical appropriateness for reimbursement purposes. Pertinent information should include an adequate definition or description of the nature, extent, and need for the service, material or supply.

2. MODIFIERS: Listed services may be modified under certain circumstances. When appropriate, the modifying circumstance is identified by adding a modifier to the basic procedure code. CPT and HCPCS National Level II modifiers may be used with CPT and HCPCS National Level II procedure codes. Modifiers commonly used with PATHOLOGY AND LABORATORY SERVICES are as follows:

   -CC   Procedure code change (use "CC" when the procedure code submitted was changed either for administrative reasons or because an incorrect code was filed)

   -LR   Laboratory round trip

   -TC   Technical component. Under certain circumstances, a charge may be made for the technical component alone. Under these circumstances, the technical component charge is identified by adding the modifier -TC to the usual procedure code. Technical component charges are institutional charges and are not billed separately by physicians. Portable x-ray suppliers bill only for the technical component however, and should use modifier -TC. The charge data from portable x-ray suppliers will then be used to build customary and prevailing profiles.

3. CPT CODE CROSS-REFERENCE: See sections for equivalent CPT code(s) for all listings in this section.

Chemistry and Toxicology Tests

P2028   Cephalin flocculation, blood

CIM: 50-34

P2029   Congo red, blood

CIM: 50-34

P2031   Hair analysis (excluding arsenic)

CIM: 50-24

P2033   Thymol turbidity, blood

CIM: 50-34

P2038   Mucoprotein, blood (seromucoid) (medical necessity procedure)

CIM: 50-34

Pathology Screening Tests

P3000   Screening Papanicolaou smear, cervical or vaginal, up to three smears, by technician under physician supervision

CIM: 50-20

P3001   Screening Papanicolaou smear, cervical or vaginal, up to three smears, requiring interpretation by physician

CIM: 50-20

Miscellaneous Pathology and Laboratory Tests

P7001   Culture, bacterial, urine; quantitative, sensitivity study CPT

P9010   Blood (whole), for transfusion, per unit

MCM: 2455A

P9011   Blood, split unit

MCM: 2455A

P9012   Cryoprecipitate, each unit

MCM: 2455 B

P9016   Red blood cells, leukocytes reduced, each unit

MCM: 2455 B

P9017   Fresh frozen plasma (single donor), frozen within 8 hours of collection, each unit

MCM: 2455 B

P9019   Platelets, each unit

MCM: 2455 B

P9020   Platelet rich plasma, each unit

MCM: 2455 B

P9021   Red blood cells, each unit

MCM: 2455A

P9022   Red blood cells, washed, each unit

MCM: 2455A

P9023   Plasma, pooled multiple donor, solvent/detergent treated, frozen, each unit

MCM: 2455 B

P9031   Platelets, leukocytes reduced, each unit

MCM: 2455

P9032   Platelets, irradiated, each unit

MCM: 2455

P9033   Platelets, leukocytes reduced, irradiated, each unit

MCM: 2455

P9034   Platelets, pheresis, each unit

MCM: 2455

P9035   Platelets, pheresis, leukocytes reduced, each unit

MCM: 2455

P9036   Platelets, pheresis, irradiated, each unit

MCM: 2455

P9037   Platelets, pheresis, leukocytes reduced, irradiated, each unit

MCM: 2455

P9038   Red blood cells, irradiated, each unit

MCM: 2455

P9039   Red blood cells, deglycerolized, each unit

MCM: 2455

P9040   Red blood cells, leukocytes reduced, irradiated, each unit

MCM: 2455

P9041   Infusion, albumin (human), 5%, 50 ml

P9043   Infusion, plasma protein fraction (human), 5%, 50 ml

MCM: 2455B

P9044   Plasma, cryoprecipitate reduced, each unit

MCM: 2455.B

P9045   Infusion, albumin (human), 5%, 250 ml

P9046   Infusion, albumin (human), 25%, 20 ml

P9047   Infusion, albumin (human), 25%, 50 ml

P9048   Infusion, plasma protein fraction (human), 5%, 250 ml

P9050   Granulocytes, pheresis, each unit

P9051   Whole blood or red blood cells, leukocytes reduced, CMV-negative, each unit

Statute: 1833T

P9052   Platelets, HLA-matched leukocytes reduced, apheresis/pheresis, each unit

Statute: 1833T

P9053   Platelets, pheresis, leukocytes reduced, CMV-negative, irradiated, each unit

Statute: 1833T

P9054   Whole blood or red blood cells, leukocytes reduced, frozen, deglycerol, washed, each unit

Statute: 1833T

P9055   Platelets, leukocytes reduced, CMV-negative, apheresis/pheresis, each unit

Not payable
by Medicare   Non-covered
by Medicare   Special coverage
instructions   Carrier
judgement   295

Statute: 1833T

P9056   Whole blood, leukocytes reduced, irradiated, each unit

Statute: 1833T

P9057   Red blood cells, frozen/deglycerolized/washed, leukocytes reduced, irradiated, each unit

Statute: 1833T

P9058   Red blood cells, leukocytes reduced, CMV-negative, irradiated, each unit

Statute: 1833T

P9059   Fresh frozen plasma between 8-24 hours of collection, each unit

Statute: 1833T

P9060   Fresh frozen plasma, donor retested, each unit

Statute: 1833T

P9070   Plasma, pooled multiple donor, pathogen reduced, frozen, each unit

Statute: 1833T

P9071   Plasma (single donor), pathogen reduced, frozen, each unit

MCM: 2455B

Statute: 1833T

(**P9072**   Code deleted December 31, 2017).

● **P9073**   Platelets, pheresis, pathogen-reduced, each unit

MCM: 2455B

● **P9100**   Pathogen(s) test for platelets

CIM: 50-34

P9603   Travel allowance one way in connection with medically necessary laboratory specimen collection drawn from home bound or nursing home bound patient; prorated miles actually travelled

MCM: 51141K

P9604   Travel allowance one way in connection with medically necessary laboratory specimen collection drawn from home bound or nursing home bound patient; prorated trip charge.

MCM: 51141K

P9612   Catheterization for collection of specimen, single patient, all places of service

MCM: 5114.1D

P9615   Catheterization for collection of specimen(s) (multiple patients)

MCM: 51141D

TEMPORARY CODES

Guidelines

In addition to the information presented in the INTRODUCTION, several other items unique to this section are defined or identified here:

1. SUBSECTION INFORMATION: Some of the listed subheadings or subsections have special needs or instructions unique to that section. Where these are indicated, special "notes" will be presented preceding or following the listings. Those subsections within the TEMPORARY CODES section that have "notes" are as follows:

Subsection	Code Numbers
Temporary codes	Q0000-Q9999

2. SPECIAL REPORT: A service, material or supply that is rarely provided, unusual, variable or new may require a special report in determining medical appropriateness for reimbursement purposes. Pertinent information should include an adequate definition or description of the nature, extent, and need for the service, material or supply.

3. MODIFIERS: Listed services may be modified under certain circumstances. When appropriate, the modifying circumstance is identified by adding a modifier to the basic procedure code. CPT and HCPCS National Level II modifiers may be used with CPT and HCPCS National Level II procedure codes. Modifiers commonly used with TEMPORARY CODES are as follows:

-CC Procedure code change (use "CC" when the procedure code submitted was changed either for administrative reasons or because an incorrect code was filed)

-LL Lease/rental (used when DME equipment rental is to be applied against the purchase price)

-LR Laboratory round trip

-QC Single channel monitoring

-QD Recording and storage in solid state memory by a digital recorder

-QE Prescribed amount of oxygen is less than 1 liter per minute (LPM)

-QF Prescribed amount of oxygen exceeds 4 liters per minute (LPM) and portable oxygen is prescribed

-QG Prescribed amount of oxygen is greater than 4 liters per minute (LPM)

-QH Oxygen conserving device is being used with an oxygen delivery system

-QT Recording and storage on tape by an analog tape recorder

-RP Replacement and repair (may be used to indicate replacement of DME, orthotic and prosthetic devices that have been in use for some time. The claim shows the code for the part, followed by the "RP" modifier and the charge for the part.)

-RR   Rental (used when DME is to be rented)

-TC   Technical component. Under certain circumstances, a charge may be made for the technical component alone. Under these circumstances, the technical component charge is identified by adding the modifier -TC to the usual procedure code. Technical component charges are institutional charges and are not billed separately by physicians. Portable x-ray suppliers bill only for the technical component however, and should use modifier -TC. The charge data from portable x-ray suppliers will then be used to build customary and prevailing profiles.

-UE   Used durable medical equipment

4.   CPT CODE CROSS-REFERENCE: See sections for equivalent CPT code(s) for all listings in this section.

Temporary Codes

NOTE: Temporary codes are national codes given by CMS on a temporary basis. The list contains current codes, as well as those which have been superseded by permanent alphanumeric codes as indicated by the cross-reference.

Q0035   Cardiokymography

CIM: 50-50

Q0081   Infusion therapy, using other than chemotherapeutic drugs, per visit

CIM: 60-14

Q0083   Chemotherapy administration by other than infusion technique only (e.g., subcutaneous, intramuscular, push), per visit

Q0084   Chemotherapy administration by infusion technique only, per visit

CIM: 60-14

Q0085   Chemotherapy administration by both infusion technique and other technique(s) (e.g., subcutaneous, intramuscular, push), per visit

Q0091   Screening Papanicolaou smear; obtaining, preparing and conveyance of cervical or vaginal smear to laboratory

CIM: 50-20

Q0092   Set-up portable x-ray equipment

MCM: 2070.4

Q0111   Wet mounts, including preparations of vaginal, cervical or skin specimens

Q0112   All potassium hydroxide (KOH) preparations

Q0113   Pinworm examinations

Q0114   Fern test

Q0115   Post-coital direct, qualitative examinations of vaginal or cervical mucous

Q0138   Injection, ferumoxytol, for treatment of iron deficiency anemia, 1 mg (non-ESRD use)

Q0139   Injection, ferumoxytol, for treatment of iron deficiency anemia, 1 mg (for ESRD on dialysis)

Q0144   Azithromycin dihydrate, oral, capsules/powder, 1 gram

Q0161   Chlorpromazine hydrochloride, 5 mg, oral, approved prescription anti-emetic, for use as a complete therapeutic substitute for an iv anti-emetic at the time of chemotherapy treatment, not to exceed a 48 hour dosage regimen

Q0162   Ondansetron 1 mg, oral, approved prescription anti-emetic, for use as a complete therapeutic substitute for an iv anti-emetic at the time of chemotherapy treatment, not to exceed a 48 hour dosage regimen

Statute: 4557

Q0163   Diphenhydramine hydrochloride, 50 mg, oral, approved prescription anti-emetic, for use as a complete therapeutic substitute for an iv anti-emetic at time of chemotherapy treatment not to exceed a 48 hour dosage regimen

Statute: 4557

Q0164   Prochlorperazine maleate, 5 mg, oral, approved prescription anti-emetic, for use as a complete therapeutic substitute for an iv anti-emetic at the time of chemotherapy treatment, not to exceed a 48 hour dosage regimen

Statute: 4557

Q0166   Granisetron hydrochloride, 1 mg, oral, approved prescription anti-emetic, for use as a complete therapeutic substitute for an iv anti-emetic at the time of chemotherapy treatment, not to exceed a 24 hour dosage regimen

Statute: 4557

Q0167   Dronabinol, 2.5 mg, oral, approved prescription anti-emetic, for use as a complete therapeutic substitute for an iv anti-emetic at the time of chemotherapy treatment, not to exceed a 48 hour dosage regimen

Statute: 4557

Q0169   Promethazine hydrochloride, 12.5 mg, oral, approved prescription anti-emetic, for use as a complete therapeutic substitute for an iv anti-emetic at the time of chemotherapy treatment, not to exceed a 48 hour dosage regimen

Statute: 4557

Q0173   Trimethobenzamide hydrochloride, 250 mg, oral, approved prescription anti-emetic, for use as a complete therapeutic substitute for an iv anti-emetic at the time of chemotherapy treatment, not to exceed a 48 hour dosage regimen

Statute: 4557

Q0174   Thiethylperazine maleate, 10 mg, oral, approved prescription anti-emetic, for use as a complete therapeutic substitute for an iv anti-emetic at the time of chemotherapy treatment, not to exceed a 48 hour dosage regimen

Statute: 4557

Q0175   Perphenazine, 4 mg, oral, approved prescription anti-emetic, for use as a complete therapeutic substitute for an iv anti-emetic at the time of chemotherapy treatment, not to exceed a 48 hour dosage regimen

Statute: 4557

Q0177   Hydroxyzine pamoate, 25 mg, oral, approved prescription anti-emetic, for use as a complete therapeutic substitute for an iv anti-emetic at the time of chemotherapy treatment, not to exceed a 48 hour dosage regimen

Statute: 4557

Q0180   Dolasetron mesylate, 100 mg, oral, approved prescription anti-emetic, for use as a complete therapeutic substitute for an iv anti-emetic at the time of chemotherapy treatment, not to exceed a 24 hour dosage regimen

Statute: 4557

Q0181   Unspecified oral dosage form, approved prescription anti-emetic, for use as a complete therapeutic substitute for a iv anti-emetic at the time of chemotherapy treatment, not to exceed a 48 hour dosage regimen

Statute: 4557

● **Q0477**   Power module patient cable for use with electric or electric/pneumatic ventricular assist device, replacement only

Q0478   Power adapter for use with electric or electric/pneumatic ventricular assist device, vehicle type

Q0479   Power module for use with electric or electric/pneumatic ventricular assist device, replacement only

Q0480   Driver for use with pneumatic ventricular assist device, replacement only

Q0481   Microprocessor control unit for use with electric ventricular assist device, replacement only

Q0482   Microprocessor control unit for use with electric/pneumatic combination ventricular assist device, replacement only

Q0483   Monitor/display module for use with electric ventricular assist device, replacement only

Q0484   Monitor/display module for use with electric or electric/pneumatic ventricular assist device, replacement only

Q0485   Monitor control cable for use with electric ventricular assist device, replacement only

Q0486   Monitor control cable for use with electric/pneumatic ventricular assist device, replacement only

Q0487   Leads (pneumatic/electrical) for use with any type electric/pneumatic ventricular assist device, replacement only

Q0488   Power pack base for use with electric ventricular assist device, replacement only

Q0489   Power pack base for use with electric/pneumatic ventricular assist device, replacement only

Q0490   Emergency power source for use with electric ventricular assist device, replacement only

Q0491   Emergency power source for use with electric/pneumatic ventricular assist device, replacement only

Q0492 Emergency power supply cable for use with electric ventricular assist device, replacement only

Q0493 Emergency power supply cable for use with electric/pneumatic ventricular assist device, replacement only

Q0494 Emergency hand pump for use with electric or electric/pneumatic ventricular assist device, replacement only

Q0495 Battery/power pack charger for use with electric or electric/pneumatic ventricular assist device, replacement only

Q0496 Battery, other than lithium-ion, for use with electric or electric/pneumatic ventricular assist device, replacement only

Q0497 Battery clips for use with electric or electric/pneumatic ventricular assist device, replacement only

Q0498 Holster for use with electric or electric/pneumatic ventricular assist device, replacement only

Q0499 Belt/vest/bag for use to carry external peripheral components of any type ventricular assist device, replacement only

Q0500 Filters for use with electric or electric/pneumatic ventricular assist device, replacement only

Q0501 Shower cover for use with electric or electric/pneumatic ventricular assist device, replacement only

Q0502 Mobility cart for pneumatic ventricular assist device, replacement only

Q0503 Battery for pneumatic ventricular assist device, replacement only, each

Q0504 Power adapter for pneumatic ventricular assist device, replacement only, vehicle type

Q0506 Battery, lithium-ion, for use with electric or electric/pneumatic ventricular assist device, replacement only

Q0507 Miscellaneous supply or accessory for use with an external ventricular assist device

Q0508 Miscellaneous supply or accessory for use with an implanted ventricular assist device

Q0509 Miscellaneous supply or accessory for use with any implanted ventricular assist device for which payment was not made under Medicare part a

Q0510 Pharmacy supply fee for initial immunosuppressive drug(s), first month following transplant

Q0511 Pharmacy supply fee for oral anti-cancer, oral anti-emetic or immunosuppressive drug(s); for the first prescription in a 30-day period

Q0512 Pharmacy supply fee for oral anti-cancer, oral anti-emetic or immunosuppressive drug(s); for a subsequent prescription in a 30-day period

Ⓟ **Q0513** Pharmacy dispensing fee for inhalation drug(s); per 30 days

Ⓟ **Q0514** Pharmacy dispensing fee for inhalation drug(s); per 90 days

Q0515 Injection, sermorelin acetate, 1 microgram

MCM: 2049

Q1004 New technology intraocular lens category 4 as defined in federal register notice

Q1005 New technology intraocular lens category 5 as defined in federal register notice

Q2004 Irrigation solution for treatment of bladder calculi, for example Renacidin, per 500 ml

MCM: 2049

Statute: 1861S2B

Q2009 Injection, fosphenytoin, 50 mg phenytoin equivalent

MCM: 2049

Statute: 1861S2B

Q2017 Injection, teniposide, 50 mg

MCM: 2049

Statute: 1861S2B

Q2026 Injection, Radiesse, 0.1 ml

Q2028 Injection, Sculptra, 0.5 mg

Q2034 Influenza virus vaccine, split virus, for intramuscular use (Agriflu)

MCM: 2049.4

Q2035 Influenza virus vaccine, split virus, when administered to individuals 3 years of age and older, for intramuscular use (Afluria)

MCM: 2049.4

Q2036 Influenza virus vaccine, split virus, when administered to individuals 3 years of age and older, for intramuscular use (FluLaval)

MCM: 2049.4

Q2037 Influenza virus vaccine, split virus, when administered to individuals 3 years of age and older, for intramuscular use (Fluvirin)

MCM: 2049.4

Q2038 Influenza virus vaccine, split virus, when administered to individuals 3 years of age and older, for intramuscular use (Fluzone)

MCM: 2049.4

Q2039 Influenza virus vaccine, not otherwise specified

MCM: 2049.4

• **Q2040** Tisagenlecleucel, up to 250 million car-positive viable t cells, including leukapheresis and dose preparation procedures, per infusion

Q2043 Sipuleucel-t, minimum of 50 million autologous cd54+ cells activated with pap-gm-csf, including leukapheresis and all other preparatory procedures, per infusion

Q2049 Injection, doxorubicin hydrochloride, liposomal, imported Lipidox, 10 mg

Q2050 Injection, doxorubicin hydrochloride, liposomal, not otherwise specified, 10 mg

MCM: 2049.4

Q2052   Services, supplies and accessories used in the home under the Medicare intravenous immune globulin (IVIG) demonstration

Q3001   Radioelements for brachytherapy, any type, each

MCM: 15022

Q3014   Telehealth originating site facility fee

Q3027   Injection, interferon beta-1a, 1 mcg for intramuscular use

MCM: 2049

Q3028   Injection, interferon beta-1a, 1 mcg for subcutaneous use

Q3031   Collagen skin test

CIM: 65-9

Q4001   Casting supplies, body cast adult, with or without head, plaster

Q4002   Cast supplies, body cast adult, with or without head, fiberglass

Q4003   Cast supplies, shoulder cast, adult (11 years +), plaster

Q4004   Cast supplies, shoulder cast, adult (11 years +), fiberglass

Q4005   Cast supplies, long arm cast, adult (11 years +), plaster

Q4006   Cast supplies, long arm cast, adult (11 years +), fiberglass

Q4007   Cast supplies, long arm cast, pediatric (0-10 years), plaster

Q4008   Cast supplies, long arm cast, pediatric (0-10 years), fiberglass

Q4009   Cast supplies, short arm cast, adult (11 years +), plaster

Q4010   Cast supplies, short arm cast, adult (11 years +), fiberglass

Q4011   Cast supplies, short arm cast, pediatric (0-10 years), plaster

Q4012   Cast supplies, short arm cast, pediatric (0-10 years), fiberglass

Q4013   Cast supplies, gauntlet cast (includes lower forearm and hand), adult (11 years +), plaster

Q4014   Cast supplies, gauntlet cast (includes lower forearm and hand), adult (11 years +), fiberglass

Q4015   Cast supplies, gauntlet cast (includes lower forearm and hand), pediatric (0-10 years), plaster

Q4016   Cast supplies, gauntlet cast (includes lower forearm and hand), pediatric (0-10 years), fiberglass

Q4017   Cast supplies, long arm splint, adult (11 years +), plaster

Q4018   Cast supplies, long arm splint, adult (11 years +), fiberglass

Q4019   Cast supplies, long arm splint, pediatric (0-10 years), plaster

Q4020   Cast supplies, long arm splint, pediatric (0-10 years), fiberglass

Q4021   Cast supplies, short arm splint, adult (11 years +), plaster

Q4022 Cast supplies, short arm splint, adult (11 years +), fiberglass

Q4023 Cast supplies, short arm splint, pediatric (0-10 years), plaster

Q4024 Cast supplies, short arm splint, pediatric (0-10 years), fiberglass

Q4025 Cast supplies, hip spica (one or both legs), adult (11 years +), plaster

Q4026 Cast supplies, hip spica (one or both legs), adult (11 years +), fiberglass

Q4027 Cast supplies, hip spica (one or both legs), pediatric (0-10 years), plaster

Q4028 Cast supplies, hip spica (one or both legs), pediatric (0-10 years), fiberglass

Q4029 Cast supplies, long leg cast, adult (11 years +), plaster

Q4030 Cast supplies, long leg cast, adult (11 years +), fiberglass

Q4031 Cast supplies, long leg cast, pediatric (0-10 years), plaster

Q4032 Cast supplies, long leg cast, pediatric (0-10 years), fiberglass

Q4033 Cast supplies, long leg cylinder cast, adult (11 years +), plaster

Q4034 Cast supplies, long leg cylinder cast, adult (11 years +), fiberglass

Q4035 Cast supplies, long leg cylinder cast, pediatric (0-10 years), plaster

Q4036 Cast supplies, long leg cylinder cast, pediatric (0-10 years), fiberglass

Q4037 Cast supplies, short leg cast, adult (11 years +), plaster

Q4038 Cast supplies, short leg cast, adult (11 years +), fiberglass

Q4039 Cast supplies, short leg cast, pediatric (0-10 years), plaster

Q4040 Cast supplies, short leg cast, pediatric (0-10 years), fiberglass

Q4041 Cast supplies, long leg splint, adult (11 years +), plaster

Q4042 Cast supplies, long leg splint, adult (11 years +), fiberglass

Q4043 Cast supplies, long leg splint, pediatric (0-10 years), plaster

Q4044 Cast supplies, long leg splint, pediatric (0-10 years), fiberglass

Q4045 Cast supplies, short leg splint, adult (11 years +), plaster

Q4046 Cast supplies, short leg splint, adult (11 years +), fiberglass

Q4047 Cast supplies, short leg splint, pediatric (0-10 years), plaster

Q4048 Cast supplies, short leg splint, pediatric (0-10 years), fiberglass

Q4049 Finger splint, static

Q4050 Cast supplies, for unlisted types and materials of casts

Q4051 Splint supplies, miscellaneous (includes thermoplastics, strapping, fasteners, padding and other supplies)

Q4074 Iloprost, inhalation solution,-approved final product, non-compounded, administered through DME, unit dose form, up to 20 micrograms

• New code ▲ Revised code ( ) Deleted code ⓣTrigger ⓟ Post Trigger DME

Injection Codes for EPO

Q4081   Injection, epoetin alfa, 100 units (for ESRD on dialysis)

MCM: 4273.1

Q4082   Drug or biological, not otherwise classified, part b drug competitive acquisition program (cap)

Q4100   Skin substitute, not otherwise specified

Q4101   Apligraf, per square centimeter

Q4102   Oasis wound matrix, per square centimeter

Q4103   Oasis burn matrix, per square centimeter

Q4104   Integra bilayer matrix wound dressing (BMWD), per square centimeter

Q4105   Integra dermal regeneration template (DRT) or Integra omnigraft dermal regeneration matrix, per square centimeter

Q4106   Dermagraft, per square centimeter

Q4107   Graftjacket, per square centimeter

Q4108   Integra matrix, per square centimeter

Q4110   Primatrix, per square centimeter

Q4111   Gammagraft, per square centimeter

Q4112   Cymetra, injectable, 1 cc

Q4113   Graftjacket xpress, injectable, 1 cc

Q4114   Integra flowable wound matrix, injectable, 1 cc

Q4115   Alloskin, per square centimeter

Q4116   AlloDerm, per square centimeter

Q4117   Hyalomatrix, per square centimeter

Q4118   Matristem micromatrix, 1 mg

(**Q4119**   Code deleted December 31, 2016).

(**Q4120**   Code deleted December 31, 2016).

Q4121   Theraskin, per square centimeter

Q4122   Dermacell, per square centimeter

Q4123   Alloskin rt, per square centimeter

Q4124   Oasis ultra tri-layer wound matrix, per square centimeter

Q4125   Arthroflex, per square centimeter

Q4126   Memoderm, dermaspan, TranZgraft or integuply, per square centimeter

Q4127   Talymed, per square centimeter

Q4128   Flex hd, allopatch hd, or matrix hd, per square centimeter

(**Q4129**   Code deleted December 31, 2016).

| | Not payable by Medicare | | Non-covered by Medicare | | Special coverage instructions | | Carrier judgement | 305 |

	Q4130	Strattice tm, per square centimeter
	Q4131	Epifix or epicord, per square centimeter
▲	**Q4132**	Grafix core and grafixpl core, per square centimeter
▲	**Q4133**	Grafix prime and grafixpl prime, per square centimeter
	Q4134	Hmatrix, per square centimeter
	Q4135	Mediskin, per square centimeter
	Q4136	Ez-derm, per square centimeter
	Q4137	Amnioexcel or biodexcel, per square centimeter
	Q4138	Biodefense dryflex, per square centimeter
	Q4139	Amniomatrix or Biomatrix, injectable, 1 cc
	Q4140	Biodefense, per square centimeter
	Q4141	Alloskin ac, per square centimeter
	Q4142	Xcm biologic tissue matrix, per square centimeter
	Q4143	Repriza, per square centimeter
	Q4145	Epifix, injectable, 1 mg
	Q4146	Tensix, per square centimeter
	Q4147	Architect, architect px, or architect fx, extracellular matrix, per square centimeter
▲	**Q4148**	Neox cord 1k, Neox cord rt, or clarix cord 1k, per square centimeter
	Q4149	Excellagen, 0.1 cc
	Q4150	Allowrap DS or dry, per square centimeter
	Q4151	Amnioband or guardian, per square centimeter
	Q4152	Dermapure, per square centimeter
	Q4153	Dermavest and Plurivest, per square centimeter
	Q4154	Biovance, per square centimeter
	Q4155	Neoxflo or Clarixflo, 1 mg
▲	**Q4156**	Neox 100 or clarix 100, per square centimeter
	Q4157	Revitalon, per square centimeter
▲	**Q4158**	Kerecis omega3, per square centimeter
	Q4159	Affinity, per square centimeter
	Q4160	Nushield, per square centimeter
	Q4161	Bio-connekt wound matrix, per square centimeter
▲	**Q4162**	Woundex flow, BioSkin flow, 0.5 cc
▲	**Q4163**	Woundex, BioSkin, per square centimeter
	Q4164	Helicoll, per square centimeter

Q4165	Keramatrix, per square centimeter
Q4166	Cytal, per square centimeter
Q4167	Truskin, per square centimeter
Q4168	Amnioband, 1 mg
Q4169	Artacent wound, per square centimeter
Q4170	Cygnus, per square centimeter
Q4171	Interfyl, 1 mg
Q4172	PuraPly or PuraPly am, per square centimeter
Q4173	Palingen or Palingen xplus, per square centimeter
Q4174	Palingen or Promatrx, 0.36 mg per 0.25 cc
Q4175	Miroderm, per square centimeter
● Q4176	Neopatch, per square centimeter
● Q4177	Floweramnioflo, 0.1 cc
● Q4178	Floweramniopatch, per square centimeter
● Q4179	Flowerderm, per square centimeter
● Q4180	Revita, per square centimeter
● Q4181	Amnio wound, per square centimeter
● Q4182	TransCyte, per square centimeter

Hospice or Home Health Care

Q5001	Hospice or home health care provided in patient's home/residence
Q5002	Hospice or home health care provided in assisted living facility
Q5003	Hospice care provided in nursing long term care facility (LTC) or non-skilled nursing facility (NF)
Q5004	Hospice care provided in skilled nursing facility (snf)
Q5005	Hospice care provided in inpatient hospital
Q5006	Hospice care provided in inpatient hospice facility
Q5007	Hospice care provided in long term care facility
Q5008	Hospice care provided in inpatient psychiatric facility
Q5009	Hospice or home health care provided in place not otherwise specified (nos)
Q5010	Hospice home care provided in a hospice facility

Miscellaneous and Osmolar Contrast Material

| Q5101 | Injection, filgrastim (g-csf), biosimilar, 1 microgram |
| Q5102 | Injection, infliximab, biosimilar, 10 mg |

MCM: 2049

Q9950 Injection, sulfur hexafluoride lipid microspheres, per ml

Q9951 Low osmolar contrast material, 400 or greater mg/ml iodine concentration, per ml
MCM: 15022

Q9953 Injection, iron-based magnetic resonance contrast agent, per ml
MCM: 15022

Q9954 Oral magnetic resonance contrast agent, per 100 ml
MCM: 15022

Q9955 Injection, perflexane lipid microspheres, per ml

Q9956 Injection, octafluoropropane microspheres, per ml

Q9957 Injection, perflutren lipid microspheres, per ml

Q9958 High osmolar contrast material, up to 149 mg/ml iodine concentration, per ml
MCM: 15022

Q9959 High osmolar contrast material, 150-199 mg/ml iodine concentration, per ml
MCM: 15022

Q9960 High osmolar contrast material, 200-249 mg/ml iodine concentration, per ml
MCM: 15022

Q9961 High osmolar contrast material, 250-299 mg/ml iodine concentration, per ml
MCM: 15022

Q9962 High osmolar contrast material, 300-349 mg/ml iodine concentration, per ml
MCM: 15022

Q9963 High osmolar contrast material, 350-399 mg/ml iodine concentration, per ml
MCM: 15022

Q9964 High osmolar contrast material, 400 or greater mg/ml iodine concentration, per ml
MCM: 15022

Q9965 Low osmolar contrast material, 100-199 mg/ml iodine concentration, per ml
MCM: 15022

Q9966 Low osmolar contrast material, 200-299 mg/ml iodine concentration, per ml
MCM: 15022

Q9967 Low osmolar contrast material, 300-399 mg/ml iodine concentration, per ml
MCM: 15022

Q9968 Injection, non-radioactive, non-contrast, visualization adjunct (e.g., methylene blue, isosulfan blue), 1 mg

Q9969 Tc-99m from non-highly enriched uranium source, full cost recovery add-on, per study dose

(**Q9980**   Code deleted December 31, 2016).

(**Q9981**   Code deleted December 31, 2016). Use J8670.

  Q9982   Flutemetamol f18, diagnostic, per study dose, up to 5 millicuries

  Q9983   Florbetaben f18, diagnostic, per study dose, up to 8.1 millicuries

(**Q9984**   Code deleted December 31, 2017). Use J7296.

(**Q9985**   Code deleted December 31, 2017).

(**Q9986**   Code deleted December 31, 2017).

(**Q9987**   Code deleted December 31, 2017).

(**Q9988**   Code deleted December 31, 2017). Use 1833T.

(**Q9989**   Code deleted December 31, 2017).

Not payable
by Medicare

Non-covered
by Medicare

Special coverage
instructions

Carrier
judgement

309

DIAGNOSTIC RADIOLOGY SERVICES

Guidelines

In addition to the information presented in the INTRODUCTION, several other items unique to this section are defined or identified here:

1. SPECIAL REPORT: A service, material or supply that is rarely provided, unusual, variable or new may require a special report in determining medical appropriateness for reimbursement purposes. Pertinent information should include an adequate definition or description of the nature, extent, and need for the service, material or supply.

2. MODIFIERS: Listed services may be modified under certain circumstances. When appropriate, the modifying circumstance is identified by adding a modifier to the basic procedure code. CPT and HCPCS National Level II modifiers may be used with CPT and HCPCS National Level II procedure codes. Modifiers commonly used with DIAGNOSTIC RADIOLOGY SERVICES are as follows:

   -CC Procedure code change (use "CC" when the procedure code submitted was changed either for administrative reasons or because an incorrect code was filed)

   -LT Left side (used to identify procedures performed on the left side of the body)

   -RT Right side (used to identify procedures performed on the right side of the body)

   -TC Technical component. Under certain circumstances, a charge may be made for the technical component alone. Under those circumstances, the technical component charge is identified by adding modifier -TC to the usual procedure number. Technical component charges are institutional charges and are not billed separately by physicians. However, portable x-ray suppliers bill only for the technical component and should use modifier -TC. The charge data from portable x-ray suppliers will then be used to build customary and prevailing profiles.

3. CPT CODE CROSS-REFERENCE: There are no equivalent CPT codes for procedures listed in this section.

Diagnostic Radiology Services

R0070 Transportation of portable x-ray equipment and personnel to home or nursing home, per trip to facility or location, one patient seen

MCM: 2070.4, 5244.B

R0075 Transportation of portable x-ray equipment and personnel to home or nursing home, per trip to facility or location, more than one patient seen

MCM: 2070.4, 5244.B

R0076 Transportation of portable ekg to facility or location, per patient

CIM: 50-15

MCM: 2070.1, 2070.4

PRIVATE PAYER CODES

Guidelines

HCPCS "S" codes are temporary national codes established by the private payers for private payer use. Prior to using "S" codes on insurance claims to private payers, you should consult with the payer to confirm that the "S" codes are acceptable. "S" codes are not valid for Medicare use.

In addition to the information presented in the INTRODUCTION, several other items unique to this section are defined or identified here.

1. SPECIAL REPORT: A service, material or supply that is rarely provided, unusual, variable or new may require a special report in determining medical appropriateness for reimbursement purposes. Pertinent information should include an adequate definition or description of the nature, extent, and need for the service, material or supply.

2. MODIFIERS: Listed services may be modified under certain circumstances. When appropriate, the modifying circumstance is identified by adding a modifier to the basic procedure code. CPT and HCPCS National Level II modifiers may be used with CPT and HCPCS National Level II procedure codes.

Private Payer Codes

S0012	Butorphanol tartrate, nasal spray, 25 mg
S0014	Tacrine hydrochloride, 10 mg
S0017	Injection, aminocaproic acid, 5 grams
S0020	Injection, Bupivicaine hydrochloride, 30 ml
S0021	Injection, cefoperazone sodium, 1 gram
S0023	Injection, cimetidine hydrochloride, 300 mg
S0028	Injection, famotidine, 20 mg
S0030	Injection, metronidazole, 500 mg
S0032	Injection, nafcillin sodium, 2 grams
S0034	Injection, ofloxacin, 400 mg
S0039	Injection, sulfamethoxazole and trimethoprim, 10 ml
S0040	Injection, ticarcillin disodium and clavulanate potassium, 3.1 grams
S0073	Injection, aztreonam, 500 mg
S0074	Injection, cefotetan disodium, 500 mg
S0077	Injection, clindamycin phosphate, 300 mg
S0078	Injection, fosphenytoin sodium, 750 mg
S0080	Injection, pentamidine isethionate, 300 mg
S0081	Injection, piperacillin sodium, 500 mg
S0088	Imatinib, 100 mg

S0090	Sildenafil citrate, 25 mg
S0091	Granisetron hydrochloride, 1 mg (for circumstances falling under the Medicare statute, use Q0166)
S0092	Injection, hydromorphone hydrochloride, 250 mg (loading dose for infusion pump)
S0093	Injection, morphine sulfate, 500 mg (loading dose for infusion pump)
S0104	Zidovudine, oral, 100 mg
S0106	Bupropion HCL sustained release tablet, 150 mg, per bottle of 60 tablets
S0108	Mercaptopurine, oral, 50 mg
S0109	Methadone, oral, 5 mg
S0117	Tretinoin, topical, 5 grams
S0119	Ondansetron, oral, 4 mg (for circumstances falling under the Medicare statute, use HCPCS q code)
S0122	Injection, menotropins, 75 iu
S0126	Injection, follitropin alfa, 75 iu
S0128	Injection, follitropin beta, 75 iu
S0132	Injection, ganirelix acetate, 250 mcg
S0136	Clozapine, 25 mg
S0137	Didanosine (ddi), 25 mg
S0138	Finasteride, 5 mg
S0139	Minoxidil, 10 mg
S0140	Saquinavir, 200 mg
S0142	Colistimethate sodium, inhalation solution administered through DME, concentrated form, per mg
S0145	Injection, pegylated interferon alfa-2a, 180 mcg per ml
S0148	Injection, pegylated interferon alfa-2b, 10 mcg
S0155	Sterile dilutant for epoprostenol, 50 ml
S0156	Exemestane, 25 mg
S0157	Becaplermin gel 0.01%, 0.5 gm
S0160	Dextroamphetamine sulfate, 5 mg
S0164	Injection, pantoprazole sodium, 40 mg
S0166	Injection, olanzapine, 2.5 mg
S0169	Calcitrol, 0.25 microgram
S0170	Anastrozole, oral, 1 mg
S0171	Injection, bumetanide, 0.5 mg
S0172	Chlorambucil, oral, 2 mg

S0174   Dolasetron mesylate, oral 50 mg (for circumstances falling under the Medicare statute, use Q0180)

S0175   Flutamide, oral, 125 mg

S0176   Hydroxyurea, oral, 500 mg

S0177   Levamisole hydrochloride, oral, 50 mg

S0178   Lomustine, oral, 10 mg

S0179   Megestrol acetate, oral, 20 mg

S0182   Procarbazine hydrochloride, oral, 50 mg

S0183   Prochlorperazine maleate, oral, 5 mg (for circumstances falling under the Medicare statute, use Q0164)

S0187   Tamoxifen citrate, oral, 10 mg

S0189   Testosterone pellet, 75 mg

S0190   Mifepristone, oral, 200 mg

S0191   Misoprostol, oral, 200 mcg

S0194   Dialysis/stress vitamin supplement, oral, 100 capsules

S0197   Prenatal vitamins, 30-day supply

S0199   Medically induced abortion by oral ingestion of medication including all associated services and supplies (e.g., patient counseling, office visits, confirmation of pregnancy by hcg, ultrasound to confirm duration of pregnancy, ultrasound to confirm completion of abortion) except drugs

S0201   Partial hospitalization services, less than 24 hours, per diem

S0207   Paramedic intercept, non-hospital-based ALS service (non-voluntary), non-transport

S0208   Paramedic intercept, hospital-based ALS service (non-voluntary), non-transport

S0209   Wheelchair van, mileage, per mile

S0215   Non-emergency transportation; mileage, per mile

S0220   Medical conference by a physician with interdisciplinary team of health professionals or representatives of community agencies to coordinate activities of patient care (patient is present); approximately 30 minutes

S0221   Medical conference by a physician with interdisciplinary team of health professionals or representatives of community agencies to coordinate activities of patient care (patient is present); approximately 60 minutes

S0250   Comprehensive geriatric assessment and treatment planning performed by assessment team

S0255   Hospice referral visit (advising patient and family of care options) performed by nurse, social worker, or other designated staff

S0257   Counseling and discussion regarding advance directives or end of life care planning and decisions, with patient and/or surrogate (list separately in addition to code for appropriate evaluation and management service)

S0260   History and physical (outpatient or office) related to surgical procedure (list separately in addition to code for appropriate evaluation and management service)

S0265   Genetic counseling, under physician supervision, each 15 minutes

S0270   Physician management of patient home care, standard monthly case rate (per 30 days)

S0271   Physician management of patient home care, hospice monthly case rate (per 30 days)

S0272   Physician management of patient home care, episodic care monthly case rate (per 30 days)

S0273   Physician visit at member's home, outside of a capitation arrangement

S0274   Nurse practitioner visit at member's home, outside of a capitation arrangement

S0280   Medical home program, comprehensive care coordination and planning, initial plan

S0281   Medical home program, comprehensive care coordination and planning, maintenance of plan

S0302   Completed early periodic screening diagnosis and treatment (EPSDT) service (list in addition to code for appropriate evaluation and management service)

S0310   Hospitalist services (list separately in addition to code for appropriate evaluation and management service)

S0311   Comprehensive management and care coordination for advanced illness, per calendar month

S0315   Disease management program; initial assessment and initiation of the program

S0316   Disease management program, follow-up/reassessment

S0317   Disease management program; per diem

S0320   Telephone calls by a registered nurse to a disease management program member for monitoring purposes; per month

S0340   Lifestyle modification program for management of coronary artery disease, including all supportive services; first quarter / stage

S0341   Lifestyle modification program for management of coronary artery disease, including all supportive services; second or third quarter / stage

S0342   Lifestyle modification program for management of coronary artery disease, including all supportive services; fourth quarter / stage

S0353   Treatment planning and care coordination management for cancer, initial treatment

S0354   Treatment planning and care coordination management for cancer, established patient with a change of regimen

S0390   Routine foot care; removal and/or trimming of corns, calluses and/or nails and preventive maintenance in specific medical conditions (e.g., diabetes), per visit

S0395   Impression casting of a foot performed by a practitioner other than the manufacturer of the orthotic

S0400   Global fee for extracorporeal shock wave lithotripsy treatment of kidney stone(s)

S0500   Disposable contact lens, per lens

S0504 Single vision prescription lens (safety, athletic, or sunglass), per lens

S0506 Bifocal vision prescription lens (safety, athletic, or sunglass), per lens

S0508 Trifocal vision prescription lens (safety, athletic, or sunglass), per lens

S0510 Non-prescription lens (safety, athletic, or sunglass), per lens

S0512 Daily wear specialty contact lens, per lens

S0514 Color contact lens, per lens

S0515 Scleral lens, liquid bandage device, per lens

S0516 Safety eyeglass frames

S0518 Sunglasses frames

S0580 Polycarbonate lens (list this code in addition to the basic code for the lens)

S0581 Nonstandard lens (list this code in addition to the basic code for the lens)

S0590 Integral lens service, miscellaneous services reported separately

S0592 Comprehensive contact lens evaluation

S0595 Dispensing new spectacle lenses for patient supplied frame

S0596 Phakic intraocular lens for correction of refractive error

S0601 Screening proctoscopy

S0610 Annual gynecological examination, new patient

S0612 Annual gynecological examination, established patient

S0613 Annual gynecological examination; clinical breast examination without pelvic evaluation

S0618 Audiometry for hearing aid evaluation to determine the level and degree of hearing loss

S0620 Routine ophthalmological examination including refraction; new patient

S0621 Routine ophthalmological examination including refraction; established patient

S0622 Physical exam for college, new or established patient (list separately in addition to appropriate evaluation and management code)

S0630 Removal of sutures; by a physician other than the physician who originally closed the wound

S0800 Laser in situ keratomileusis (LASIK)

S0810 Photorefractive keratectomy (PRK)

S0812 Phototherapeutic keratectomy (ptk)

S1001 Deluxe item, patient aware (list in addition to code for basic item)

S1002 Customized item (list in addition to code for basic item)

S1015 IV tubing extension set

S1016 Non-pvc (polyvinyl chloride) intravenous administration set, for use with drugs that are not stable in pvc e.g., paclitaxel

S1030 Continuous noninvasive glucose monitoring device, purchase (for physician interpretation of data, use CPT code)

S1031 Continuous noninvasive glucose monitoring device, rental, including sensor, sensor replacement, and download to monitor (for physician interpretation of data, use CPT code)

S1034 Artificial pancreas device system (e.g., low glucose suspend (LGS) feature) including continuous glucose monitor, blood glucose device, insulin pump and computer algorithm that communicates with all of the devices

S1035 Sensor; invasive (e.g., subcutaneous), disposable, for use with artificial pancreas device system

S1036 Transmitter; external, for use with artificial pancreas device system

S1037 Receiver (monitor); external, for use with artificial pancreas device system

S1040 Cranial remolding orthosis, pediatric, rigid, with soft interface material, custom fabricated, includes fitting and adjustment(s)

S1090 Mometasone furoate sinus implant, 370 micrograms

S2053 Transplantation of small intestine and liver allografts

S2054 Transplantation of multivisceral organs

S2055 Harvesting of donor multivisceral organs, with preparation and maintenance of allografts; from cadaver donor

S2060 Lobar lung transplantation

S2061 Donor lobectomy (lung) for transplantation, living donor

S2065 Simultaneous pancreas kidney transplantation

S2066 Breast reconstruction with gluteal artery perforator (gap) flap, including harvesting of the flap, microvascular transfer, closure of donor site and shaping the flap into a breast, unilateral

S2067 Breast reconstruction of a single breast with "stacked" deep inferior epigastric perforator (diep) flap(s) and/or gluteal artery perforator (gap) flap(s), including harvesting of the flap(s), microvascular transfer, closure of donor site(s) and shaping the flap into a breast, unilateral

S2068 Breast reconstruction with deep inferior epigastric perforator (diep) flap or superficial inferior epigastric artery (siea) flap, including harvesting of the flap, microvascular transfer, closure of donor site and shaping the flap into a breast, unilateral

S2070 Cystourethroscopy, with ureteroscopy and/or pyeloscopy; with endoscopic laser treatment of ureteral calculi (includes ureteral catheterization)

S2079 Laparoscopic esophagomyotomy (Heller type)

S2080 Laser-assisted uvulopalatoplasty (LAUP)

S2083 Adjustment of gastric band diameter via subcutaneous port by injection or aspiration of saline

S2095 Transcatheter occlusion or embolization for tumor destruction, percutaneous, any method, using yttrium-90 microspheres

• New code ▲ Revised code ( ) Deleted code ⓉTrigger ⓅPost Trigger DME

S2102	Islet cell tissue transplant from pancreas; allogeneic
S2103	Adrenal tissue transplant to brain
S2107	Adoptive immunotherapy i.e. development of specific anti-tumor reactivity (e.g., tumor-infiltrating lymphocyte therapy) per course of treatment
S2112	Arthroscopy, knee, surgical for harvesting of cartilage (chondrocyte cells)
S2115	Osteotomy, periacetabular, with internal fixation
S2117	Arthroereisis, subtalar
S2118	Metal-on-metal total hip resurfacing, including acetabular and femoral components
S2120	Low density lipoprotein (LDL) apheresis using heparin-induced extracorporeal LDL precipitation
S2140	Cord blood harvesting for transplantation, allogeneic
S2142	Cord blood-derived stem-cell transplantation, allogeneic
S2150	Bone marrow or blood-derived stem cells (peripheral or umbilical), allogeneic or autologous, harvesting, transplantation, and related complications; including: pheresis and cell preparation/storage; marrow ablative therapy; drugs, supplies, hospitalization with outpatient follow-up; medical/surgical, diagnostic, emergency, and rehabilitative services; and the number of days of pre-and post-transplant care in the global definition
S2152	Solid organ(s), complete or segmental, single organ or combination of organs; deceased or living donor(s), procurement, transplantation, and related complications; including: drugs; supplies; hospitalization with outpatient follow-up; medical/surgical, diagnostic, emergency, and rehabilitative services, and the number of days of pre- and post-transplant care in the global definition
S2202	Echosclerotherapy
S2205	Minimally invasive direct coronary artery bypass surgery involving mini-thoracotomy or mini-sternotomy surgery, performed under direct vision; using arterial graft(s), single coronary arterial graft
S2206	Minimally invasive direct coronary artery bypass surgery involving mini-thoracotomy or mini-sternotomy surgery, performed under direct vision; using arterial graft(s), two coronary arterial grafts
S2207	Minimally invasive direct coronary artery bypass surgery involving mini-thoracotomy or mini-sternotomy surgery, performed under direct vision; using venous graft only, single coronary venous graft
S2208	Minimally invasive direct coronary artery bypass surgery involving mini-thoracotomy or mini-sternotomy surgery, performed under direct vision; using single arterial and venous graft(s), single venous graft
S2209	Minimally invasive direct coronary artery bypass surgery involving mini-thoracotomy or mini-sternotomy surgery, performed under direct vision; using two arterial grafts and single venous graft
S2225	Myringotomy, laser-assisted
S2230	Implantation of magnetic component of semi-implantable hearing device on ossicles in middle ear

| Not payable by Medicare | Non-covered by Medicare | Special coverage instructions | Carrier judgement | 319 |

S2235	Implantation of auditory brain stem implant
S2260	Induced abortion, 17 to 24 weeks
S2265	Induced abortion, 25 to 28 weeks
S2266	Induced abortion, 29 to 31 weeks
S2267	Induced abortion, 32 weeks or greater
S2300	Arthroscopy, shoulder, surgical; with thermally-induced capsulorrhaphy
S2325	Hip core decompression
S2340	Chemodenervation of abductor muscle(s) of vocal cord
S2341	Chemodenervation of adductor muscle(s) of vocal cord
S2342	Nasal endoscopy for post-operative debridement following functional endoscopic sinus surgery, nasal and/or sinus cavity(s), unilateral or bilateral
S2348	Decompression procedure, percutaneous, of nucleus pulposus of intervertebral disc, using radiofrequency energy, single or multiple levels, lumbar
S2350	Diskectomy, anterior, with decompression of spinal cord and/or nerve root(s), including osteophytectomy; lumbar, single interspace
S2351	Diskectomy, anterior, with decompression of spinal cord and/or nerve root(s), including osteophytectomy; lumbar, each additional interspace (list separately in addition to code for primary procedure)
S2400	Repair, congenital diaphragmatic hernia in the fetus using temporary tracheal occlusion, procedure performed in utero
S2401	Repair, urinary tract obstruction in the fetus, procedure performed in utero
S2402	Repair, congenital cystic adenomatoid malformation in the fetus, procedure performed in utero
S2403	Repair, extralobar pulmonary sequestration in the fetus, procedure performed in utero
S2404	Repair, myelomeningocele in the fetus, procedure performed in utero
S2405	Repair of sacrococcygeal teratoma in the fetus, procedure performed in utero
S2409	Repair, congenital malformation of fetus, procedure performed in utero, not otherwise classified
S2411	Fetoscopic laser therapy for treatment of twin-to-twin transfusion syndrome
S2900	Surgical techniques requiring use of robotic surgical system (list separately in addition to code for primary procedure)
S3000	Diabetic indicator; retinal eye exam, dilated, bilateral
S3005	Performance measurement, evaluation of patient self assessment, depression
S3600	Stat laboratory request (situations other than s3601)
S3601	Emergency stat laboratory charge for patient who is homebound or residing in a nursing facility

S3620   Newborn metabolic screening panel, includes test kit, postage and the laboratory tests specified by the state for inclusion in this panel (e.g. galactose; hemoglobin, electrophoresis; hydroxyprogesterone, 17-d; phenylalanine (PKU); and thyroxine, total)

S3630   Eosinophil count, blood, direct

S3645   HIV-1 antibody testing of oral mucosal transudate

S3650   Saliva test, hormone level; during menopause

S3652   Saliva test, hormone level; to assess preterm labor risk

S3655   Antisperm antibodies test (immunobead)

S3708   Gastrointestinal fat absorption study

S3722   Dose optimization by area under the curve (AUC) analysis, for infusional 5-fluorouracil

S3800   Genetic testing for amyotrophic lateral sclerosis (ALS)

S3840   DNA analysis for germline mutations of the ret proto-oncogene for susceptibility to multiple endocrine neoplasia type 2

S3841   Genetic testing for retinoblastoma

S3842   Genetic testing for von Hippel-Lindau disease

S3844   DNA analysis of the connexin 26 gene (gjb2) for susceptibility to congenital, profound deafness

S3845   Genetic testing for alpha-thalassemia

S3846   Genetic testing for hemoglobin e beta-thalassemia

S3849   Genetic testing for Niemann-pick disease

S3850   Genetic testing for sickle cell anemia

S3852   DNA analysis for apoe epsilon 4 allele for susceptibility to Alzheimer's disease

S3853   Genetic testing for myotonic muscular dystrophy

S3854   Gene expression profiling panel for use in the management of breast cancer treatment

S3861   Genetic testing, sodium channel, voltage-gated, type v, alpha subunit (scn5a) and variants for suspected Brugada syndrome

S3865   Comprehensive gene sequence analysis for hypertrophic cardiomyopathy

S3866   Genetic analysis for a specific gene mutation for hypertrophic cardiomyopathy (HCM) in an individual with a known HCM mutation in the family

S3870   Comparative genomic hybridization (CGH) microarray testing for developmental delay, autism spectrum disorder and/or intellectual disability

S3900   Surface electromyography (EMG)

S3902   Ballistocardiogram

S3904   Masters two step

S4005   Interim labor facility global (labor occurring but not resulting in delivery)

S4011 In vitro fertilization; including but not limited to identification and incubation of mature oocytes, fertilization with sperm, incubation of embryo(s), and subsequent visualization for determination of development

S4013 Complete cycle, gamete intrafallopian transfer (gift), case rate

S4014 Complete cycle, zygote intrafallopian transfer (zift), case rate

S4015 Complete in vitro fertilization cycle, not otherwise specified, case rate

S4016 Frozen in vitro fertilization cycle, case rate

S4017 Incomplete cycle, treatment cancelled prior to stimulation, case rate

S4018 Frozen embryo transfer procedure cancelled before transfer, case rate

S4020 In vitro fertilization procedure cancelled before aspiration, case rate

S4021 In vitro fertilization procedure cancelled after aspiration, case rate

S4022 Assisted oocyte fertilization, case rate

S4023 Donor egg cycle, incomplete, case rate

S4025 Donor services for in vitro fertilization (sperm or embryo), case rate

S4026 Procurement of donor sperm from sperm bank

S4027 Storage of previously frozen embryos

S4028 Microsurgical epididymal sperm aspiration (mesa)

S4030 Sperm procurement and cryopreservation services; initial visit

S4031 Sperm procurement and cryopreservation services; subsequent visit

S4035 Stimulated intrauterine insemination (IUI), case rate

S4037 Cryopreserved embryo transfer, case rate

S4040 Monitoring and storage of cryopreserved embryos, per 30 days

S4042 Management of ovulation induction (interpretation of diagnostic tests and studies, non-face-to-face medical management of the patient), per cycle

S4981 Insertion of levonorgestrel-releasing intrauterine system

S4989 Contraceptive intrauterine device (e.g., Progestasert iud), including implants and supplies

S4990 Nicotine patches, legend

S4991 Nicotine patches, non-legend

S4993 Contraceptive pills for birth control

S4995 Smoking cessation gum

S5000 Prescription drug, generic

S5001 Prescription drug, brand name

S5010 5% dextrose and 0.45% normal saline, 1000 ml

S5012 5% dextrose with potassium chloride, 1000 ml

S5013 5% dextrose/0.45% normal saline with potassium chloride and magnesium sulfate, 1000 ml

S5014 5% dextrose/0.45% normal saline with potassium chloride and magnesium sulfate, 1500 ml

S5035 Home infusion therapy, routine service of infusion device (e.g., pump maintenance)

S5036 Home infusion therapy, repair of infusion device (e.g., pump repair)

S5100 Day care services, adult; per 15 minutes

S5101 Day care services, adult; per half day

S5102 Day care services, adult; per diem

S5105 Day care services, center-based; services not included in program fee, per diem

S5108 Home care training to home care client, per 15 minutes

S5109 Home care training to home care client, per session

S5110 Home care training, family; per 15 minutes

S5111 Home care training, family; per session

S5115 Home care training, non-family; per 15 minutes

S5116 Home care training, non-family; per session

S5120 Chore services; per 15 minutes

S5121 Chore services; per diem

S5125 Attendant care services; per 15 minutes

S5126 Attendant care services; per diem

S5130 Homemaker service, nos; per 15 minutes

S5131 Homemaker service, nos; per diem

S5135 Companion care, adult (e.g., iadl/ADL); per 15 minutes

S5136 Companion care, adult (e.g., iadl/ADL); per diem

S5140 Foster care, adult; per diem

S5141 Foster care, adult; per month

S5145 Foster care, therapeutic, child; per diem

S5146 Foster care, therapeutic, child; per month

S5150 Unskilled respite care, not hospice; per 15 minutes

S5151 Unskilled respite care, not hospice; per diem

S5160 Emergency response system; installation and testing

S5161 Emergency response system; service fee, per month (excludes installation and testing)

S5162 Emergency response system; purchase only

S5165 Home modifications; per service

S5170 Home delivered meals, including preparation; per meal

S5175	Laundry service, external, professional; per order
S5180	Home health respiratory therapy, initial evaluation
S5181	Home health respiratory therapy, nos, per diem
S5185	Medication reminder service, non-face-to-face; per month
S5190	Wellness assessment, performed by non-physician
S5199	Personal care item, nos, each
S5497	Home infusion therapy, catheter care / maintenance, not otherwise classified; includes administrative services, professional pharmacy services, care coordination, and all necessary supplies and equipment (drugs and nursing visits coded separately), per diem
S5498	Home infusion therapy, catheter care / maintenance, simple (single lumen), includes administrative services, professional pharmacy services, care coordination and all necessary supplies and equipment, (drugs and nursing visits coded separately), per diem
S5501	Home infusion therapy, catheter care / maintenance, complex (more than one lumen), includes administrative services, professional pharmacy services, care coordination, and all necessary supplies and equipment (drugs and nursing visits coded separately), per diem
S5502	Home infusion therapy, catheter care / maintenance, implanted access device, includes administrative services, professional pharmacy services, care coordination and all necessary supplies and equipment, (drugs and nursing visits coded separately), per diem (use this code for interim maintenance of vascular access not currently in use)
S5517	Home infusion therapy, all supplies necessary for restoration of catheter patency or declotting
S5518	Home infusion therapy, all supplies necessary for catheter repair
S5520	Home infusion therapy, all supplies (including catheter) necessary for a peripherally inserted central venous catheter (PICC) line insertion
S5521	Home infusion therapy, all supplies (including catheter) necessary for a midline catheter insertion
S5522	Home infusion therapy, insertion of peripherally inserted central venous catheter (PICC), nursing services only (no supplies or catheter included)
S5523	Home infusion therapy, insertion of midline venous catheter, nursing services only (no supplies or catheter included)
S5550	Insulin, rapid onset, 5 units
S5551	Insulin, most rapid onset (lispro or aspart); 5 units
S5552	Insulin, intermediate acting (NPH or lente); 5 units
S5553	Insulin, long acting; 5 units
S5560	Insulin delivery device, reusable pen; 1.5 ml size
S5561	Insulin delivery device, reusable pen; 3 ml size
S5565	Insulin cartridge for use in insulin delivery device other than pump; 150 units
S5566	Insulin cartridge for use in insulin delivery device other than pump; 300 units

S5570   Insulin delivery device, disposable pen (including insulin); 1.5 ml size

S5571   Insulin delivery device, disposable pen (including insulin); 3 ml size

S8030   Scleral application of tantalum ring(s) for localization of lesions for proton beam therapy

(S8032   Code deleted 09/30/16). Use G0297

S8035   Magnetic source imaging

S8037   Magnetic resonance cholangiopancreatography (MRCP)

S8040   Topographic brain mapping

S8042   Magnetic resonance imaging (MRI), low-field

S8055   Ultrasound guidance for multifetal pregnancy reduction(s), technical component (only to be used when the physician doing the reduction procedure does not perform the ultrasound, guidance is included in the CPT code for multifetal pregnancy reduction - 59866)

S8080   Scintimammography (radioimmunoscintigraphy of the breast), unilateral, including supply of radiopharmaceutical

S8085   Fluorine-18 fluorodeoxyglucose (f-18 fdg) imaging using dual-head coincidence detection system (non-dedicated pet scan)

S8092   Electron beam computed tomography (also known as ultrafast ct, cine ct)

S8096   Portable peak flow meter

S8097   Asthma kit (including but not limited to portable peak expiratory flow meter, instructional video, brochure, and/or spacer)

S8100   Holding chamber or spacer for use with an inhaler or nebulizer; without mask

S8101   Holding chamber or spacer for use with an inhaler or nebulizer; with mask

S8110   Peak expiratory flow rate (physician services)

S8120   Oxygen contents, gaseous, 1 unit equals 1 cubic foot

S8121   Oxygen contents, liquid, 1 unit equals 1 pound

S8130   Interferential current stimulator, 2 channel

S8131   Interferential current stimulator, 4 channel

S8185   Flutter device

S8186   Swivel adapter

S8189   Tracheostomy supply, not otherwise classified

S8210   Mucus trap

S8265   Haberman feeder for cleft lip/palate

S8270   Enuresis alarm, using auditory buzzer and/or vibration device

S8301   Infection control supplies, not otherwise specified

S8415   Supplies for home delivery of infant

S8420   Gradient pressure aid (sleeve and glove combination), custom made

S8421	Gradient pressure aid (sleeve and glove combination), ready made
S8422	Gradient pressure aid (sleeve), custom made, medium weight
S8423	Gradient pressure aid (sleeve), custom made, heavy weight
S8424	Gradient pressure aid (sleeve), ready made
S8425	Gradient pressure aid (glove), custom made, medium weight
S8426	Gradient pressure aid (glove), custom made, heavy weight
S8427	Gradient pressure aid (glove), ready made
S8428	Gradient pressure aid (gauntlet), ready made
S8429	Gradient pressure exterior wrap
S8430	Padding for compression bandage, roll
S8431	Compression bandage, roll
S8450	Splint, prefabricated, digit (specify digit by use of modifier)
S8451	Splint, prefabricated, wrist or ankle
S8452	Splint, prefabricated, elbow
S8460	Camisole, post-mastectomy
S8490	Insulin syringes (100 syringes, any size)
S8930	Electrical stimulation of auricular acupuncture points; each 15 minutes of personal one-on-one contact with the patient
S8940	Equestrian/hippotherapy, per session
S8948	Application of a modality (requiring constant provider attendance) to one or more areas; low-level laser; each 15 minutes
S8950	Complex lymphedema therapy, each 15 minutes
S8990	Physical or manipulative therapy performed for maintenance rather than restoration
S8999	Resuscitation bag (for use by patient on artificial respiration during power failure or other catastrophic event)
S9001	Home uterine monitor with or without associated nursing services
S9007	Ultrafiltration monitor
S9024	Paranasal sinus ultrasound
S9025	Omnicardiogram/cardiointegram
S9034	Extracorporeal shockwave lithotripsy for gall stones (if performed with ERCP, use 43265)
S9055	Procuren or other growth factor preparation to promote wound healing
S9056	Coma stimulation per diem
S9061	Home administration of aerosolized drug therapy (e.g., pentamidine); administrative services, professional pharmacy services, care coordination, all necessary supplies and equipment (drugs and nursing visits coded separately), per diem

S9083 Global fee urgent care centers

S9088 Services provided in an urgent care center (list in addition to code for service)

S9090 Vertebral axial decompression, per session

S9097 Home visit for wound care

S9098 Home visit, phototherapy services (e.g., bili-lite), including equipment rental, nursing services, blood draw, supplies, and other services, per diem

S9110 Telemonitoring of patient in their home, including all necessary equipment; computer system, connections, and software; maintenance; patient education and support; per month

S9117 Back school, per visit

S9122 Home health aide or certified nurse assistant, providing care in the home; per hour

S9123 Nursing care, in the home; by registered nurse, per hour (use for general nursing care only, not to be used when CPT codes 99500-99602 can be used)

S9124 Nursing care, in the home; by licensed practical nurse, per hour

S9125 Respite care, in the home, per diem

S9126 Hospice care, in the home, per diem

S9127 Social work visit, in the home, per diem

S9128 Speech therapy, in the home, per diem

S9129 Occupational therapy, in the home, per diem

S9131 Physical therapy; in the home, per diem

S9140 Diabetic management program, follow-up visit to non-md provider

S9141 Diabetic management program, follow-up visit to md provider

S9145 Insulin pump initiation, instruction in initial use of pump (pump not included)

S9150 Evaluation by ocularist

S9152 Speech therapy, re-evaluation

S9208 Home management of preterm labor, including administrative services, professional pharmacy services, care coordination, and all necessary supplies or equipment (drugs and nursing visits coded separately), per diem (do not use this code with any home infusion per diem code)

S9209 Home management of preterm premature rupture of membranes (pprom), including administrative services, professional pharmacy services, care coordination, and all necessary supplies or equipment (drugs and nursing visits coded separately), per diem (do not use this code with any home infusion per diem code)

S9211 Home management of gestational hypertension, includes administrative services, professional pharmacy services, care coordination and all necessary supplies and equipment (drugs and nursing visits coded separately); per diem (do not use this code with any home infusion per diem code)

S9212 Home management of postpartum hypertension, includes administrative services, professional pharmacy services, care coordination, and all necessary supplies and equipment (drugs and nursing visits coded separately), per diem (do not use this code with any home infusion per diem code)

S9213 Home management of preeclampsia, includes administrative services, professional pharmacy services, care coordination, and all necessary supplies and equipment (drugs and nursing services coded separately); per diem (do not use this code with any home infusion per diem code)

S9214 Home management of gestational diabetes, includes administrative services, professional pharmacy services, care coordination, and all necessary supplies and equipment (drugs and nursing visits coded separately); per diem (do not use this code with any home infusion per diem code)

S9325 Home infusion therapy, pain management infusion; administrative services, professional pharmacy services, care coordination, and all necessary supplies and equipment, (drugs and nursing visits coded separately), per diem (do not use this code with s9326, s9327 or s9328)

S9326 Home infusion therapy, continuous (twenty-four hours or more) pain management infusion; administrative services, professional pharmacy services, care coordination and all necessary supplies and equipment (drugs and nursing visits coded separately), per diem

S9327 Home infusion therapy, intermittent (less than twenty-four hours) pain management infusion; administrative services, professional pharmacy services, care coordination, and all necessary supplies and equipment (drugs and nursing visits coded separately), per diem

S9328 Home infusion therapy, implanted pump pain management infusion; administrative services, professional pharmacy services, care coordination, and all necessary supplies and equipment (drugs and nursing visits coded separately), per diem

S9329 Home infusion therapy, chemotherapy infusion; administrative services, professional pharmacy services, care coordination, and all necessary supplies and equipment (drugs and nursing visits coded separately), per diem (do not use this code with s9330 or s9331)

S9330 Home infusion therapy, continuous (twenty-four hours or more) chemotherapy infusion; administrative services, professional pharmacy services, care coordination, and all necessary supplies and equipment (drugs and nursing visits coded separately), per diem

S9331 Home infusion therapy, intermittent (less than twenty-four hours) chemotherapy infusion; administrative services, professional pharmacy services, care coordination, and all necessary supplies and equipment (drugs and nursing visits coded separately), per diem

S9335 Home therapy, hemodialysis; administrative services, professional pharmacy services, care coordination, and all necessary supplies and equipment (drugs and nursing services coded separately), per diem

S9336 Home infusion therapy, continuous anticoagulant infusion therapy (e.g., heparin), administrative services, professional pharmacy services, care coordination and all necessary supplies and equipment (drugs and nursing visits coded separately), per diem

S9338 Home infusion therapy, immunotherapy, administrative services, professional pharmacy services, care coordination, and all necessary supplies and equipment (drugs and nursing visits coded separately), per diem

S9339 Home therapy; peritoneal dialysis, administrative services, professional pharmacy services, care coordination and all necessary supplies and equipment (drugs and nursing visits coded separately), per diem

S9340 Home therapy; enteral nutrition; administrative services, professional pharmacy services, care coordination, and all necessary supplies and equipment (enteral formula and nursing visits coded separately), per diem

S9341 Home therapy; enteral nutrition via gravity; administrative services, professional pharmacy services, care coordination, and all necessary supplies and equipment (enteral formula and nursing visits coded separately), per diem

S9342 Home therapy; enteral nutrition via pump; administrative services, professional pharmacy services, care coordination, and all necessary supplies and equipment (enteral formula and nursing visits coded separately), per diem

S9343 Home therapy; enteral nutrition via bolus; administrative services, professional pharmacy services, care coordination, and all necessary supplies and equipment (enteral formula and nursing visits coded separately), per diem

S9345 Home infusion therapy, anti-hemophilic agent infusion therapy (e.g., factor viii); administrative services, professional pharmacy services, care coordination, and all necessary supplies and equipment (drugs and nursing visits coded separately), per diem

S9346 Home infusion therapy, alpha-1-proteinase inhibitor (e.g., Prolastin); administrative services, professional pharmacy services, care coordination, and all necessary supplies and equipment (drugs and nursing visits coded separately), per diem

S9347 Home infusion therapy, uninterrupted, long-term, controlled rate intravenous or subcutaneous infusion therapy (e.g., epoprostenol); administrative services, professional pharmacy services, care coordination, and all necessary supplies and equipment (drugs and nursing visits coded separately), per diem

S9348 Home infusion therapy, sympathomimetic/inotropic agent infusion therapy (e.g., dobutamine); administrative services, professional pharmacy services, care coordination, all necessary supplies and equipment (drugs and nursing visits coded separately), per diem

S9349 Home infusion therapy, tocolytic infusion therapy; administrative services, professional pharmacy services, care coordination, and all necessary supplies and equipment (drugs and nursing visits coded separately), per diem

S9351 Home infusion therapy, continuous or intermittent anti-emetic infusion therapy; administrative services, professional pharmacy services, care coordination, and all necessary supplies and equipment (drugs and visits coded separately), per diem

S9353 Home infusion therapy, continuous insulin infusion therapy; administrative services, professional pharmacy services, care coordination, and all necessary supplies and equipment (drugs and nursing visits coded separately), per diem

S9355 Home infusion therapy, chelation therapy; administrative services, professional pharmacy services, care coordination, and all necessary

S9357 Home infusion therapy, enzyme replacement intravenous therapy; (e.g., imiglucerase); administrative services, professional pharmacy services, care coordination, and all necessary supplies and equipment (drugs and nursing visits coded separately), per diem

S9359 Home infusion therapy, anti-tumor necrosis factor intravenous therapy; (e.g., infliximab); administrative services, professional pharmacy services, care coordination, and all necessary supplies and equipment (drugs and nursing visits coded separately), per diem

S9361 Home infusion therapy, diuretic intravenous therapy; administrative services, professional pharmacy services, care coordination, and all necessary supplies and equipment (drugs and nursing visits coded separately), per diem

S9363 Home infusion therapy, anti-spasmotic therapy; administrative services, professional pharmacy services, care coordination, and all necessary supplies and equipment (drugs and nursing visits coded separately), per diem

S9364 Home infusion therapy, total parenteral nutrition (tpn); administrative services, professional pharmacy services, care coordination, and all necessary supplies and equipment including standard tpn formula (lipids, specialty amino acid formulas, drugs other than in standard formula and nursing visits coded separately), per diem (do not use with home infusion codes S9365-S9368 using daily volume scales)

S9365 Home infusion therapy, total parenteral nutrition (tpn); one liter per day, administrative services, professional pharmacy services, care coordination, and all necessary supplies and equipment including standard tpn formula (lipids, specialty amino acid formulas, drugs other than in standard formula and nursing visits coded separately), per diem

S9366 Home infusion therapy, total parenteral nutrition (tpn); more than one liter but no more than two liters per day, administrative services, professional pharmacy services, care coordination, and all necessary supplies and equipment including standard tpn formula (lipids, specialty amino acid formulas, drugs other than in standard formula and nursing visits coded separately), per diem

S9367 Home infusion therapy, total parenteral nutrition (tpn); more than two liters but no more than three liters per day, administrative services, professional pharmacy services, care coordination, and all necessary supplies and equipment including standard tpn formula (lipids, specialty amino acid formulas, drugs other than in standard formula and nursing visits coded separately), per diem

S9368 Home infusion therapy, total parenteral nutrition (tpn); more than three liters per day, administrative services, professional pharmacy services, care coordination, and all necessary supplies and equipment including standard tpn formula (lipids, specialty amino acid formulas, drugs other than in standard formula and nursing visits coded separately), per diem

S9370 Home therapy, intermittent anti-emetic injection therapy; administrative services, professional pharmacy services, care coordination, and all necessary supplies and equipment (drugs and nursing visits coded separately), per diem

S9372 Home therapy; intermittent anticoagulant injection therapy (e.g., heparin); administrative services, professional pharmacy services, care coordination, and all necessary supplies and equipment (drugs and nursing visits coded separately), per diem (do not use this code for flushing of infusion devices with heparin to maintain patency)

S9373 Home infusion therapy, hydration therapy; administrative services, professional pharmacy services, care coordination, and all necessary supplies and equipment (drugs and nursing visits coded separately), per diem (do not use with hydration therapy codes s9374-s9377 using daily volume scales)

S9374 Home infusion therapy, hydration therapy; one liter per day, administrative services, professional pharmacy services, care coordination, and all necessary supplies and equipment (drugs and nursing visits coded separately), per diem

S9375 Home infusion therapy, hydration therapy; more than one liter but no more than two liters per day, administrative services, professional pharmacy services, care coordination, and all necessary supplies and equipment (drugs and nursing visits coded separately), per diem

S9376 Home infusion therapy, hydration therapy; more than two liters but no more than three liters per day, administrative services, professional pharmacy services, care coordination, and all necessary supplies and equipment (drugs and nursing visits coded separately), per diem

S9377 Home infusion therapy, hydration therapy; more than three liters per day, administrative services, professional pharmacy services, care coordination, and all necessary supplies (drugs and nursing visits coded separately), per diem

S9379 Home infusion therapy, infusion therapy, not otherwise classified; administrative services, professional pharmacy services, care coordination, and all necessary supplies and equipment (drugs and nursing visits coded separately), per diem

S9381 Delivery or service to high risk areas requiring escort or extra protection, per visit

S9401 Anticoagulation clinic, inclusive of all services except laboratory tests, per session

S9430 Pharmacy compounding and dispensing services

S9433 Medical food nutritionally complete, administered orally, providing 100% of nutritional intake

S9434 Modified solid food supplements for inborn errors of metabolism

S9435 Medical foods for inborn errors of metabolism

S9436 Childbirth preparation/Lamaze classes, non-physician provider, per session

S9437 Childbirth refresher classes, non-physician provider, per session

S9438 Cesarean birth classes, non-physician provider, per session

S9439 VBAC (vaginal birth after cesarean) classes, non-physician provider, per session

S9441 Asthma education, non-physician provider, per session

S9442 Birthing classes, non-physician provider, per session

S9443 Lactation classes, non-physician provider, per session

S9444 Parenting classes, non-physician provider, per session

S9445 Patient education, not otherwise classified, non-physician provider, individual, per session

S9446 Patient education, not otherwise classified, non-physician provider, group, per session

S9447	Infant safety (including CPR) classes, non-physician provider, per session
S9449	Weight management classes, non-physician provider, per session
S9451	Exercise classes, non-physician provider, per session
S9452	Nutrition classes, non-physician provider, per session
S9453	Smoking cessation classes, non-physician provider, per session
S9454	Stress management classes, non-physician provider, per session
S9455	Diabetic management program, group session
S9460	Diabetic management program, nurse visit
S9465	Diabetic management program, dietitian visit
S9470	Nutritional counseling, dietitian visit
S9472	Cardiac rehabilitation program, non-physician provider, per diem
S9473	Pulmonary rehabilitation program, non-physician provider, per diem
S9474	Enterostomal therapy by a registered nurse certified in enterostomal therapy, per diem
S9475	Ambulatory setting substance abuse treatment or detoxification services, per diem
S9476	Vestibular rehabilitation program, non-physician provider, per diem
S9480	Intensive outpatient psychiatric services, per diem
S9482	Family stabilization services, per 15 minutes
S9484	Crisis intervention mental health services, per hour
S9485	Crisis intervention mental health services, per diem
S9490	Home infusion therapy, corticosteroid infusion; administrative services, professional pharmacy services, care coordination, and all necessary supplies and equipment (drugs and nursing visits coded separately), per diem
S9494	Home infusion therapy, antibiotic, antiviral, or antifungal therapy; administrative services, professional pharmacy services, care coordination, and all necessary supplies and equipment (drugs and nursing visits coded separately), per diem (do not use this code with home infusion codes for hourly dosing schedules s9497-s9504)
S9497	Home infusion therapy, antibiotic, antiviral, or antifungal therapy; once every 3 hours; administrative services, professional pharmacy services, care coordination, and all necessary supplies and equipment (drugs and nursing visits coded separately), per diem
S9500	Home infusion therapy, antibiotic, antiviral, or antifungal therapy; once every 24 hours; administrative services, professional pharmacy services, care coordination, and all necessary supplies and equipment (drugs and nursing visits coded separately), per diem
S9501	Home infusion therapy, antibiotic, antiviral, or antifungal therapy; once every 12 hours; administrative services, professional pharmacy services, care coordination, and all necessary supplies and equipment (drugs and nursing visits coded separately), per diem
S9502	Home infusion therapy, antibiotic, antiviral, or antifungal therapy; once every 8 hours, administrative services, professional pharmacy services, care coordination, and all necessary supplies and equipment (drugs and nursing visits coded separately), per diem

S9503 Home infusion therapy, antibiotic, antiviral, or antifungal; once every 6 hours; administrative services, professional pharmacy services, care coordination, and all necessary supplies and equipment (drugs and nursing visits coded separately), per diem

S9504 Home infusion therapy, antibiotic, antiviral, or antifungal; once every 4 hours; administrative services, professional pharmacy services, care coordination, and all necessary supplies and equipment (drugs and nursing visits coded separately), per diem

S9529 Routine venipuncture for collection of specimen(s), single home bound, nursing home, or skilled nursing facility patient

S9537 Home therapy; hematopoietic hormone injection therapy (e.g., erythropoietin, g-csf, gm-csf); administrative services, professional pharmacy services, care coordination, and all necessary supplies and equipment (drugs and nursing visits coded separately), per diem

S9538 Home transfusion of blood product(s); administrative services, professional pharmacy services, care coordination and all necessary supplies and equipment (blood products, drugs, and nursing visits coded separately), per diem

S9542 Home injectable therapy, not otherwise classified, including administrative services, professional pharmacy services, care coordination, and all necessary supplies and equipment (drugs and nursing visits coded separately), per diem

S9558 Home injectable therapy; growth hormone, including administrative services, professional pharmacy services, care coordination, and all necessary supplies and equipment (drugs and nursing visits coded separately), per diem

S9559 Home injectable therapy, interferon, including administrative services, professional pharmacy services, care coordination, and all necessary supplies and equipment (drugs and nursing visits coded separately), per diem

S9560 Home injectable therapy; hormonal therapy (e.g.; leuprolide, goserelin), including administrative services, professional pharmacy services, care coordination, and all necessary supplies and equipment (drugs and nursing visits coded separately), per diem

S9562 Home injectable therapy, palivizumab, including administrative services, professional pharmacy services, care coordination, and all necessary supplies and equipment (drugs and nursing visits coded separately), per diem

S9590 Home therapy, irrigation therapy (e.g., sterile irrigation of an organ or anatomical cavity); including administrative services, professional pharmacy services, care coordination, and all necessary supplies and equipment (drugs and nursing visits coded separately), per diem

S9810 Home therapy; professional pharmacy services for provision of infusion, specialty drug administration, and/or disease state management, not otherwise classified, per hour (do not use this code with any per diem code)

S9900 Services by a journal-listed Christian science practitioner for the purpose of healing, per diem

S9901 Services by a journal-listed Christian science nurse, per hour

S9960 Ambulance service, conventional air service, nonemergency transport, one way (fixed wing)

S9961 Ambulance service, conventional air service, nonemergency transport, one way (rotary wing)

S9970 Health club membership, annual

S9975 Transplant related lodging, meals and transportation, per diem

S9976 Lodging, per diem, not otherwise classified

S9977 Meals, per diem, not otherwise specified

S9981 Medical records copying fee, administrative

S9982 Medical records copying fee, per page

S9986 Not medically necessary service (patient is aware that service not medically necessary)

S9988 Services provided as part of a phase i clinical trial

S9989 Services provided outside of the united states of America (list in addition to code(s) for service(s))

S9990 Services provided as part of a phase ii clinical trial

S9991 Services provided as part of a phase iii clinical trial

S9992 Transportation costs to and from trial location and local transportation costs (e.g., fares for taxicab or bus) for clinical trial participant and one caregiver/companion

S9994 Lodging costs (e.g., hotel charges) for clinical trial participant and one caregiver/companion

S9996 Meals for clinical trial participant and one caregiver/companion

S9999 Sales tax

STATE MEDICAID AGENCY CODES

Guidelines

"T" codes were added to HCPCS in 2002. These codes are exclusively for the use of state Medicaid agencies. Prior to using "T" codes on health insurance claims to your state Medicaid processor, you should verify that these codes are acceptable. "T" codes are not valid for Medicare use.

In addition to the information presented in the INTRODUCTION, several other items unique to this section are defined or identified here.

1. SPECIAL REPORT: A service, material or supply that is rarely provided, unusual, variable or new may require a special report in determining medical appropriateness for reimbursement purposes. Pertinent information should include an adequate definition or description of the nature, extent, and need for the service, material or supply.

2. MODIFIERS: Listed services may be modified under certain circumstances. When appropriate, the modifying circumstance is identified by adding a modifier to the basic procedure code. CPT and HCPCS National Level II modifiers may be used with CPT and HCPCS National Level II procedure codes.

State Medicaid Agency Codes

Code	Description
T1000	Private duty / independent nursing service(s) - licensed, up to 15 minutes
T1001	Nursing assessment / evaluation
T1002	Rn services, up to 15 minutes
T1003	LPN/LVN services, up to 15 minutes
T1004	Services of a qualified nursing aide, up to 15 minutes
T1005	Respite care services, up to 15 minutes
T1006	Alcohol and/or substance abuse services, family/couple counseling
T1007	Alcohol and/or substance abuse services, treatment plan development and/or modification
T1009	Child sitting services for children of the individual receiving alcohol and/or substance abuse services
T1010	Meals for individuals receiving alcohol and/or substance abuse services (when meals not included in the program)
T1012	Alcohol and/or substance abuse services, skills development
T1013	Sign language or oral interpretive services, per 15 minutes
T1014	Telehealth transmission, per minute, professional services bill separately
T1015	Clinic visit/encounter, all-inclusive
T1016	Case management, each 15 minutes
T1017	Targeted case management, each 15 minutes

T1018 School-based individualized education program (iep) services, bundled

T1019 Personal care services, per 15 minutes, not for an inpatient or resident of a hospital, nursing facility, icf/mr or imd, part of the individualized plan of treatment (code may not be used to identify services provided by home health aide or certified nurse assistant)

T1020 Personal care services, per diem, not for an inpatient or resident of a hospital, nursing facility, icf/mr or imd, part of the individualized plan of treatment (code may not be used to identify services provided by home health aide or certified nurse assistant)

T1021 Home health aide or certified nurse assistant, per visit

T1022 Contracted home health agency services, all services provided under contract, per day

T1023 Screening to determine the appropriateness of consideration of an individual for participation in a specified program, project or treatment protocol, per encounter

T1024 Evaluation and treatment by an integrated, specialty team contracted to provide coordinated care to multiple or severely handicapped children, per encounter

T1025 Intensive, extended multidisciplinary services provided in a clinic setting to children with complex medical, physical, mental and psychosocial impairments, per diem

T1026 Intensive, extended multidisciplinary services provided in a clinic setting to children with complex medical, physical, medical and psychosocial impairments, per hour

T1027 Family training and counseling for child development, per 15 minutes

T1028 Assessment of home, physical and family environment, to determine suitability to meet patient's medical needs

T1029 Comprehensive environmental lead investigation, not including laboratory analysis, per dwelling

T1030 Nursing care, in the home, by registered nurse, per diem

T1031 Nursing care, in the home, by licensed practical nurse, per diem

T1040 Medicaid certified community behavioral health clinic services, per diem

T1041 Medicaid certified community behavioral health clinic services, per month

T1502 Administration of oral, intramuscular and/or subcutaneous medication by health care agency/professional, per visit

T1503 Administration of medication, other than oral and/or injectable, by a health care agency/professional, per visit

T1505 Electronic medication compliance management device, includes all components and accessories, not otherwise classified

T1999 Miscellaneous therapeutic items and supplies, retail purchases, not otherwise classified; identify product in "remarks"

T2001 Non-emergency transportation; patient attendant/escort

T2002 Non-emergency transportation; per diem

T2003 Non-emergency transportation; encounter/trip

T2004 Non-emergency transport; commercial carrier, multi-pass

T2005	Non-emergency transportation; stretcher van
T2007	Transportation waiting time, air ambulance and non-emergency vehicle, one-half (1/2) hour increments
T2010	Preadmission screening and resident review (pasrr) level i identification screening, per screen
T2011	Preadmission screening and resident review (pasrr) level ii evaluation, per evaluation
T2012	Habilitation, educational; waiver, per diem
T2013	Habilitation, educational, waiver; per hour
T2014	Habilitation, prevocational, waiver; per diem
T2015	Habilitation, prevocational, waiver; per hour
T2016	Habilitation, residential, waiver; per diem
T2017	Habilitation, residential, waiver; 15 minutes
T2018	Habilitation, supported employment, waiver; per diem
T2019	Habilitation, supported employment, waiver; per 15 minutes
T2020	Day habilitation, waiver; per diem
T2021	Day habilitation, waiver; per 15 minutes
T2022	Case management, per month
T2023	Targeted case management; per month
T2024	Service assessment/plan of care development, waiver
T2025	Waiver services; not otherwise specified (nos)
T2026	Specialized childcare, waiver; per diem
T2027	Specialized childcare, waiver; per 15 minutes
T2028	Specialized supply, not otherwise specified, waiver
T2029	Specialized medical equipment, not otherwise specified, waiver
T2030	Assisted living, waiver; per month
T2031	Assisted living; waiver, per diem
T2032	Residential care, not otherwise specified (nos), waiver; per month
T2033	Residential care, not otherwise specified (nos), waiver; per diem
T2034	Crisis intervention, waiver; per diem
T2035	Utility services to support medical equipment and assistive technology/devices, waiver
T2036	Therapeutic camping, overnight, waiver; each session
T2037	Therapeutic camping, day, waiver; each session
T2038	Community transition, waiver; per service
T2039	Vehicle modifications, waiver; per service
T2040	Financial management, self-directed, waiver; per 15 minutes

| T2041 | Supports brokerage, self-directed, waiver; per 15 minutes |

T2041 Supports brokerage, self-directed, waiver; per 15 minutes

T2042 Hospice routine home care; per diem

T2043 Hospice continuous home care; per hour

T2044 Hospice inpatient respite care; per diem

T2045 Hospice general inpatient care; per diem

T2046 Hospice long term care, room and board only; per diem

T2048 Behavioral health; long-term care residential (non-acute care in a residential treatment program where stay is typically longer than 30 days), with room and board, per diem

T2049 Non-emergency transportation; stretcher van, mileage; per mile

T2101 Human breast milk processing, storage and distribution only

T4521 Adult sized disposable incontinence product, brief/diaper, small, each

CIM: 60-9

T4522 Adult sized disposable incontinence product, brief/diaper, medium, each

CIM: 60-9

T4523 Adult sized disposable incontinence product, brief/diaper, large, each

CIM: 60-9

T4524 Adult sized disposable incontinence product, brief/diaper, extra large, each

CIM: 60-9

T4525 Adult sized disposable incontinence product, protective underwear/pull-on, small size, each

CIM: 60-9

T4526 Adult sized disposable incontinence product, protective underwear/pull-on, medium size, each

CIM: 60-9

T4527 Adult sized disposable incontinence product, protective underwear/pull-on, large size, each

CIM: 60-9

T4528 Adult sized disposable incontinence product, protective underwear/pull-on, extra large size, each

CIM: 60-9

T4529 Pediatric sized disposable incontinence product, brief/diaper, small/medium size, each

CIM: 60-9

T4530 Pediatric sized disposable incontinence product, brief/diaper, large size, each

CIM: 60-9

T4531 Pediatric sized disposable incontinence product, protective underwear/pull-on, small/medium size, each

CIM: 60-9

T4532 Pediatric sized disposable incontinence product, protective underwear/pull-on, large size, each

CIM: 60-9

T4533 Youth sized disposable incontinence product, brief/diaper, each

CIM: 60-9

T4534 Youth sized disposable incontinence product, protective underwear/pull-on, each

CIM: 60-9

T4535 Disposable liner/shield/guard/pad/undergarment, for incontinence, each

CIM: 60-9

T4536 Incontinence product, protective underwear/pull-on, reusable, any size, each

CIM: 60-9

T4537 Incontinence product, protective underpad, reusable, bed size, each

CIM: 60-9

T4538 Diaper service, reusable diaper, each diaper

CIM: 60-9

T4539 Incontinence product, diaper/brief, reusable, any size, each

CIM: 60-9

T4540 Incontinence product, protective underpad, reusable, chair size, each

CIM: 60-9

T4541 Incontinence product, disposable underpad, large, each

T4542 Incontinence product, disposable underpad, small size, each

T4543 Adult sized disposable incontinence product, protective brief/diaper, above extra large, each

CIM: 60-9

T4544 Adult sized disposable incontinence product, protective underwear/pull-on, above extra large, each

CIM: 60-9

T5001 Positioning seat for persons with special orthopedic needs

T5999 Supply, not otherwise specified

| | Not payable by Medicare | | Non-covered by Medicare | | Special coverage instructions | | Carrier judgement | 339 |

Guidelines

In addition to the information presented in the INTRODUCTION, several other items unique to this section are defined or identified here:

1. SUBSECTION INFORMATION: Some of the listed subheadings or subsections have special needs or instructions unique to that section. Where these are indicated, special "notes" will be presented preceding or following the listings. Those subsections within the VISION SERVICES section that have "notes" are as follows:

Subsection	Code Numbers
Spectacle lenses	V2100-V2499
Contact lenses	V2500-V2599
Low vision aids	V2600-V2615

2. UNLISTED SERVICE OR PROCEDURE: A service or procedure may be provided that is not listed in this edition of HCPCS. When reporting such a service, the appropriate "unlisted procedure" code may be used to indicate the service, identifying it by "special report" as defined below. HCPCS terminology is inconsistent in defining unlisted procedures. The procedure definition may include the term(s) "unlisted", "not otherwise classified", "unspecified", "unclassified", "other" and "miscellaneous". Prior to using these codes, try to determine if a Local Level III code or CPT code is available. The "unlisted procedures" and accompanying codes for VISION SERVICES are as follows:

V2199   Not otherwise classified, single vision lens, bifocal, glass or plastic
V2499   Variable sphericity lens, other type
V2599   Not otherwise classified, contact lens
V2629   Prosthetic eye, other type
V2799   Vision service, miscellaneous

3. SPECIAL REPORT: A service, material or supply that is rarely provided, unusual, variable or new may require a special report in determining medical appropriateness for reimbursement purposes. Pertinent information should include an adequate definition or description of the nature, extent, and need for the service, material or supply.

4. MODIFIERS: Listed services may be modified under certain circumstances. When appropriate, the modifying circumstance is identified by adding a modifier to the basic procedure code. CPT and HCPCS National Level II modifiers may be used with CPT and HCPCS National Level II procedure codes. Modifiers commonly used with VISION SERVICES are as follows:

-AP   Determination of refractive state was not performed in the course of diagnostic ophthalmological examination

-CC   Procedure code change (use "CC" when the procedure code submitted was changed either for administrative reasons or because an incorrect code was filed)

-LS   FDA-monitored intraocular lens implant

-LT   Left side (used to identify procedures performed on the left side of the body)

-PL   Progressive addition lenses

-RT   Right side (used to identify procedures performed on the right side of the body)

-SF   Second opinion ordered by a professional review organization (PRO) per section 9401, P.L. 99-272. (100 percent reimbursement; no Medicare deductible or coinsurance)

-TC   Technical component. Under certain circumstances, a charge may be made for the technical component alone. Under those circumstances, the technical component charge is identified by adding modifier -TC to the usual procedure number. Technical component charges are institutional charges and are not billed separately by physicians. However, portable x-ray suppliers bill only for the technical component and should use modifier -TC. The charge data from portable x-ray suppliers will then be used to build customary and prevailing profiles.

-VP   Aphakic patient

5.   CPT CODE CROSS-REFERENCE: See sections for equivalent CPT code(s) for all listings in this section.

Frames

V2020	Frames, purchases
	MCM: 2130
V2025	Deluxe frame
	MCM: 3045.4

Spectacle Lenses

NOTE: If CPT code 92390 or 92395 is reported, recode with the specific lens type listed below. For aphakic temporary spectacle correction, see CPT code 92358.

V2100	Sphere, single vision, plano to plus or minus 4.00, per lens
V2101	Sphere, single vision, plus or minus 4.12 to plus or minus 7.00d, per lens
V2102	Sphere, single vision, plus or minus 7.12 to plus or minus 20.00d, per lens
V2103	Spherocylinder, single vision, plano to plus or minus 4.00d sphere, .12 to 2.00d cylinder, per lens
V2104	Spherocylinder, single vision, plano to plus or minus 4.00d sphere, 2.12 to 4.00d cylinder, per lens
V2105	Spherocylinder, single vision, plano to plus or minus 4.00d sphere, 4.25 to 6.00d cylinder, per lens
V2106	Spherocylinder, single vision, plano to plus or minus 4.00d sphere, over 6.00d cylinder, per lens

V2107   Spherocylinder, single vision, plus or minus 4.25 to plus or minus 7.00 sphere, .12 to 2.00d cylinder, per lens

V2108   Spherocylinder, single vision, plus or minus 4.25d to plus or minus 7.00d sphere, 2.12 to 4.00d cylinder, per lens

V2109   Spherocylinder, single vision, plus or minus 4.25 to plus or minus 7.00d sphere, 4.25 to 6.00d cylinder, per lens

V2110   Spherocylinder, single vision, plus or minus 4.25 to 7.00d sphere, over 6.00d cylinder, per lens

V2111   Spherocylinder, single vision, plus or minus 7.25 to plus or minus 12.00d sphere, .25 to 2.25d cylinder, per lens

V2112   Spherocylinder, single vision, plus or minus 7.25 to plus or minus 12.00d sphere, 2.25d to 4.00d cylinder, per lens

V2113   Spherocylinder, single vision, plus or minus 7.25 to plus or minus 12.00d sphere, 4.25 to 6.00d cylinder, per lens

V2114   Spherocylinder, single vision, sphere over plus or minus 12.00d, per lens

V2115   Lenticular, (myodisc), per lens, single vision

V2118   Aniseikonic lens, single vision

V2121   Lenticular lens, per lens, single

   MCM: 2130.B

V2199   Not otherwise classified, single vision lens

V2200   Sphere, bifocal, plano to plus or minus 4.00d, per lens

V2201   Sphere, bifocal, plus or minus 4.12 to plus or minus 7.00d, per lens

V2202   Sphere, bifocal, plus or minus 7.12 to plus or minus 20.00d, per lens

V2203   Spherocylinder, bifocal, plano to plus or minus 4.00d sphere, .12 to 2.00d cylinder, per lens

V2204   Spherocylinder, bifocal, plano to plus or minus 4.00d sphere, 2.12 to 4.00d cylinder, per lens

V2205   Spherocylinder, bifocal, plano to plus or minus 4.00d sphere, 4.25 to 6.00d cylinder, per lens

V2206   Spherocylinder, bifocal, plano to plus or minus 4.00d sphere, over 6.00d cylinder, per lens

V2207   Spherocylinder, bifocal, plus or minus 4.25 to plus or minus 7.00d sphere,.12 to 2.00d cylinder, per lens

V2208   Spherocylinder, bifocal, plus or minus 4.25 to plus or minus 7.00d sphere, 2.12 to 4.00d cylinder, per lens

V2209   Spherocylinder, bifocal, plus or minus 4.25 to plus or minus 7.00d sphere, 4.25 to 6.00d cylinder, per lens

V2210   Spherocylinder, bifocal, plus or minus 4.25 to plus or minus 7.00d sphere, over 6.00d cylinder, per lens

V2211 Spherocylinder, bifocal, plus or minus 7.25 to plus or minus 12.00d sphere, .25 to 2.25d cylinder, per lens

V2212 Spherocylinder, bifocal, plus or minus 7.25 to plus or minus 12.00d sphere, 2.25 to 4.00d cylinder, per lens

V2213 Spherocylinder, bifocal, plus or minus 7.25 to plus or minus 12.00d sphere, 4.25 to 6.00d cylinder, per lens

V2214 Spherocylinder, bifocal, sphere over plus or minus 12.00d, per lens

V2215 Lenticular (myodisc), per lens, bifocal

V2218 Aniseikonic, per lens, bifocal

V2219 Bifocal seg width over 28 mm

V2220 Bifocal add over 3.25d

V2221 Lenticular lens, per lens, bifocal

MCM: 2130.B

V2299 Specialty bifocal (by report)

V2300 Sphere, trifocal, plano to plus or minus 4.00d, per lens

V2301 Sphere, trifocal, plus or minus 4.12 to plus or minus 7.00d, per lens

V2302 Sphere, trifocal, plus or minus 7.12 to plus or minus 20.00, per lens

V2303 Spherocylinder, trifocal, plano to plus or minus 4.00d sphere, .12-2.00d cylinder, per lens

V2304 Spherocylinder, trifocal, plano to plus or minus 4.00d sphere, 2.25-4.00d cylinder, per lens

V2305 Spherocylinder, trifocal, plano to plus or minus 4.00d sphere, 4.25 to 6.00 cylinder, per lens

V2306 Spherocylinder, trifocal, plano to plus or minus 4.00d sphere, over 6.00d cylinder, per lens

V2307 Spherocylinder, trifocal, plus or minus 4.25 to plus or minus 7.00d sphere, .12 to 2.00d cylinder, per lens

V2308 Spherocylinder, trifocal, plus or minus 4.25 to plus or minus 7.00d sphere, 2.12 to 4.00d cylinder, per lens

V2309 Spherocylinder, trifocal, plus or minus 4.25 to plus or minus 7.00d sphere, 4.25 to 6.00d cylinder, per lens

V2310 Spherocylinder, trifocal, plus or minus 4.25 to plus or minus 7.00d sphere, over 6.00d cylinder, per lens

V2311 Spherocylinder, trifocal, plus or minus 7.25 to plus or minus 12.00d sphere, .25 to 2.25d cylinder, per lens

V2312 Spherocylinder, trifocal, plus or minus 7.25 to plus or minus 12.00d sphere, 2.25 to 4.00d cylinder, per lens

• New code   ▲ Revised code   ( ) Deleted code   ⓉTrigger   ℗ Post Trigger DME

V2313	Spherocylinder, trifocal, plus or minus 7.25 to plus or minus 12.00d sphere, 4.25 to 6.00d cylinder, per lens
V2314	Spherocylinder, trifocal, sphere over plus or minus 12.00d, per lens
V2315	Lenticular, (myodisc), per lens, trifocal
V2318	Aniseikonic lens, trifocal
V2319	Trifocal seg width over 28 mm
V2320	Trifocal add over 3.25d
V2321	Lenticular lens, per lens, trifocal
	MCM: 2130.B
V2399	Specialty trifocal (by report)
V2410	Variable asphericity lens, single vision, full field, glass or plastic, per lens
V2430	Variable asphericity lens, bifocal, full field, glass or plastic, per lens
V2499	Variable sphericity lens, other type

Contact Lenses (CPT 92391 or 92396)

NOTE: If CPT code 92391 or 92396 is reported, recode with specific lens type listed below, per lens.

V2500	Contact lens, PMMA, spherical, per lens
V2501	Contact lens, PMMA, toric or prism ballast, per lens
V2502	Contact lens, PMMA, bifocal, per lens
V2503	Contact lens, PMMA, color vision deficiency, per lens
V2510	Contact lens, gas permeable, spherical, per lens
V2511	Contact lens, gas permeable, toric, prism ballast, per lens
V2512	Contact lens, gas permeable, bifocal, per lens
V2513	Contact lens, gas permeable, extended wear, per lens
V2520	Contact lens, hydrophilic, spherical, per lens
	CIM: 45-7, 65-1
V2521	Contact lens, hydrophilic, toric, or prism ballast, per lens
	CIM: 45-7, 65-1
V2522	Contact lens, hydrophilic, bifocal, per lens
	CIM: 45-7, 65-1
V2523	Contact lens, hydrophilic, extended wear, per lens
	CIM: 45-7, 65-1
V2530	Contact lens, scleral, gas impermeable, per lens (for contact lens modification, see 92325)
V2531	Contact lens, scleral, gas permeable, per lens (for contact lens modification, see 92325)

Not payable by Medicare	Non-covered by Medicare	Special coverage instructions	Carrier judgement

CIM: 65-3

V2599   Contact lens, other type

Low Vision Aids (CPT 92392)

NOTE: If CPT code 92392 is reported, record with specific systems listed below.

V2600   Hand held low vision aids and other nonspectacle mounted aids

V2610   Single lens spectacle mounted low vision aids

V2615   Telescopic and other compound lens system, including distance vision telescopic, near vision telescopes and compound microscopic lens system

Prosthetic Eye (CPT 92330 or 92393)

V2623   Prosthetic eye, plastic, custom

MCM: 2133

V2624   Polishing/resurfacing of ocular prosthesis

V2625   Enlargement of ocular prosthesis

V2626   Reduction of ocular prosthesis

V2627   Scleral cover shell

CIM: 65-3

V2628   Fabrication and fitting of ocular conformer

V2629   Prosthetic eye, other type

Intraocular Lenses

V2630   Anterior chamber intraocular lens

MCM: 2130

V2631   Iris supported intraocular lens

MCM: 2130

V2632   Posterior chamber intraocular lens

MCM: 2130

Miscellaneous

V2700   Balance lens, per lens

V2702   Deluxe lens feature

MCM: 2130B

V2710   Slab off prism, glass or plastic, per lens

V2715   Prism, per lens

V2718   Press-on lens, Fresnell prism, per lens

V2730 Special base curve, glass or plastic, per lens

V2744 Tint, photochromatic, per lens

MCM: 2130B

V2745 Addition to lens; tint, any color, solid, gradient or equal, excludes photochromatic, any lens material, per lens

MCM: 2130.B

V2750 Anti-reflective coating, per lens

MCM: 2130B

V2755 U-V lens, per lens

MCM: 2130B

V2756 Eye glass case

V2760 Scratch resistant coating, per lens

V2761 Mirror coating, any type, solid, gradient or equal, any lens material, per lens

MCM: 2130.B

V2762 Polarization, any lens material, per lens

MCM: 2130.B

V2770 Occluder lens, per lens

V2780 Oversize lens, per lens

V2781 Progressive lens, per lens

V2782 Lens, index 1.54 to 1.65 plastic or 1.60 to 1.79 glass, excludes polycarbonate, per lens

MCM: 2130.B

V2783 Lens, index greater than or equal to 1.66 plastic or greater than or equal to 1.80 glass, excludes polycarbonate, per lens

MCM: 2130.B

V2784 Lens, polycarbonate or equal, any index, per lens

MCM: 2130.B

V2785 Processing, preserving and transporting corneal tissue

V2786 Specialty occupational multifocal lens, per lens

MCM: 2130.B

V2787 Astigmatism correcting function of intraocular lens

Statute: 1862(a)(7)

V2788 Presbyopia correcting function of intraocular lens

Statute: 1862(a)(7)

V2790 Amniotic membrane for surgical reconstruction, per procedure

V2797 Vision supply, accessory and/or service component of another HCPCS vision code

V2799   Vision item or service, miscellaneous

Guidelines

In addition to the information presented in the INTRODUCTION, several other items unique to this section are defined or identified here:

1. PROSTHETIC DEVICES: Prosthetic devices that replace all or part of an internal body organ or the function of a permanently inoperative or malfunctioning internal body organ are covered when furnished on a physician's order. If the medical record and attending physician indicate the condition will be indefinite, the test of permanence is met.

2. SPEECH PATHOLOGY: Services necessary for diagnosing and treating speech disorders that result in communication disabilities, and swallowing disorders, regardless of the presence of a disability, are covered Medicare services if reasonable and necessary. The services must be considered to be an effective treatment for the patient's condition, and the patient's condition must be at a level of severity that requires the service of a qualified speech pathologist.

3. UNLISTED SERVICE OR PROCEDURE: A service or procedure may be provided that is not listed in this edition of HCPCS. When reporting such a service, the appropriate "unlisted procedure" code may be used to indicate the service, identifying it by "special report" as defined below. HCPCS terminology is inconsistent in defining unlisted procedures. The procedure definition may include the term(s) "unlisted", "not otherwise classified", "unspecified", "unclassified", "other" and "miscellaneous". Prior to using these codes, try to determine if a Local Level III code or CPT code is available. The "unlisted procedures" and accompanying codes for HEARING SERVICES are as follows:

    V5299   Hearing service, miscellaneous

4. SPECIAL REPORT: A service, material or supply that is rarely provided, unusual, variable or new may require a special report in determining medical appropriateness for reimbursement purposes. Pertinent information should include an adequate definition or description of the nature, extent, and need for the service, material or supply.

5. MODIFIERS: Listed services may be modified under certain circumstances. When appropriate, the modifying circumstance is identified by adding a modifier to the basic procedure code. CPT and HCPCS National Level II modifiers may be used with CPT and HCPCS National Level II procedure codes. Modifiers commonly used with HEARING SERVICES are as follows:

    -CC   Procedure code change (use "CC" when the procedure code submitted was changed either for administrative reasons or because an incorrect code was filed)

    -LT   Left side (used to identify procedures performed on the left side of the body)

    -RT   Right side (used to identify procedures performed on the right side of the body)

    -SF   Second opinion ordered by a professional review organization (PRO) per section 9401, P.L. 99-272 (100 percent reimbursement; no Medicare deductible or coinsurance)

-TC Technical component. Under certain circumstances, a charge may be made for the technical component alone. Under those circumstances, the technical component charge is identified by adding modifier -TC to the usual procedure number. Technical component charges are institutional charges and are not billed separately by physicians. However, portable x-ray suppliers bill only for the technical component and should use modifier -TC. The charge data from portable x-ray suppliers will then be used to build customary and prevailing profiles.

6. CPT CODE CROSS-REFERENCE: See sections for equivalent CPT code(s) for all listings in this section.

Hearing Services

V5008 Hearing screening

MCM: 2320

V5010 Assessment for hearing aid

Statute: 1862A7

V5011 Fitting/orientation/checking of hearing aid

Statute: 1862A7

V5014 Repair/modification of a hearing aid

Statute: 1862A7

V5020 Conformity evaluation

Statute: 1862A7

V5030 Hearing aid, monaural, body worn, air conduction

Statute: 1862A7

V5040 Hearing aid, monaural, body worn, bone conduction

Statute: 1862A7

V5050 Hearing aid, monaural, in the ear

Statute: 1862A7

V5060 Hearing aid, monaural, behind the ear

Statute: 1862A7

V5070 Glasses, air conduction

Statute: 1862A7

V5080 Glasses, bone conduction

Statute: 1862A7

V5090 Dispensing fee, unspecified hearing aid

Statute: 1862A7

V5095 Semi-implantable middle ear hearing prosthesis

Statute: 1862A7

V5100 Hearing aid, bilateral, body worn

Statute: 1862A7

V5110   Dispensing fee, bilateral

Statute: 1862A7

V5120   Binaural, body

Statute: 1862A7

V5130   Binaural, in the ear

Statute: 1862A7

V5140   Binaural, behind the ear

Statute: 1862A7

V5150   Binaural, glasses

Statute: 1862A7

V5160   Dispensing fee, binaural

Statute: 1862A7

V5170   Hearing aid, cros, in the ear

Statute: 1862A7

V5180   Hearing aid, cros, behind the ear

Statute: 1862A7

V5190   Hearing aid, cros, glasses

Statute: 1862A7

V5200   Dispensing fee, cros

Statute: 1862A7

V5210   Hearing aid, bicros, in the ear

Statute: 1862A7

V5220   Hearing aid, bicros, behind the ear

Statute: 1862A7

V5230   Hearing aid, bicros, glasses

Statute: 1862A7

V5240   Dispensing fee, bicros

Statute: 1862A7

V5241   Dispensing fee, monaural hearing aid, any type

Statute: 1862A7

V5242   Hearing aid, analog, monaural, cic (completely in the ear canal)

Statute: 1862A7

V5243   Hearing aid, analog, monaural, itc (in the canal)

Statute: 1862A7

V5244 Hearing aid, digitally programmable analog, monaural, cic

Statute: 1862A7

V5245 Hearing aid, digitally programmable, analog, monaural, itc

Statute: 1862A7

V5246 Hearing aid, digitally programmable analog, monaural, ite (in the ear)

Statute: 1862A7

V5247 Hearing aid, digitally programmable analog, monaural, bte (behind the ear)

Statute: 1862A7

V5248 Hearing aid, analog, binaural, cic

Statute: 1862A7

V5249 Hearing aid, analog, binaural, itc

Statute: 1862A7

V5250 Hearing aid, digitally programmable analog, binaural, cic

Statute: 1862A7

V5251 Hearing aid, digitally programmable analog, binaural, itc

Statute: 1862A7

V5252 Hearing aid, digitally programmable, binaural, ite

Statute: 1862A7

V5253 Hearing aid, digitally programmable, binaural, bte

Statute: 1862A7

V5254 Hearing aid, digital, monaural, cic

Statute: 1862A7

V5255 Hearing aid, digital, monaural, itc

Statute: 1862A7

V5256 Hearing aid, digital, monaural, ite

Statute: 1862A7

V5257 Hearing aid, digital, monaural, bte

Statute: 1862A7

V5258 Hearing aid, digital, binaural, cic

Statute: 1862A7

V5259 Hearing aid, digital, binaural, itc

Statute: 1862A7

V5260 Hearing aid, digital, binaural, ite

Statute: 1862A7

V5261 Hearing aid, digital, binaural, bte

Statute: 1862A7

V5262 Hearing aid, disposable, any type, monaural

Statute: 1862A7

V5263 Hearing aid, disposable, any type, binaural

Statute: 1862A7

V5264 Ear mold/insert, not disposable, any type

Statute: 1862A7

V5265 Ear mold/insert, disposable, any type

Statute: 1862A7

V5266 Battery for use in hearing device

Statute: 1862A7

V5267 Hearing aid or assistive listening device/supplies/accessories, not otherwise specified

Statute: 1862A7

V5268 Assistive listening device, telephone amplifier, any type

Statute: 1862A7

V5269 Assistive listening device, alerting, any type

Statute: 1862A7

V5270 Assistive listening device, television amplifier, any type

Statute: 1862A7

V5271 Assistive listening device, television caption decoder

Statute: 1862A7

V5272 Assistive listening device, tdd

Statute: 1862A7

V5273 Assistive listening device, for use with cochlear implant

Statute: 1862A7

V5274 Assistive listening device, not otherwise specified

Statute: 1862A7

V5275 Ear impression, each

Statute: 1862A7

V5281 Assistive listening device, personal fm/dm system, monaural, (1 receiver, transmitter, microphone), any type

Statute: 1862a7

V5282 Assistive listening device, personal fm/dm system, binaural, (2 receivers, transmitter, microphone), any type

Statute: 1862a7

V5283 Assistive listening device, personal fm/dm neck, loop induction receiver

Statute: 1862a7

V5284 Assistive listening device, personal fm/dm, ear level receiver

Statute: 1862a7

V5285 Assistive listening device, personal fm/dm, direct audio input receiver

Statute: 1862a7

V5286 Assistive listening device, personal blue tooth fm/dm receiver

Statute: 1862a7

V5287 Assistive listening device, personal fm/dm receiver, not otherwise specified

Statute: 1862a7

V5288 Assistive listening device, personal fm/dm transmitter assistive listening device

Statute: 1862a7

V5289 Assistive listening device, personal fm/dm adapter/boot coupling device for receiver, any type

Statute: 1862a7

V5290 Assistive listening device, transmitter microphone, any type

Statute: 1862a7

V5298 Hearing aid, not otherwise classified

Statute: 1862A7

V5299 Hearing service, miscellaneous

MCM: 2320

V5336 Repair/modification of augmentative communicative system or device (excludes adaptive hearing aid)

Statute: 1862A7

V5362 Speech screening

Statute: 1862(a)(7)

V5363 Language screening

Statute: 1862(a)(7)

V5364 Dysphagia screening

Statute: 1862(a)(7)

ALPHABETIC INDEX

Questions regarding coding and billing guidance should be submitted to the insurer in whose jurisdiction a claim would be filed. For private sector health insurance systems, please contact the individual private insurance entity. For Medicaid systems, please contact the Medicaid Agency in the state in which the claim is being filed. For Medicare, contact the Medicare contractor.

A

Activated carbon filter	A4680
Activity therapy	G0176, H2032
Acyclovir	J0133, J8499
Adagen	J2504
Adalimumab	J0135
Adapter replacement	A4282
Adaptor/extension, pacing lead or neurostimulator lead (implantable)	C1883
Additive	B4104
Adenoma(s) or colorectal cancer	G9933, G9935
Adenosine	J0151, J0153
Adhesion barrier	C1765
Adhesive	
bandage	A6413
disc or foam pad	A5126
disc	A7506
liquid or equal	A4364
remover	A4455, A4456
support, breast prosthesis	A4280
Adjunctive blue light cystoscopy	C9738
Adjustable angle footplate	K0040
Adjustable chair	E1570
Adjustment gastric band diameter	S2083
Administration	
hepatitis b vaccine	G0010
influenza virus vaccine	G0008
medication	T1503
oral, im and/or subcutaneous medication	T1502
pneumococcal vaccine	G0009
Administration set	A7003, A7005, A7006
Administrative, Miscellaneous and Investigational	A9000-A9999
Adoptive immunotherapy	S2107
Ado-trastuzumab	J9354
Adrenal tissue transplant to brain	S2103
Adrenalin	J0171
Adrucil	J9190
Adult sized disposable incontinence product	
brief/diaper	T4521
protective brief/diaper	T4543
protective underwear	T4525
Advanced life support	
level 2 (advanced life support 2)	A0433

Amitriptyline HCL	G6030, J1320
Ammonia N-13	A9526
Ammonia test paper	A4774
Amnioband or guardian	Q4151
Amnioexcel or biodexcel	Q4137
Amniomatrix or Biomatrix	Q4139
Amniopro flow, BioSkin flow, Biorenew flow, Woundex flow, Aminogen-a,	
Aminogen-c	Q4162, Q4163
Amnio wound	Q4181
Amniotic membrane	V2790
Amobarbital	J0300
Amphadase	J3470
Amphetamine or methamphetamine	G6042
Amphotericin B	J0285
cholesteryl sulfate complex	J0288
lipid complex	J0287, J0287-J0289
liposome	J0289
Ampicillin	J0290, J0295
Amputee	
adapter, wheelchair	E0959
prosthesis	L5000-L7510, L7520, L7900, L8400-L8465
stump sock	L8470-L8485
wheelchair	E1170-E1190, E1200, K0100
Amygdalin	J3570
Anastrozole	J8999
Anastrozole, oral	S0170
Anchor/screw	C1713
Androgen deprivation therapy	G9894
Anectine	J0330
Anestacaine	J0330
Angiomax	J0583
Anidulafungin	J0348
Aniseikonic lens	
bifocal	V2218
single vision	V2118
trifocal	V2318
Anistreplase	J0350
Ankle control orthosis stirrup style, rigid	L4350
Ankle foot orthosis	
double upright free plantar dorsiflexion	L1990
fracture orthosis	L2106

Anti-reflective coating, per lens	V2750
Antisperm antibodies test (immunobead)	S3655
Antithrombin III	J7197
Antithrombin recombinant	J7196
Anzemet	J1260, Q0180
Apidra	Q0180
Apligraf	Q4101
Apnea monitor	E0618, E0619
Apomorphine HCL	J0364
Appliance cleaner	A5131
incontinence and ostomy appliances	A5131
pneumatic	E0655-E0673
Application a modality	S8948
Application low cost skin substitute graft	
face, scalp, eyelids, mouth, neck, ears, orbits, genitalia, hands, feet, and/or multiple digits	C5275
trunk, arms, legs	C5271
Aprepitant, oral	J8501
Aprotinin	J0365
Aqueous shunt	L8612
Aralast Np	J0256
Aranesp	J0881
sterile	J7051
Arbutamine HCL	J0395
Arch support	L3040-L3100
Architect, architect px, or architect fx, extracellular matrix	Q4147
Arformoterol, inhalation solution	J7605
Argatroban	J0883-J0884
Arimidex	J0881
Aripiprazole	J0400, J0401
Aristospan	J3303
Arixtra	J1652
Arm	
pad	K0019
rest	E0994
wheelchair	E0973
Aromasin	J1652
Arranon	J9261
Arsenic trioxide	J9017
Arthroereisis, subtalar	S2117
Arthroflex	Q4125
Arthroscopy	

Atgam	J7504
Ativan	J7504
Atropine sulfate	J0461
Atropine inhalation solution	J7635, J7636
Attendant care services	S5125, S5126
Audiologic assessment	V5008-V5020
Audiometry	S0618
Auditory osseointegrated device	L8690, L8690-L8693, L8691, L8692
transducer/actuator, replacement only, each	L8694
Auricular prosthesis	L8045
Aurothioglucose	J2910
Autologous cultured chondrocytes, implant	J7330
Autologous platelet rich plasma	G0460
Automatic blood pressure monitor	A4670
Automatic external defibrillator	K0606
Automatic grasp feature	L6881
Automatic intermittent peritoneal dialysis system	E1592
Avastin	J9035
Avelox iv	J2280
Avonex pen	J1826
Axillary crutch extension	L0978
Azacitidine	J9025
Azasan	J1826
Azathioprine	J1826, J7500, J7501
Azithromycin	J0456
Azithromycin dihydrate, oral, capsules/powder	Q0144
Aztreonam	S0073

B

Baci-IM	J0456
Bacitracin	J0456
Back school	S9117
Back supports	L0621-L0861, L0960
Back, contoured	E2293
Back, planar	E2291
Back pain	
Back pain measured by the visual analog scale (vas)	G9941, G9944
Back pain not measured by the visual analog scale (vas)	G9943, G9946
Baclofen	J0475, J0475, J0476
Bacterial sensitivity study	P7001

Bag

drainage	A4357
irrigation supply	A4398
urinary	A5112, A4358

Balance lens — V2700

Ballistocardiogram — S3902

Banaril — J1200

Banophen — J1200

Barbiturates, not elsewhere specified — G6043

Basic life support

mileage (per mile)	A0380
routine disposable supplies	A0382
specialized service disposable supplies	A0384

Basiliximab — J0480

Bath conductivity meter — E1550

Bathtub

chair	E0240
stool or bench	E0245, E0247-E0248
transfer rail	E0246
wall rail	E0241, E0242

Battery

cables replacement	A4612
charger replacement	A4613
charger	E1066, L7362, L7366, L7360, L7364-L7368, Q0503
clips electric or electric/pneumatic ventricular assist device	Q0497
heavy duty replacement	A4611
lithium-ion electric or electric/pneumatic ventricular assist device	Q0506
other than lithium-ion electric or electric/pneumatic ventricular assist device	Q0496
replacement for blood glucose monitor	A4233-A4236
replacement for cochlear implant device	L8623-L8624
replacement for TENS	A4630, V5266
ventilator	A4611-A4613

Battery/power pack charger electric or electric/pneumatic ventricular assist device — Q0495

BayHep b — J1200

BCG live, intravesical — J9031

BCG vaccine — J1200

Becaplermin gel — S0157

Beclomethasone inhalation solution — J7622

Bed

accessory board, table, or support device	E0315
air fluidized	E0194

board — E0273

cradle — E0280

cradle — E0280

drainage bag, bottle — A4357, A5102

hospital — E0250-E0270, E0300-E0329

rail — E0305, E0310

safety enclosure frame/canopy — E0316

side rails, full length — E0310

side rails, half length — E0305

Bed pan

fracture, metal or plastic — E0276

standard, metal or plastic — E0275

Bedside

drainage bag — A4357

drainage bottle — A5102

Behavioral health

counseling and therapy — H0004

day treatment — H2012

hotline service — H0030

long-term care residential — T2048

long-term residential — H0019

outreach service — H0023

prevention education service — H0025

prevention information dissemination service — H0024

residential — H0017

screening to determine eligibility — H0002

short-term residential — H0018

Belatacept — J0485

Belimumab — J0490

Belinostat — J9032

belt, strap, sleeve, garment, or covering, any type — A4467

extremity — E0945

ostomy — A4367

pelvic — E0944

safety — K0031

wheelchair — E0978, E0979

Belt/vest/bag — Q0499

Benadryl — J1200

Bench, bathtub (*see also* **Bathtub**) — E0245

Bendamustine HCL — J9033

BeneFIX — J7195

Benesch boot	L3212-L3214
Benesch boot, pair	
child	L3213
infant	L3212
junior	L3214
Bentyl	J0500
Benzacot	J3250
Benzocaine	J3250
Benzodiazepines	G6031
Benztropine	J0515
Beta-1a	J1826, Q3027, Q3028
Beta-1b	J1830
Betadine	A4246, A4247
Betadine or iodine swabs/wipes, per box	A4247
Betadine or pHisoHex solution	A4246
Betameth	J0704
Betamethasone acetate and betamethasone sodium phosphate	J0702
Betamethasone acetate micronized	J0515
Betamethasone dipropionate	J7624
Betamethasone inhalation solution	J7624
Betaseron	J1830
Bethanechol chloride	J0520
Bethkis	J0520
Bevacizumab	C9257, J9035, J9035, Q2024
Bicarbonate concentrate,	
powder	A4707
solution	A4706
Bicillin l-a	J0561
BiCNU	J9050
Bifocal	
add over 3.25d	V2220
glass or plastic	V2200-V2299
seg width over 28mm	V2219
vision prescription lens	S0506
Bilirubin (phototherapy) light	E0202
Binaural	
behind the ear	V5140
body	V5120
glasses	V5150
in the ear	V5130
Binder	A4465

ytterbium-169	C2637
yttrium-90	C2616
stranded	C2638
cesium-131	C2642
iodine-125	C2638
nos	C2698
palladium-103	C2640
Brake attachment	E0159
Breast prosthesis	
adhesive skin support	A4280, L8000-L8035, L8600, L8020, L8039
mastectomy bra	L8000
mastectomy sleeve	L8010
silicone or equal	L8030
Breast pump	
accessories	A4281-A4286
electric	E0603
heavy duty, hospital grade	E0604
manual	E0602
Breast reconstruction	S2066-S2068
Breast shield and splash protector	A4284
Breathing circuits	A4618
Brentuximab Vedotin	J9042
Brief face-to-face behavioral counseling	G0443
Brompheniramine maleate	J0945
Broncho saline	A4216
Brovana	J7605
Budesonide inhalation solution	J7626, J7627, J7633, J7634
Bulking agent	L8604, L8607
Bumetanide	J7626, S0171
Bupivacaine	J7626
Bupivacaine liposome	C9290
Bupivicaine HCL	S0020
Bupperenorphine HCL	J0592
Bupperenorphine/naloxone, oral	J0571, J0572, J0573, J0574, J0575
Bupperopion HCL	S0106
Buprenex	J0592
Buprenorphine HCL	J0592
Buprenorphine/naloxone	J0571-J0575
Bus, nonemergency transportation	A0110
Busulfan	J0594, J0594, J8510, J8510
Butorphanol tartrate	J0595

Butorphanol tartrate, nasal spray   S0012

C

Cefotetan   J0698

Cefotetan disodium   S0074

Cefoxitin   J0694

Ceftaroline fosamil   J0712

Ceftazidime   J0713, J0713, J0714

Ceftizoxime sodium   J0715

Ceftolozane 50 mg and tazobactam 25 mg   J0695

Ceftriaxone sodium   J0696

Cefuroxime sodium   J0697

Celestone Soluspan   J0702

CellCept   J7517, K0412

Cellular therapy   M0075

Cement, ostomy   A4364

Centrifuge   A4650, E1500

Centruroides Immune F(ab)   J0716

Cephalin flocculation, blood   P2028

Cephalothin sodium   J1890

Cephapirin sodium   J0710

Ceprotin   J2724

Certolizumab pegol   J0717

Cervical

     halo   L0810-L0830

     head harness/halter   E0942

     orthosis   L0100-L0200

     traction   E0855, E0856

Cervical cap contraceptive   A4261

Cervical collar

     flexible, non-adjustable, prefabricated, off-the-shelf (foam collar)   L0120

     flexible, thermoplastic molded to patient   L0130

     molded to patient model   L0170

     multiple post occipital/mandibular supports   L0190, L0200, L0180

     semi-rigid

         adjustable (plastic collar)   L0140

         adjustable molded chin cup   L0150

         thermoplastic foam   L0172, L0174

         wire frame occipital/mandibular support   L0160

Cervical head harness/halter   E0942

Cervical or vaginal cancer screening pelvic and clinical breast examination   G0101

Cervical thoracic lumbar sacral orthosis immobilizer, infant size, prefabricated   L1001

Cervical traction device   E0856

Cervical traction equipment   E0855

Chlorpromazine HCL	J3230, Q0161
Chore services	S5120, S5121
Chorionic gonadotropin	J0725
Chromic phosphate p-32 suspension	A9564
Chromium cr-51 sodium chromate, diagnostic	A9553
Cidofovir	J0740
Cilastatin sodium, imipenem	J0743
Cimetidine HCL	S0023
Cinacalcet, oral, 1 mg, (for esrd on dialysis)	J0604
Ciprofloxacin	
for intravenous infusion	J0744
octic suspension	J7342
Cisplatin	J9060
Cladribine	J9065
Claforan	J0698
Clamp	
dialysis	A4918
external urethral	A4356
Cleaning device tracheoesophageal voice prosthesis	L8513
Cleanser, wound	A6260
Cleansing agent, dialysis equipment	A4790
Cleocin phosphate	J0698
Clevidipine butyrate	C9248
Clinically node negative invasive breast cancer	G9911
Clinacort	J0698
Clindamycin	J0698
Clindamycin phosphate	J0698, S0077
Clinic visit/encounter, all-inclusive	T1015
Clofarabine	J9027
Clolar	J9027
Clonidine	J0735
Closure device vascular (implantable/insertable)	C1760
Clotting time tube	A4771
Clozapine	S0136
Clubfoot wedge	L3380
Cobalt co-57/58, not otherwise classified cyanocobalamin	A9546, A9559
Cobolin-m	J0735
Cocaine or metabolite	G6044
Cochlear device	L8614
Cochlear implant	
external controller component, replacement	L8628

D

Delatestryl	J0895
Delestrogen	J1380
Delivery and/or installation charges	E1600
Delivery or service to high risk areas	S9381
Delivery/set-up/dispensing	A9901
Deltasone	J1380
Deluxe frame	V2025
Deluxe item	S1001
Deluxe lens feature	V2702
Demerol HCL	J1380
Denileukin diftitox	J9160
Denosumab	J0897
Depo-Cobolin	J1380
DepoCyt	J9098
Depo-estradiol cypionate	J1000
Depo-Medrol	J1030
Depo-Provera contraceptive	J1050
Depo-testosterone	J1071
Dermacell	Q4122
Dermagraft	Q4106
Dermal filler injection(s)	G0429
Dermal substitute, native, non-denatured collagen	
fetal bovine origin (Surgimend collagen matrix)	C9358
neonatal bovine origin (Surgimend collagen matrix)	C9360
Dermapure	Q4152
Dermavest and Plurivest	Q4153
Desferal	J0895
Desipramine	G6032
Desmopressin acetate	J2597
Destruction localized lesion choroid	G0186
Detachable, adjustable height armrest	
base	K0017
upper portion	K0018
Detachable, non-adjustable height armrest	K0015
Detector, blood leak, dialysis	E1560
Development cognitive skills to improve attention, memory, problem solving	G0515
Development testing interpretation and report	G0451
Developmental delay prevention activities, dependent child client	H2037
Dexamethasone	J2597
acetate	J1094
inhalation solution	J7637, J7638

Dialysis equipment, nos	E1699
Dialysis/stress vitamin supplement, oral	S0194
Dialyzer	A4690
Diaper	T1500, T4521-T4540, T4543, T4544
Diaper service	T4538
Diaper, adult	
incontinence garment	A4520
incontinence supply, rectal insert , each	A4337
Diaphragm	A4266
Diazepam	J3360
Diazoxide	J1730
Dicyclocot	J0500
Dicyclomine HCL	J0500
Didanosine (ddi)	S0137
Diethylstilbestrol diphosphate	J9165
Digoxin	J1160
Digoxin immune Fab (ovine)	J1162
Dihydrocodeinone	G6045
Dihydroergotamine mesylate	J1110
Dihydromorphinone	G6046
Dihydrotestosterone	G6047
Dilated macular exam	G9890, G9893, G9974, G9977
Dilaudid	J1170
Dimenhydrinate	J1240
Dimercaprol	J0470
Dimethadione	G6048
Dimethyl sulfoxide (DMSO)	J1212
Diphedryl	J1212
Diphenhist	J1212
Diphenhydramine HCL	J1200
oral	Q0163
Diphenyl	J1200
Diphenyl elixir	J1200
Diprivan	J1200
Dipyridamole	J1245
Direct (face-to-face	G0128
Direct admission patient	G0379
Direct skilled nursing services	
license practical nurse (LPN)	G0300
registered nurse (RN)	G0299

Dopamine HCL J1265

Doripenem J1267

Dormin sleep aid J1265

Dornase alfa, inhalation solution J7639

Dose optimization S3722

Doxepin G6034

Doxercalciferol J1270

Doxil J9001

Doxorubicin HCL J9000, J9000, J9002

Doxorubicin HCL, liposomal

    imported Lipidox Q2049

    nos Q2050

Drain bag/bottle A4911

Drainage

    bag A4357, A4358

    board, postural E0606

    bottle A5102

Drainage extension line A4672

Dressing (see also Bandage)

    alginate A6196-A6199

    collagen A6020-A6024

    composite A6200-A6205

    contact layer A6206-A6208

    foam A6209-A6215

    gauze A6216-A6230, A6402-A6406

    holder/binder A4462

    hydrocolloid A6234-A6241

    hydrogel A6242-A6248

    specialty absorptive A6251-A6256

    transparent film A6257-A6259

    tubular A6457

Drive belt K0098

Driver Q0480

Dronabinol Q0167

Droperidol J1790

Droperidol and fentanyl citrate J1810

Dropper A4649

Droxia J1790

Drug confirmation procedure G6058

Drug or biological, not otherwise classified Q4082

E

Endarterectomy, chemical	M0300
Endoscope sheath	A4270
Endoscope, retrograde imaging/illumination colonoscope device	C1749
Endoskeletal ankle foot system	L5973
Endoskeletal system, addition	L5848, L5856-L5857, L5925, L5969
Enema bag	A4458
Enfuvirtide	J1324
Engerix-B	J1438
Enlargement ocular prosthesis	V2625
Enoxaparin sodium	J1650
Enteral	
feeding supply kit (syringe) (pump) (gravity)	B4034-B4036
formula	B4102, B4103, B4158, B4159, B4160, B4161, B4162
hydrolyzed proteins (amino acids and peptide chain)	B4153
inherited disease of metabolism	B4157
intact nutrients	B4150
manufactured blenderized natural foods	B4149
nutritionally complete	B4154
Enteral nutrition infusion pump	B9000, B9002
Enterostomal therapy by a registered nurse	S9474
Enuresis alarm	S8270
Envarsus XR	J7503
Eosinophil count, blood, direct	S3630
Epiandrosterone	G6049
Epifix	Q4131
Epifix, injectable	Q4145
Epinephrine	J0171
Epirubicin HCL	J0171, J9178
Epoetin alfa	
for esrd on dialysis	Q4081
for non-esrd use	J0885
Epoetin beta	J0887-J0888
for esrd on dialysis	J0887
Epogen	J0885
Epoprostenol	J1325
Eptifibatide	J1327
Equestrian/hippotherapy	S8940
Erbitux	J9055
Ergonovine maleate	J1330
Eribulin mesylate	J9179
Erivedge	J9055

F

dialysis carbon A4680

ostomy A4368

tracheostoma A4481

ultrasonic generator A7014

Filter holder and integrated filter A7507

Filter holder and integrated filter housing, and adhesive A7509

Filter holder or filter cap, reusable A7503

Filter

disposable

aerosol compressor or ultrasonic generator A7013

positive airway pressure device A7038

nondisposable A7014

Filters electric or electric/pneumatic ventricular assist device Q0500

Financial management, self-directed, waiver T2040

Finasteride S0138

Finger orthosis L3933

nontorsion joint L3935

proximal interphalangeal (pip)/distal interphalangeal (dip) L3925

Finger splint, static Q4049

Fistula cannulation set A4730

Fitting/orientation/checking hearing aid V5011

Fixed wing air mileage, per statute mile A0435

Fixed, adjustable height armrest, pair K0020

Flebogamma J1572

Flex hd, allopatch hd, or matrix hd Q4128

Flolan J1325

Florbetapir F18 .... A9586

Floweramnioflo Q4177

Floweramniopatch Q4178

Flowerderm Q4179

Flowmeter E0440, E0555, E0580

Floxuridine J9200

Fluconazole, injection J1450

Fludarabine phosphate J8562, J9185, J9185

Fluid barrier, dialysis E1575

Flunisolide, inhalation solution J7641

Fluocinolone J7311, J7313

Fluorine-18 fluorodeoxyglucose (f-18 fdg) imaging S8085

Fluorodeoxyglucose F-18 FDG A9552

Fluorouracil J7641, J9190

Fluphenazine decanoate J2680

Frozen in vitro fertilization cycle	S4016
Full face mask positive airway pressure device	A7030
Full sole and heel wedge, between sole	L3420
Fully-reclining wheelchair	
detachable arms (desk or full length)	E1070
detachable arms, desk or full length)	E1060
fixed full length arms	E1050
Fulvestrant	J9395
Functional electrical stimulator	E0770
Functional neuromuscular stimulation	E0764
Functional status not performed	G9918
Functional status performed	G9916
Furosemide	J1940
Fuzeon	J1324

G

Gadobenate dimeglumine (MultiHance)	A9577, A9578
Gadobutrol	A9585
Gadofosveset trisodium	A9583
Gadolinium-based magnetic resonance contrast agent, nos	A9579
Gadoterate meglumine	A9575
Gadoteridol, (ProHance multipack)	A9576
Gadoxetate disodium	A9581
Gait trainer	E8000-E8002
Gait trainer, pediatric size	
anterior support	E8002
posterior support	E8000
pediatric size, upright support	E8001
Gallium ga67	A9556
Gallium nitrate	J1457
Galsulfase	J1458
GamaSTAN s	J1460
Gamma	J9216
Gamma globulin	J1460, J1560
Gammagard liquid	J1569
Gammagard s	J1566
Gammagraft	Q4111
Gammaked	J1561
Gammaplex	J1557
Gamunex	J1561

Ganciclovir sodium	J1570
Ganciclovir, implant	J7310
Ganirelix acetate	J1561, S0132
Garamycin	J1580
Garment, belt, sleeve or other covering	A4466
Gas system	
compressed	E0424, E0425
gaseous	E0430, E0431, E0441, E0443
liquid	E0434-E0440, E0442, E0444
Gasket or seal, for use with prosthetic socket insert	L7700
Gastric suction pump home model	E2000
Gastrointestinal fat absorption study	S3708
Gastrostomy/jejunostomy tube	
low-profile, any material	B4088
standard, any material	B4087
Gatifloxacin	J1590
Gauze (*see also* Bandage)	
impregnated	A6222-A6233, A6266
impregnated, hydrogel	A6231
impregnated, water or normal saline	A6228
non-impregnated	A6219
non-impregnated	A6402-A6404
non-impregnated, non-sterile	A6216
Gefitinib	J8565
Gel	
conductive	A4558
pressure pad	E0185, E0196
Gel or gel-like pressure pad	E0185
Gel pressure mattress	E0196
Gel sheet	A6025
Gelatin capsule, application device	L8515
Gelatin capsules or equivalent	L8512
Gemcitabine	J1561
Gemcitabine HCL	J9201
Gemtuzumab ozogamicin	J9300
Gemzar	J9201
Genahist	J9201
General use wheelchair	
back cushion	E2611, E2612
seat cushion	E2601, E2602
Generator	

H

detachable arms desk or full length, swing away detachable footrests ... E1086

Hemodialysis machine ... E1590

Hemodialyzer, portable ... E1635

Hemofil M ... J7190

Hemophilia clotting factor ... J7190-J7198, J7199

Hemostats ... A4850, E1637

Hemostix ... A4773

HepaGam B

   IM ... J1571

   IV ... J1573

Heparin infusion pump, dialysis ... E1520

Heparin lock flush ... J1642

Heparin sodium ... J1644

Hepatitis B immune globulin

   HepaGam b), im ... J1571

   HepaGam b), iv ... J1573

Hepatitis b virus (HBV) status assessed ... G9912

Hepatitis b virus (HBV) status not assessed ... G9913

Hepatitis C antibody screening ... G0472

Hep-Lock (U/P) ... J1642

Herceptin ... J9355

Hexalite ... A4590

Hexaminolevulinate HCL, per study dose ... C9275

High compression bandage, elastic, knitted/woven ... A6452

High frequency chest wall oscillation

   air-pulse generator system ... E0483

   system hose, replacement ... A7026

   system vest, replacement ... A7025

High intensity behavioral counseling to prevent sexually transmitted infection ... G0445

High mount flip-up footrest ... K0037

High osmolar contrast material ... Q9958, Q9958-Q9964, Q9959, Q9960, Q9961, Q9962, Q9963, Q9964

High strength lightweight wheelchair ... E1087, E1088, E1089, K004

Hip

   disarticulation prosthesis ... L5250, L5270

   orthosis (HO) ... L1600-L1690

Hip core decompression ... S2325

Hip disarticulation

   Canadian type ... L5250

   Canadian type, molded socket ... L5331

   tilt table type ... L5270

diuretic IV therapy   S9361

enzyme replacement IV therapy   S9357

hydration therapy   S9373

immunotherapy   S9338

implanted pump pain management infusion   S9328

infusion therapy   S9379

insertion of midline venous catheter   S5523

insertion of peripherally inserted central venous catheter (PICC)   S5522

intermittent (less than twenty-four hours) chemotherapy infusion   S9331

intermittent (less than twenty-four hours) pain management infusion   S9327

pain management infusion   S9325

repair of infusion device (e.g. pump repair)   S5036

routine service of infusion device   S5035, S5517, S5518, S5520, S5521

sympathomimetic/inotropic agent infusion therapy   S9348

tocolytic infusion therapy   S9349

total parenteral nutrition (tpn)   S9364

uninterrupted, long-term, controlled rate IV or subcutaneous infusion therapy   S9347

Home injectable therapy

growth hormone   S9558

hormonal therapy   S9560

interferon   S9559

palivizumab   S9562, S9542

Home management

gestational diabetes   S9214

gestational hypertension   S9211

postpartum hypertension   S9212

preeclampsia   S9213

preterm labor   S9208

preterm premature rupture   S9209

Home modifications   S5165

Home sleep test (hst)   G0398-G0400

Home therapy

enteral nutrition   S9340

enteral nutrition via bolus   S9343

enteral nutrition via gravity   S9341

enteral nutrition via pump   S9342

hematopoietic hormone injection therapy (e.g. erythropoietin, g-csf, gm-csf)   S9537

hemodialysis   S9335

intermittent anticoagulant injection therapy (e.g. heparin)   S9372

intermittent anti-emetic injection therapy   S9370

irrigation therapy   S9590

I

Imitrex — J9208

Imlygic — J9208

Immediate post surgical or early fitting

    application of initial rigid dressing — L5400

    application of non-weight bearing rigid dressing — L5450

    application of rigid dressing — L6388, L6386

Immersion external heater — E1372

Immune globulin

    Bivigam — J1556

    Flebogamma/Flebogamma dif, iv, non-lyophilized (e.g. liquid) — J1572

    Gammagard liquid), non-lyophilized, (e.g. liquid) — J1569

    Gammaplex, iv, non-lyophilized (e.g. liquid) — J1557

    Gamunex-c/gammaked, non-lyophilized (e.g. liquid) — J1561

    HepaGam B — J1571

    Hizentra — J1559, J1575

    lyophilized (e.g. powder), nos — J1566

    non-lyophilized (e.g. liquid), nos — J1599

    Octagam, iv, non-lyophilized (e.g. liquid) — J1568

    Privigen, iv, non-lyophilized (e.g. liquid) — J1459

    Vivaglobin — J1562

Immune globulin/hyaluronidase, (hyqvia) immunoglobulin — J1575

Immunosuppressive drug, not otherwise classified — J7599

Implant

    access system — A4301

    aqueous shunt — L8612

    breast — L8600

    cochlear — L8614, L8619

    collagen, urinary tract — L8603

    dextranomer/hyaluronic acid copolymer — L8604

    ganciclovir — J7310

    hallux — L8642

    infusion pump, programmable — E0783, E0786

    joint — L8630, L8641, L8658

    lacrimal duct — A4262, A4263

    metacarpophalangeal joint — L8630

    metatarsal joint — L8641

    neurostimulator pulse generator — L8679, L8681-L8688

    not otherwise specified — L8699

    ocular — L8610

    ossicular — L8613

    osteogenesis stimulator — E0749

rectal insert	A4337
urethral insert	A4336
Incontinence treatment system pelvic floor stimulator	E0740
Increlex	J2170
Indium IN-111	
capromab pendetide	A9507
ibritumomab tiuxetan	A9542
labeled autologous platelets	A9571
labeled autologous white blood cells	A9570
oxyquinoline	A9547
pentetate	A9548
pentetreotide	A9572
satumomab	A4642
Induced abortion	S2260, S2265, S2266, S2267
Indwelling catheter	
Foley type, three way	A4346
Foley type, two-way latex	A4338
Foley type, two-way, all silicone	A4344
specialty type, eg	A4340
Infant safety (including CPR) classes, non-physician provider	S9447
Infection control supplies	S8301
Infectious agent antibody detection HIV-1 and/or HIV-2, screening	G0432, G0433
Infectious agent detection by nucleic acid (DNA or RNA)	G0476
INFeD	J1750
Infliximab injection	J1745
Influenza virus vaccine, split virus	Q2034, Q2035, Q2036, Q2037, Q2038, Q2039
Infrared heating pad system	E0221
Infumorph	J1750
Infusion	
albumin (human)	P9041
d5w	J7070
dextran 40	J7100
dextran 75	J7110
normal saline solution	J7030
plasma protein fraction (human)	P9043
pump	C1772
ambulatory, with administrative equipment	E0781
heparin, dialysis	E1520
implantable	E0782, E0783
implantable, refill kit	A4220
insulin	E0784

passive restoration (shoulder cap only)   L6370

Interscapular-thoracic, external power, molded inner socket   L6970

Interspinous process distraction device (implantable)   C1821

Intra-fraction localization and tracking target or patient motion   G6017

Intragastric hypothermia using gastric freezing   M0100

Intralesional   J3302

Intraocular lenses   V2630-V2632

Intrapulmonary percussive ventilation system   E0481

Intrauterine copper contraceptive   J7300

Intravenous infusion initiation prolonged infusion   C8957

Intravenous services, supplies and accessories   Q2052

Introducer/sheath, guiding, intracardiac electrophysiological

     fixed-curve, other than peel-away   C1893

     fixed-curve, peel-away   C1892

     steerable, other than peel-away   C1766

Introducer/sheath, other than guiding

     laser   C2629

     non-laser   C1894

Intron a   J9214

Invanz   J1335

Inversion/eversion correction device   A9285

Iodine I-123

     iobenguane   A9582

     ioflupane   A9584

     sodium iodide   A9509, A9516

Iodine I-125

     serum albumin   A9532

     sodium iodide   A9527

     sodium iothalamate   A9554

Iodine I-131

     iodinated serum albumin   A9524

     sodium iodide capsule   A9517, A9528

     sodium iodide solution   A9529-A9531

Iodine Iobenguane sulfate I-131   A9508

Iodine swabs/wipes   A4247

IPD system   E1592

Ipilimumab   J9228

IPPB machine   E0500

Ipratropium bromide   J3535, J7644, J7645

Ipratropium bromide and albuterol sulfate   J7620

Iressa   J8565

J

K

L

Larynx, artificial   L8500
Laser blood collection device and accessory   E0620, A4257
Laser in situ keratomileusis (LASIK)   S0800
Laser-assisted uvulopalatoplasty (LAUP)   S2080
Laundry service   S5175
L-carnitine HCL   J7120
Lead
   cardioverter-defibrillator
      endocardial dual coil (implantable)   C1895
      endocardial single coil   C1777
      other than endocardial single or dual coil (implantable)   C1896
   left ventricular coronary venous system   C1900
   neurostimulator
      (implantable)   C1778
      test kit (implantable)   C1897
   pacemaker
      other than transvenous VDD single pass   C1898
      transvenous VDD single pass   C1779
   pacemaker/cardioverter-defibrillator combination (implantable)   C1899
Lead investigation   T1029
Lead wires, per pair   A4557
Leads (pneumatic/electrical) replacement only   Q0487
Leg
   bag   A4358, A5105, A5112
   extensions for walker   E0158
   rest, elevating   K0195
   rest, wheelchair   E0990
   strap
      foam or fabric   A5114, K0038
      h style   K0039
      latex   A5113
      replacement   A5113-A5114
Leg pain measured by the visual analog scale (vas)   G9947
Leg pain not measured by the visual analog scale (vas)   G9949
Legg Perthes   L1700-L1755
   multiple post collar   L0180-L0200
   pneumatic splint   L4350-L4380
   pronation/supination   E1818
   repair or replacement   L4000-L4210
   replace soft interface material   L4390-L4394
   sacroiliac   L0600-L0620

Levocarnitine	J1955
Levofloxacin	J1955, J1956
Levoleucovorin	J0641
Levoleucovorin calcium	J0641
Levonorgestrel, (contraceptive), implants and supplies	J7306
Levonorgestrel-releasing intrauterine contraceptive system	J7297, J7298, J7301
kyleena	J7296
Levorphanol tartrate	J0641, J1960
Levulan Kerastick 20%	J7308
Lexidronam	A9604, A9605
Lidocaine	J7308
Lidocaine 70 mg/tetracaine 70 mg, per patch	C9285
Lidocaine HCL	J2001
Lifestyle modification program for management coronary artery disease	S0340, S0341, S0342
Lift	
patient (includes seat lift)	E0621-E0635
Lift, elevation	
elevation, heel, per inch	L3334
elevation, heel, tapered to metatarsals	L3300
elevation, inside shoe, tapered	L3332
elevation, metal extension (skate)	L3330
heel and sole, cork, per inch	L3320
heel and sole, neoprene, per inch	L3310
Light compression bandage, elastic, knitted/woven	A6448, A6449, A6450
Lightweight portable motorized/power wheelchair	K0012
Lightweight wheelchair	
detachable arms (desk or full length)	E1260
detachable arms, (desk or full length)	E1240
fixed full length arms	E1270, K0003
Lincocin	J7308
Lincomycin HCL	J2010
Linezolid	J2010, J2020
Lioresal intrathecal refill kit	J0475
Lioresal intrathecal screening kit	J0476
Liquid barrier, ostomy	A4363
Lithium ion battery	
cochlear implant device speech processor	L8623
rechargeable	A4601
rechargeable, replacement	L7367
replacement only	L7368
LMD in dextrose	J7100

M

Medically induced abortion	S0199
Medication reminder service	S5185
Medication training and support	H0034
Mediphedryl	Q0167
Mediskin	Q4135
Medrol	J7509
Medroxyprogesterone acetate	J1050
Megace	J1050
Megestrol acetate	J1050
Megestrol acetate, oral	S0179
Melphalan	J8600
Melphalan HCL	J9245
Melphalan, oral	J8600
Memoderm, dermaspan, TranZgraft or integuply	Q4126
Menadione	J3430
Menotropins	S0122
Mental health	
assessment, by non-physician	H0031
clubhouse services	H2030, H2031
partial hospitalization, treatment	H0035
service plan development by non-physician	H0032
services, nos	H0046
Meperidine	J2175
Meperidine and promethazine HCL	J2180
Meperidine HCL	J2175, J3430
Mepivacaine HCL	J0670
Mepolizumab	J2182
Meprobamate	G6052
Mercaptopurine	J0670
oral	S0108
Meropenem	J2185
Merrem iv	J2185
Mesh (implantable)	C1781
Mesna	J9209
Metacarpophalangeal joint, prosthetic implant	L8630, L8631
Metal-on-metal total hip resurfacing	S2118
Metaproterenol sulfate, inhalation solution	J7667-J7670
Metaraminol bitartrate	J0380
Metatarsal bar wedge	
between sole	L3410
rocker	L3400

Morphine sulfate

    epidural or intrathecal use J2274, J2270, J2274, S0093

Mouthpiece (for respiratory equipment) A4617

Moxifloxacin J2280

Moxifloxacin HCL J2274

Mucoprotein, blood P2038

Mucus trap S8210

Multiaxial ankle L5986

Multidisciplinary services H2000-H2001, T1023-T1028

Multiple post collar, cervical L0180-L0200

Multiple vitamins A9153

Multi-Podus type AFO L4396

Multi-positional patient support system E0636

Multi-positional patient transfer system E1035, E1036

Multisystemic therapy H2033

Muromonab-CD3 .... J7505

Mycamine J2248

Mycophenolate mofetil J7517

Mycophenolic acid J7517, J7518

Myfortic J7518

Myobloc J0587

Myringotomy, laser-assisted S2225

N

Nabi-HB J0587

Nabilone J8650

Nafcillin sodium J0587, S0032

Naglazyme J1458

Nalbuphine HCL J1458, J2300

Naloxone HCL J2310

Naltrexone HCL J2310, J2315

Nandrolone decanoate J2320

Naropin J2795

Narrowing device, wheelchair E0969

Nasal

    application device K0183

    endoscopy S2342

    interface (mask or cannula type) A7034

    pillows A7029

    pillows/seals (for nasal application device) K0184

prosthesis provided by a non-physician	L8040
septal prosthesis provided by a non-physician	L8047
vaccine inhalation	J3530
Nasal endoscopy, surgical	C9745
Nasogastric tubing	B4081, B4082
Natalizumab	J2323
Natrecor	J2325
Navelbine	J2325
Nebulizer	
aerosol	
compressor	E0571
mask	A7015
corrugated tubing, disposable	A7010, E0570, E0570-E0585, E0585
durable, glass or autoclavable plastic	
bottle type regulator or flowmeter	E0580
bottle type, not oxygen	A7017
filter	
disposable	A7013
non-disposable	A7014
heater	E1372
large volume, disposable	
prefilled	A7008
unfilled	A7007
not used with oxygen, durable, glass	A7017
pneumatic	
administration set	A7003, A7005, A7006
nonfiltered	A7004
portable	E0570
small volume	A7003-A7005
ultrasonic	E0575
dome and mouthpiece	A7016
large volume	E0575
reservoir bottle, non-disposable	A7009
water collection device, large volume nebulizer	A7012
NebuPent	J2545
Necitumumab	J9295
Needle	A4215
non-coring	A4212
sterile	A4215
with syringe	A4206-A4209

inhalation solution administered through dme	J7699
other than inhalation drugs, administered through dme	J7799
NOC for enteral supplies	B9998
NOC for parenteral supplies	B9999
Nolvadex	J9268
Non-impregnated gauze dressing	A6216-A6221, A6402-A6404
Non-chemotherapy drug, oral, NOS	J8499
Non-contact wound warming device	E0231
Non-contact wound warming wound cover	A6000
Non-coring needle or stylet	A4212
Non-covered	
ambulance mileage.	A0888
item or service	A9270
procedure(s)	G0294
services	A9270
surgical procedure(s) using conscious sedation	G0293
Non-elastic binder	A4465
Non-emergency transportation	A0080-A0210
commercial carrier, multi-pass	T2004
encounter/trip	T2003
patient attendant/escort	T2001, S0215
stretcher van	T2005
stretcher van, mileage	T2049, T2002
taxi	A0100
Non-emergency transportation and air travel	A0140
Non-emergency transportation and bus	A0110
Non-emergency transportation, ancillary	A0190, A0210
lodging escort	A0200
lodging-recipient	A0180
Non-emergency transportation, mini-bus	A0120
Non-emergency transportation, per mile	A0160
vehicle provided by individual	A0090
vehicle provided by volunteer	A0080
Non-emergency transportation, wheel-chair van	A0130
Non-medical family planning education	H1010
Non-ophthalmic fluorescent vascular angiography	C9733
Non-powered advanced pressure reducing mattress	E0373
Non-powered advanced pressure reducing overlay	E0371
Non-prescription drugs	A9150
Non-prescription lens (safety, athletic, or sunglass), per lens	S0510
Non-pvc (polyvinyl chloride) IV administration set	S1016

O

not otherwise specified	L0999, L1499, L2999, L3999, L5999, L7499, L8039, L8239
pneumatic splint	L4350-L4380
pronation/supination	E1818
repair or replacement	L4000-L4210
replace soft interface material	L4390-L4394
sacroiliac	L0600-L0620
scoliosis	L1000-L1499
shoe, *see* Orthopedic shoes	
shoulder (SO)	L1840, L3650, L3674
shoulder-elbow-wrist-hand (SEWHO)	L3960-L3978
side bar disconnect	L2768
spinal, cervical	L0100-L0200
spinal, DME	K0112-K0116
thoracic	L0210
thoracic-hip-knee-ankle (THKO)	L1500-L1520
toe	E1830
wrist-hand-finger (WHFO)	E1805, E1806, E1825, L3900-L3954
Orthotic side bar disconnect device	L2768
Orthovisc	J7324
Oscillatory positive expiratory pressure device	E0484
Osmitrol	J7324
Ossicula prosthetic implant	L8613
Osteogenesis stimulator, electrical	
low intensity ultrasound, non-invasive	E0760
non-invasive, other than spinal applications	E0747
non-invasive, spinal applications	E0748
surgically implanted	E0749
Osteotomy, periacetabular internal fixation	S2115
Ostomy	
accessories	A5093
belt	A4396
pouches	A4416-A4435
skin barrier	A4401-A4449
supplies	A4361-A4421, A5051-A5149
Ostomy absorbent material	A4422
Ostomy accessory	A5093
Ostomy belt	A4367, A4396
Ostomy clamp , replacement only	A4363
Ostomy deodorant	A4394
solid, per tablet	A4395
Ostomy faceplate	A4361

P

brief/diaper	T4529
protective underwear	T4531
Pediculosis (lice infestation) treatment, topical	A9180
PEFR, peak expiratory flow rate meter	A4614
Peg intron rp	J2440
Pegademase bovine	J2504
Pegaptanib	J2503
Pegaspargase	J9266
Pegasys	J3490
Pegfilgrastim	J2505
Peginesatide	J0890
Peg-intron	J3490
Pegloticase	J2507
Pegylated interferon alfa-2a	S0145
Pegylated interferon alfa-2b	S0148
Pelvic belt/harness/boot	E0944
Pembrolizumab	J9271
Pemetrexed	J9305
Penicillin	
G benzathine/G benzathine and penicillin G procaine	J0558, J0561
G potassium	J2540
G procaine, aqueous	J2510
Pentam	J7676
Pentamidine isethionate	J2545, J7676, S0080
Pentastarch, 10% solution	J2513
Pentazocine HCL	J3070
Pentobarbital sodium	J2515
Pentostatin	J9268
Peramivir	J2547
Percussor	E0480
Percutaneous	
access system	A4301
catheter/tube anchoring device	A5200
islet cell transplant	G0341
skeletal fixation	G0413
transcatheter placement of drug eluting intracoronary stent(s)	C9600, C9601
transluminal coronary atherectomy	C9602, C9603
transluminal revascularization of acute total/subtotal occlusion	C9606
transluminal revascularization of chronic total occlusion	C9607, C9608
transluminal revascularization of or through coronary artery bypass graft	C9605, C9604
Perflexane lipid microspheres	Q9955

Perflutren lipid microspheres	Q9957
Performance measurement, evaluation patient self assessment, depression	S3005
Perforomist	J7606
Perianal fecal collection pouch	A4330
Peritoneal dialysis	
catheter anchoring device	A4653
dialysis clamps	E1634
Peritoneal straps, prefabricated, off-the-shelf, pair	L0980
Permanent implantable contraceptive intratubal occlusion device(s)	A4264
Permanent, long term, non-dissolvable lacrimal duct implant	A4263
Peroneal strap	L0980
Peroxide	A4244
Perphenazine	J3310, Q0169, Q0175
Personal care item, nos	S5199
Personal care services	T1019-T1021
Personal care services, not	T1019, T1020
Pertuzumab	J9306
Pessary	
non rubber	A4562
rubber	A4561
PET imaging	
any site, nos	G0235
full and partial-ring pet scanners only	G0252
whole body	G0219
Pfizerpen	J2540
Phakic intraocular lens	S0596
Pharmacy compounding and dispensing services	S9430
Pharmacy dispensing fee	G0333, Q0513, Q0514
Pharmacy supply fee	Q0510, Q0511, Q0512
Phenadoz	J2540
Phenergan	J2540
Phenobarbital sodium	J2540, J2560
Phenothiazine	G6057
Phentolamine mesylate	J2760
Phenylephrine and ketorolac, 4 ml vial	C9447
Phenylephrine HCL	J2370, J2760
Phenytoin sodium	J1165
PHisoHex solution	A4246
Photofrin, *see* Porfimer sodium Phototherapy light	E0202
Photorefractive keratectomy (PRK)	S0810
Phototherapeutic keratectomy (PTK)	S0812

Phototherapy (bilirubin) light	E0202
Physical exam	S0622
Physical or manipulative therapy performed	S8990
Physical therapy	S9131
Physician certification with home health agency	G0180
Physician documentation face-to-face visit	G0454
Physician management patient home care	
episodic care monthly case rate (per 30 days)	S0272
hospice monthly case rate (per 30 days)	S0271
standard monthly case rate (per 30 days)	S0270
Physician re-certification	G0179
Physician review, interpretation, and patient management home INR testing	G0250
Physician service required to establish and document the need	G0372
Physician supervision a patient receiving Medicare-covered services	G0181
Physician supervision a patient under a Medicare-approved hospice	G0182
Physician visit at member's home	S0273
Phytonadione	J1165, J3430
Pillow A7033	
Pillow, cervical	E0943
Pinworm examination	Q0113
Piperacillin and tazobactam	J1165
Piperacillin sodium	S0081
Piperacillin sodium/tazobactam sodium	J2543
Pitocin	J1165
Placement and removal (if performed) applicator into breast	C9726
Placement endorectal intracavitary applicator	C9725
Placement interstitial device(s)	C9728
Placement occlusive device into either a venous or arterial access site	G0269
Plasma	
cryoprecipitate reduced unit	P9044
multiple donor, pooled, frozen	P9023, P9070
pooled multiple donor	
pathogen reduced, frozen unit	P9070
solvent/detergent treated, frozen unit	P9023
single donor	
fresh frozen	P9017, P9071
pathogen reduced, frozen unit	P9071
Plastazote	L3002, L3252, L3253, L3265, L5654-L5658
Platelet	
concentrate, each unit	P9019, P9072
rich plasma, each unit	P9020

Polocaine-mpf	J0670
Polycarbonate bottle breast pump	A4285
Polycarbonate lens	S0580
Polygam	J0670
Porcine implant, Permacol	C9364
Porfimer	J9600
Porous purified collagen matrix bone void filler	C9359, C9362
Port, indwelling (implantable)	C1788
Portable	
equipment transfer	R0070-R0076
hemodialyzer system	E1635
x-ray equipment	Q0092
Portable gaseous oxygen system	
purchase	E0430
rental	E0431
Portable liquid oxygen system	
purchase	E0435
rental	E0433
Portable oxygen concentrator, rental	E1392
Portable oxygen contents	
gaseous, 1 month's supply = 1 unit	E0443
liquid, 1 month's supply = 1 unit	E0444
Portable peak flow meter	S8096
Positioning cushion/pillow/wedge	E0190
Positioning seat	T5001
Positioning wheelchair back cushion	
planar back	E2620
posterior	E2613
posterior-lateral	E2615
Positioning wheelchair seat cushion	E2605, E2606
Positive airway pressure device, accessories	A7030-A7039,
Positive expiratory pressure device	E0484
Post-coital examination	Q0115
Post-discharge pulmonary surgery services after LVRS	G0305
Posterior chamber intraocular lens	V2632
Postural drainage board	E0606
Potassium chloride	J0670, J3480
Potassium hydroxide (KOH) preparation	Q0112
Pouch	
fecal collection	A4330
ostomy	A4375-A4378, A5051-A5054, A5061-A5065

group 34 non-sealed lead acid battery — E2358

group 34 sealed lead acid battery — E2359

hand control interface — E2321

hand or chin control interface — E2374

harness — E2313

head control interface — E2330

head control or extremity control interface — E2328

insert — E2383, K0733

lithium-based battery — E2397

nonstandard seat frame — E2340

pneumatic caster tire — E2384

pneumatic drive wheel tire — E2381

sip and puff interface — E2325

solid (rubber/plastic) caster tire — E2392

solid (rubber/plastic) caster tire (removable) — E2391

solid (rubber/plastic) drive wheel tire — E2390

specialty joystick handle — E2323

tube — E2382

u-1 non-sealed lead acid battery — E2364

u-1 sealed lead acid battery (e.g. gel cell, absorbed glassmat) — E2365

Power wheelchair component

actuator, replacement only — E2378

drive wheel gear box, replacement only — E2369

drive wheel motor, replacement only — E2368

integrated drive wheel motor and gear box combination, replacement only — E2370

Powered air flotation bed (low air loss therapy) — E0193

Powered air overlay — E0372

Powered bone marrow biopsy needle — C1830

Powered pressure reducing mattress overlay/pad, alternating — E0181

Powered pressure-reducing air mattress — E0277

Pralatrexate — J9307

Pralidoxime chloride — J2730

Preadmission screening and resident review (PASRR) — T2010, T2011

Prednicot — J2730

Prednisolone

acetate — J2650

oral — J7510

Prednisone — J7510, J7512

Pregnyl — J0725

Prehensile actuator, switch controlled — L7040

Prelone — J0725

Premarin intravenous	J1410
Premierpro rx ampicillin	J0290
Premierpro rx furosemide	J0290
Prenatal care	
at risk enhanced service	H1002
at-risk assessment	H1000
at-risk enhanced service	H1001
at-risk enhanced service package (includes H1001-H1004)	H1005
Prenatal vitamins, 30-day supply	S0197
Pre-operative pulmonary surgery services	G0302, G0303, G0304
Preparation instillation fecal microbiota	G0455
Preparation kits, dialysis	A4914
Preparatory prosthesis	
chemotherapy	J8999
nonchemotherapy	J8499
Preparatory, above knee - knee disarticulation ischial level socket	L5570
pylon no cover, SACH foot, laminated socket	L5590
pylon, no cover, SACH foot, thermoplastic or equal	L5580
Preparatory, below knee 'ptb' type socket, non-alignable system	
no cover, SACH foot, prefabricated, adjustable open end socket	L5535
pylon, no cover, SACH foot, laminated socket	L5540
pylon, no cover, SACH foot, plaster socket	L5510
pylon, no cover, SACH foot, thermoplastic or equal	L5530
pylon, no cover, SACH foot, thermoplastic or equal, direct	L5520
Preparatory, elbow disarticulation or above elbow	
single wall plastic socket	L6584
single wall socket	L6586
Preparatory, hip disarticulation-hemipelvectomy	L5595, L5600
Preparatory, shoulder disarticulation	L6588, L6590
Preparatory, wrist disarticulation	
single wall plastic socket	L6580
single wall socket	L6582
Presbyopia correcting function intraocular lens	V2788
Prescription drug	
brand name	S5001
generic	S5000
oral, chemotherapeutic, nos	J8999
oral, non chemotherapeutic, nos	J8499
Press-on lens Fresnell prism	V2718
Pressure	
alarm, dialysis	E1540

pad	A4640, E0180-E0199
Prialt	J2278
Primatrix	Q4110
Primatrix dermal repair scaffold	Q4110
Primaxin iv	J0743
Prism, per lens	V2715
Private duty / independent nursing service(s)	T1000
Privigen	J1459
Probe, percutaneous lumbar discectomy	C2614
Probe/needle, cryoablation	C2618
Procainamide HCL	J2690
Procarbazine HCL, oral	S0182
Processing, preserving and transporting corneal tissue	V2785
Prochlorperazine	J0780, J2690
Prochlorperazine edisylate	J0780
Prochlorperazine maleate, oral	Q0164, S0183
Procrit	J0885
Procurement donor sperm from sperm bank	S4026
Procuren or other growth factor preparation	S9055
Progesterone	J0885, J2675
Prograf	J2675, J7525
Progressive lens	V2781
Prolastin-c	J0256
Proleukin	J9015
Prolia	J0897
Prolotherapy	M0076
Promacot	Q0169
Promazine HCL	J2950
Promethazine	Q0169
Promethazine and meperidine	J2180
Promethazine HCL	J2550, Q0169
Promethegan	J2550
Propofol	J2550, J2704
Propranolol	J1800, J2550
Prostaglandin e1	J0270
Prostate cancer screening	
digital rectal examination	G0102
prostate specific antigen test (PSA)	G0103
Prosthesis	
artificial larynx battery/accessory	L8505
breast	L8000-L8035, L8600

Q

R

2 separate treatment areas, use of multiple blocks

    11-19 mev   G6009

    20 mev or greater   G6010

    6-10 mev   G6008

    up to 5 mev   G6007

3 or more separate treatment areas, custom blocking   G6011

single treatment area, simple blocks or no blocks

    11-19 mev   G6005

    20 mev or greater   G6006

    6-10 mev   G6004

    up to 5 mev   G6003

Radiesse   Q2026

Radioelements for brachytherapy   Q3001

Radiofrequency transmitter (external)   L8683, L8684

Radiolabeled product provided during hospital inpatient stay   C9898

Radiology service   R0070-R0076

Radiopharmaceutical diagnostic and therapeutic imaging agent   A4641, A4642, A9500-A9699

Radiopharmaceutical, diagnostic   A9599

    diagnostic, not otherwise classified   A4641

    therapeutic, not otherwise classified   A9699

Radium ra-223 dichloride, therapeutic   A9606

Rail

    bathtub   E0241, E0242, E0246

    bed   E0305, E0310

    toilet   E0243

Raised toilet seat   E0244

Ramucirumab   J9308

Ranibizumab   J2778

Ranitidine HCL   J0330, J2780

Rapamune   J7520

Rapidpaq dicopanol   J7520

Rasburicase   J2783

Ratchet assembly   K0050

Reaching/grabbing device   A9281

Reagent strip   A4252

Rear wheel assembly, complete   K0069, K0070

Receiver (monitor)

    with artificial pancreas device system   S1037

    with interstitial continuous glucose monitoring system   A9278

Receiver (monitor), dedicated   K0554

Receiver and/or transmitter, neurostimulator (implantable)	C1816
Reciprocating peritoneal dialysis system	E1630
Reclast	J3488
Reclining back, addition to pediatric size wheelchair	E1014
Recombivax HB	J7520
Reconstruction, computed tomographic angiography aorta	G0288
Rectal thermometer	A4932
Red blood cells	P9021, P9022
deglycerolized unit	P9039
frozen/deglycerolized/washed, leukocytes reduced, irradiated unit	P9057
irradiated unit	P9038
leukocytes reduced unit	P9016
leukocytes reduced, CMV-negative, irradiated unit	P9058
leukocytes reduced, irradiated unit	P9040
unit	P9021
washed unit	P9022
Reduction ocular prosthesis	V2626
Refill kit	A4220
Regadenoson	J2785
Regular insulin	J1820
Regulator, oxygen	E1353
Rehabilitation program	H2001
Remicade	J1745
Remodulin	J3285
Removal impacted cerumen	G0268
Removal sutures	S0630
Removal non-biodegradable drug delivery implants)	G0517
Removal with reinsertion, non-biodegradable drug delivery implants	G0518
Renacidin	Q2004
ReoPro	J0130
Repair	
congenital cystic adenomatoid malformation in the fetus	S2402
congenital diaphragmatic hernia in the fetus	S2400
congenital malformation of fetus	S2409
Contract, ESRD	A4890
durable medical equipment	E1340
extralobar pulmonary sequestration in the fetus	S2403
maxillofacial prosthesis	L8049
myelomeningocele in the fetus	S2404
orthotic device	L4205
prosthetic device	L7510

cover   E2619

cushions   E1701

diaphragm/faceplate   A7502

electrodes automated external defibrillator   K0609

garment automated external defibrillator   K0608

handgrip, cane, crutch, or walker   A4636

lens shield cartridge laser skin piercing device   A4257

measuring scales   E1702

pad   A4639, A4640

socket

    above knee/knee disarticulation   L5701

    above elbow/elbow disarticulation   L6884

    below elbow/wrist disarticulation   L6883

    below knee   L5700

    hip disarticulation   L5702

    shoulder disarticulation/interscapular thoracic   L6885

soft interface material

    cuffs   E1821

    dynamic adjustable extension/flexion device   E1820

    static AFO   L4392

strap, any orthosis   L4002

tip, cane, crutch, walker   A4637

Repriza   Q4143

Resectisol   J0130

Reservoir bottle, non-disposable   A7009

Residential care, nos, waiver   T2032, T2033

Residual extremity support system   E1020

Reslizumab   J2786

RespiGam, *see* **Respiratory syncytial virus immune**

Respiratory assist device   E0470

Respiratory suction pump   E0600

Respite care services

not in the home   H0045

up to 15 minutes   T1005

Respite care, in the home   S9125

Restall globulin Restraint   E0710, J0130

Restraints (body, chest, wrist or ankle)   E0710

Resuscitation bag   S8999

Reteplase   J2993

Retinal prosthesis   C1841

Retinal tamponade device   C1814

Retisert	J7311
Retrieval device insertable	C1773
Reverse osmosis water purification system	E1610
Revita	Q4180
Revitalon	Q4157
Rho d immune globulin	
human, full dose	J2790
human, minidose	J2788
human, solvent detergent	J2792
Rho(D) immune globulin, human	J2788, J2790, J2791, J2792
RhoGAM ultra-filtered plus	J2790
Rhophylac	J2791
Rib belt, thoracic	A4572, L0220
Rifadin iv	J2791
Rifampin	J2791
Right heart catheterization	C9741
Rilonacept	J2793
RimabotulinumtoxinB	J0587
Rimso-50	J1212
Ring, ostomy	A4404
Ringers lactate infusion	J7120
Risperdal Consta	J2794
Risperidone	J2794
Rite aid allergy	J2794
Rituxan	J9310
Rituximab	J9310
RN services	T1002
Robaxin	J9310
Robin-aids	L6000, L6010, L6020, L6855, L6860
Robinul	J9310
Rocking bed	E0462
Rodex	J9310
Rolapitant	J8670
Rollabout chair	E1031
Romidepsin	J9315
Romiplostim	J2796
Ropivacaine HCL	J2795, J9310
Rotary wing air mileage	A0436
Routine foot care	G0247, S0390
Routine ophthalmological examination	S0620, S0621
Routine venipuncture	S9529

Rubidium rb-82 A9555

S

Sacral nerve stimulation test lead A4290

Sacroiliac orthosis

   flexible L0621

   provides pelvic-sacral support L0623

Safety enclosure frame/canopy hospital bed E0316

Safety equipment E0700

   vest, wheelchair E0980

Safety eyeglass frames S0516

Safety vest, wheelchair E0980

Safety concerns screen provided G9922, G9923

Safety concerns screening not provided G9925

Safety concerns screening positive screen G9926

Saizen click easy cartridge J9310

Sales tax S9999

Salicylate G6038

Saline

   hypertonic J7130

   solution J7030-J7050, A4216-A4218

Saliva test, hormone level S3650, S3652

Samarium SM-153 lexidronam A9604

Sandimmune A4216, J7516

Sandostatin J2353, J2354

Saquinavir S0140

Sargramostim (GM-CSF) J2820

Scale E1639

Scheduled interdisciplinary team conference G0175

School-based individualized education program T1018

Scintimammography S8080

Scleral application tantalum ring(s) S8030

Scleral cover shell V2627

Scleral lens S0515

Scoliosis L1010-L1120, L1210-L1290, L1000-L1499

Scratch resistant coating, per lens V2760

Screening

   cytopathology G0123

   mammography G0202

   Papanicolaou smear P3000, P3001, Q0091

performed and negative	G9920
performed and positive	G9919
proctoscopy	S0601
smears, cervical or vaginal	G0141
Sculptra	Q2028
Sealant	
skin	A6250
pulmonary, liquid	C2615
Seat	
attachment, walker	E0156
contoured	E2294
insert, wheelchair	E0992
lift (patient)	E0621, E0627-E0629
lift mechanism placed over or on top of toilet	E0172
planar	E2292
upholstery, wheelchair	E0975
Sebelipase alfa	J2840
Secretin	J2850
Segmental gradient pressure pneumatic appliance	
full arm	E0672
full leg	E0671
half leg	E0673
Segmental pneumatic appliance	
pneumatic compressor, chest	E0657
pneumatic compressor, full arm	E0668
pneumatic compressor, full leg	E0667
pneumatic compressor, half leg	E0669
pneumatic compressor, integrated, 2 full legs and trunk	E0670
pneumatic compressor, trunk	E0656
Self-adherent bandage, elastic, non-knitted/non-woven	A6453, A6454, A6455
Self-help/peer services	H0038
Semen analysis	G0027
Semi-implantable middle ear hearing prosthesis	V5095
Semi-reclining wheelchair	
detachable arms (desk or full length)	E1110
fixed full length arms	E1100
Sensitivity study	P7001
Sensor invasive (e.g. subcutaneous), disposable	A9276, S1035
Sensorcaine-mpf	J2353
Separate seat lift mechanism	
patient owned furniture-non-electric	E0629

Skills training and development   H2014

Skin

    barrier, ostomy   A4362, A4363, A4369-A4373, A4385, A5120

    bond or cement, ostomy   A4364

    sealant, protectant, moisturizer   A6250

    substitute   Q4100-Q4165

Skin barrier

    solid, 4 x 4 or equivalent   A4362

    solid, 6 x 6 or equivalent   A5121

    solid, 8 x 8 or equivalent   A5122

    wipes or swabs   A5120

Skin piercing device   E0620

Skin protection and positioning wheelchair seat cushion   E2607, E2608, E2624

Skin protection wheelchair seat cushion   E2603, E2604, E2622

Skin sealants, protectants, moisturizers, ointments , any size   A6250

Skin substitute

    Integra meshed bilayer wound matrix   C9363

    nos   Q4100

Slab off prism, glass or plastic, per lens   V2710

Sleepinal   J0480

Sleep-tabs   J0480

Sleeve replacement only   A4600

Sling or seat, patient lift, canvas or nylon   E0621, E0630, E0635

Slings   A4565

Small volume nonfiltered pneumatic nebulizer   A7004

Smoking cessation classes, non-physician provider   S9453

Smoking cessation gum   S4995

Smz-tmp   J0480

Social work and psychological services   G0409

Social work visit, in the home   S9127

Social worker, nonemergency transport   A0160

Sock

    body sock   L0984

    prosthetic sock   L8420-L8435, L8470, L8480, L8485

    stump sock   L8470-L8485

Sodium

    chloride injection   J2912

    ferric gluconate complex in sucrose   J2916

    fluoride F-18   A9580

    Hyalgan   J7321

    hyaluronate Euflexxa   J7323

Speech generating device	
digitized speech	E2504, E2500-E2599
synthesized speech	E2510
Speech generating software program	E2511
Speech screening	V5362
Speech therapy	S9128, S9152
Sperm procurement and cryopreservation services	S4030, S4031
Sphere	
bifocal	V2200
single vision	V2100
trifocal	V2300
Spherocylinder	
bifocal	V2203
single vision	V2103
trifocal	V2303
Sphygmomanometer/blood pressure apparatus	A4660
Spinal orthosis	
cervical	L0100-L0200
cervical-thoracic-lumbar-sacral (CTLSO)	L0700, L0710
DME	K0112-K0116
halo	L0810-L0830
multiple post collar	L0180-L0200
scoliosis	L1000-L1499
torso supports	L0960
Spirometer	
electronic	E0487
non-electronic	A9284
Splint	A4570, A4570, L3100, L4350-L4380
ankle	L4390-L4398
dynamic	E1800, E1805, E1810, E1815, E1825, E1830, E1840
footdrop	L4398
prefabricated, digit	S8450
prefabricated, elbow	S8452
prefabricated, wrist or ankle	S8451
Splint supplies	Q4051
Spoke protectors	K0065
Spring-powered device	A4258
Stadol	J0595
Stand/rack	E1355
Standard - weight frame motorized/power wheelchair	K0010, K0011
Standard hemi (low seat) wheelchair	K0002

Stocking supporter grips, prefabricated, off-the-shelf	L0982
Stoma cap	A5055
Stoma plug or seal	A5081
Stomach tube	B4083
Storage previously frozen embryos	S4027
Strattice tm	Q4130
Streptokinase	J2995
Streptomycin sulfate	J0595, J3000
Streptozocin	J9320
Stress management classes, non-physician provider	S9454
Strip, blood glucose test	A4253, A4772
urine reagent	A4250
Strontium sr-89 chloride	A9600
Stump sock	L8470-L8485
Stylet	A4212
Subcutaneous	J1562
Succinylcholine chloride	J0330
Suction pump	
gastric, home model	E2000
home model	K0743
respiratory, home model	E0600
Sufentanil citrate	J3000
Sulfamethoxazole and trimethoprim	S0039
Sulfur hexafluoride lipid microspheres	Q9950
Sumatriptan succinate	J3030
Sumavel DosePro	J3030
Sunglasses frames	S0518
Supartz	J7321
Supplies	A4211
per week (list drug separately)	A4221, S8415
syringe type cartridge	K0552
Supply	T5999
Supply allowance for therapeutic continuous glucose monitor (cgm)	K0553
Supply injectable contrast material	A9700
Supply/accessory/service	A9900
Support	
arch	L3040-L3090
cervical	L0100-L0200
spinal	L0960
stockings	L8100-L8239
Supported employment	H2023, H2024

Syrex	A4216
Syringe	A4213, A4657
sterile	A4213
with needle	A4206
Systemic antimicrobials not prescribed	G9959
Systemic antimicrobials prescribed	G9961

T

Tables, bed	E0274, E0315
Tacrine HCL	S0014
Tacrolimus	A4216, J7507
oral	J7503, J7507, J7508
parenteral	J7525
Taliglucerase	J3060
Talwin lactate	J3070
Talymed	Q4127
Tamoxifen citrate	J3070
oral	S0187
Tape	
non-waterproof	A4450
waterproof	A4452
Targeted case management	T1017, T2023
Taxi, non emergency transportation	A0100
Tazicef	J0713
TBO-filgrastim	J1447
Technetium TC 99M	
Arcitumomab	A9568
Bicisate	A9557
Depreotide	A9536
Disofenin	A9510
Exametazime	A9521
Exametazime labeled autologous white blood cells	A9569
Fanolesomab	A9566
Gluceptate	A9550
Labeled red blood cells	A9560
Macroaggregated albumin	A9540
Mebrofenin	A9537
Mertiatide	A9562
Oxidronate	A9561
Pentetate	A9539, A9567

sport/recreational/work attachment, any material	L6704
Terminal devices	L6700-L6895
Testopel pellets	J7681
Testosterone	
cypionate and estradiol cypionate	J1071
enanthate	J3121
undecanoate	J3145
Testosterone pellet	S0189
Tetanus immune globulin, human	J1670
Tetracycline	J0120
Thallous chloride tl 201	A9505
Theophylline	J2810, J3121
Therapeutic agent	A4321
Therapeutic behavioral services	H2019, H2020
Therapeutic camping	
day, waiver	T2037
overnight, waiver	T2036
Therapeutic light box	A4634, E0203
Therapeutic procedures	
improve respiratory function	G0238, G0239
increase strength or endurance respiratory muscles	G0237
Therapy occupational	H5300
Theraskin	Q4121
Thermometer	A4931-A4932
dialysis	A4910
Thiamine HCL	J3411
Thiethylperazine maleate	J3280, Q0174
Thiotepa	J9340
Thoracic orthosis	L0210
Thoracic, rib belt, custom fabricated	L0220
Thoracic-hip-knee-ankle (THKAO)	L1500-L1520
Thoracic-lumbar-sacral-orthosis (TLSO)	
scoliosis	L1200-L1290
spinal	L0430-L0492
Thrombate iii	J7197
Thymoglobulin	J7511
Thymol turbidity, blood	P2033
Thyrogen	J3240
Thyrotropin alfa	J3240
Ticarcillin disodium and clavulanate potassium	S0040
Tice BCG	J9031

cleaning brush	A4626
inner cannula	A4623
mask	A7525
shower protector	A7523
speaking valve	L8501
supply	S8189
tube collar/holder	A7526

Tracheostomy/laryngectomy

cuffed	A7521
non-cuffed	A7520
stainless steel or equal	A7522
tube plug/stop	A7527

Tracheotomy mask or collar	A7525-A7526
Traction device, ambulatory	E0830
Traction equipment	E0840-E0948
cervical, free-standing stand/frame, pneumatic	E0849
overdoor, cervical	E0860

Traction frame

attached to footboard, extremity traction, (e.g. Buck's)	E0870
attached to footboard, pelvic traction	E0890
attached to headboard, cervical traction	E0840

Traction stand

free standing, cervical traction	E0850
free standing, extremity traction, (e.g., Buck's)	E0880
free standing, pelvic traction, (e.g., Buck's)	E0900

Training and educational services	G0177
Transcarpal/metacarpal or partial hand disarticulation prosthesis	L6026
Transcatheter occlusion or embolization	S2095
TransCyte	Q4182
Transcutaneous electrical joint stimulation device system	E0762
Transcutaneous electrical nerve stimulator (TENS)	E0720-E0770
Transducer protector, dialysis	E1575
Transesophageal echocardiography (tee)	C8926, C8927
Transfer (shoe orthosis)	L3600-L3640
Transfer bench	E0247
Transfer bench, heavy duty	E0248
Transfer device	E0705

Transfer an orthosis from one shoe to another

caliper plate, existing	L3600
caliper plate, new	L3610
Dennis Browne splint (Riveton), both shoes	L3640

Trasylol	J0365
Trauma response team associated hospital critical care service	G0390
Travel allowance one way in connection	P9603, P9604
Tray	
insertion	A4310-A4316
irrigation	A4320
surgical (*see also* kits)	A4550
wheelchair	E0950
Treanda	J0365
Treated water (deionized, distilled, or reverse osmosis)	A4714
Treatment planning and care coordination management	S0353
with a change of regimen	S0354
Trelstar depot	J3315
Treprostinil	J3285
inhalation solution	J7686
Tretinoin, topical	S0117
Triam cot	J3302
Triamcinolone	
acetonide	J3300, J3301
diacetate	J3302
hexacetonide	J3303
inhalation solution	
concentrated	J7683
unit dose	J7684
Triesence	J7684
Triethylenethiophosphoramide	J7684
Trifluopromazine HCL	J3400
Trifocal	
glass or plastic	V2300-V2399
add over 3.25d	V2320
seg width over 28 mm	V2319
vision prescription lens	S0508
Trimethobenzamide HCL	J3250, Q0173
Trimetrexate glucoronate	J3305
Trimming dystrophic nails	G0127
Triptorelin pamoate	J3315
Trisenox	Q0173
Truss	L8300-L8330
addition to standard pad, scrotal pad	L8330
addition to standard pad, water pad	L8320
double	L8310

single	L8300
Truxadryl	J1200
Tub stool or bench	E0245
Tube/tubing	
anchoring device	A5200
blood	A4750, A4755
corrugated tubing, non-disposable	A4337
drainage extension	A4331
gastrostomy	B4087, B4088
integrated heating element	A4604
irrigation	A4355
laryngectomy	A4622
nasogastric	B4081, B4082
oxygen	A4616
positive airway pressure device	A7037
replacement	A4281
serum clotting time	A4771
stomach	B4083
suction pump	A7002
tire	K0091, K0093, K0095, K0097
tracheostomy	A4622
urinary drainage	K0280
Tubular dressing	A6457
Twelve volt battery	L7364
Twilite	J1200
Twinrix	J1200
Tygacil	J3243
Tyvaso	J7686

U

Ultrafiltration monitor	S9007
Ultra lightweight wheelchair	K0005
Ultrasonic guidance	G6001
Ultrasonic nebulizer	E0575
Ultrasonic/electronic aerosol generator	E0574
Ultrasound guidance multifetal pregnancy reduction	S8055
Ultraviolet light therapy system	A4633, E0691-E0694, E0691
Unasyn	J0295
Unclassified biologics	J3590
Unclassified drug	J3490

Unclassified drugs or biologicals   C9399

Underarm pad, crutch, replacement   A4635

Unipuncture control system, dialysis   E1580

Unlisted ambulance service   A0999

Unlisted procedure   L8499

Unscheduled or emergency dialysis treatment   G0257

Unskilled respite care, not hospice   S5150, S5151

Unspecified maxillofacial prosthesis   L8048

Unspecified oral dosage   Q0181

Upper extremity addition, locking elbow   L6693

Upper extremity fracture orthosis   L3980-L3999

Upper limb prosthesis   L6000-L7499

Urea   J3350

Ureterostomy supplies   A4454-A4590

Urethral suppository, Alprostadil   J0275

Urinal

    female, jug-type, any material   E0326

    male, jug-type, any material   E0325

Urinary

    catheter   A4338-A4346, A4351-A4353

    collection and retention (supplies)   A4310-A4360

    tract implant   L8603, L8606

Urinary catheter anchoring device

    adhesive skin attachment   A4333

    leg strap   A4334

Urinary drainage bag leg or abdomen

    latex   A5112

    vinyl   A4358

Urinary suspensory leg bag   A5105

Urine

    sensitivity study   P7001

    tests   A4250

Urine test or reagent strips or tablets   A4250

Urofollitropin   J3355

Urokinase   J3364, J3364, J3365

Ustekinumab   J3357, J3358

Utility services to support medical equipment and assistive technology/devices   T2035

U-V lens   V2755

V

W

heavy duty	E0148
heavy duty, multiple braking system	E0147
heavy duty, wheeled, rigid or folding	E0149
rigid (pickup), adjustable or fixed height	E0130
rigid, wheeled, adjustable or fixed height	E0141
Walking boot	
non-pneumatic	L4386, L4387
pneumatic and/or vacuum	L4360, L4361
Walking splint	L4386
Warfarin or another fad-approved anticoagulant not prescribed, reason not given	G9928
Warming card	E0232
Water	
distilled (for nebulizer)	A7018
for inhalation	A4216
for injection	A4216
for irrigation	A4217
pressure pad/mattress	E0187, E0198
purification system (ESRD)	E1610, E1615
softening system (ESRD)	E1625
Water chamber	A7046
Water circulating cold pad	E0218
Water circulating heat pad	E0217
Water collection device	A7012
Water pressure mattress	E0187
Water pressure pad	E0198
Water seal drainage container and tubing	A7041
Water softening system	E1625
Water, distilled	A7018
Wearable artificial kidney	E1632
Wedges, shoe	L3340-L3420
Weight management classes, non-physician provider	S9449
Wellness assessment, performed by non-physician	S5190
Wet mount	Q0111
Wheel attachment, rigid pickup walker	E0155
Wheelchair accessory	E0192, E0950-E1030, E1065-E1069, E2211-E2230, E2300-E2399
addition to mobile arm support	E2631
addition to power seating system	E1009
adjustable height, detachable armrest	E0973
amputee	E1170-E1200
back upholstery	E0982
back, fully reclining, manual	E1226

bearings	E2210
calf rest/pad	E0995
component or accessory	K0108
crutch and cane holder	E2207
cushions	E2601-E2625
cylinder tank carrier	E2208, E0956
detachable arms, desk or full length)	E1140, E1150, E0950-E1298, K0001-K0108, E1223, E1224
elevating leg rest, complete assembly	E0990
fixed arm, elevating leg rests	E1222
fixed arm, footrests	E1221
fixed full length arms	E1160
foot box, any type	E0954
headrest, cushioned	E0955
lateral thigh or knee support	E0953
manual fully reclining back	E1226
manual semi-reclining back	E1225
manual Swing-Away	E1028
medial thigh support	E0957
narrowing device	E0969
pediatric size	E1236
positioning belt/safety belt/pelvic strap	E0978
power add-on	E0983-E0984
power seat elevation system	E2300
power seating system	E1002
power seating system	E1005
power standing system	E2301
powered	E2610
seat lift mechanism	E0985
seat upholstery	E0981
shock absorber	E1015-E1018
shoulder elbow	E2626
shoulder harness/straps or chest strap	E0960
specially sized	E1220, E1230
stump support system	K0551
transfer board or device	E0705, E0950
van, non-emergency	A0130
ventilator tray, fixed	E1029
ventilator tray, gimbaled	E1030
wheelchair seat or back cushion	K0669
youth	E1091
Wheelchair van, mileage, per mile	S0209

dynamic flexor hinge L3900

    external powered, electric L3904, L3806, L3807, L3809, L3931

    rigid L3808

Wrist hand orthosis L3905, L3906, L3915, L3916

    wrist extension control cock-up L3908

X

XCM biologic tissue matrix Q4142

Xenon Xe 133 . . . . A9558

Xeomin J0588

Xgeva J0897

Xolair J2357

Xopenex J7612, J7614

X-ray equipment, portable Q0092, R0070, R0075

Xylocaine J7614

Xylocaine HCL J2000

Y

Y set tubing A4719

Yondelis J7614

Youth sized disposable incontinence product

    brief/diaper T4533

    protective underwear T4534

Yttrium Y-90 ibritumomab A9543

Z

Zanosar J9320

Zantac J2780

Zembrace symtouch J2780

Zemplar J2501

Ziconotide J2278

Zidovudine J3485

Zidovudine, oral S0104

Zinc air battery L8621

Zinc paste impregnated bandage, non-elastic, knitted/woven A6456

Ziprasidone mesylate J3486

Zithromax J0456, Q0144

APPENDIX A: MODIFIERS

HCPCS National Level II Modifiers

The following list is the complete list of HCPCS National Level II modifiers and descriptions.

- A1	Dressing for one wound
- A2	Dressing for two wounds
- A3	Dressing for three wounds
- A4	Dressing for four wounds
- A5	Dressing for five wounds
- A6	Dressing for six wounds
- A7	Dressing for seven wounds
- A8	Dressing for eight wounds
- A9	Dressing for nine or more wounds
- AA	Anesthesia services performed personally by anesthesiologist
- AD	Medical supervision by a physician: more than four concurrent anesthesia procedures
- AE	Registered dietician
- AF	Specialty physician
- AG	Primary physician
- AH	Clinical psychologist
- AI	Principal physician of record
- AJ	Clinical social worker
- AK	Non participating physician
- AM	Physician, team member service
- AO	Alternate payment method declined by provider of service
- AP	Determination of refractive state was not performed in the course of diagnostic ophthalmological examination
- AQ	Physician providing a service in an unlisted health professional shortage area (hpsa)
- AR	Physician provider services in a physician scarcity area
- AS	Physician assistant, nurse practitioner, or clinical nurse specialist services for assistant at surgery
- AT	Acute treatment (this modifier should be used when reporting service 98940, 98941, 98942)

- AU	Item furnished in conjunction with a urological, ostomy, or tracheostomy supply
- AV	Item furnished in conjunction with a prosthetic device, prosthetic or orthotic
- AW	Item furnished in conjunction with a surgical dressing
- AX	Item furnished in conjunction with dialysis services
- AY	Item or service furnished to an esrd patient that is not for the treatment of esrd
- AZ	Physician providing a service in a dental health professional shortage area for the purpose of an electronic health record incentive payment
- BA	Item furnished in conjunction with parenteral enteral nutrition (pen) services
- BL	Special acquisition of blood and blood products
- BO	Orally administered nutrition, not by feeding tube
- BP	The beneficiary has been informed of the purchase and rental options and has elected to purchase the item
- BR	The beneficiary has been informed of the purchase and rental options and has elected to rent the item
- BU	The beneficiary has been informed of the purchase and rental options and after 30 days has not informed the supplier of his/her decision
- CA	Procedure payable only in the inpatient setting when performed emergently on an outpatient who expires prior to admission
- CB	Service ordered by a renal dialysis facility (rdf) physician as part of the esrd beneficiary's dialysis benefit, is not part of the composite rate, and is separately reimbursable
- CC	Procedure code change (use 'cc' when the procedure code submitted was changed either for administrative reasons or because an incorrect code was filed)
- CD	AMCC test has been ordered by an esrd facility or MCP physician that is part of the composite rate and is not separately billable
- CE	AMCC test has been ordered by an esrd facility or MCP physician that is a composite rate test but is beyond the normal frequency covered under the rate and is separately reimbursable based on medical necessity
- CF	AMCC test has been ordered by an esrd facility or MCP physician that is not part of the composite rate and is separately billable
- CG	Policy criteria applied
- CH	0 percent impaired, limited or restricted
- CI	At least 1 percent but less than 20 percent impaired, limited or restricted
- CJ	At least 20 percent but less than 40 percent impaired, limited or restricted
- CK	At least 40 percent but less than 60 percent impaired, limited or restricted
- CL	At least 60 percent but less than 80 percent impaired, limited or restricted
- CM	At least 80 percent but less than 100 percent impaired, limited or restricted

- CN   100 percent impaired, limited or restricted

(**- CP**   Code deleted December 31, 2017).

- CR   Catastrophe/disaster related

- CS   Item or service related, in whole or in part, to an illness, injury, or condition that was caused by or exacerbated by the effects, direct or indirect, of the 2010 oil spill in the gulf of Mexico, including but not limited to subsequent clean-up activities

- CT   Computed tomography services furnished using equipment that does not meet each of the attributes of the national electrical manufacturers association (nema) xr-29-2013 standard

- DA   Oral health assessment by a licensed health professional other than a dentist

- E1   Upper left, eyelid

- E2   Lower left, eyelid

- E3   Upper right, eyelid

- E4   Lower right, eyelid

- EA   Erythropoietic stimulating agent (esa) administered to treat anemia due to anti-cancer chemotherapy

- EB   Erythropoietic stimulating agent (esa) administered to treat anemia due to anti-cancer radiotherapy

- EC   Erythropoietic stimulating agent (esa) administered to treat anemia not due to anti-cancer radiotherapy or anti-cancer chemotherapy

- ED   Hematocrit level has exceeded 39% (or hemoglobin level has exceeded 13.0 g/dl) for 3 or more consecutive billing cycles immediately prior to and including the current cycle

- EE   Hematocrit level has not exceeded 39% (or hemoglobin level has not exceeded 13.0 g/dl) for 3 or more consecutive billing cycles immediately prior to and including the current cycle

- EJ   Subsequent claims for a defined course of therapy, e.g., EPO, sodium hyaluronate, infliximab

- EM   Emergency reserve supply (for esrd benefit only)

- EP   Service provided as part of medicaid early periodic screening diagnosis and treatment (EPSDT) program

- ET   Emergency services

- EX   Expatriate beneficiary

- EY   No physician or other licensed health care provider order for this item or service

- F1   Left hand, second digit

- F2   Left hand, third digit

- F3   Left hand, fourth digit

- F4   Left hand, fifth digit

- F5	Right hand, thumb
- F6	Right hand, second digit
- F7	Right hand, third digit
- F8	Right hand, fourth digit
- F9	Right hand, fifth digit
- FA	Left hand, thumb
- FB	Item provided without cost to provider, supplier or practitioner, or full credit received for replaced device (examples, but not limited to, covered under warranty, replaced due to defect, free samples)
- FC	Partial credit received for replaced device
- FP	Service provided as part of family planning program
- FX	X-ray taken using film
• - FY	X-ray taken using computed radiography technology/cassette-based imaging
- G1	Most recent URR reading of less than 60
- G2	Most recent URR reading of 60 to 64.9
- G3	Most recent URR reading of 65 to 69.9
- G4	Most recent URR reading of 70 to 74.9
- G5	Most recent URR reading of 75 or greater
- G6	Esrd patient for whom less than six dialysis sessions have been provided in a month
- G7	Pregnancy resulted from rape or incest or pregnancy certified by physician as life threatening
- G8	Monitored anesthesia care (mac) for deep complex, complicated, or markedly invasive surgical procedure
- G9	Monitored anesthesia care for patient who has history of severe cardio-pulmonary condition
- GA	Waiver of liability statement issued as required by payer policy, individual case
- GB	Claim being re-submitted for payment because it is no longer covered under a global payment demonstration
- GC	This service has been performed in part by a resident under the direction of a teaching physician
- GD	Units of service exceeds medically unlikely edit value and represents reasonable and necessary services
- GE	This service has been performed by a resident without the presence of a teaching physician under the primary care exception

- GF   Non-physician (e.g. nurse practitioner (np), certified registered nurse anesthetist (crna), certified registered nurse (crn), clinical nurse specialist (cns), physician assistant (pa)) services in a critical access hospital

- GG   Performance and payment of a screening mammogram and diagnostic mammogram on the same patient, same day

- GH   Diagnostic mammogram converted from screening mammogram on same day

- GJ   "opt out" physician or practitioner emergency or urgent service

- GK   Reasonable and necessary item/service associated with a -GA or -GZ modifier

- GL   Medically unnecessary upgrade provided instead of non-upgraded item, no charge, no advance beneficiary notice (abn)

- GM   Multiple patients on one ambulance trip

- GN   Services delivered under an outpatient speech language pathology plan of care

- GO   Services delivered under an outpatient occupational therapy plan of care

- GP   Services delivered under an outpatient physical therapy plan of care

- GQ   Via asynchronous telecommunications system

- GR   This service was performed in whole or in part by a resident in a department of veterans affairs medical center or clinic, supervised in accordance with va policy

- GS   Dosage of erythropoietin stimulating agent has been reduced and maintained in response to hematocrit or hemoglobin level

- GT   Via interactive audio and video telecommunication systems

- GU   Waiver of liability statement issued as required by payer policy, routine notice

- GV   Attending physician not employed or paid under arrangement by the patient's hospice provider

- GW   Service not related to the hospice patient's terminal condition

- GX   Notice of liability issued, voluntary under payer policy

- GY   Item or service statutorily excluded, does not meet the definition of any medicare benefit or, for non-medicare insurers, is not a contract benefit

- GZ   Item or service expected to be denied as not reasonable and necessary

- H9   Court-ordered

- HA   Child/adolescent program

- HB   Adult program, non geriatric

- HC   Adult program, geriatric

- HD   Pregnant/parenting women's program

- HE   Mental health program

- HF	Substance abuse program
- HG	Opioid addiction treatment program
- HH	Integrated mental health/substance abuse program
- HI	Integrated mental health and intellectual disability/developmental disabilities program
- HJ	Employee assistance program
- HK	Specialized mental health programs for high-risk populations
- HL	Intern
- HM	Less than bachelor degree level
- HN	Bachelors degree level
- HO	Masters degree level
- HP	Doctoral level
- HQ	Group setting
- HR	Family/couple with client present
- HS	Family/couple without client present
- HT	Multi-disciplinary team
- HU	Funded by child welfare agency
- HV	Funded state addictions agency
- HW	Funded by state mental health agency
- HX	Funded by county/local agency
- HY	Funded by juvenile justice agency
- HZ	Funded by criminal justice agency
- J1	Competitive acquisition program no-pay submission for a prescription number
- J2	Competitive acquisition program, restocking of emergency drugs after emergency administration
- J3	Competitive acquisition program (cap), drug not available through cap as written, reimbursed under average sales price methodology
- J4	DMEPOS item subject to DMEPOS competitive bidding program that is furnished by a hospital upon discharge
- JA	Administered intravenously
- JB	Administered subcutaneously
- JC	Skin substitute used as a graft
- JD	Skin substitute not used as a graft

- **- JE**   Administered via dialysate

• **- JG**   Drug or biological acquired with 340b drug pricing program discount

- **- JW**   Drug amount discarded/not administered to any patient

- **- K0**   Lower extremity prosthesis functional level 0 - does not have the ability or potential to ambulate or transfer safely with or without assistance and a prosthesis does not enhance their quality of life or mobility.

- **- K1**   Lower extremity prosthesis functional level 1 - has the ability or potential to use a prosthesis for transfers or ambulation on level surfaces at fixed cadence. typical of the limited and unlimited household ambulator.

- **- K2**   Lower extremity prosthesis functional level 2 - has the ability or potential for ambulation with the ability to traverse low level environmental barriers such as curbs, stairs or uneven surfaces. typical of the limited community ambulator.

- **- K3**   Lower extremity prosthesis functional level 3 - has the ability or potential for ambulation with variable cadence. typical of the community ambulator who has the ability to transverse most environmental barriers and may have vocational, therapeutic, or exercise activity that demands prosthetic utilization beyond simple locomotion.

- **- K4**   Lower extremity prosthesis functional level 4 - has the ability or potential for prosthetic ambulation that exceeds the basic ambulation skills, exhibiting high impact, stress, or energy levels, typical of the prosthetic demands of the child, active adult, or athlete.

- **- KA**   Add on option/accessory for wheelchair

- **- KB**   Beneficiary requested upgrade for abn, more than 4 modifiers identified on claim

- **- KC**   Replacement of special power wheelchair interface

- **- KD**   Drug or biological infused through dme

- **- KE**   Bid under round one of the DMEPOS competitive bidding program for use with non-competitive bid base equipment

- **- KF**   Item designated by FDA as class iii device

- **- KG**   DMEPOS item subject to DMEPOS competitive bidding program number 1

- **- KH**   DMEPOS item, initial claim, purchase or first month rental

- **- KI**   DMEPOS item, second or third month rental

- **- KJ**   DMEPOS item, parenteral enteral nutrition (pen) pump or capped rental, months four to fifteen

- **- KK**   DMEPOS item subject to DMEPOS competitive bidding program number 2

- **- KL**   DMEPOS item delivered via mail

- **- KM**   Replacement of facial prosthesis including new impression/moulage

- **- KN**   Replacement of facial prosthesis using previous master model

- **- KO**   Single drug unit dose formulation

- **KP**   First drug of a multiple drug unit dose formulation

- **KQ**   Second or subsequent drug of a multiple drug unit dose formulation

- **KR**   Rental item, billing for partial month

- **KS**   Glucose monitor supply for diabetic beneficiary not treated with insulin

- **KT**   Beneficiary resides in a competitive bidding area and travels outside that competitive bidding area and receives a competitive bid item

- **KU**   DMEPOS item subject to DMEPOS competitive bidding program number 3

- **KV**   DMEPOS item subject to DMEPOS competitive bidding program that is furnished as part of a professional service

- **KW**   DMEPOS item subject to DMEPOS competitive bidding program number 4

- **KX**   Requirements specified in the medical policy have been met

- **KY**   DMEPOS item subject to DMEPOS competitive bidding program number 5

- **KZ**   New coverage not implemented by managed care

- **LC**   Left circumflex coronary artery

- **LD**   Left anterior descending coronary artery

- **LL**   Lease/rental (use the -LL modifier when dme equipment rental is to be applied against the purchase price)

- **LM**   Left main coronary artery

- **LR**   Laboratory round trip

- **LS**   Fda-monitored intraocular lens implant

- **LT**   Left side (used to identify procedures performed on the left side of the body)

- **M2**   Medicare secondary payer (msp)

- **MS**   Six month maintenance and servicing fee for reasonable and necessary parts and labor which are not covered under any manufacturer or supplier warranty

- **NB**   Nebulizer system, any type,-cleared for use with specific drug

- **NR**   New when rented (use the 'nr' modifier when dme which was new at the time of rental is subsequently purchased)

- **NU**   New equipment

- **P1**   A normal healthy patient

- **P2**   A patient with mild systemic disease

- **P3**   A patient with severe systemic disease

- **P4**   A patient with severe systemic disease that is a constant threat to life

- **P5**   A moribund patient who is not expected to survive without the operation

- P6	A declared brain-dead patient whose organs are being removed for donor purposes
- PA	Surgical or other invasive procedure on wrong body part
- PB	Surgical or other invasive procedure on wrong patient
- PC	Wrong surgery or other invasive procedure on patient
- PD	Diagnostic or related non diagnostic item or service provided in a wholly owned or operated entity to a patient who is admitted as an inpatient within 3 days
- PI	Positron emission tomography (pet) or pet/computed tomography (ct) to inform the initial treatment strategy of tumors that are biopsy proven or strongly suspected of being cancerous based on other diagnostic testing
- PL	Progressive addition lenses
- PM	Post mortem
- PN	Non-excepted service provided at an off-campus, outpatient, provider-based department of a hospital
- PO	Excepted service provided at an off-campus, outpatient, provider-based department of a hospital
- PS	Positron emission tomography (pet) or pet/computed tomography (ct) to inform the subsequent treatment strategy of cancerous tumors when the beneficiary's treating physician determines that the pet study is needed to inform subsequent anti-tumor strategy
- PT	Colorectal cancer screening test; converted to diagnostic test or other procedure
- Q0	Investigational clinical service provided in a clinical research study that is in an approved clinical research study
- Q1	Routine clinical service provided in a clinical research study that is in an approved clinical research study
- Q2	Demonstration procedure/service
- Q3	Live kidney donor surgery and related services
- Q4	Service for ordering/referring physician qualifies as a service exemption
▲ - Q5	Service furnished under a reciprocal billing arrangement by a substitute physician or by a substitute physical therapist furnishing outpatient physical therapy services in a health professional shortage area, a medically underserved area, or a rural area
▲ - Q6	Service furnished under a fee-for-time compensation arrangement by a substitute physician or by a substitute physical therapist furnishing outpatient physical therapy services in a health professional shortage area, a medically underserved area, or a rural area
- Q7	One class a finding
- Q8	Two class b findings
- Q9	One class b and two class c findings

- QC   Single channel monitoring

- QD   Recording and storage in solid state memory by a digital recorder

- QE   Prescribed amount of oxygen is less than 1 liter per minute (lpm)

- QF   Prescribed amount of oxygen exceeds 4 liters per minute (lpm) and portable oxygen is prescribed

- QG   Prescribed amount of oxygen is greater than 4 liters per minute(lpm)

- QH   Oxygen conserving device is being used with an oxygen delivery system

- QJ   Services/items provided to a prisoner or patient in state or local custody, however the state or local government, as applicable, meets the requirements in 42 cfr 411.4 (b)

- QK   Medical direction of two, three, or four concurrent anesthesia procedures involving qualified individuals

- QL   Patient pronounced dead after ambulance called

- QM   Ambulance service provided under arrangement by a provider of services

- QN   Ambulance service furnished directly by a provider of services

- QP   Documentation is on file showing that the laboratory test(s) was ordered individually or ordered as a cpt-recognized panel other than automated profile codes 80002-80019, g0058, g0059, and g0060.

- QQ   Ordering professional consulted a qualified clinical decision support mechanism for this service and the related data was provided to the furnishing professional

- QS   Monitored anesthesia care service

- QT   Recording and storage on tape by an analog tape recorder

- QW   CLIA waived test

- QX   Crna service: with medical direction by a physician

- QY   Medical direction of one certified registered nurse anesthetist (crna) by an anesthesiologist

- QZ   Crna service: without medical direction by a physician

- RA   Replacement of a dme, orthotic or prosthetic item

- RB   Replacement of a part of a dme, orthotic or prosthetic item furnished as part of a repair

- RC   Right coronary artery

- RD   Drug provided to beneficiary, but not administered "incident-to"

- RE   Furnished in full compliance with-mandated risk evaluation and mitigation strategy (rems)

- RI   Ramus intermedius coronary artery

- RR   Rental (use the -RR modifier when dme is to be rented)

- RT	Right side (used to identify procedures performed on the right side of the body)
- SA	Nurse practitioner rendering service in collaboration with a physician
- SB	Nurse midwife
- SC	Medically necessary service or supply
- SD	Services provided by registered nurse with specialized, highly technical home infusion training
- SE	State and/or federally-funded programs/services
- SF	Second opinion ordered by a professional review organization (pro) per section 9401, p.l. 99-272 (100% reimbursement - no medicare deductible or coinsurance)
- SG	Ambulatory surgical center (asc) facility service
- SH	Second concurrently administered infusion therapy
- SJ	Third or more concurrently administered infusion therapy
- SK	Member of high risk population (use only with codes for immunization)
- SL	State supplied vaccine
- SM	Second surgical opinion
- SN	Third surgical opinion
- SQ	Item ordered by home health
- SS	Home infusion services provided in the infusion suite of the iv therapy provider
- ST	Related to trauma or injury
- SU	Procedure performed in physician's office (to denote use of facility and equipment)
- SV	Pharmaceuticals delivered to patient's home but not utilized
- SW	Services provided by a certified diabetic educator
- SY	Persons who are in close contact with member of high-risk population (use only with codes for immunization)
(**- SZ**	Code deleted December 31, 2017).
- T1	Left foot, second digit
- T2	Left foot, third digit
- T3	Left foot, fourth digit
- T4	Left foot, fifth digit
- T5	Right foot, great toe
- T6	Right foot, second digit
- T7	Right foot, third digit

- **T8**   Right foot, fourth digit

- **T9**   Right foot, fifth digit

- **TA**   Left foot, great toe

• - **TB**   Drug or biological acquired with 340b drug pricing program discount, reported for informational purposes

- **TC**   Technical component; under certain circumstances, a charge may be made for the technical component alone; under those circumstances the technical component charge is identified by adding modifier 'tc' to the usual procedure number; technical component charges are institutional charges and not billed separately by physicians; however, portable x-ray suppliers only bill for technical component and should utilize modifier tc; the charge data from portable x-ray suppliers will then be used to build customary and prevailing profiles

- **TD**   Rn

- **TE**   LPN/LVN

- **TF**   Intermediate level of care

- **TG**   Complex/high tech level of care

- **TH**   Obstetrical treatment/services, prenatal or postpartum

- **TJ**   Program group, child and/or adolescent

- **TK**   Extra patient or passenger, non-ambulance

- **TL**   Early intervention/individualized family service plan (ifsp)

- **TM**   Individualized education program (iep)

- **TN**   Rural/outside providers' customary service area

- **TP**   Medical transport, unloaded vehicle

- **TQ**   Basic life support transport by a volunteer ambulance provider

- **TR**   School-based individualized education program (iep) services provided outside the public school district responsible for the student

- **TS**   Follow-up service

- **TT**   Individualized service provided to more than one patient in same setting

- **TU**   Special payment rate, overtime

- **TV**   Special payment rates, holidays/weekends

- **TW**   Back-up equipment

- **U1**   Medicaid level of care 1, as defined by each state

- **U2**   Medicaid level of care 2, as defined by each state

- **U3**   Medicaid level of care 3, as defined by each state

- U4	Medicaid level of care 4, as defined by each state
- U5	Medicaid level of care 5, as defined by each state
- U6	Medicaid level of care 6, as defined by each state
- U7	Medicaid level of care 7, as defined by each state
- U8	Medicaid level of care 8, as defined by each state
- U9	Medicaid level of care 9, as defined by each state
- UA	Medicaid level of care 10, as defined by each state
- UB	Medicaid level of care 11, as defined by each state
- UC	Medicaid level of care 12, as defined by each state
- UD	Medicaid level of care 13, as defined by each state
- UE	Used durable medical equipment
- UF	Services provided in the morning
- UG	Services provided in the afternoon
- UH	Services provided in the evening
- UJ	Services provided at night
- UK	Services provided on behalf of the client to someone other than the client (collateral relationship)
- UN	Two patients served
- UP	Three patients served
- UQ	Four patients served
- UR	Five patients served
- US	Six or more patients served
- V1	Demonstration modifier 1
- V2	Demonstration modifier 2
- V3	Demonstration modifier 3
- V5	Vascular catheter (alone or with any other vascular access)
- V6	Arteriovenous graft (or other vascular access not including a vascular catheter)
- V7	Arteriovenous fistula only (in use with two needles)
● - VM	Medicare diabetes prevention program (mdpp) virtual make-up session
- VP	Aphakic patient

- **- X1**   Continuous/broad services: for reporting services by clinicians, who provide the principal care for a patient, with no planned endpoint of the relationship; services in this category represent comprehensive care, dealing with the entire scope of patient problems, either directly or in a care coordination role; reporting clinician service examples include, but are not limited to: primary care, and clinicians providing comprehensive care to patients in addition to specialty care

- **- X2**   Continuous/focused services: for reporting services by clinicians whose expertise is needed for the ongoing management of a chronic disease or a condition that needs to be managed and followed with no planned endpoint to the relationship; reporting clinician service examples include but are not limited to: a rheumatologist taking care of the patient's rheumatoid arthritis longitudinally but not providing general primary care services

- **- X3**   Episodic/broad services: for reporting services by clinicians who have broad responsibility for the comprehensive needs of the patient that is limited to a defined period and circumstance such as a hospitalization; reporting clinician service examples include but are not limited to the hospitalist's services rendered providing comprehensive and general care to a patient while admitted to the hospital

- **- X4**   Episodic/focused services: for reporting services by clinicians who provide focused care on particular types of treatment limited to a defined period and circumstance; the patient has a problem, acute or chronic, that will be treated with surgery, radiation, or some other type of generally time-limited intervention; reporting clinician service examples include but are not limited to, the orthopedic surgeon performing a knee replacement and seeing the patient through the postoperative period

- **- X5**   Diagnostic services requested by another clinician: for reporting services by a clinician who furnishes care to the patient only as requested by another clinician or subsequent and related services requested by another clinician; this modifier is reported for patient relationships that may not be adequately captured by the above alternative categories; reporting clinician service examples include but are not limited to, the radiologist's interpretation of an imaging study requested by another clinician

   - XE   Separate encounter, a service that is distinct because it occurred during a separate encounter

   - XP   Separate practitioner, a service that is distinct because it was performed by a different practitioner

   - XS   Separate structure, a service that is distinct because it was performed on a separate organ/structure

   - XU   Unusual non-overlapping service, the use of a service that is distinct because it does not overlap usual components of the main service

   - ZA   Novartis/Sandoz

   - ZB   Pfizer/Hospira

- **- ZC**   Merck/Samsung bioepis

AMBULANCE SERVICE MODIFIERS

For ambulance service, one-digit modifiers are combined to form a two-digit modifier that identifies the ambulance's place of origin with the first digit, and ambulance's destination with the second digit. They are used in items 12 and 13 on the CMS Form 1491.

One digit modifiers:

-D   Diagnostic or therapeutic site other than-P or-H when these are used as origin codes

-E   Residential, domiciliary, custodial facility (other than an 1819 facility)

-G   Hospital-based dialysis facility (hospital or hospital related)

-H   Hospital

-I   Site of transfer (for example, airport or helicopter pad) between types of ambulance

-J   Non-hospital-based dialysis facility

-N   Skilled nursing facility (SNF) (1819 facility)

-P   Physician's office (includes HMO non-hospital facility, clinic, etc.)

-R   Residence

-S   Scene of accident or acute event

-X   (Destination code only) Intermediate stop at physician's office on the way to the hospital (includes HMO non-hospital facility, clinic, etc.)

PET SCAN MODIFIERS

Use these single-digit alpha characters in combination as two-character modifiers to indicate the results of a current PET scan and a previous test.

-N   Negative

-E   Equivocal

-P   Positive, but not suggestive of extensive ischemia

-S   Positive and suggestive of extensive ischemia (>20 percent of the left ventricle)

APPENDIX B:
SUMMARY OF CHANGES

Summary of Official HCPCS Additions, Changes, and Deletions for 2018

(**-CP**   Code deleted December 31, 2017).

▲   **-FY**   X-ray taken using computed radiography technology/cassette-based imaging

▲   **-JG**   Drug or biological acquired with 340b drug pricing program discount

▲   **-Q5**   Service furnished under a reciprocal billing arrangement by a substitute physician or by a substitute physical therapist furnishing outpatient physical therapy services in a health professional shortage area, a medically underserved area, or a rural area

▲   **-Q6**   Service furnished under a fee-for-time compensation arrangement by a substitute physician or by a substitute physical therapist furnishing outpatient physical therapy services in a health professional shortage area, a medically underserved area, or a rural area

▲   **-QQ**   Ordering professional consulted a qualified clinical decision support mechanism for this service and the related data was provided to the furnishing professional

(**-SZ**   Habilitative services

▲   **-TB**   Drug or biological acquired with 340b drug pricing program discount, reported for informational purposes

▲   **-VM**   Medicare diabetes prevention program (mdpp) virtual make-up session

▲   **-X1**   Continuous/broad services: for reporting services by clinicians, who provide the principal care for a patient, with no planned endpoint of the relationship; services in this category represent comprehensive care, dealing with the entire scope of patient problems, either directly or in a care coordination role; reporting clinician service examples include, but are not limited to: primary care, and clinicians providing comprehensive care to patients in addition to specialty care

▲   **-X2**   Continuous/focused services: for reporting services by clinicians whose expertise is needed for the ongoing management of a chronic disease or a condition that needs to be managed and followed with no planned endpoint to the relationship; reporting clinician service examples include but are not limited to: a rheumatologist taking care of the patient's rheumatoid arthritis longitudinally but not providing general primary care services

▲   **-X3**   Episodic/broad services: for reporting services by clinicians who have broad responsibility for the comprehensive needs of the patient that is limited to a defined period and circumstance such as a hospitalization; reporting clinician service examples include but are not limited to the hospitalist's services rendered providing comprehensive and general care to a patient while admitted to the hospital

▲   **-X4**   Episodic/focused services: for reporting services by clinicians who provide focused care on particular types of treatment limited to a defined period and circumstance; the patient has a problem, acute or chronic, that will be treated with surgery, radiation, or some other type of generally time-limited intervention; reporting clinician service examples

---

include but are not limited to, the orthopedic surgeon performing a knee replacement and seeing the patient through the postoperative period

▲ **-X5** Diagnostic services requested by another clinician: for reporting services by a clinician who furnishes care to the patient only as requested by another clinician or subsequent and related services requested by another clinician; this modifier is reported for patient relationships that may not be adequately captured by the above alternative categories; reporting clinician service examples include but are not limited to, the radiologist's interpretation of an imaging study requested by another clinician

▲ **-ZC** Merck/Samsung bioepis

(**A9599** Code deleted December 31, 2017).

• **C9014** Injection, cerliponase alfa, 1 mg

• **C9015** Injection, c-1 esterase inhibitor (human), haegarda, 10 units

▲ **C9016** Injection, triptorelin extended release, 3.75 mg

▲ **C9024** Injection, liposomal, 1 mg daunorubicin and 2.27 mg cytarabine

▲ **C9028** Injection, inotuzumab ozogamicin, 0.1 mg

▲ **C9029** Injection, guselkumab, 1 mg

(**C9140** Code deleted December 31, 2017). Use J7210.

(**C9483** Code deleted December 31, 2017). Use J9022.

(**C9484** Code deleted December 31, 2017). Use J1428.

(**C9485** Code deleted December 31, 2017). Use J9285.

(**C9486** Code deleted December 31, 2017). Use J1627.

(**C9487** Code deleted July 1, 2017).

▲ **C9488** Injection, conivaptan hydrochloride, 1 mg

(**C9489** Code deleted December 31, 2017). Use J2326.

(**C9490** Code deleted December 31, 2017). Use J0565.

(**C9491** Code deleted December 31, 2017). Use J9023.

▲ **C9492** Injection, durvalumab, 10 mg

▲ **C9493** Injection, edaravone, 1 mg

(**C9494** Code deleted December 31, 2017). Use J2350.

▲ **C9738** Adjunctive blue light cystoscopy with fluorescent imaging agent (list separately in addition to code for primary procedure)

▲ **C9745** Nasal endoscopy, surgical; balloon dilation of eustachian tube

▲ **C9746** Transperineal implantation of permanent adjustable balloon continence device, with cystourethroscopy, when performed and/or fluoroscopy, when performed

▲ **C9747** Ablation of prostate, transrectal, high intensity focused ultrasound (hifu), including imaging guidance

▲ **C9748** Transurethral destruction of prostate tissue; by radiofrequency water vapor (steam)

▲ New code   ▲ Revised code   ( ) Deleted code

thermal therapy

▲ **E0953** Wheelchair accessory, lateral thigh or knee support, any type including fixed mounting hardware, each

▲ **E0954** Wheelchair accessory, foot box, any type, includes attachment and mounting hardware, each foot

(**G0202** Code deleted December 31, 2017). Use 77067.

(**G0204** Code deleted December 31, 2017). Use 77066.

(**G0206** Code deleted December 31, 2017). Use 77065.

(**G0364** Code deleted December 31, 2017).

(**G0502** Code deleted December 31, 2017). Use 99492.

(**G0503** Code deleted December 31, 2017). Use 99493.

(**G0504** Code deleted December 31, 2017). Use 99494.

(**G0505** Code deleted December 31, 2017). Use 99483.

(**G0507** Code deleted December 31, 2017). Use 99484.

▲ **G0511** Rural health clinic or federally qualified health center (RHC or fqhc) only, general care management, 20 minutes or more of clinical staff time for chronic care management services or behavioral health integration services directed by an RHC or fqhc practitioner (physician, np, pa, or CNM), per calendar month

▲ **G0512** Rural health clinic or federally qualified health center (RHC/fqhc) only, psychiatric collaborative care model (psychiatric cocm), 60 minutes or more of clinical staff time for psychiatric cocm services directed by an RHC or fqhc practitioner (physician, np, pa, or CNM) and including services furnished by a behavioral health care manager and consultation with a psychiatric consultant, per calendar month

▲ **G0513** Prolonged preventive service(s) (beyond the typical service time of the primary procedure), in the office or other outpatient setting requiring direct patient contact beyond the usual service; first 30 minutes (list separately in addition to code for preventive service)

▲ **G0514** Prolonged preventive service(s) (beyond the typical service time of the primary procedure), in the office or other outpatient setting requiring direct patient contact beyond the usual service; each additional 30 minutes (list separately in addition to code g0513 for additional 30 minutes of preventive service)

▲ **G0515** Development of cognitive skills to improve attention, memory, problem solving (includes compensatory training), direct (one-on-one) patient contact, each 15 minutes

▲ **G0516** Insertion of non-biodegradable drug delivery implants, 4 or more (services for subdermal rod implant)

▲ **G0517** Removal of non-biodegradable drug delivery implants, 4 or more (services for subdermal implants)

▲ **G0518** Removal with reinsertion, non-biodegradable drug delivery implants, 4 or more (services for subdermal implants)

▲ **G8442** Pain assessment not documented as being performed, documentation the patient is not

---

eligible for a pain assessment using a standardized tool at the time of the encounter

▲ G8535   Elder maltreatment screen not documented; documentation that patient is not eligible for the elder maltreatment screen at the time of the encounter

▲ G8540   Functional outcome assessment not documented as being performed, documentation the patient is not eligible for a functional outcome assessment using a standardized tool at the time of the encounter

(G8696   Code deleted December 31, 2017).

(G8697   Code deleted December 31, 2017).

(G8698   Code deleted December 31, 2017).

▲ G8808   Trans-abdominal or trans-vaginal ultrasound not performed, reason not given

▲ G8869   Patient has documented immunity to hepatitis b and initiating anti-TNF therapy

(G8879   Code deleted December 31, 2017).

▲ G8880   Documentation of reason(s) sentinel lymph node biopsy not performed (e.g., reasons could include but not limited to; non-invasive cancer, incidental discovery of breast cancer on prophylactic mastectomy, incidental discovery of breast cancer on reduction mammoplasty, pre-operative biopsy proven lymph node (ln) metastases, inflammatory carcinoma, stage 3 locally advanced cancer, recurrent invasive breast cancer, clinically node positive after neoadjuvant systemic therapy, patient refusal after informed consent)

▲ G8939   Pain assessment documented as positive, follow-up plan not documented, documentation the patient is not eligible at the time of the encounter

▲ G8941   Elder maltreatment screen documented as positive, follow-up plan not documented, documentation the patient is not eligible for follow-up plan at the time of the encounter

(G8947   Code deleted December 31, 2017).

▲ G8967   Warfarin or another FDA approved oral anticoagulant is prescribed

▲ G8968   Documentation of medical reason(s) for not prescribing warfarin or another-approved anticoagulant (e.g., atrial appendage device in place)

▲ G8969   Documentation of patient reason(s) for not prescribing warfarin or another-approved oral anticoagulant that is approved for the prevention of thromboembolism (e.g., patient choice of having atrial appendage device placed)

(G8971   Code deleted December 31, 2017).

(G8972   Code deleted December 31, 2017).

▲ G9227   Functional outcome assessment documented, care plan not documented, documentation the patient is not eligible for a care plan at the time of the encounter

▲ G9263   Documentation of patient discharged alive following endovascular aaa repair

▲ G9313   Amoxicillin, with or without clavulanate, not prescribed as first line antibiotic at the time of diagnosis for documented reason

▲ G9348   Ct scan of the paranasal sinuses ordered at the time of diagnosis for documented reasons

(G9381   Code deleted December 31, 2017).

(G9496   Code deleted December 31, 2017).

     ▲ New code   ▲ Revised code   ( ) Deleted code

▲ **G9504** Documented reason for not assessing hepatitis b virus (HBV) status (e.g., patient not initiating anti-TNF therapy, patient declined) prior to initiating anti-TNF therapy

▲ **G9607** Documented medical reasons for not performing intraoperative cystoscopy (e.g., urethral pathology precluding cystoscopy, any patient who has a congenital or acquired absence of the urethra) or in the case of patient death

▲ **G9624** Patient not screened for unhealthy alcohol use using a systematic screening method or patient did not receive brief counseling if identified as an unhealthy alcohol user, reason not given

▲ **G9637** At least two orders for the same high-risk medication

▲ **G9638** At least two orders for the same high-risk medications not ordered

▲ **G9656** Patient transferred directly from anesthetizing location to PACU or other non-ICU location

▲ **G9758** Patient in hospice at any time during the measurement period

▲ **G9762** Patient had at least two HPV vaccines (with at least 146 days between the two) or three HPV vaccines on or between the patient's 9th and 13th birthdays

▲ **G9763** Patient did not have at least two HPV vaccines (with at least 146 days between the two) or three HPV vaccines on or between the patient's 9th and 13th birthdays

▲ **G9764** Patient has been treated with an oral systemic or biologic medication for psoriasis vulgaris

▲ **G9765** Documentation that the patient declined therapy change or alternative therapies were unavailable, has documented contraindications, or has not been treated with an oral systemic or biologic for at least six consecutive months (e.g., experienced adverse effects or lack of efficacy with all other therapy options) in order to achieve better disease control as measured by pga, bsa, pasi, or dlqi

▲ **G9785** Pathology report diagnosing cutaneous basal cell carcinoma or squamous cell carcinoma (to include in situ disease) sent from the pathologist/dermatopathologist to the biopsying clinician for review within 7 days from the time when the tissue specimen was received by the pathologist

▲ **G9786** Pathology report diagnosing cutaneous basal cell carcinoma or squamous cell carcinoma (to include in situ disease) was not sent from the pathologist/dermatopathologist to the biopsying clinician for review within 7 days from the time when the tissue specimen was received by the pathologist

▲ **G9794** Documentation of medical reason(s) for not on a daily aspirin or other antiplatelet (e.g., history of gastrointestinal bleed, intra-cranial bleed, idiopathic thrombocytopenic purpura (ITP), gastric bypass or documentation of active anticoagulant use during the measurement period)

▲ **G9814** Death occurring during the index acute care hospitalization

▲ **G9815** Death did not occur during the index acute care hospitalization

▲ **G9816** Death occurring after discharge from the hospital but within 30 days post procedure

▲ **G9817** Death did not occur after discharge from the hospital within 30 days post procedure

▲ **G9840** Ras (KRAS and NRAS) gene mutation testing performed before initiation of anti-EGFR

---

moab

▲ **G9841**   Ras (KRAS and NRAS) gene mutation testing not performed before initiation of anti-EGFR moab

▲ **G9843**   Ras (KRAS or NRAS) gene mutation

▲ **G9890**   Dilated macular exam performed, including documentation of the presence or absence of macular thickening or geographic atrophy or hemorrhage and the level of macular degeneration severity

▲ **G9891**   Documentation of medical reason(s) for not performing a dilated macular examination

▲ **G9892**   Documentation of patient reason(s) for not performing a dilated macular examination

▲ **G9893**   Dilated macular exam was not performed, reason not otherwise specified

▲ **G9894**   Androgen deprivation therapy prescribed/administered in combination with external beam radiotherapy to the prostate

▲ **G9895**   Documentation of medical reason(s) for not prescribing/administering androgen deprivation therapy in combination with external beam radiotherapy to the prostate (e.g., salvage therapy)

▲ **G9896**   Documentation of patient reason(s) for not prescribing/administering androgen deprivation therapy in combination with external beam radiotherapy to the prostate

▲ **G9897**   Patients who were not prescribed/administered androgen deprivation therapy in combination with external beam radiotherapy to the prostate, reason not given

▲ **G9898**   Patient age 65 or older in institutional special needs plans (snp) or residing in long-term care with pos code 32, 33, 34, 54, or 56 any time during the measurement period

▲ **G9899**   Screening, diagnostic, film, digital or digital breast tomosynthesis (3d) mammography results documented and reviewed

▲ **G9900**   Screening, diagnostic, film, digital or digital breast tomosynthesis (3d) mammography results were not documented and reviewed, reason not otherwise specified

▲ **G9901**   Patient age 65 or older in institutional special needs plans (snp) or residing in long-term care with pos code 32, 33, 34, 54, or 56 any time during the measurement period

▲ **G9902**   Patient screened for tobacco use and identified as a tobacco user

▲ **G9903**   Patient screened for tobacco use and identified as a tobacco non-user

▲ **G9904**   Documentation of medical reason(s) for not screening for tobacco use (e.g., limited life expectancy, other medical reason)

▲ **G9905**   Patient not screened for tobacco use, reason not given

▲ **G9906**   Patient identified as a tobacco user received tobacco cessation intervention (counseling and/or pharmacotherapy)

▲ **G9907**   Documentation of medical reason(s) for not providing tobacco cessation intervention (e.g., limited life expectancy, other medical reason)

▲ **G9908**   Patient identified as tobacco user did not receive tobacco cessation intervention (counseling and/or pharmacotherapy), reason not given

▲ **G9909**   Documentation of medical reason(s) for not providing tobacco cessation intervention if identified as a tobacco user (eg, limited life expectancy, other medical reason)

▲ New code   ▲ Revised code   ( ) Deleted code

▲ **G9910** Patients age 65 or older in institutional special needs plans (snp) or residing in long-term care with pos code 32, 33, 34, 54 or 56 anytime during the measurement period

▲ **G9911** Clinically node negative (t1n0m0 or t2n0m0) invasive breast cancer before or after neoadjuvant systemic therapy

▲ **G9912** Hepatitis b virus (HBV) status assessed and results interpreted prior to initiating anti-TNF (tumor necrosis factor) therapy

▲ **G9913** Hepatitis b virus (HBV) status not assessed and results interpreted prior to initiating anti-TNF (tumor necrosis factor) therapy, reason not given

▲ **G9914** Patient receiving an anti-TNF agent

▲ **G9915** No record of HBV results documented

▲ **G9916** Functional status performed once in the last 12 months

▲ **G9917** Documentation of medical reason(s) for not performing functional status (e.g., patient is severely impaired and caregiver knowledge is limited, other medical reason)

▲ **G9918** Functional status not performed, reason not otherwise specified

▲ **G9919** Screening performed and positive and provision of recommendations

▲ **G9920** Screening performed and negative

▲ **G9921** No screening performed, partial screening performed or positive screen without recommendations and reason is not given or otherwise specified

▲ **G9922** Safety concerns screen provided and if positive then documented mitigation recommendations

▲ **G9923** Safety concerns screen provided and negative

▲ **G9924** Documentation of medical reason(s) for not providing safety concerns screen or for not providing recommendations, orders or referrals for positive screen (e.g., patient in palliative care, other medical reason)

▲ **G9925** Safety concerns screening not provided, reason not otherwise specified

▲ **G9926** Safety concerns screening positive screen is without provision of mitigation recommendations, including but not limited to referral to other resources

▲ **G9927** Documentation of system reason(s) for not prescribing warfarin or another-approved anticoagulation due to patient being currently enrolled in a clinical trial related to af/atrial flutter treatment

▲ **G9928** Warfarin or another-approved anticoagulant not prescribed, reason not given

▲ **G9929** Patient with transient or reversible cause of af (e.g., pneumonia, hyperthyroidism, pregnancy, cardiac surgery)

▲ **G9930** Patients who are receiving comfort care only

▲ **G9931** Documentation of cha2ds2-vasc risk score of 0 or 1

▲ **G9932** Documentation of patient reason(s) for not having records of negative or managed positive tb screen (e.g., patient does not return for Mantoux (PPD) skin test evaluation)

▲ **G9933** Adenoma(s) or colorectal cancer detected during screening colonoscopy

▲ **G9934** Documentation that neoplasm detected is only diagnosed as traditional serrated adenoma,

---

▲ New code   ▲ Revised code   ( ) Deleted code

sessile serrated polyp, or sessile serrated adenoma

▲ **G9935**   Adenoma(s) or colorectal cancer not detected during screening colonoscopy

▲ **G9936**   Surveillance colonoscopy - personal history of colonic polyps, colon cancer, or other malignant neoplasm of rectum, rectosigmoid junction, and anus

▲ **G9937**   Diagnostic colonoscopy

▲ **G9938**   Patients age 65 or older in institutional special needs plans (snp) or residing in long-term care with pos code 32, 33, 34, 54, or 56 any time during the measurement period

▲ **G9939**   Pathologists/dermatopathologists is the same clinician who performed the biopsy

▲ **G9940**   Documentation of medical reason(s) for not on a statin (e.g., pregnancy, in vitro fertilization, clomiphene rx, esrd, cirrhosis, muscular pain and disease during the measurement period or prior year)

▲ **G9941**   Back pain was measured by the visual analog scale (vas) within three months preoperatively and at three months (6 - 20 weeks) postoperatively

▲ **G9942**   Patient had any additional spine procedures performed on the same date as the lumbar discectomy/laminotomy

▲ **G9943**   Back pain was not measured by the visual analog scale (vas) within three months preoperatively and at three months (6 - 20 weeks) postoperatively

▲ **G9944**   Back pain was measured by the visual analog scale (vas) within three months preoperatively and at one year (9 to 15 months) postoperatively

▲ **G9945**   Patient had cancer, fracture or infection related to the lumbar spine or patient had idiopathic or congenital scoliosis

▲ **G9946**   Back pain was not measured by the visual analog scale (vas) within three months preoperatively and at one year (9 to 15 months) postoperatively

▲ **G9947**   Leg pain was measured by the visual analog scale (vas) within three months preoperatively and at three months (6 to 20 weeks) postoperatively

▲ **G9948**   Patient had any additional spine procedures performed on the same date as the lumbar discectomy/laminotomy

▲ **G9949**   Leg pain was not measured by the visual analog scale (vas) within three months preoperatively and at three months (6 to 20 weeks) postoperatively

▲ **G9954**   Patient exhibits 2 or more risk factors for post-operative vomiting

▲ **G9955**   Cases in which an inhalational anesthetic is used only for induction

▲ **G9956**   Patient received combination therapy consisting of at least two prophylactic pharmacologic anti-emetic agents of different classes preoperatively and/or intraoperatively

▲ **G9957**   Documentation of medical reason for not receiving combination therapy consisting of at least two prophylactic pharmacologic anti-emetic agents of different classes preoperatively and/or intraoperatively (e.g., intolerance or other medical reason)

▲ **G9958**   Patient did not receive combination therapy consisting of at least two prophylactic pharmacologic anti-emetic agents of different classes preoperatively and/or intraoperatively

▲ **G9959**   Systemic antimicrobials not prescribed

▲ **G9960**   Documentation of medical reason(s) for prescribing systemic antimicrobials

▲ **G9961**   Systemic antimicrobials prescribed

▲ **G9962**   Embolization endpoints are documented separately for each embolized vessel and ovarian artery angiography or embolization performed in the presence of variant uterine artery anatomy

▲ **G9963**   Embolization endpoints are not documented separately for each embolized vessel or ovarian artery angiography or embolization not performed in the presence of variant uterine artery anatomy

▲ **G9964**   Patient received at least one well-child visit with a pcp during the performance period

▲ **G9965**   Patient did not receive at least one well-child visit with a pcp during the performance period

▲ **G9966**   Children who were screened for risk of developmental, behavioral and social delays using a standardized tool with interpretation and report

▲ **G9967**   Children who were not screened for risk of developmental, behavioral and social delays using a standardized tool with interpretation and report

▲ **G9968**   Patient was referred to another provider or specialist during the performance period

▲ **G9969**   Provider who referred the patient to another provider received a report from the provider to whom the patient was referred

▲ **G9970**   Provider who referred the patient to another provider did not receive a report from the provider to whom the patient was referred

▲ **G9974**   Dilated macular exam performed, including documentation of the presence or absence of macular thickening or geographic atrophy or hemorrhage and the level of macular degeneration severity

▲ **G9975**   Documentation of medical reason(s) for not performing a dilated macular examination

▲ **G9976**   Documentation of patient reason(s) for not performing a dilated macular examination

▲ **G9977**   Dilated macular exam was not performed, reason not otherwise specified

▲ **J0565**   Injection, Bezlotoxumab, 10 mg

▲ **J0604**   Cinacalcet, oral, 1 mg, (for esrd on dialysis)

▲ **J0606**   Injection, etelcalcetide, 0.1 mg

▲ **J1428**   Injection, eteplirsen, 10 mg

▲ **J1555**   Injection, immune globulin (cuvitru), 100 mg

▲ **J1627**   Injection, granisetron, extended-release, 0.1 mg

(**J1725**   Code deleted December 31, 2017).

▲ **J1726**   Injection, hydroxyprogesterone caproate, (Makena), 10 mg

▲ **J1729**   Injection, hydroxyprogesterone caproate, not otherwise specified, 10 mg

▲ **J2326**   Injection, nusinersen, 0.1 mg

▲ **J2350**   Injection, ocrelizumab, 1 mg

▲ New code   ▲ Revised code   ( ) Deleted code   511

▲ **J3358** Ustekinumab, for intravenous injection, 1 mg

▲ **J7210** Injection, factor viii, (antihemophilic factor, recombinant), (afstyla), 1 i.u.

▲ **J7211** Injection, factor viii, (antihemophilic factor, recombinant), (kovaltry), 1 i.u.

▲ **J7296** Levonorgestrel-releasing intrauterine contraceptive system, (kyleena), 19.5 mg

▲ **J7321** Hyaluronan or derivative, Hyalgan, Supartz or visco-3, for intra-articular injection, per dose

▲ **J7345** Aminolevulinic acid HCl for topical administration, 10% gel, 10 mg

▲ **J9022** Injection, atezolizumab, 10 mg

▲ **J9023** Injection, avelumab, 10 mg

▲ **J9203** Injection, gemtuzumab ozogamicin, 0.1 mg

▲ **J9285** Injection, olaratumab, 10 mg

(**J9300** Code deleted December 31, 2017).

▲ **K0553** Supply allowance for therapeutic continuous glucose monitor (cgm), includes all supplies and accessories, 1 month supply = 1 unit of service

▲ **K0554** Receiver (monitor), dedicated, for use with therapeutic glucose continuous monitor system

▲ **L3760** Elbow orthosis (EO), with adjustable position locking joint(s), prefabricated, item that has been trimmed, bent, molded, assembled, or otherwise customized to fit a specific patient by an individual with expertise

▲ **L3761** Elbow orthosis (EO), with adjustable position locking joint(s), prefabricated, off-the-shelf

▲ **L7700** Gasket or seal, for use with prosthetic socket insert, any type, each

▲ **L8618** Transmitter cable for use with cochlear implant device or auditory osseointegrated device, replacement

▲ **L8624** Lithium ion battery for use with cochlear implant or auditory osseointegrated device speech processor, ear level, replacement, each

▲ **L8625** External recharging system for battery for use with cochlear implant or auditory osseointegrated device, replacement only, each

▲ **L8691** Auditory osseointegrated device, external sound processor, excludes transducer/actuator, replacement only, each

▲ **L8694** Auditory osseointegrated device, transducer/actuator, replacement only, each

(**P9072** Code deleted December 31, 2017).

▲ **P9073** Platelets, pheresis, pathogen-reduced, each unit

▲ **P9100** Pathogen(s) test for platelets

▲ **Q0477** Power module patient cable for use with electric or electric/pneumatic ventricular assist device, replacement only

▲ **Q2040** Tisagenlecleucel, up to 250 million car-positive viable t cells, including leukapheresis and dose preparation procedures, per infusion

---

▲ New code   ▲ Revised code   ( ) Deleted code

▲ **Q4132** Grafix core and grafixpl core, per square centimeter

▲ **Q4133** Grafix prime and grafixpl prime, per square centimeter

▲ **Q4148** Neox cord 1k, Neox cord rt, or Clarix cord 1k, per square centimeter

▲ **Q4156** Neox 100 or Claris 100, per square centimeter

▲ **Q4158** Kerecis omega3, per square centimeter

▲ **Q4162** Woundex flow, BioSkin flow, 0.5 cc

▲ **Q4163** Woundex, BioSkin, per square centimeter

▲ **Q4176** Neopatch, per square centimeter

▲ **Q4177** Floweramnioflo, 0.1 cc

▲ **Q4178** Floweramniopatch, per square centimeter

▲ **Q4179** Flowerderm, per square centimeter

▲ **Q4180** Revita, per square centimeter

▲ **Q4181** Amnio wound, per square centimeter

▲ **Q4182** TransCyte, per square centimeter

(**Q9984** Code deleted December 31, 2017). Use J7296.

(**Q9985** Code deleted December 31, 2017).

(**Q9986** Code deleted December 31, 2017).

(**Q9987** Code deleted December 31, 2017).

(**Q9988** Code deleted December 31, 2017). Use 1833T.

(**Q9989** Code deleted December 31, 2017).

▲ New code ▲ Revised code ( ) Deleted code

▲ New code   ▲ Revised code   ( ) Deleted code

APPENDIX C: TABLE OF DRUGS

HCPCS Table of Drugs

Directions for the Use of the Table:

1. All drugs are listed in strict alphabetical order by generic drug name.

2. HCPCS code numbers for drugs are listed only under the generic drug name. Users should first look for entries under generic names of drugs. When a drug is known only by brand name, look for the brand name and you will be directed to the generic name of the drug (see "generic name".

3. Information which is indented and appears beneath the first line for a drug is to be considered a continuation of the line preceding it. All drug entries should be checked for indented lines beneath it as a continuation of that entry.

4. When one drug has more than one entry as a result of different routes of administration or different amounts, the drug name is not repeated. All entries for the same drug are listed beneath that drug.

5. The following abbreviations are used in the "routes of administration" column:

amp	=	ampule
DME	=	durable medical equipment
EPI	=	epidural
G	=	gram
IA	=	intra-arterial administration
IM	=	intramuscular administration
INF	=	infusion
INH	=	administration by inhaled solution
INJ	=	injection
IO	=	intraocular
IT	=	intrathecal
IU	=	international unit
IV	=	intravenous administration
mcg	=	microgram
mg	=	milligram
ml	=	milliliter
ORAL	=	administered orally
OTH	=	other routes of administration
PAR	=	parenteral
SC	=	subcutaneous administration
TABS	=	tablets
U	=	units
VAR	=	various routes of administration

DRUG	DOSE	ROUTE	HCPCS
A			
Abatacept	10 mg	IV	J0129
Abbokinase, *see* Urokinase			
Abbokinase, Open Cath, *see* Urokinase			
Abciximab	10 mg	IV	J0130
Abelcet, *see* Amphotericin B Lipid Complex			
ABLC, *see* Amphotericin B			
Abobotulinumtoxin type A	5 units	IM	J0586
Acetaminophen	10 mg	IV	J0131
Acetazolamide sodium	up to 500 mg	IM, IV	J1120
Acetylcysteine, Injection	100 mg	IV	J0132
Acetylcysteine, unit dose form	per gram	INH	J7604, J7608
Achromycin, *see* Tetracycline			
Actemra, *see* Tocilizumab			
ACTH, *see* Corticotropin			
Acthar, *see* Corticotropin			
Actimmune, *see* Interferon gamma 1-B			
Activase, *see* Alteplase recombinant			
Acyclovir	5 mg		J0133
Adalimumab	20 mg	SC	J0135
Adcetris, *see* Brentuximab Vedotin			
Adenocard, *see* Adenosine			
Adenoscan, *see* Adenosine			
Adenosine	1 mg	IV	J0153
Ado-trastuzumab Emtansine	1 mg	IV	J9354
Adrenalin Chloride, *see* Adrenalin, epinephrine			
Adrenalin, epinephrine	0.1 mg	SC, IM	J0171
Adriamycin PFS, *see* Doxorubicin HCl			
Adriamycin RDF, *see* Doxorubicin HCl			
Adrucil, *see* Fluorouracil			
Aflibercept	1 mg	OTH	J0178
Agalsidase beta	1 mg	IV	J0180

DRUG	DOSE	ROUTE	HCPCS
Aggrastat, *see* Tirofiban hydrochloride			
A-hydroCort, *see* Hydrocortisone sodium phosphate			
Akineton, *see* Biperiden			
Alatrofloxacin mesylate, injection	100 mg	IV	J0200
Albuterol	0.5 mg	INH	J7620
Albuterol, concentrated form	1 mg	INH	J7610, J7611
Albuterol, unit dose form	1 mg	INH	J7609, J7613
Aldesleukin	per single use vial	IM, IV	J9015
Aldomet, *see* Methyldopate HCl			
Alefacept	0.5 mg	IM, IV	J0215
Alferon N, *see* Interferon alfa-n3			
Alglucerase	per 10 units	IV	J0205
Alglucosidase alfa	10 mg	IV	J0220, J0221
Alkaban-AQ, *see* Vinblastine sulfate			
Alkeran, *see* Melphalan, oral			
Alpha 1-proteinase inhibitor, human	10 mg	IV	J0256, J0257
Alphanate			J7186
Alprostadil, Injection	1.25 mcg	OTH	J0270
Alprostadil, urethral suppository		OTH	J0275
Alteplase recombinant	1 mg	IV	J2997
Alupent, *see* Metaproterenol sulfate or Metaproterenol, compounded			
Amcort, *see* Triamcinolone diacetate			
A-methaPred, *see* Methylprednisolone sodium succinate			
Amgen, *see* Interferon alphacon-1			
Amifostine	500 mg	IV	J0207
Amikacin sulfate	100 mg		J0278
Aminolevulinic acid HCl unit dose (354 mg)	OTH		J7308
Aminolevulinic acid HCl 10% Gel	10 mg	OTH	J7345
Aminolevulinate	1 gm	OTH	J7309
Aminophylline/Aminophyllin	up to 250 mg	IV	J0280

DRUG	DOSE	ROUTE	HCPCS
Amiodarone HCl	30 mg	IV	J0282
Amitriptyline HCl	up to 20 mg	IM	J1320
Amobarbital	up to 125 mg	IM, IV	J0300
Amphocin, *see* Amphotericin B			
Amphotericin B	50 mg	IV	J0285
Amphotericin B, lipid complex	10 mg	IV	J0287-J0289
Ampicillin sodium	up to 500 mg	IM, IV	J0290
Ampicillin sodium/sulbactam sodium	per 1.5 gm	IM, IV	J0295
Amygdalin, *see* Laetrile, Amygdalin, vitamin B-17			
Amytal, *see* Amobarbital			
Anabolin LA 100, *see* Nandrolone decanoate			
Anidulafungin	1 mg	IV	J0348
Anascorp, *see* Centruroides Immune F(ab)			
Ancef, *see* Cefazolin sodium			
Andrest 90-4, *see* Testosterone enanthate and estradiol valerate			
Andro-Cyp, *see* Testosterone cypionate			
Andro-Cyp 200, *see* Testosterone cypionate			
Andro L.A. 200, *see* Testosterone enanthate			
Andro-Estro 90-4, *see* Testosterone enanthate and estradiol valerate			
Andro/Fem, *see* Testosterone cypionate and estradiol cypionate			
Androgyn L.A., *see* Testosterone enanthate and estradiol valerate			
Androlone-50, *see* Nandrolone phenpropionate			
Androlone-D 100, *see* Nandrolone decanoate			
Andronaq-50, *see* Testosterone suspension			
Andronaq-LA, *see* Testosterone cypionate			
Andronate-200, *see* Testosterone cypionate			
Andronate-100, *see* Testosterone cypionate			
Andropository 100, *see* Testosterone enanthate			
Andryl 200, *see* Testosterone enanthate			
Anectine, *see* Succinylcholine chloride			

DRUG	DOSE	ROUTE	HCPCS
Anergan 25, *see* Promethazine HCl			
Anergan 50, *see* Promethazine HCl			
Anistreplase	30 units	IV	J0350
Anti-Inhibitor	per IU	IV	J7198
Antispas, *see* Dicyclomine HCl			
Antithrombin III (human)	per IU	IV	J7197
Antithrombin recombinant	50 IU	IV	J7196
Anzemet, *see* Dolasetron mesylate Injection			
A.P.L., *see* Chorionic gonadotropin			
Apomorphine Hydrochloride	1 mg	SC	J0364
Apresoline, *see* Hydralazine HCl			
Aprotinin	10,000 kiu		J0365
AquaMEPHYTON, *see* Vitamin K			
Aralen, *see* Chloroquine HCl			
Aramine, *see* Metaraminol			
Aranesp, *see* Darbepoetin Alfa			
Arbutamine	1 mg	IV	J0395
Arcalyst, *see* Rilonaceptt			
Aredia, *see* Pamidronate disodium			
Arfonad, *see* Trimethaphan camsylate			
Arformoterol tartrate	15 mcg	INH	J7605
Argatroban (for non-esrd use)	1 mg	IV	J0883
(for esrd use)	1 mg	IV	J0884
Aridol, *see* Mannitol			
Aripiprazole	0.25 mg	IM	J0400
Aripiprazole, extended release	1 mg	IV	J0401
Aripiprazole lauroxil	1 mg	IV	J1942
Aristocort Forte, *see* Triamcinolone diacetate			
Aristocort Intralesional, *see* Triamcinolone diacetate			
Aristospan Intra-Articular, *see* Triamcinolone hexacetonide			
Aristospan Intralesional, *see* Triamcinolone hexacetonide			

DRUG	DOSE	ROUTE	HCPCS
Arrestin, *see* Trimethobenzamide HCl			
Arsenic trioxide	1 mg	IV	J9017
Arzerra, *see* Ofatumumab			
Asparaginase	1,000 units	IV, IM	J9019
	10,000 units	IV, IM	J9020
Astramorph PF, *see* Morphine sulfate			
Atezolizumab	10 mg	IV	J9022
Atgam, *see* Lymphocyte Immune globulin			
Ativan, *see* Lorazepam			
Atropine, concentrated form	per mg	INH	J7635
Atropine, unit dose form	per mg	INH	J7636
Atropine sulfate	0.01 mg	IV, IM, SC	J0461
Atrovent, *see* Ipratropium bromide			
Atryn, *see* Antithrombin recombinant			
Aurothioglucose	up to 50 mg	IM	J2910
Autologous cultured chondrocytes Implant		OTH	J7330
Autoplex T, *see* Hemophilia clotting factors			
Avelumab	10 mg	IV	J9023
Avonex, *see* Interferon beta-1a			
Azacitidine	1 mg	SC	J9025
Azathioprine	50 mg	ORAL	J7500
Azathioprine, parenteral	100 mg	IV	J7501
Azithromycin, dihydrate	1 gm	ORAL	Q0144
Azithromycin, Injection	500 mg	IV	J0456
B			
Baclofen	10 mg	IT	J0475
	50 mcg	OTH	J0476
Bactocill, *see* Oxacillin sodium			
BAL in oil, *see* Dimercaprol			
Banflex, *see* Orphenadrine citrate			
Basiliximab	20 mg	J0480	

DRUG	DOSE	ROUTE	HCPCS
BCG (Bacillus Calmette and Guérin), live	per vial instillation	IV	J9031
Beclomethasone inhalation solution, unit dose form	per mg	INH	J7622
Belatacept	1 mg	IV	J0485
Belimumab	10 mg	IV	J0490
Belinostat	10 mg	IV	J9032
Bena-D 10, *see* Diphenhydramine HCl			
Bena-D 50, *see* Diphenhydramine HCl			
Benadryl, *see* Diphenhydramine HCl			
Benahist 10, *see* Diphenhydramine HCl			
Benahist 50, *see* Diphenhydramine HCl			
Ben-Allergin-50, *see* Diphenhydramine HCl			
Bendamustine HCl (Treanda)	1 mg	IV	J9033
Bendamustine HCl (Bendeka)	1 mg	IV	J9034
BeneFIX, *see* Factor IX, recombinant			
Benlysta, *see* Belimumab			
Benoject-10, *see* Diphenhydramine HCl			
Benoject-50, *see* Diphenhydramine HCl			
Bentyl, *see* Dicyclomine			
Benztropine mesylate	per 1 mg	IM, IV	J0515
Berinert, *see* C-1 esterase inhibitor			
Berubigen, *see* Vitamin B-12 cyanocobalamin			
Beta amyloid	per study dose	OTH	A9599
Betalin 12, *see* Vitamin B-12 cyanocobalamin			
Betameth, *see* Betamethasone sodium phosphate			
Betamethasone acetate & betamethasone sodium phosphate	per 3 mg	IM	J0702
Betamethasone inhalation solution, unit dose form	per mg	INH	J7624
Betaseron, *see* Interferon beta-1b			
Bethanechol chloride	up to 5 mg	SC	J0520
Bevacizumab	10 mg	IV	J9035
Bezlotoxumab	10 mg	IV	J0565

DRUG	DOSE	ROUTE	HCPCS
Bicillin L-A, *see* Penicillin G benzathine			
Bicillin C-R 900/300, *see* Penicillin G procaine and penicillin G benzathine			
Bicillin C-R, *see* Penicillin G benzathine and penicillin G procaine			
BiCNU, *see* Carmustine			
Biperiden lactate	per 5 mg	IM, IV	J0190
Bitolterol mesylate, concentrated form	per mg	INH	J7628
Bitolterol mesylate, unit dose form	per mg	INH	J7629
Bivalirudin	1 mg	IV	J0583
Blenoxane, *see* Bleomycin sulfate			
Bleomycin sulfate	15 units	IM, IV, SC	J9040
Blinatumomab	1 microgram	IV	J9039
Bortezomib	0.1 mg	IV	J9041
Botox, *see* OnabotulinumtoxinA			
Brentuximab Vedotin	1 mg	IV	J9042
Brethine, *see* Terbutaline sulfate or Terbutaline, compounded			
Bricanyl Subcutaneous, *see* Terbutaline sulfate			
Brompheniramine maleate	per 10 mg	IM, SC, IV	J0945
Bronkephrine, *see* Ethylnorepinephrine HCl			
Bronkosol, *see* Isoetharine HCl			
Budesonide inhalation solution, concentrated form	0.25 mg	INH	J7633, J7634
Budesonide inhalation solution, unit dose form	0.5 mg	INH	J7626, J7627
Buprenorphine Hydrochloride	0.1 mg	IM	J0592
Buprenorphine/Naloxone	1 mg	ORAL	J0571
	< = 3 mg	ORAL	J0572
	> 3 mg but < = 6 mg	ORAL	J0573
	> 6 mg but < = 10 mg	ORAL	J0574
	> 10 mg	ORAL	J0575
Busulfan	1 mg	IV	J0594
Busulfan	2 mg	ORAL	J8510

DRUG	DOSE	ROUTE	HCPCS
Butorphanol tartrate	1 mg		J0595
C			
C1 Esterase Inhibitor	10 units	IV	J0596-J0598
Cabazitaxel	1 mg	IV	J9043
Cabergoline	.25 mg	ORAL	J8515
Cafcit, *see* Caffeine citrate			
Caffeine citrate	5 mg	IV	J0706
Caine-1, *see* Lidocaine HCl			
Caine-2, *see* Lidocaine HCl			
Calcijex, *see* Calcitriol			
Calcimar, *see* Calcitonin-salmon			
Calcitonin-salmon	up to 400 units	SC, IM	J0630
Calcitriol	0.1 mcg	IM	J0636
Calcium Disodium Versenate, *see* Edetate calcium disodium			
Calcium gluconate	per 10 ml	IV	J0610
Calcium glycerophosphate & calcium lactate	per 10 ml	IM, SC	J0620
Caldolor, *see* Ibuprofen			
Calphosan, *see* Calcium glycerophosphate and calcium lactate			
Camptosar, *see* Irinotecan			
Canakinumab	1 mg	SC	J0638
Capecitabine	150 mg	ORAL	J8520
	500 mg	ORAL	J8521
Capsaicin patch	per sq cm	OTH	J7336
Carbidopa 5 mg/levodopa	20 mg enteral suspension	IV	J7340
Carbocaine with Neo-Cobefrin, *see* Mepivacaine			
Carbocaine, *see* Mepivacaine			
Carboplatin	50 mg	IV	J9045
Carfilzomib	1 mg	IV	J9047
Carmustine	100 mg	IV	J9050

DRUG	DOSE	ROUTE	HCPCS
Carnitor, *see* Levocarnitine			
Carticel, *see* Autologous cultured chondrocytes			
Caspofungin acetate	5 mg	IV	J0637
Cayston, *see* Aztreonam			
Cefadyl, *see* Cephapirin Sodium			
Cefazolin sodium	500 mg	IV, IM	J0690
Cefepime hydrochloride	500 mg	IV	J0692
Cefizox, *see* Ceftizoxime sodium			
Cefotaxime sodium	per 1 g	IV, IM	J0698
Cefoxitin sodium	1 g	IV, IM	J0694
Ceftaroline fosamil	1 mg		J0712
Ceftazidime	per 500 mg	IM, IV	J0713
Ceftazidime and Avibactam	0.5 g/0.125 g	IV	J0714
Ceftizoxime sodium	per 500 mg	IV, IM	J0715
Ceftriaxone sodium	per 250 mg	IV, IM	J0696
Ceftolozane 50 mg and tazobactam 25 mg		IV	J0695
Cefuroxime sodium, sterile	per 750 mg	IM, IV	J0697
Celestone Soluspan, *see* Betamethasone acetate and betamethasone sodium phosphate			
CellCept, *see* Mycophenolate mofetil			
Cel-U-Jec, *see* Betamethasone sodium phosphate			
Cenacort Forte, *see* Triamcinolone diacetate			
Cenacort A-40, *see* Triamcinolone acetonide			
Centruroides Immune F(ab)	up to 120 mg	IV	J0716
Cephalothin sodium	up to 1 g	IM, IV	J1890
Cephapirin sodium	up to 1 g IV,	IM	J0710
Ceredase, *see* Alglucerase			
Certolizumab pegol	1 mg	SC	J0717
Cerubidine, *see* Daunorubicin HCl			
Cetuximab	10 mg	IV	J9055
Chealamide, *see* Endrate ethylenediamine-tetra-acetic acid			
Chloramphenicol sodium succinate	up to 1 g	IV	J0720

DRUG	DOSE	ROUTE	HCPCS
Chlordiazepoxide HCl	up to 100 mg	IM, IV	J1990
Chloromycetin Sodium Succinate, *see* Chloramphenicol sodium succinate			
Chloroprocaine HCl	per 30 ml	VAR	J2400
Chlorpromazine	5 mg	ORAL	Q0161
Chloroquine HCl	up to 250 mg	IM	J0390
Chlorothiazide sodium	per 500 mg	IV	J1205
Chlorpromazine HCl	up to 50 mg	IM, IV	J3230
Chorex-5, *see* Chorionic gonadotropin			
Chorex-10, *see* Chorionic gonadotropin			
Chorignon, *see* Chorionic gonadotropin			
Chorionic gonadotropin	per 1,000 USP units	IM	J0725
Choron 10, *see* Chorionic gonadotropin			
Cidofovir	375 mg	IV	J0740
Cilastatin sodium, Imipenem	per 250 mg	IM, IV	J0743
Cimzia, *see* Certolizumab pegol			
Cinacalcet		ORAL	J0604
Cinryze, *see* C1 Esterase Inhibitor			
Cipro IV, *see* Ciprofloxacin			
Ciprofloxacin	200 mg	IV	J0706
octic suspension 6 mg		OTH	J7342
Cisplatin, powder or solution	per 10 mg	IV	J9060
Cladribine	per mg	IV	J9065
Claforan, *see* Cefotaxime sodium			
Clofarabine	1 mg	IV	J9027
Clonidine Hydrochloride	1 mg	epidural	J0735
Cobex, *see* Vitamin B-12 cyanocobalamin			
Codeine phosphate	per 30 mg	IM, IV, SC	J0745
Codimal-A, *see* Brompheniramine maleate			
Cogentin, *see* Benztropine mesylate			
Collagenase, Clostridium Histolyticum	0.01 mg	OTH	J0775
Colistimethate sodium	up to 150 mg	IM, IV	J0770

DRUG	DOSE	ROUTE	HCPCS
Coly-Mycin M, *see* Colistimethate sodium			
Compa-Z, *see* Prochlorperazine			
Compazine, *see* Prochlorperazine			
Compounded drug, not otherwise classified			J7999
Cophene-B, *see* Brompheniramine maleate			
Copper contraceptive, intrauterine		OTH	J7300
Cordarone, *see* Amiodarone HCl			
Corgonject-5, *see* Chorionic gonadotropin			
Corticorelin ovine triflutate	1 mcg		J0795
Corticotropin	up to 40 units	IV, IM, SC	J0800
Cortrosyn, *see* Cosyntropin			
Cosmegen, *see* Dactinomycin			
Cosyntropin	per 0.25 mg	IM, IV	J0833, J0834
Cotranzine, *see* Prochlorperazine			
CroFab, *see* Crotalidae Polyvalent Immune Fab			
Cromolyn sodium, unit dose form	per 10 mg	INH	J7631, J7632
Crotalidae Polyvalent Immune Fab	up to 1 gram	IV	J0840
Crysticillin 300 A.S., *see* Penicillin G procaine			
Crysticillin 600 A.S., *see* Penicillin G procaine			
Cyclophosphamide	100 mg	IV	J9070
Cyclophosphamide, oral	25 mg	ORAL	J8530
Cyclosporine, oral	25 mg	ORAL	J7515
	100 mg	ORAL	J7502
Cyclosporine, parenteral	250 mg	IV	J7516
Cytarabine	100 mg	SC, IV	J9100
Cytarabine liposome	10 mg	IT	J9098
Cytomegalovirus Immune globulin intravenous(human)per vial			
Cytosar-U, *see* Cytarabine			
Cytovene, *see* Ganciclovir sodium			
Cytoxan, *see* Cyclophosphamide; cyclophosphamide, lyophilized; and cyclophosphamide, oral			

DRUG	DOSE	ROUTE	HCPCS
D			
D-5-W, infusion	1000 cc	IV	J7070
Dacarbazine	100 mg	IV	J9130
Daclizumab	25 mg	IV	J7513
Dactinomycin	0.5 mg		
Dalalone, *see* Dexamethasone sodium phosphate			
Dalalone L.A., *see* Dexamethasone acetate			
Dalbavancin	5 mg	IV	J0875
Dalteparin sodium	per 2500 IU	SC	J1645
Daptomycin	1 mg	IV	J0878
Daratumumab	10 mg	IV	J9145
Darbepoetin Alfa	1 mcg	IV, SC	J0881, J0882
Daunorubicin citrate, liposomal formulation	10 mg	IV	J9151
Daunorubicin HCl	10 mg	IV	J9150
DaunoXome, *see* Daunorubicin citrate			
DDAVP, *see* Desmopressin acetate			
Decadron Phosphate, *see* Dexamethasone sodium phosphate			
Decadron, *see* Dexamethasone sodium phosphate			
Decadron-LA, *see* Dexamethasone acetate			
Deca-Durabolin, *see* Nandrolone decanoate			
Decaject, *see* Dexamethasone sodium phosphate			
Decaject-L.A., *see* Dexamethasone acetate			
Decitabine	1 mg	IV	J0894
Decolone-50, *see* Nandrolone decanoate			
Decolone-100, *see* Nandrolone decanoate			
De-Comberol, *see* Testosterone cypionate and estradiol cypionate			
Deferoxamine mesylate	500 mg	IM, SC, IV	J0895
Degarelix	1 mg	SC	J9155
Dehist, *see* Brompheniramine maleate			
Deladumone OB, *see* Testosterone enanthate and estradiol valerate			

DRUG	DOSE	ROUTE	HCPCS
Deladumone, *see* Testosterone enanthate and estradiol valerate			
Delatest, *see* Testosterone enanthate			
Delatestadiol, *see* Testosterone enanthate and estradiol valerate			
Delatestryl, *see* Testosterone enanthate			
Delta-Cortef, *see* Prednisolone, oral			
Delestrogen, *see* Estradiol valerate			
Demadex, *see* Torsemide			
Demerol HCl, *see* Meperidine HCl			
Denileukin diftitox	300 mcg	IV	J9160
Denosumab	1 mg	SC	J0897
DepAndro 100, *see* Testosterone cypionate			
DepAndro 200, *see* Testosterone cypionate			
DepAndrogyn, *see* Testosterone cypionate and estradiol cypionate			
DepGynogen, *see* Depo-estradiol cypionate			
DepMedalone 40, *see* Methylprednisolone acetate			
DepMedalone 80, *see* Methylprednisolone acetate			
Depo-estradiol cypionate	up to 5 mg	IM	J1000
Depogen, *see* Depo-estradiol cypionate			
Depoject, *see* Methylprednisolone acetate			
Depo-Medrol, *see* Methylprednisolone acetate			
Depopred-40, *see* Methylprednisolone acetate			
Depopred-80, *see* Methylprednisolone acetate			
Depo-Provera, *see* Medroxyprogesterone acetate			
Depotest, *see* Testosterone cypionate			
Depo-Testadiol, *see* Testosterone cypionate and estradiol cypionate			
Depotestogen, *see* Testosterone cypionate and estradiol cypionate			
Depo-Testosterone, *see* Testosterone cypionate			
Desferal Mesylate, *see* Deferoxamine mesylate			
Desmopressin acetate	1 mcg	IV, SC	J2597

DRUG	DOSE	ROUTE	HCPCS
Dexacen LA-8, *see* Dexamethasone acetate			
Dexacen-4, *see* Dexamethasone sodium phosphate			
Dexamethasone, concentrated form	per mg	INH	J7637
Dexamethasone, unit form	per mg	INH	J7638
Dexamethasone, intravitreal Implant	0.1 mg	OTH	J7312
Dexamethasone, oral	0.25 mg	ORAL	J8540
Dexamethasone acetate	1 mg	IM	J1094
Dexamethasone sodium phosphate	1 mg	IM, IV,	OTH J1100
Dexasone, *see* Dexamethasone sodium phosphate			
Dexasone L.A., *see* Dexamethasone acetate			
Dexferrum, *see* Iron Dextran			
Dexone, *see* Dexamethasone sodium phosphate			
Dexone LA, *see* Dexamethasone acetate			
Dexrazoxane hydrochloride	250 mg	IV	J1190
Dextran 40	500 ml	IV	J7100
Dextran 75	500 ml	IV	J7110
Dextrose 5%/normal saline solution,	500 ml = 1 unit	IV	J7042
Dextrose/water (5%)	500 ml = 1 unit	IV	J7060
D.H.E. 45, *see* Dihydroergotamine			
Diamox, *see* Acetazolamide sodium			
Diazepam	up to 5 mg	IM, IV	J3360
Diazoxide	up to 300 mg	IV	J1730
Dibent, *see* Dicyclomine HCl			
Diclofenac sodium	37.5	IV	J1130
Dicyclomine HCl	up to 20 mg	IM	J0500
Didronel, *see* Etidronate disodium			
Diethylstilbestrol diphosphate	250 mg	IV	J9165
Diflucan, *see* Fluconazole			
Digoxin	up to 0.5 mg	IM, IV	J1160
Digoxin Immune Fab (ovine)	per vial		J1162
Dihydrex, *see* Diphenhydramine HCl			

DRUG	DOSE	ROUTE	HCPCS
Dihydroergotamine mesylate	per 1 mg	IM, IV	J1110
Dilantin, *see* Phenytoin sodium			
Dilaudid, *see* Hydromorphone HCl			
Dilocaine, *see* Lidocaine HCl			
Dilomine, *see* Dicyclomine HCl			
Dilor, *see* Dyphylline			
Dimenhydrinate	up to 50 mg	IM, IV	J1240
Dimercaprol	per 100 mg	IM	J0470
Dimethyl sulfoxide, *see* DMSO, Dimethylsulfoxide			
Dinate, *see* Dimenhydrinate			
Dioval, *see* Estradiol valerate			
Dioval 40, *see* Estradiol valerate			
Dioval XX, *see* Estradiol valerate			
Diphenacen-50, *see* Diphenhydramine HCl			
Diphenhydramine HCl, Injection	up to 50 mg	IV, IM	J1200
Diphenhydramine HCl, oral	50 mg	ORAL	Q0163
Dipyridamole	per 10 mg	IV	J1245
Disotate, *see* Endrate ethylenediamine-tetra-acetic acid			
Di-Spaz, *see* Dicyclomine HCl			
Ditate-DS, *see* Testosterone enanthate and estradiol valerate			
Diuril Sodium, *see* Chlorothiazide sodium			
D-Med 80, *see* Methylprednisolone acetate			
DMSO, Dimethyl sulfoxide 50%,	50 ml	OTH	J1212
Dobutamine HCl	per 250 mg	IV	J1250
Dobutrex, *see* Dobutamine HCl			
Docetaxel	20 mg	IV	J9170
Dolasetron mesylate, Injection	10 mg	IV	J1260
Dolasetron mesylate, tablets	100 mg	ORAL	Q0180
Dolophine HCl, *see* Methadone HCl			
Dommanate, *see* Dimenhydrinate			
Donbax, *see* Doripenem			
Dopamine HCl	40 mg		J1265

DRUG	DOSE	ROUTE	HCPCS
Doribax, *see* Doripenem			
Doripenem	10 mg	IV	J1267
Dornase alpha, unit dose form	per mg	INH	J7639
Doxercalciferol	1 mcg	IV	J1270
Doxil, *see* Doxorubicin HCL, lipid			
Doxorubicin HCL	10 mg	IV	J9000
Dramamine, *see* Dimenhydrinate			
Dramanate, *see* Dimenhydrinate			
Dramilin, *see* Dimenhydrinate			
Dramocen, *see* Dimenhydrinate			
Dramoject, *see* Dimenhydrinate			
Dronabinol, oral	2.5 mg	ORAL	Q0167
Droperidol	up to 5 mg	IM, IV	J1790
Drug administered through a metered dose inhaler		INH	J3535
Droperidol and fentanyl citrate	up to 2 ml ampule	IM, IV	J1810
DTIC-Dome, *see* Dacarbazine			
Dua-Gen L.A., *see* Testosterone enanthate and estradiol valerate cypionate			
Duoval P.A., *see* Testosterone enanthate and estradiol valerate			
Durabolin, *see* Nandrolone phenpropionate			
Duraclon, *see* Clonidine Hydrochloride			
Dura-Estrin, *see* Depo-estradiol cypionate			
Duracillin A.S., *see* Penicillin G procaine			
Duragen-10, *see* Estradiol valerate			
Duragen-20, *see* Estradiol valerate			
Duragen-40, *see* Estradiol valerate			
Duralone-40, *see* Methylprednisolone acetate			
Duralone-80, *see* Methylprednisolone acetate			
Duralutin, *see* Hydroxyprogesterone Caproate			
Duramorph, *see* Morphine sulfate			
Duratest-100, *see* Testosterone cypionate			

DRUG	DOSE	ROUTE	HCPCS
Duratest-200, *see* Testosterone cypionate			
Duratestrin, *see* Testosterone cypionate and estradiol cypionate			
Durathate-200, *see* Testosterone enanthate			
Dymenate, *see* Dimenhydrinate			
Dyphylline	up to 500 mg	IM	J1180
Dysport, *see* Abobotulinum toxin type A			
E			
Ecallantide	1 mg	SC	J1290
Eculizumab	10 mg	IV	J1300
Edetate calcium disodium	up to 1000 mg	IV, SC, IM	J0600
Edetate disodium	per 150 mg	IV	J3520
Elavil, *see* Amitriptyline HCl			
Ellence, *see* Epirubicin HCl			
Elliotts b solution	1 ml	OTH	J9175
Elosulfase alfa	1 mg	IV	J1322
Elotuzumab	1 mg	IV	J9176
Elspar, *see* Asparaginase			
Emend, *see* Fosaprepitant			
Emete-Con, *see* Benzquinamide			
Eminase, *see* Anistreplase			
Enbrel, *see* Etanercept			
Endrate ethylenediamine-tetra-acetic acid, *see* Edetate disodium			
Enfuvirtide	1 mg	SC	J1324
Enovil, *see* Amitriptyline HCl			
Enoxaparin sodium	10 mg	SC	J1650
Eovist, *see* Gadoxetate disodium			
Epinephrine, adrenalin	0.1 mg	SC, IM	J0171
Epirubicin hydrochloride	2 mg		J9178
Epoetin alfa	100 units	IV, SC	Q4081
Epoetin alfa, non-ESRD use	1000 units	IV	J0885

DRUG	DOSE	ROUTE	HCPCS
Epoetin beta, esrd use	1 mcg	IV	J0887
Epoetin beta, non-esrd use	1 mcg	IV	J0888
Epoprostenol	0.5 mg	IV	J1325
Eptifibatide, Injection	5 mg	IM, IV	J1327
Ergonovine maleate	up to 0.2 mg	IM, IV	J1330
Eribulin mesylate	0.1 mg	IV	J9179
Ertapenem sodium	500 mg	IM, IV	J1335
Erwinase, *see* Asparaginase			
Erythromycin lactobionate	500 mg	IV	J1364
Estra-D, *see* Depo-estradiol cypionate			
Estra-L 20, *see* Estradiol valerate			
Estra-L 40, *see* Estradiol valerate			
Estra-Testrin, *see* Testosterone enanthate and estradiol valerate			
Estradiol Cypionate, *see* Depo-estradiol cypionate			
Estradiol L.A., *see* Estradiol valerate			
Estradiol L.A. 20, *see* Estradiol valerate			
Estradiol L.A. 40, *see* Estradiol valerate			
Estradiol valerate	up to 10 mg	IM	J1380
Estro-Cyp, *see* Depo-estradiol cypionate			
Estrogen, conjugated	per 25 mg	IV, IM	J1410
Estroject L.A., *see* Depo-estradiol cypionate			
Estrone	per 1 mg	IM	J1435
Estrone 5, *see* Estrone			
Estrone Aqueous, *see* Estrone			
Estronol, *see* Estrone			
Estronol-L.A., *see* Depo-estradiol cypionate			
Etanercept, Injection	25 mg	IM, IV	J1438
Etelcalcetide	0.1 mg	IV	J0606
Eteplirsen	10 mg	IV	J1428
Ethanolamine	100 mg		J1430
Ethyol, *see* Amifostine			
Etidronate disodium	per 300 mg	IV	J1436

DRUG	DOSE	ROUTE	HCPCS
Etonogestrel Implant			J7307
Etopophos, *see* Etoposide			
Etoposide	10 mg	IV	J9181
Etoposide, oral	50 mg	ORAL	J8560
Euflexxa	per dose	OTH	J7323
Everolimus, oral	0.25 mg	ORAL	J7527
Everone, *see* Testosterone Enanthate			
Eylea, *see* Aflibercept			
F			
Factor VIIa (coagulation factor, recombinant)	1 mcg	IV	J7189
Factor VIII (anti-hemophilic factor, human)	per IU	IV	J7190
Factor VIII (anti-hemophilic factor, porcine)	per IU	IV	J7191
Factor VIII (anti-hemophilic factor, recombinant)	per IU	IV	J7182, J7185, J7192, J7188
Factor VIII fc fusion (recombinant)	per IU	IV	J7205, J7207, J7209
Factor VIII (anti-hemophilic factor recombinant)			
(Afstyla)	per IU	IV	J7210
(Kovaltry)	per IU	IV	J7211
Factor IX (anti-hemophilic factor, purified, non-recombinant)	per IU	IV	J7193
Factor IX (anti-hemophilic factor, recombinant)	per IU	IV	J7195, J7200-J7202
Factor IX, complex	per IU	IV	J7194
Factor X (human)	per IU	IV	J7175
Factor XIII A-subunit (recombinant)	per IU	IV	J7181
Factors, other hemophilia clotting	per IU	IV	J7196
Factrel, *see* Gonadorelin HCl			
Feiba VH Immuno, *see* Factors, other hemophilia clotting			
Fentanyl citrate	0.1 mg	IM, IV	J3010
Feraheme, *see* Ferumoxytol			
Ferric Carboxymaltose	1 mg	IV	J1439

DRUG	DOSE	ROUTE	HCPCS
Ferric pyrophosphate citrate solution	0.1 mg of iron	IV	J1443
Ferrlecit, *see* Sodium ferric gluconate complex in sucrose			
Ferumoxytol	1 mg		Q0138, Q0139
Filgrastim (G-CSF)	1 mcg	SC, IV	J1442, Q5101
Filgrastim (TBO)	1 mcg	IV	J1447
Firazyr, *see* Icatibant			
Firmagon, *see* Degarelix			
Flebogamma	500 mg	IV	J1572
Flexoject, *see* Orphenadrine citrate			
Flexon, *see* Orphenadrine citrate			
Flolan, *see* Epoprostenol			
Florbetaben f18, diagnostic	per study dose	IV	Q9983
Floxuridine	500 mg	IV	J9200
Fluconazole	200 mg	IV	J1450
Fludara, *see* Fludarabine phosphate			
Fludarabine phosphate	1 mg	ORAL	J8562
	50 mg	IV	J9185
Flunisolide inhalation solution, unit dose form	per mg	INH	J7641
Fluocinolone		OTH	J7311, J7313
Fluorouracil	500 mg	IV	J9190
Flutemetamol f18, diagnostic	per study dose	IV	Q9982
Folex, *see* Methotrexate sodium			
Folex PFS, *see* Methotrexate sodium			
Follutein, *see* Chorionic gonadotropin			
Folotyn, *see* Pralatrexate			
Fomepizole	15 mg		J1451
Fomivirsen sodium	1.65 mg	Intraocular	J1452
Fondaparinux sodium	0.5 mg	SC	J1652
Formoterol	12 mcg	INH	J7640

DRUG	DOSE	ROUTE	HCPCS
Formoterol fumarate	20 mcg	INH	J7606
Fortaz, *see* Ceftazidime			
Fosaprepitant	1 mg	IV	J1453
Foscarnet sodium	per 1,000 mg	IV	J1455
Foscavir, *see* Foscarnet sodium			
Fosphenytoin	50 mg	IV	Q2009
FUDR, *see* Floxuridine			
Fulvestrant	25 mg	IM	J9395
Fungizone Intravenous, *see* Amphotericin B			
Furomide M.D., *see* Furosemide			
Furosemide	up to 20 mg	IM, IV	J1940
G			
Gadoxetate disodium	1 ml	IV	A9581
Gallium nitrate	1 mg	IV	J1457
Galsulfase	1 mg	IV	J1458
GamaSTAN, *see* Gamma globulin and Immune globulin			
Gammagard Liquid	500 mg	IV	J1569
Gamma globulin	1 cc	IM	J1460
	over 10 cc	IM	J1560
Gammaplex	500 mg	IV	J1557
Gammar, *see* Gamma globulin and Immune globulin			
Gammar-IV, *see* Immune globulin intravenous (human)			
Gamulin RH, *see* Rho(D) Immune globulin			
Gamunex	500 mg	IV	J1561
Ganciclovir, Implant	4.5 mg	OTH	J7310
Ganciclovir sodium	500 mg	IV	J1570
Garamycin, gentamicin	up to 80 mg	IM, IV	J1580
Gatifloxacin	10 mg	IV	J1590
Gefitinib	250 mg	ORAL	J8565
Gel-One	per dose	OTH	J7326
Gemcitabine HCl	200 mg	IV	J9201

DRUG	DOSE	ROUTE	HCPCS
Gemsar, *see* Gemcitabine HCl			
Gemtuzumab ozogamicin	0.1 mg	IV	J9203
Gentamicin Sulfate, *see* Garamycin, gentamicin			
Gentran, *see* Dextran 40			
Gentran 75, *see* Dextran 75			
Gesterol 50, *see* Progesterone			
Glassia	10 mg	IV	J0257
Glatiramer Acetate	20 mg	SC	J1595
Glucagon HCl	per 1 mg	SC, IM, IV	J1610
Glukor, *see* Chorionic gonadotropin Glycopyrrolate, concentrated form	per 1 mg	INH	J7642
Glycopyrrolate, unit dose form	per 1 mg	INH	J7643
Gold sodium thiomalate	up to 50 mg	IM	J1600
Golimumab	1 mg	IV	J1602
Gonadorelin HCl	per 100 mcg	SC, IV	J1620
Gonic, *see* Chorionic gonadotropin			
Goserelin acetate Implant	per 3.6 mg	SC	J9202
Granisetron, extended release	0.1 mg	IV	J1627
Granisetron HCl, Injection	100 mcg	IV	J1626
Granisetron HCl, oral	1 mg	ORAL	Q0166
Gynogen L.A. A10,@ *see* Estradiol valerate			
Gynogen L.A. A20,@ *see* Estradiol valerate			
Gynogen L.A. A40,@ *see* Estradiol valerate			
H			
Halaven, *see* Eribulin mesylate			
Haldol, *see* Haloperidol			
Haloperidol	up to 5 mg	IM, IV	J1630
Haloperidol decanoate			
Hectorol, *see* Doxercalciferol			
Hemin	1 mg		J1640
Hemofil M, *see* Factor VIII			
Hemophilia clotting factors(e.g., anti-inhibitors)	per IU	IV	J7198

DRUG	DOSE	ROUTE	HCPCS
Hemophilia clotting factors, NOC	per IU	IV	J7199
HepaGam B	0.5 ml	IM	J1571
	0.5 ml	IV	J1573
Hep-Lock, *see* Heparin sodium (heparin lock flush)			
Hep-Lock U/P, *see* Heparin sodium (heparin lock flush)			
Heparin sodium	1,000 units	IV, SC	J1644
Heparin sodium (heparin lock flush)	10 units	IV	J1642
Herceptin, *see* Trastuzumab			
Hexadrol Phosphate, *see* Dexamethasone sodium phosphate			
Histaject, *see* Brompheniramine maleate			
Histerone 50, *see* Testosterone suspension			
Histerone 100, *see* Testosterone suspension			
Histrelin acetate	10 mcg		J1675
Histrelin Implant	50 mg	OTH	J9225
Hizentra, *see* Immune globulin			
Human fibrinogen concentrate	100 mg	IV	J7178
Hyalgan, Supartz or VISCO-3		IA	J7321
Hyaluronan or derivative	per dose	IV	J7327
Gel-Syn	0.1 mg	IA	J7328
Gen Visc 850	1 mg	IA	J7320
Hymovis	1 mg	IA	J7322
Gelsyn-3	0.1	IV	J7328
Hyaluronidase	up to 150 units	SC, IV	J3470
Hyaluronidase, ovine	up to 999 units	VAR	J3471
Hyaluronidase, ovine	per 1000 units	VAR	J3472
Hyaluronidase recombinant	1 usp	SC	J3473
Hyate:C, *see* Factor VIII (anti-hemophilic factor (porcine))			
Hybolin Improved, *see* Nandrolone phenpropionate			

DRUG	DOSE	ROUTE	HCPCS
Hybolin Decanoate, *see* Nandrolone decanoate			
Hycamtin, *see* Topotecan			
Hydralazine HCl	up to 20 mg	IV, IM	J0360
Hydrate, *see* Dimenhydrinate			
Hydrocortisone acetate	up to 25 mg IV,	IV, IM, SC	J1700
Hydrocortisone sodium phosphate	up to 50 mg	IV, IM, SC	J1710
Hydrocortisone succinate sodium	up to 100 mg	IV, IM, SC	J1720
Hydrocortone Acetate, *see* Hydrocortisone acetate			
Hydrocortone Phosphate, *see* Hydrocortisone sodium phosphate			
Hydromorphone HCl	up to 4 mg	SC, IM, IV	J1170
Hydroxyprogesterone Caproate	1 mg	IM	J1725
Hydroxyprogesterone Caproate, NOS	10 mg	IV	J1729
Hydroxyprogesterone Caproate, (Makena)	10 mg	IV	J1726
Hydroxyzine HCl	up to 25 mg	IM	J3410
Hydroxyzine Pamoate	25 mg	ORAL	Q0177
Hylan G-F	20	OTH	J7322
Hyoscyamine sulfate	up to 0.25 mg	SC, IM, IV	J1980
Hyperstat IV, *see* Diazoxide			
Hyper-Tet, *see* Tetanus Immune globulin, human			
HypRho-D, *see* Rho(D) Immune globulin			
Hyrexin-50, *see* Diphenhydramine HCl			
Hyzine-50, *see* Hydroxyzine HCl			
I			
Ibandronate sodium	1 mg	IV	J1740
Ibuprofen	100 mg	IV	J1741
Ibutilide fumarate	1 mg	IV	J1742
Icatibant	1 mg	SC	J1744
Idamycin, *see* Idarubicin HCl			
Idarubicin HCl	5 mg	IV	J9211
Idursulfase	1 mg	IV	J1743
Ifex, *see* Ifosfamide			

DRUG	DOSE	ROUTE	HCPCS
Ifosfamide	1 g	IV	J9208
Ilaris, *see* Canakinumab			
Iloprost	20 mcg	INH	Q4074
Ilotycin, *see* Erythromycin gluceptate			
Imferon, *see* Iron dextran			
Imiglucerase	10 units	IV	J1786
Imitrex, *see* Sumatriptan succinate			
Immune globulin			
Bivigam	500 mg	IV	J1556
Flebogamma	500 mg	IV	J1572
Gammagard Liquid	500 mg	IV	J1569
Gammaplex	500 mg	IV	J1557
Gamunex	500 mg	IV	J1561
HepaGam B	0.5 ml	IM	J1571
HepaGam B	0.5 ml	IV	J1573
Hizentra	100 mg	SC	J1559
Hyaluronidase, (hyqvia)	100 mcg	IV	J1575
NOS	500 mg	IV	J1566, J1599
Octagam	500 mg	IV	J1568
Privigen	500 mg	IV	J1459
Rhophylac	100 IU	IM	J2791
Subcutaneous	100 mg	SC	J1562
Cuvitru	100 mg	IV	J1555
Immunosuppressive drug, not otherwise classified			J7599
Imuran, *see* Azathioprine			
Inapsine, *see* Droperidol			
Incobotulinumtoxin type A	1 unit	IM	J0588
Inderal, *see* Propranolol HCl			
INFeD, *see* Iron Dextran			
Infergen, *see* Interferon alfa-1			
Infliximab, Injection	10 mg	IM, IV	J1745, Q5102
Innohep, *see* Tinzaparin			

DRUG	DOSE	ROUTE	HCPCS
Innovar, *see* Droperidol with fentanyl citrate			
Insulin	5 units	SC	J1815
Insulin lispro	50 units	SC	J1817
Intal, *see* Cromolyn sodium or Cromolyn sodium, compounded			
Integrilin, Injection, *see* Eptifibatide			
Interferon alphacon-1, recombinant	1 mcg	SC	J9212
Interferon alfa-2a, recombinant	3 million units	SC, IM	J9213
Interferon alfa-2b, recombinant	1 million units	SC, IM	J9214
Interferon alfa-n3 (human leukocyte derived)	250,000 IU	IM	J9215
Interferon beta-1a	30 mcg	IM	J1826
Interferon beta-1a	1 mcg	IM	Q3027
Interferon beta-1a	1 mcg	SC	Q3028
Interferon beta-1b	0.25 mg	SC	J1830
Interferon gamma-1b	3 million units	SC	J9216
Intrauterine copper contraceptive, *see* Copper contraceptive, intrauterine			
Invega Sustenna, *see* Paliperidone Palmitate			
Ipilimumab	1 mg	IV	J9228
Ipratropium bromide, unit dose form	per mg	INH	J7644, J7645
Irinotecan	20 mg	IV	J9206, J9205
Iron dextran	50 mg	IV	J1750
Iron sucrose	1 mg	IV	J1756
Irrigation solution for Tx of bladder calculi	per 50 ml	OTH	Q2004
Isavuconazonium	1 mg	IV	J1833
Isocaine HCl, *see* Mepivacaine			
Isoetharine HCl, concentrated form	per mg	INH	J7647, J7648
Isoetharine HCl, unit dose form	per mg	INH	J7649, J7650
Isoproterenol HCl, concentrated form	per mg	INH	J7657, J7658
Isoproterenol HCl, unit dose form	per mg	INH	J7659, J7660
Istodax, *see* Romidepsin			

DRUG	DOSE	ROUTE	HCPCS
Isuprel, *see* Isoproterenol HCl			
Itraconazole	50 mg	IV	J1835
Ixabepilone	1 mg	IV	J9207
Ixempra, *see* Ixabepilone			
J			
Jenamicin, *see* Garamycin, gentamicin			
Jevtana, *see* Cabazitaxel			
K			
Kabikinase, *see* Streptokinase			
Kalbitor, *see* Ecallantide			
Kaleinate, *see* Calcium gluconate			
Kanamycin sulfate	up to 75 mg	IM, IV	J1850
Kanamycin sulfate	up to 500 mg	IM, IV	J1840
Kantrex, *see* Kanamycin sulfate			
Keflin, *see* Cephalothin sodium			
Kefurox, *see* Cefuroxime sodium			
Kefzol, *see* Cefazolin sodium			
Kenaject-40, *see* Triamcinolone acetonide			
Kenalog-10, *see* Triamcinolone acetonide			
Kenalog-40, *see* Triamcinolone acetonide			
Keppra, *see* Levetiracetam			
Kestrone 5, *see* Estrone			
Ketorolac tromethamine	per 15 mg	IM, IV	J1885
Key-Pred 25, *see* Prednisolone acetate			
Key-Pred 50, *see* Prednisolone acetate			
Key-Pred-SP, *see* Prednisolone sodium phosphate			
K-Flex, *see* Orphenadrine citrate			
Klebcil, *see* Kanamycin sulfate			
Koate-HP, *see* Factor VIII Kogenate, *see* Factor VIII			
Konakion, *see* Vitamin K, phytonadione, etc.			
Konyne-80, *see* Factor IX, complex			
Krystexxa, *see* Pegloticase			

DRUG	DOSE	ROUTE	HCPCS
Kytril, *see* Granisetron HCl			
Kyleena	19.5 mg		
L			
L.A.E. 20, *see* Estradiol valerate			
Laetrile, Amygdalin, vitamin B-17			J3570
Lanoxin, *see* Digoxin			
Lanreotide	1 mg	SC	J1930
Largon, *see* Propiomazine HCl			
Laronidase	0.1 mg	IV	J1931
Lasix, *see* Furosemide			
L-Caine, *see* Lidocaine HCl			
Lepirudin	50 mg		J1945
Leucovorin calcium	per 50 mg	IM, IV	J0640
Leukine, *see* Sargramostim (GM-CSF)			
Leuprolide acetate (for depot suspension)	per 3.75 mg	IM	J1950
	7.5 mg	IM	J9217
Leuprolide acetate	per 1 mg	IM	J9218
Leuprolide acetate Implant	65 mg	OTH	J9219
Leustatin, *see* Cladribine			
Levalbuterol HCl, concentrated form	0.5 mg	INH	J7607, J7612
Levalbuterol HCl, unit dose form	0.5 mg	INH	J7614, J7615
Levaquin I.U., *see* Levofloxacin			
Levetiracetam	10 mg	IV	J1953
Levocarnitine	per 1 gm	IV	J1955
Levo-Dromoran, *see* Levorphanol tartrate			
Levofloxacin	250 mg	IV	J1956
Levoleucovorin calcium	0.5 mg	IV	J0641
Levonorgestrel Implant		OTH	J7306
Levonorgestrel releasing intrauterine contraceptive	52 mg	OTH	J7297, J7298
KYLEENA	19.5 mg	OTH	J7296
Levorphanol tartrate	up to 2 mg	SC, IV	J1960
Levsin, *see* Hyoscyamine sulfate			

DRUG	DOSE	ROUTE	HCPCS
Levulan Kerastick, *see* Aminolevulinic acid HCl			
Lexiscan, *see* Regadenoson			
Librium, *see* Chlordiazepoxide HCl			
Lidocaine HCl	10 mg	IV	J2001
Lidoject-1, *see* Lidocaine HCl			
Lidoject-2, *see* Lidocaine HCl			
Lincocin, *see* Lincomycin HCl			
Lincomycin HCl	up to 300 mg	IV	J2010
Linezolid	200 mg	IV	J2020
Liquaemin Sodium, *see* Heparin sodium			
Lioresal, *see* Baclofen			
LMD (10%), *see* Dextran 40			
Lovenox, *see* Enoxaparin sodium			
Lorazepam	2 mg	IM, IV	J2060
Lufyllin, *see* Dyphylline			
Luminal Sodium, *see* Phenobarbital sodium			
Lumizyme, *see* Alglucosidase alfa			
Lunelle, *see* Medroxyprogesterone acetate/estradiol cypionate			
Lupron, *see* Leuprolide acetate			
Lyophilized, *see* Cyclophosphamide, lyophilized			
M			
Magnesium sulfate	500 mg		J3475
Makena, *see* Hydroxyprogesterone Caproate			
Mannitol	25% in 50 ml	IV	J2150
	5mg	INH	J7665
Marmine, *see* Dimenhydrinate			
Maxipime, *see* Cefepime hydrochloride			
Mecasermin	1 mg	SC	J2170
Mechlorethamine HCl (nitrogen mustard), HN2	10 mg	IV	J9230
Medralone 40, *see* Methylprednisolone acetate			
Medralone 80, *see* Methylprednisolone acetate			

DRUG	DOSE	ROUTE	HCPCS
Medrol, *see* Methylprednisolone			
Medroxyprogesterone acetate	1 mg	IM	J1050
Mefoxin, *see* Cefoxitin sodium			
Melphalan HCl	50 mg	IV	J9245
Melphalan, oral	2 mg	ORAL	J8600
Menoject LA, *see* Testosterone cypionate and estradiol cypionate			
Mepergan Injection, *see* Meperidine and promethazine HCl			
Meperidine HCl	per 100 mg	IM, IV, SC	J2175
Meperidine and promethazine HCl	up to 50 mg	IM, IV	J2180
Mepivacaine HCL	per 10 ml	VAR	J0670
Mepolizumab	1 mg	IV	J2182
Meropenem	100 mg	IV	J2185
Mesna	200 mg	IV	J9209
Mesnex, *see* Mesna			
Metaprel, *see* Metaproterenol sulfate			
Metaproterenol sulfate, concentrated form	per 10 mg	INH	J7667, J7668
Metaproterenol sulfate, unit dose form	per 10 mg	INH	J7669, J7670
Metaraminol bitartrate	per 10 mg	IV, IM, SC	J0380
Metastron, *see* Strontium-89 chloride			
Methacholine chloride	1 mg	INH	J7674
Methadone HCl	up to 10 mg	IM, SC	J1230
Methergine, *see* Methylergonovine maleate			
Methocarbamol	up to 10 ml	IV, IM	J2800
Methotrexate, oral	2.5 mg	ORAL	J8610
Methotrexate sodium	5 mg	IV, IM, IT, IA	J9250
	50 mg	IV, IM, IT, IA	J9260
Methotrexate LPF, *see* Methotrexate sodium			
Methyldopate HCl	up to 250 mg	IV	J0210
Methylnaltrexone	0.1 mg	SC	J2212
Methylprednisolone, oral	per 4 mg	ORAL	J7509

DRUG	DOSE	ROUTE	HCPCS
Methylprednisolone acetate	20 mg	IM	J1020
	40 mg	IM	J1030
	80 mg	IM	J1040
Methylprednisolone sodium succinate	up to 40 mg	IM, IV	J2920
	up to 125 mg	IM, IV	J2930
Metoclopramide HCl	up to 10 mg	IV	J2765
Metvixia, *see* Aminolevulinate			
Miacalcin, *see* Calcitonin-salmon			
Micafungin sodium	1 mg		J2248
Midazolam HCl	per 1 mg	IM, IV	J2250
Milrinone lactate	5 mg	IV	J2260
Minocin, *see* Minocycline Hydrochloride			
Minocycline Hydrochloride	1 mg	IV	J2265
Mirena, *see* Levonorgestrel releasing intrauterine contraceptive			
Mithracin, *see* Plicamycin			
Mitomycin	0.2 mg	Ophthalmic	J7315
	5 mg	IV	J9280
Mitosol, *see* Mitomycin			
Mitoxantrone HCl	per 5 mg	IV	J9293
Monocid, *see* Cefonicid sodium			
Monoclate-P, *see* Factor VIII			
Monoclonal antibodies, parenteral	5 mg	IV	J7505
Mononine, *see* Factor IX, purified, non-recombinant			
Morphine sulfate	up to 10 mg	IM, IV, SC	J2270
Morphine sulfate, preservative-free	10 mg	SC, IM, IV	J2274
Moxifloxacin	100 mg	IV	J2280
Mozobil, *see* Plerixafor			
M-Prednisol-40, *see* Methylprednisolone acetate			
M-Prednisol-80, *see* Methylprednisolone acetate			
Mucomyst, *see* Acetylcysteine or Acetylcysteine, compounded			
Mucosol, *see* Acetylcysteine			

DRUG	DOSE	ROUTE	HCPCS
Muromonab-CD3	5 mg	IV	J7505
Muse, *see* Alprostadil			
Mustargen, *see* Mechlorethamine HCl			
Mutamycin, *see* Mitomycin			
Mycophenolic acid	180 mg	ORAL	J7518
Mycophenolate Mofetil	250 mg	ORAL	J7517
Myleran, *see* Busulfan			
Mylotarg, *see* Gemtuzumab ozogamicin			
Myobloc, *see* RimabotulinumtoxinB			
Myochrysine, *see* Gold sodium thiomalate			
Myolin, *see* Orphenadrine citrate			
N			
Nabilone	1 mg	ORAL	J8650
Nalbuphine HCl	per 10 mg	IM, IV, SC	J2300
Naloxone HCl	per 1 mg	IM, IV, SC	J2310
Naltrexone, depot form	1 mg	IM	J2315
Nandrobolic L.A., *see* Nandrolone decanoate			
Nandrolone decanoate	up to 50 mg	IM	J2320
Narcan, *see* Naloxone HCl			
Naropin, *see* Ropivacaine HCl			
Nasahist B, *see* Brompheniramine maleate			
Nasal vaccine inhalation		INH	J3530
Natalizumab	1 mg	IV	J2323
Navane, *see* Thiothixene			
Navelbine, *see* Vinorelbine tartrate			
ND Stat, *see* Brompheniramine maleate			
Nebcin, *see* Tobramycin sulfate			
NebuPent, *see* Pentamidine isethionate			
Necitumumab	1 mg	IV	J9295
Nelarabine	50 mg	IV	J9261
Nembutal Sodium Solution, *see* Pentobarbital sodium			
Neocyten, *see* Orphenadrine citrate			

DRUG	DOSE	ROUTE	HCPCS
Neo-Durabolic, *see* Nandrolone decanoate			
Neoquess, *see* Dicyclomine HCl			
Neosar, *see* Cyclophosphamide			
Neostigmine methylsulfate	up to 0.5 mg	IM, IV, SC	J2710
Neo-Synephrine, *see* Phenylephrine HCl			
Nervocaine 1%, *see* Lidocaine HCl			
Nervocaine 2%, *see* Lidocaine HCl			
Nesacaine, *see* Chloroprocaine HCL			
Nesacaine-MPF, *see* Chloroprocaine HCl			
Nesiritide	0.1 mg	IV	J2325
Neumega, *see* Oprelvekin			
Neupogen, *see* Filgrastim (G-CSF)			
Neutrexin, *see* Trimetrexate glucuronate			
Nipent, *see* Pentostatin			
Nivolumab	1 mg	IV	J9299
Nordryl, *see* Diphenhydramine HCl			
Norflex, *see* Orphenadrine citrate			
Norzine, *see* Thiethylperazine maleate			
Not otherwise classified drugs			J3490
Not otherwise classified drugs other than administered thru DME		INH	J7799
Not otherwise classified drugs administered thru DME		INH	J7699
Not otherwise classified drugs, anti-neoplastic			J9999
Not otherwise classified drugs, chemotherapeutic		ORAL	J8999
Not otherwise classified drugs, Immunosuppressive			J7599
Not otherwise classified drugs, non-chemotherapeutic		ORAL	J8499
Novantrone, *see* Mitoxantrone HCl			
Novo Seven, *see* Factor VIIa NPH, *see* Insulin			
Nplate, *see* Romiplostim			
Nubain, *see* Nalbuphine HCl			
Nulicaine, *see* Lidocaine HCl			
Nulojix, *see* Belatacept			
Numorphan, *see* Oxymorphone HCl			

DRUG	DOSE	ROUTE	HCPCS
Numorphan H.P., *see* Oxymorphone HCl			
Nusinersen	0.1 mg	IV	J2326
O			
Ocriplasmin	0.125 mg	IV	J7316
Octagam	500 mg	IV	J1568
Ocrelizumab	1 mg	IV	J2350
Octreotide Acetate, Injection	1 mg	IM	J2353
	25 mcg	IV, SQ	J2354
Oculinum, *see* Botulinum toxin type A			
Ofatumumab	10 mg	IV	J9302
Ofirmev, *see* Acetaminophen			
O-Flex, *see* Orphenadrine citrate			
Oforta, *see* Fludarabine phosphate			
Olanzapine	1 mg	IM	J2358
Olaratumab	10 mg	IV	J9285
Omacetaxine Mepesuccinate	0.01 mg	IV	J9262
Omalizumab	5 mg	SC	J2357
Omnipen-N, *see* Ampicillin			
Omontys, *see* Peginesatide			
OnabotulinumtoxinA	1 unit	IM	J0585
Oncaspar, *see* Pegaspargase			
Oncovin, *see* Vincristine sulfate			
Ondansetron HCl	1 mg	IV	J2405
Ondansetron HCl, oral	1 mg	ORAL	Q0162
Oprelvekin	5 mg	SC	J2355
Oraminic II, *see* Brompheniramine maleate			
Oritavancin	10 mg	IV	J2407
Ormazine, *see* Chlorpromazine HCl			
Orphenadrine citrate	up to 60 mg	IV, IM	J2360
Orphenate, *see* Orphenadrine citrate			
Orthovisc		OTH	J7324
Or-Tyl, *see* Dicyclomine			

DRUG	DOSE	ROUTE	HCPCS
Oxacillin sodium	up to 250 mg	IM, IV	J2700
Oxaliplatin	0.5 mg	IV	J9263
Oxymorphone HCl	up to 1 mg	IV, SC, IM	J2410
Oxytetracycline HCl	up to 50 mg	IM	J2460
Oxytocin	up to 10 units	IV, IM	J2590
Ozurdex, *see* Dexamethasone, intravitreal Implant			
P			
Paclitaxel	1 mg	IV	J9267
Paclitaxel protein-bound particles	1 mg	IV	J9264
Palifermin	50 mcg	IV	J2425
Paliperidone Palmitate	1 mg	IM	J2426
Palonosetron HCl	25 mcg	IV	J2469
Netupitant 300 mg and palonosetron	0.5 mg	ORAL	J8655
Pamidronate disodium	per 30 mg	IV	J2430
Panitumumab	10 mg	IV	J9303
Papaverine HCl	up to 60 mg	IV, IM	J2440
ParaGard T 380 A, *see* Copper contraceptive, intrauterine			
Paraplatin, *see* Carboplatin			
Paricalcitol, Injection	1 mcg	IV, IM	J2501
Pasireotide, long acting	1 mg	IV	J2502
Pegademase bovine	25 iu		J2504
Pegaptanib	0.3 mg	OTH	J2503
Pegaspargase	per single dose vial	IM, IV	J9266
Pegfilgrastim	6 mg	SC	J2505
Peginesatide	0.1 mg	IV, SC	J0890
Pegloticase	1 mg	IV	J2507
Pemetrexed	10 mg	IV	J9305
Pembrolizumab	1 mg	IV	J9271
Penicillin G benzathine	100,000 units	IM	J0561
Penicillin G benzathine and penicillin G procaine	100,000 units	IM	J0558

DRUG	DOSE	ROUTE	HCPCS
Penicillin G potassium	up to 600,000 units	IM, IV	J2540
Penicillin G procaine, aqueous	up to 600,000 units	IM, IV	J2510
Pentamidine isethionate	per 300 mg	INH	J2545,J7676
Pentastarch, 10%	100 ml		J2513
Pentazocine HCl	30 mg	IM, SC, IV	J3070
Pentobarbital sodium	per 50 mg	IM, IV, OTH	J2515
Pentostatin	per 10 mg	IV	J9268
Perforomist, *see* Formoterol fumarate			
Peramivir	1 mg	IV	J2547
Permapen, *see* Penicillin G benzathine			
Perphenazine, Injection	up to 5 mg	IM, IV	J3310
Perphenazine, tablets	4 mg	ORAL	Q0175
Persantine IV, *see* Dipyridamole			
Pertuzumab	1 mg	IV	J9306
Pet Imaging			
Gallium Ga-68, dotatate, diagnostic	0.1 millicurie	IV	A9587
Fluciclovine F-18, diagnostic	1 millicurie	IV	A9588
Positron emission tomography radiopharmaceutical, diagnostic			
for tumor identification, NOC		IV	A9597
for non-tumor identification, NOC		IV	A9598
Pfizerpen, *see* Penicillin G potassium			
Pfizerpen A.S., *see* Penicillin G procaine			
Phenazine 25, *see* Promethazine HCl			
Phenazine 50, *see* Promethazine HCl			
Phenergan, *see* Promethazine HCl			
Phenobarbital sodium	up to 120 mg	IM, IV	J2560
Phentolamine mesylate	up to 5 mg	IM, IV	J2760
Phenylephrine HCl	up to 1 ml	SC, IM, IV	J2370
Phenytoin sodium	per 50 mg	IM, IV	J1165
Photofrin, *see* Porfimer sodium			

DRUG	DOSE	ROUTE	HCPCS
Phytonadione (Vitamin K)	per 1 mg	IM, SC, IV	J3430
Piperacillin/Tazobactam Sodium, Injection	1.125 g	IV	J2543
Pitocin, *see* Oxytocin			
Platinol AQ, *see* Cisplatin			
Plas+SD, *see* Plasma, pooled multiple donor			
Plasma, cryoprecipitate reduced	each unit	IV	P9044
Plasma, pooled multiple donor, frozen, each unit		IV	P9023, P9070
Plasma (single donor), pathogen reduced, frozen each unit		IV	P9071
Platelets, pheresis, pathogen reduced each unit		IV	P9073
Pathogen(s) test for platelets		OTH	P9100
Platinol, *see* Cisplatin			
Plerixafor	1 mg	SC	J2562
Plicamycin	2,500 mcg	IV	J9270
Polocaine, *see* Mepivacaine			
Polycillin-N, *see* Ampicillin			
Porfimer Sodium	75 mg	IV	J9600
Potassium chloride	per 2 mEq	IV	J3480
Pralatrexate	1 mg	IV	J9307
Pralidoxime chloride	up to 1 g	IV, IM, SC	J2730
Predalone-50, *see* Prednisolone acetate			
Predcor-25, *see* Prednisolone acetate			
Predcor-50, *see* Prednisolone acetate			
Predicort-50, *see* Prednisolone acetate			
Prednisone, Immediate release or delayed release	1 mg	ORAL	J7512
Prednisolone, oral	5 mg	ORAL	J7510
Prednisolone acetate	up to 1 ml	IM	J2650
Predoject-50, *see* Prednisolone acetate			
Pregnyl, *see* Chorionic gonadotropin			
Premarin Intravenous, *see* Estrogen, conjugated			
Prescription, chemotherapeutic, not otherwise specified		ORAL	J8999

DRUG	DOSE	ROUTE	HCPCS
Prescription, nonchemotherapeutic, not otherwise specified		ORAL	J8499
Primacor, *see* Milrinone lactate			
Primaxin I.M., *see* Cilastatin sodium, Imipenem			
Primaxin I.V., *see* Cilastatin sodium, Imipenem			
Priscoline HCl, *see* Tolazoline HCl			
Privigen	500 mg	IV	J1459
Pro-Depo, *see* Hydroxyprogesterone Caproate			
Procainamide HCl	up to 1 g	IM, IV	J2690
Prochlorperazine	up to 10 mg	IM, IV	J0780
Prochlorperazine maleate, oral	5 mg	ORAL	Q0164
Profasi HP, *see* Chorionic gonadotropin			
Profilnine Heat-Treated, *see* Factor IX			
Progestaject, *see* Progesterone			
Progesterone	per 50 mg	IM	J2675
Prograf, *see* Tacrolimus, oral or parenteral			
Prokine, *see* Sargramostim (GM-CSF)			
Prolastin, *see* Alpha 1-proteinase inhibitor, human			
Proleukin, *see* Aldesleukin			
Prolixin Decanoate, *see* Fluphenazine decanoate			
Promazine HCl	up to 25 mg	IM	J2950
Promethazine HCl, Injection	up to 50 mg	IM, IV	J2550
Promethazine HCl, oral	12.5 mg	ORAL	Q0169
Pronestyl, *see* Procainamide HCl			
Proplex T, *see* Factor IX			
Proplex SX-T, *see* Factor IX			
Propofol	10 mg	IV	J2704
Propranolol HCl	up to 1 mg	IV	J1800
Prorex-25, *see* Promethazine HCl			
Prorex-50, *see* Promethazine HCl			
Prostaphlin, *see* Procainamide HCl			
Prostigmin, *see* Neostigmine methylsulfate			
Protamine sulfate	per 10 mg	IV	J2720

DRUG	DOSE	ROUTE	HCPCS
Protein C Concentrate	10 IU	IV	J2724
Protirelin	per 250 mcg	IV	J2725
Prothazine, *see* Promethazine HCl			
Protopam Chloride, *see* Pralidoxime chloride			
Proventil, *see* Albuterol sulfate, compounded			
Prozine-50, *see* Promazine HCl			
Pulmicort Respules, *see* Budesonide			
Pyridoxine HCl	100 mg		J3415
Q			
Quelicin, *see* Succinylcholine chloride			
Quinupristin/dalfopristin	500 mg (150/350)	IV	J2770
Qutenza, *see* Capsaicin patch			
R			
Ramucirumab	5 mg	IV	J9308
Ranibizumab	0.1 mg	OTH	J2778
Ranitidine HCL, Injection	25 mg	IV, IM	J2780
Rapamune, *see* Sirolimus			
Rasburicase	0.5 mg	IV	J2783
Recombinate, *see* Factor VIII			
Redisol, *see* Vitamin B-12 cyanocobalamin			
Regadenoson	0.1 mg	IV	J2785
Regitine, *see* Phentolamine mesylate			
Reglan, *see* Metoclopramide HCl			
Regular, *see* Insulin			
Relefact TRH, *see* Protirelin			
Relistor, *see* methylnaltrexone			
Remicade, *see* Infliximab, Injection			
Reo Pro, *see* Abciximab			
Rep-Pred 40, *see* Methylprednisolone acetate			
Rep-Pred 80, *see* Methylprednisolone acetate			
Reslizumab	1 mg	IV	J2786

DRUG	DOSE	ROUTE	HCPCS
RespiGam, *see* Respiratory Syncytial Virus			
Retavase, *see* Reteplase			
Reteplase	18.8 mg	IV	J2993
Retrovir, *see* Zidovudine			
Rheomacrodex, *see* Dextran 40			
Rhesonativ, *see* Rho(D) Immune globulin, human			
Rheumatrex Dose Pack, *see* Methotrexate, oral			
Rho(D) Immune globulin		IM, IV	J2791
Rho(D) Immune globulin, human 1 dose package,	300 mcg	IM	J2790
	50 mg	IM	J2788
Rho(D)immune globulin, human, solvent detergent	100 IU	IV	J2792
RhoGAM, *see* Rho(D) Immune globulin, human			
Rhophylac	100 IU	IM, IV	J2791
RiaSTAP, *see* Human Fibrinogen concentrate			
Rilonacept	1 mg	SC	J2793
RimabotulinumtoxinB	100 units	IM	J0587
Ringers lactate infusion	up to 1,000 cc	IV	J7120, J7121
Risperidone	0.5 mg	IM	J2794
Rituxan, *see* Rituximab			
Rituximab	100 mg	IV	J9310
Robaxin, *see* Methocarbamol			
Rocephin, *see* Ceftriaxone sodium			
Roferon-A, *see* Interferon alfa-2A, recombinant			
Rolapitant, oral, 1 mg	1 mg	ORAL	J8670
Romidepsin	1 mg	IV	J9315
Romiplostim	10 mcg	SC	J2796
Ropivacaine Hydrochloride	1 mg	OTH	J2795
Rubex, *see* Doxorubicin HCl			
Rubramin PC, *see* Vitamin B-12 cyanocobalamin			
S			
Saline solution	5% dextrose, 500 ml	IV	J7042

DRUG	DOSE	ROUTE	HCPCS
	infusion, 250 cc	IV	J7050
	infusion, 1,000 cc	IV	J7030
Saline solution, sterile	500 ml = 1 unit	IV, OTH	J7040
Sandimmune, *see* Cyclosporine			
Sandoglobulin, *see* Immune globulin intravenous (human)			
Sandostatin Lar Depot, *see* Octreotide			
Sargramostim (GM-CSF)	50 mcg	IV	J2820
Sculptra	0.5 mg	IV	Q2028
Sebelelipase alfa	1 mg	IV	J2840
Selestoject, *see* Betamethasone sodium phosphate			
Sermorelin acetate	1 mcg	SC	Q0515
Siltuximab	10 mg	IV	J2860
Sincalide	5 mcg	IV	J2805
Sinusol-B, *see* Brompheniramine maleate			
Sirolimus	1 mg	ORAL	J7520
Skyla	13.5 mg	OTH	J7301
Sodium ferric gluconate in sucrose	12.5 mg		J2916
Sodium Hyaluronate			
Euflexxa			J7323
Hyalgan, Supartz, Visco-3			J7321
Orthovisc			J7324
Solganal, *see* Aurothioglucose			
Solu-Cortef, *see* Hydrocortisone sodium phosphate (J1710)			
Solu-Medrol, *see* Methylprednisolone sodium succinate			
Solurex, *see* Dexamethasone sodium phosphate			
Solurex LA, *see* Dexamethasone acetate			
Somatrem	1 mg	SC	J2940
Somatropin	1 mg	SC	J2941

DRUG	DOSE	ROUTE	HCPCS
Somatuline Depot, *see* Lanreotide			
Sparine, *see* Promazine HCl			
Spasmoject, *see* Dicyclomine HCl			
Spectinomycin HCl	up to 2 g	IM	J3320
Sporanox, *see* Itraconazole			
Staphcillin, *see* Methicillin sodium			
Stelara, *see* Ustekinumab			
Stilphostrol, *see* Diethylstilbestrol diphosphate			
Streptase, *see* Streptokinase			
Streptokinase	per 250,000 IU	IV	J2995
Streptomycin Sulfate, *see* Streptomycin			
Streptomycin	up to 1 g	IM	J3000
Streptozocin	1 gm		
Strontium-89 chloride	per millicurie		
Sublimaze, *see* Fentanyl citrate			
Succinylcholine chloride	up to 20 mg	IV, IM	J0330
Injection, sulfur hexafluoride lipid microspheres	per ml	IV	Q9950
Sumatriptan succinate	6 mg	SC	J3030
Supartz		OTH	J7321
Sucostrin, *see* Succinylcholine chloride			
Sus-Phrine, *see* Adrenalin, epinephrine			
Synercid, *see* Quinupristin/dalfopristin			
Synkavite, *see* Vitamin K, phytonadione, etc.			
Syntocionon, *see* Oxytocin			
Synvisc and Synvisc-One	1 mg	OTH	J7325
Sytobex, *see* Vitamin B-12 cyanocobalamin			
T			
Tacrolimus, oral, extended release	0.1 mg	ORAL	J7508
(Envarsus XR)	0.25 mg	ORAL	J7503
Tacrolimus, oral, Immediate release	per 1 mg	ORAL	J7507
Tacrolimus, parenteral	5 mg	IV	J7525

DRUG	DOSE	ROUTE	HCPCS
Taliglucerase Alfa	10 units	IV	J3060
Talimogene laherparepvec	per 1 million plaque forming units	IV	J9325
Talwin, *see* Pentazocine HCl			
Taractan, *see* Chlorprothixene			
Taxol, *see* Paclitaxel			
Taxotere, *see* Docetaxel			
Tazidime, *see* Ceftazidime			
Technetium TC Sestamibi	per dose		A9500
Tedizolid phosphate	1 mg	IV	J3090
TEEV, *see* Testosterone enanthate and estradiol valerate			
Teflaro, *see* Ceftaroline fosamil			
Telavancin	10 mg	IV	J3095
Temozolomide	1 mg	IV	J9328
	5 mg	ORAL	J8700
Temsirolimus	1 mg	IV	J9330
Tenecteplase	1 mg	IV	J3101
Teniposide	50 mg		Q2017
Tequin, *see* Gatifloxacin			
Terbutaline sulfate	up to 1 mg	SC, IV	J3105
Terbutaline sulfate, concentrated form	per 1 mg	INH	J7680
Terbutaline sulfate, unit dose form	per 1 mg	INH	J7681
Teriparatide	10 mcg	SC	J3110
Terramycin IM, *see* Oxytetracycline HCl			
Testa-C, *see* Testosterone cypionate			
Testadiate, *see* Testosterone enanthate and estradiol valerate			
Testadiate-Depo, *see* Testosterone cypionate			
Testoject-LA, *see* Testosterone cypionate			
Testaqua, *see* Testosterone suspension			
Test-Estro Cypionates, *see* Testosterone cypionate and estradiol cypionate			

DRUG	DOSE	ROUTE	HCPCS
Test-Estro-C, *see* Testosterone cypionate and estradiol cypionate			
Testex, *see* Testosterone propionate			
Testoject-50, *see* Testosterone suspension			
Testoject-LA, *see* Testosterone cypionate			
Testone LA 200, *see* Testosterone enanthate			
Testone LA 100, *see* Testosterone enanthate			
Testosterone Aqueous, *see* Testosterone suspension			
Testosterone enanthate	1 mg	IM	J3121
Testosterone cypionate	1 mg	IM	J1071
Testosterone undecanoate	1 mg	IM	J3145
Testradiol 90/4, *see* Testosterone enanthate and estradiol valerate			
Testrin PA, *see* Testosterone enanthate			
Tetanus Immune globulin, human	up to 250 units	IM	J1670
Tetracycline	up to 250 mg	IM, IV	J0120
Thallous Chloride TL 201	per MCI		A9505
Theelin Aqueous, *see* Estrone			
Theophylline per MCI	per 40 mg	IV	J2810
TheraCys, *see* BCG live			
Thiamine HCl	100 mg		J3411
Thiethylperazine maleate, Injection	up to 10 mg	IM	J3280
Thiethylperazine maleate, oral	10 mg	ORAL	Q0174
Thiotepa	15 mg	IV	J9340
Thorazine, *see* Chlorpromazine HCl			
Thymoglobulin, also *see* Immune globulin			
anti-thymocyte globulin, equine	250 mg	IV	J7504
anti-thymocyte globulin, rabbit	25 mg	IV	J7511
Thypinone, *see* Protirelin			
Thyrogen, *see* Thyrotropin Alfa			
Thyrotropin Alfa, Injection	0.9 mg	IM, SC	J3240
Tice BCG, *see* BCG live			

DRUG	DOSE	ROUTE	HCPCS
Ticon, *see* Trimethobenzamide HCl			
Tigan, *see* Trimethobenzamide HCl			
Tigecycline	1 mg	IV	J3243
Tiject-20, *see* Trimethobenzamide HCl			
Tinzaparin	1000 IU	SC	J1655
Tirofiban Hydrochloride, Injection	0.25 mg	IM, IV	J3246
TNKase, *see* Tenecteplase			
TOBI, *see* Tobramycin, inhalation solution			
Tobramycin, inhalation solution	300 mg	INH	J7682, J7685
Tobramycin sulfate	up to 80 mg	IM, IV	J3260
Tocilizumab	1 mg	IV	J3262
Tofranil, *see* Imipramine HCl			
Tolazoline HCl	up to 25 mg	IV	J2670
Topotecan	0.25 mg	ORAL	J8705
	0.1 mg	IV	J9351
Toradol, *see* Ketorolac tromethamine			
Torecan, *see* Thiethylperazine maleate			
Torisel, *see* Temsirolimus			
Tornalate, *see* Bitolterol mesylate			
Torsemide	10 mg/ml	IV	J3265
Totacillin-N, *see* Ampicillin			
Trabectedin	0.1 mg	IV	J9352
Trastuzumab	10 mg	IV	J9355
Treanda, *see* Bendamustine HCl			
Treprostinil	1 mg		J3285
Tri-Kort, *see* Triamcinolone acetonide			
Triam-A, *see* Triamcinolone acetonide			
Triamcinolone, concentrated form	per 1 mg	INH	J7683
Triamcinolone, unit dose	per 1 mg	INH	J7684
Triamcinolone acetonide	1 mg per 10 mg	IM	J3300 J3301
Triamcinolone diacetate	per 5 mg	IM	J3302
Triamcinolone hexacetonide	per 5 mg	VAR	J3303

DRUG	DOSE	ROUTE	HCPCS
Triesence, *see* Triamcinolone acetonide			
Triflupromazine HCl	up to 20 mg	IM, IV	J3400
Trilafon, *see* perphenazine			
Trilog, *see* Triamcinolone acetonide			
Trilone, *see* Triamcinolone diacetate			
Trimethobenzamide HCl, Injection	up to 200 mg	IM	J3250
Trimethobenzamide HCl, oral	250 mg	ORAL	Q0173
Trimetrexate glucuronate	per 25 mg	IV	J3305
Triptorelin Pamoate Trisenox, *see* Arsenic trioxide			
Trobicin, *see* Spectinomycin HCl			
Trovan, *see* Alatrofloxacin mesylate			
Tysabri, *see* Natalizumab	3.75 mg	SC	J3315
U			
Ultrazine-10, *see* Prochlorperazine			
Unasyn, *see* Ampicillin sodium/sulbactam sodium			
Unclassified drugs (see also Not elsewhere classified)		J3490	
Unspecified oral antiemetic			Q0181
Urea	up to 40 g	IV	J3350
Ureaphil, *see* Urea			
Urecholine, *see* Bethanechol chloride			
Urofollitropin	75 iu	IV	J3355
Urokinase	5,000 IU vial	IV	J3364
	250,000 IU vial	IV	J3365
Ustekinumab	1 mg	SC	J3357
Ustekinumab	1 mg	IV	J3358
V			
V-Gan 25, *see* Promethazine HCl			
V-Gan 50, *see* Promethazine HCl			
Valergen 10, *see* Estradiol valerate			
Valergen 20, *see* Estradiol valerate			
Valergen 40, *see* Estradiol valerate			

DRUG	DOSE	ROUTE	HCPCS
Valertest No. 1, *see* Testosterone enanthate and estradiol valerate			
Valertest No. 2, *see* Testosterone enanthate and estradiol valerate			
Valium, *see* Diazepam			
Valrubicin, intravesical	200 mg	OTH	J9357
Valstar, *see* Valrubicin			
Vancocin, *see* Vancomycin HCl			
Vancoled, *see* Vancomycin HCl			
Vancomycin HCl	500 mg	IV, IM	J3370
Vasoxyl, *see* Methoxamine HCl			
Vedolizumab	1 mg	IV	J3380
Velaglucerase alfa	100 units	IV	J3385
Velban, *see* Vinblastine sulfate			
Velsar, *see* Vinblastine sulfate			
Venofer, *see* Iron sucrose			
Ventolin, *see* Albuterol sulfate			
VePesid, *see* Etoposide and Etoposide, oral			
Versed, *see* Midazolam HCl			
Verteporfin	0.1 mg	IV	J3396
Vesprin, *see* Triflupromazine HCl			
Viadur, *see* Leuprolide acetate Implant			
Vibativ, *see* Telavancin			
Vinblastine sulfate	1 mg	IV	J9360
Vincasar PFS, *see* Vincristine sulfate			
Vincristine sulfate	1 mg	IV	J9370
Vincristine sulfate Liposome	1 mg	IV	J9371
Vinorelbine tartrate	per 10 mg	IV	J9390
Vistaject-25, *see* Hydroxyzine HCl			
Vistaril, *see* Hydroxyzine HCl			
Vistide, *see* cidofovir			
Visudyne, *see* Verteporfin			

DRUG	DOSE	ROUTE	HCPCS
Vitamin K, phytonadione, menadione, menadiol sodium diphosphate	per 1 mg	IM, SC, IV	J3430
Vitamin B-12 cyanocobalamin	up to 1,000 mcg	IM, SC	J3420
Von Willebrand Factor Complex, human	per IU VWF:RCo	IV	J7187
	per IU VWF:RCo	IV	J7183
Vonvendi	per IU VWF:RCp	IV	J7179
Voriconazole	10 mg	IV	J3465
Vpriv, *see* Velaglucerase alfa			

W

DRUG	DOSE	ROUTE	HCPCS
Wehamine, *see* Dimenhydrinate			
Wehydryl, *see* Diphenhydramine HCl			
Wellcovorin, *see* Leucovorin calcium			
Wilate, *see* Von Willebrand Factor complex (human)			
Win Rho SD, *see* Rho(D) immuglobulin, human, solvent detergent			
Wyamine Sulfate, *see* Mephentermine sulfate			
Wycillin, *see* Penicillin G procaine			
Wydase, *see* Hyaluronidase			

X

DRUG	DOSE	ROUTE	HCPCS
Xeloda, *see* Capecitabine			
Xeomin, *see* Incobotulinumtoxin type A			
Xgeva, *see* Denosumab			
Xiaflex, *see* Collagenase			
Xopenex, *see* Albuterol			
Xylocaine HCl, *see* Lidocaine HCl			
Xyntha, *see* Factor VIII (anti-hemophilic factor, recombinant)			

Y

DRUG	DOSE	ROUTE	HCPCS
Yervoy, *see* Ipilimumab			

DRUG	DOSE	ROUTE	HCPCS
Z			
Zanosar, *see* Streptozocin			
Zantac, *see* Ranitidine HCL			
Zemplar, *see* Paricalcitol			
Zenapax, *see* Daclizumab			
Zetran, *see* Diazepam Ziconotide	1 mcg	OTH	J2278
Zidovudine	10 mg	IV	J3485
Zinacef, *see* Cefuroxime sodium			
Ziprasidone Mesylate	10 mg	IM	J3486
Zithromax, *see* Azithromycin dihydrate			
Zithromax I.V., *see* Azithromycin, Injection			
Ziv-Aflibercept	1 mg	IV	J9400
Zofran, *see* Ondansetron HCl			
Zoladex, *see* Goserelin acetate Implant			
Zoledronic Acid	1 mg	IV	J3489
Zolicef, *see* Cefazolin sodium			
Zortress, *see* Everolimus			
Zosyn, *see* Piperacillin			
Zyprexa Relprevv, *see* Olanzapine			
Zyvox, *see* Linezolid			

APPENDIX D: MEDICARE REFERENCES

COVERAGE INSTRUCTION MANUAL (CIM) REFERENCES

The following Medicare references refer to policy issues identified in the main body of the HCPCS code section. Coverage Instruction Manual references are identified with the term CIM: followed by the reference number(s).

35-10 HYPERBARIC OXYGEN THERAPY

For purposes of coverage under Medicare, hyperbaric oxygen (HBO) therapy is a modality in which the entire body is exposed to oxygen under increased atmospheric pressure.

A. Covered Conditions.—Program reimbursement for HBO therapy will be limited to that which is administered in a chamber (including the one man unit) and is limited to the following conditions:

1. Acute carbon monoxide intoxication, (ICD-9 -CM diagnosis 986).
2. Decompression illness, (ICD-9-CM diagnosis 993.2, 993.3).
3. Gas embolism, (ICD-9-CM diagnosis 958.0, 999.1).
4. Gas gangrene, (ICD-9-CM diagnosis 0400).
5. Acute traumatic peripheral ischemia. HBO therapy is an adjunctive treatment to be used in combination with accepted standard therapeutic measures when loss of function, limb, or life is threatened. (ICD-9-CM diagnosis 902.53, 903.01, 903.1, 904.0, 904.41.)
6. Crush injuries and suturing of severed limbs. As in the previous conditions, HBO therapy would be an adjunctive treatment when loss of function, limb, or life is threatened. (ICD-9-CM diagnosis 927.00-927.03, 927.09-927.11, 927.20-927.21, 927.8-927.9, 928.00-928.01, 928.10-928.11, 928.20-928.21, 928.3, 928.8-928.9, 929.0, 929.9, 996.90-996.99.)
7. Progressive necrotizing infections (necrotizing fasciitis), (ICD-9-CM diagnosis 728.86).
8. Acute peripheral arterial insufficiency, (ICD-9-CM diagnosis 444.21, 444.22, 444.81).
9. Preparation and preservation of compromised skin grafts (not for primary management of wounds), (ICD-9CM diagnosis 996.52; excludes artificial skin graft).
10. Chronic refractory osteomyelitis, unresponsive to conventional medical and surgical management, (ICD-9-CM diagnosis 730.10-730.19).
11. Osteoradionecrosis as an adjunct to conventional treatment, (ICD-9-CM diagnosis 526.89).
12. Soft tissue radionecrosis as an adjunct to conventional treatment, (ICD-9-CM diagnosis 990).
13. Cyanide poisoning, (ICD-9-CM diagnosis 987.7, 989.0).
14. Actinomycosis, only as an adjunct to conventional therapy when the disease process is refractory to antibiotics and surgical treatment, (ICD-9-CM diagnosis 039.0-039.4, 039.8, 039.9).
15. Diabetic wounds of the lower extremities in patients who meet the following three criteria:

    a) Patient has type I or type II diabetes and has a lower extremity wound that is due to diabetes;
    b) Patient has a wound classified as Wagner grade III or higher; and
    c) Patient has failed an adequate course of standard wound therapy.

The use of HBO therapy is covered as adjunctive therapy only after there are no measurable signs of healing for at least 30-days of treatment with standard wound therapy and must be used in addition to standard wound care. Standard wound care in patients with diabetic wounds includes: assessment of a patient's vascular status and correction of any vascular problems in the affected limb if possible, optimization of nutritional status, optimization of glucose control, debridement by any means to remove devitalized tissue, maintenance of a clean, moist bed of granulation tissue with appropriate moist dressings, appropriate off-loading, and necessary treatment to resolve any infection that might be present. Failure to respond to standard wound care occurs when there are no measurable signs of healing for at least 30 consecutive days. Wounds must be evaluated at least every 30 days during administration of HBO therapy. Continued treatment with HBO therapy is not covered if measurable signs of healing have not been demonstrated within any 30-day period of treatment.

B. Noncovered Conditions.—All other indications not specified under §35-10 (A) are not covered under the Medicare program. No program payment may be made for any conditions other than those listed in §35-10(A).

No program payment may be made for HBO in the treatment of the following conditions:

1. Cutaneous, decubitus, and stasis ulcers.
2. Chronic peripheral vascular insufficiency.
3. Anaerobic septicemia and infection other than clostridial.
4. Skin burns (thermal).
5. Senility.
6. Myocardial infarction.
7. Cardiogenic shock.
8. Sickle cell anemia.
9. Acute thermal and chemical pulmonary damage, i.e., smoke inhalation with pulmonary insufficiency.
10. Acute or chronic cerebral vascular insufficiency.
11. Hepatic necrosis.
12. Aerobic septicemia.
13. Nonvascular causes of chronic brain syndrome (Pick's disease, Alzheimer's disease, Korsakoff's disease).
14. Tetanus.
15. Systemic aerobic infection.
16. Organ transplantation.
17. Organ storage.
18. Pulmonary emphysema.
19. Exceptional blood loss anemia.
20. Multiple Sclerosis.
21. Arthritic Diseases.
22. Acute cerebral edema.

C. Topical Application of Oxygen.—This method of administering oxygen does not meet the definition of HBO therapy as stated above. Also, its clinical efficacy has not been established. Therefore, no Medicare reimbursement may be made for the topical application of oxygen. (Cross reference: §35-31.)

D. Physician Supervision Requirement--For HBO therapy to be covered under the Medicare program, the physician must be in constant attendance during the entire treatment. This is a professional activity that cannot be delegated in that it requires independent medical judgement by the physician. The physician must be present, carefully monitoring the patient during the hyperbaric oxygen therapy session and be immediately available should a complication occur. This requirement applies in all settings: no payment will be made under Part A or Part B, unless the physician is in constant attendance during the HBO therapy procedure.

E. Credentials--A physician qualified in HBO therapy treatment is defined by Medicare for this purpose to be credentialed by the hospital in which HBO therapy is being performed specifically in hyperbaric medicine and the management of acute cardiopulmonary emergencies, including placement of chest tube. Credentialing includes, at a minimum, the following:

- Training, experience and privileges within the institution to manage acute cardiopulmonary emergencies, including advanced cardiac life support, and emergency myringotomy;
- Completion of a recognized hyperbaric medicine training program as established by either the American College of Hyperbaric Medicine or the Undersea and Hyperbaric Medical Society (UHMS) with a minimum of 60 hours of training and documented by a certificate of completion or an equivalent program; and
- Continuing medical education in hyperbaric medicine of a minimum of 16 hours every 2 years after initial credentialing.

An additional requirement that must be met for Medicare's payment for hyperbaric medical therapy is that cardiopulmonary resuscitation team coverage must be immediately available during the hours of the hyperbaric chamber operations.

35-13 PROLOTHERAPY, JOINT SCLEROTHERAPY, AND LIGAMENTOUS INJECTIONS WITH SCLEROSING AGENTS—NOT COVERED

The medical effectiveness of the above therapies has not been verified by scientifically controlled studies. Accordingly, reimbursement for these modalities should be denied on the ground that they are not reasonable and necessary as required by §1862(a)(1) of the law.

35-20 TREATMENT OF MOTOR FUNCTION DISORDERS WITH ELECTRIC NERVE STIMULATION—NOT COVERED

While electric nerve stimulation has been employed to control chronic intractable pain for some time, its use in the treatment of motor function disorders, such as multiple sclerosis, is a recent innovation, and the medical effectiveness of such therapy has not been verified by scientifically controlled studies. Therefore, where electric nerve stimulation is employed to treat motor function disorders, no reimbursement may be made for the stimulator or for the services related to its implantation since this treatment cannot be considered reasonable and necessary.

See §§35-27 and 65-8.

NOTE: For Medicare coverage of deep brain stimulation for essential tremor and Parkinson's disease, see §65-19.

35-27 BIOFEEDBACK THERAPY

Biofeedback therapy provides visual, auditory or other evidence of the status of certain body functions so that a person can exert voluntary control over the functions, and thereby alleviate an abnormal bodily condition. Biofeedback therapy often uses electrical devices to transform bodily signals indicative of such functions as heart rate, blood pressure, skin temperature, salivation, peripheral vasomotor activity, and gross muscle tone into a tone or light, the loudness or brightness of which shows the extent of activity in the function being measured.

Biofeedback therapy differs from electromyography, which is a diagnostic procedure used to record and study the electrical properties of skeletal muscle. An electromyography device may be used to provide feedback with certain types of biofeedback.

Biofeedback therapy is covered under Medicare only when it is reasonable and necessary for the individual patient for muscle re-education of specific muscle groups or for treating pathological muscle abnormalities of spasticity, incapacitating muscle spasm, or weakness, and more conventional treatments (heat, cold, massage, exercise, support) have not been successful. This therapy is not covered for treatment of ordinary muscle tension states or for psychosomatic conditions.

See HCFA-Pub. 14-3, §§2200ff, 2215, and 4161; HCFA-Pub. 13-3, §§3133.3, 3148, and 3149; HCFA-Pub. 10, §§242 and 242.5 for special physical therapy requirements. See also §35-20 and 65-8.)

35-34 FABRIC WRAPPING OF ABDOMINAL ANEURYSMS—NOT COVERED

Fabric wrapping of abdominal aneurysms is not a covered Medicare procedure. This is a treatment for abdominal aneurysms which involves wrapping aneurysms with cellophane or fascia lata. This procedure has not been shown to prevent eventual rupture. In extremely rare instances, external wall reinforcement may be indicated when the current accepted treatment (excision of the aneurysm and reconstruction with synthetic materials) is not a viable alternative, but external wall reinforcement is not fabric wrapping. Accordingly, fabric wrapping of abdominal aneurysms is not considered reasonable and necessary within the meaning of §1862(a)(1) of the Act.

35-46 ASSESSING PATIENT'S SUITABILITY FOR ELECTRICAL NERVE STIMULATION THERAPY

Electrical nerve stimulation is an accepted modality for assessing a patient's suitability for ongoing treatment with a transcutaneous or an implanted nerve stimulator. Accordingly, program payment may be made for the following techniques when used to determine the potential therapeutic usefulness of an electrical nerve stimulator:

A. <u>Transcutaneous Electrical Nerve Stimulation (TENS)</u>.--This technique involves attachment of a transcutaneous nerve stimulator to the surface of the skin over the peripheral nerve to be stimulated. It is used by the patient on a trial basis and its effectiveness in modulating pain is monitored by the physician, or physical therapist. Generally, the physician or physical therapist is able to determine whether the patient is likely to derive a significant therapeutic benefit from continuous use of a transcutaneous stimulator within a trial period of 1 month; in a few cases this determination may take longer to make. Document the medical necessity for such services which are furnished beyond the first month. (See §45-25 for an explanation of coverage of medically necessary supplies for the effective use of TENS.)

If TENS significantly alleviates pain, it may be considered as primary treatment; if it produces no relief or greater discomfort than the original pain electrical nerve stimulation therapy is ruled out.

However, where TENS produces incomplete relief, further evaluation with percutaneous electrical nerve stimulation may be considered to determine whether an implanted peripheral nerve stimulator would provide significant relief from pain. (See §35-46B.)

Usually, the physician or physical therapist providing the services will furnish the equipment necessary for assessment. Where the physician or physical therapist advises the patient to rent the TENS from a supplier during the trial period rather than supplying it himself/herself, program payment may be made for rental of the TENS as well as for the services of the physician or physical therapist who is evaluating its use. However, the combined program payment which is made for the physician's or physical therapist's services and the rental of the stimulator from a supplier should not exceed the amount which would be payable for the total service, including the stimulator, furnished by the physician or physical therapist alone.

B. <u>Percutaneous Electrical Nerve Stimulation (PENS).</u>--This diagnostic procedure which involves stimulation of peripheral nerves by a needle electrode inserted through the skin is performed only in a physician's office, clinic, or hospital outpatient department. Therefore, it is covered only when performed by a physician or incident to physician's service. If pain is effectively controlled by percutaneous stimulation, implantation of electrodes is warranted.

As in the case of TENS (described in subsection A), generally the physician should be able to determine whether the patient is likely to derive a significant therapeutic benefit from continuing use of an implanted nerve stimulator within a trial period of 1 month. In a few cases, this determination may take longer to make. The medical necessity for such diagnostic services which are furnished beyond the first month must be documented.

NOTE: Electrical nerve stimulators do not prevent pain but only alleviate pain as it occurs. A patient can be taught how to employ the stimulator, and once this is done, can use it safely and effectively without direct physician supervision. Consequently, it is inappropriate for a patient to visit his/her physician, physical therapist, or an outpatient clinic on a continuing basis for treatment of pain with electrical nerve stimulation. Once it is determined that electrical nerve stimulation should be continued as therapy and the patient has been trained to use the stimulator, it is expected that a stimulator will be implanted or the patient will employ the TENS on a continual basis in his/her home. Electrical nerve stimulation treatments furnished by a physician in his/her office, by a physical therapist or outpatient clinic are excluded from coverage by §1862(a)(1) of the Act. (See §65-8 for an explanation of coverage of the therapeutic use of implanted peripheral nerve stimulators under the prosthetic devices benefit. See §60-20 for an explanation of coverage of the therapeutic use of TENS under the durable medical equipment benefit.)

35-47 OSTEOGENIC STIMULATION

Electrical stimulation to augment bone repair can be attained either invasively or noninvasively. Invasive devices provide electrical stimulation directly at the fracture site either through percutaneously placed cathodes or by implantation of a coiled cathode wire into the fracture site. The power pack for the latter device is implanted into soft tissue near the fracture site and subcutaneously connected to the cathode, creating a self-contained system with no external components. The power supply for the former device is externally placed and the leads connected to the inserted cathodes. With the noninvasive device, opposing pads, wired to an external power supply, are placed over the cast. An electromagnetic field is created between the pads at the fracture site.

1. <u>Noninvasive Stimulator</u>.—The noninvasive stimulator device is covered only for the following indications:

   - Nonunion of long bone fractures;
   - Failed fusion, where a minimum of nine months has elapsed since the last surgery;
   - Congenital pseudarthroses; and
   - As an adjunct to spinal fusion surgery for patients at high risk of pseudarthrosis due to previously failed spinal fusion at the same site or for those undergoing multiple level fusion. A multiple level fusion involves 3 or more vertebrae (e.g., L3-L5, L4-S1, etc).

2. <u>Invasive (Implantable) Stimulator</u>.—The invasive stimulator device is covered only for the following indications:

   - Nonunion of long bone fractures; and
   - As an adjunct to spinal fusion surgery for patients at high risk of pseudarthrosis due to previously failed spinal fusion at the same site or for those undergoing multiple level fusion.

   A multiple level fusion involves 3 or more vertebrae (e.g., L3-L5, L4-S1, etc). Effective for services performed on or after September 15, 1980, nonunion of long bone fractures, for both noninvasive and invasive devices, is considered to exist only after 6 or more months have elapsed without healing of the fracture.

   Effective for services performed on or after April 1, 2000, nonunion of long bone fractures, for both noninvasive and invasive devices, is considered to exist only when serial radiographs have confirmed that fracture healing has ceased for three or more months prior to starting treatment with the electrical osteogenic stimulator. Serial radiographs must include a minimum of two sets of radiographs, each including multiple views of the fracture site, separated by a minimum of 90 days.

3. <u>Ultrasonic Osteogenic Stimulators</u>.—An ultrasonic osteogenic stimulator is a non-invasive device that emits low intensity, pulsed ultrasound. The ultrasound signal is applied to the skin surface at the fracture location via ultrasound, conductive gel in order to stimulate fracture healing.

   Effective for services performed on or after January 1, 2001, ultrasonic osteogenic stimulators are covered as medically reasonable and necessary for the treatment of non-union fractures. In demonstrating nonunion of fractures, we would expect:

   - A minimum of two sets of radiographs obtained prior to starting treatment with the osteogenic stimulator, separated by a minimum of 90 days. Each radiograph must include multiple views of the fracture site accompanied with a written interpretation by a physician stating that there has been no clinically significant evidence of fracture healing between the two sets of radiographs.
   - Indications that the patient failed at least one surgical intervention for the treatment of the fracture.

Non-unions of the skull, vertebrae, and those that are tumor-related are excluded from coverage. The ultrasonic osteogenic stimulator may not be used concurrently with other non-invasive osteogenic devices. The national non-coverage policy related to ultrasonic osteogenic stimulators for fresh fractures and delayed unions remains in place. This policy relates only to non-union as defined above.

35-50 COCHLEOSTOMY WITH NEUROVASCULAR TRANSPLANT FOR MENIERE'S DISEASE—NOT COVERED

Ménière's disease (or syndrome) is a common cause of paroxysmal vertigo. Ménière's syndrome is usually treated medically. When medical treatment fails, surgical treatment may be required.

While there are two recognized surgical procedures used in treating Ménière's disease (decompression of the endolymphatic hydrops and labyrinthectomy), there is no scientific evidence supporting the safety and effectiveness of cochleostomy with neurovascular transplant in treatment of Ménière's syndrome. Accordingly, Medicare does not cover cochleostomy with neurovascular transplant for treatment of Ménière's disease.

35-64 CHELATION THERAPY FOR TREATMENT OF ATHEROSCLEROSIS

Chelation therapy is the application of chelation techniques for the therapeutic or preventive effects of removing unwanted metal ions from the body. The application of chelation therapy using ethylenediamine-tetra-acetic acid (EDTA) for the treatment and prevention of atherosclerosis is controversial. There is no widely accepted rationale to explain the beneficial effects attributed to this therapy. Its safety is questioned and its clinical effectiveness has never been established by well designed, controlled clinical trials. It is not widely accepted and practiced by American physicians. EDTA chelation therapy for atherosclerosis is considered experimental. For these reasons, EDTA chelation therapy for the treatment or prevention of atherosclerosis is not covered.

Some practitioners refer to this therapy as chemoendarterectomy and may also show a diagnosis other than atherosclerosis, such as arteriosclerosis or calcinosis. Claims employing such variant terms should also be denied under this section.

Cross-reference: §45-20

35-74 EXTERNAL COUNTERPULSATION (ECP) FOR SEVERE ANGINA— COVERED

External counterpulsation (ECP), commonly referred to as enhanced external counterpulsation, is a non-invasive outpatient treatment for coronary artery disease refractory to medical and/or surgical therapy. Although ECP devices are cleared by the Food and Drug Administration (FDA) for use in treating a variety of cardiac conditions, including stable or unstable angina pectoris, acute myocardial infarction and cardiogenic shock, the use of this device to treat cardiac conditions other than stable angina pectoris is not covered, since only that use has developed sufficient evidence to demonstrate its medical effectiveness. Non-coverage of hydraulic versions of these types of devices remains in force.

Coverage is provided for the use of ECP for patients who have been diagnosed with disabling angina (Class III or Class IV, Canadian Cardiovascular Society Classification or equivalent classification) who, in the opinion of a cardiologist or cardiothoracic surgeon, are not readily amenable to surgical intervention, such as PTCA or cardiac bypass because: (1) their condition is inoperable, or at high risk of operative complications or post-operative failure; (2) their coronary anatomy is not readily amenable to such procedures; or (3) they have co-morbid states which create excessive risk.

A full course of therapy usually consists of 35 one-hour treatments, which may be offered once or twice daily, usually 5 days per week. The patient is placed on a treatment table where their lower trunk and lower extremities are wrapped in a series of three compressive air cuffs which inflate and deflate in synchronization with the patient's cardiac cycle.

During diastole the three sets of air cuffs are inflated sequentially (distal to proximal) compressing the vascular beds within the muscles of the calves, lower thighs and upper thighs. This action results in an increase in diastolic pressure, generation of retrograde arterial blood flow and an increase in venous return. The cuffs are deflated simultaneously just prior to systole, which produces a rapid drop in vascular impedance, a decrease in ventricular workload and an increase in cardiac output.

The augmented diastolic pressure and retrograde aortic flow appear to improve myocardial perfusion, while systolic unloading appears to reduce cardiac workload and oxygen requirements. The increased venous return coupled with enhanced systolic flow appears to increase cardiac output. As a result of this treatment, most patients experience increased time until onset of ischemia, increased exercise tolerance, and a reduction in the number and severity of anginal episodes. Evidence was presented that this effect lasted well beyond the immediate post-treatment phase, with patients symptom-free for several months to two years.

This procedure must be done under direct supervision of a physician.

35-77 NEUROMUSCULAR ELECTRICAL STIMULATION (NMES)

Neuromuscular electrical stimulation (NMES) involves the use of a device that transmits an electrical impulse to activate muscle groups by way of electrodes. There are two broad categories of NMES. One type of device stimulates the muscle when the patient is in a resting state to treat muscle atrophy. The second type is used to enhance functional activity of neurologically impaired patients.

Treatment of Muscle Atrophy

Coverage of NMES to treat muscle atrophy is limited to the treatment of patients with disuse atrophy where the nerve supply to the muscle is intact, including brain, spinal cord and peripheral nerves and other non-neurological reasons for disuse atrophy. Examples include casting or splinting of a limb, contracture due to scarring of soft tissue as in burn lesions, and hip orthotic training begins). (See CIM 45-25 for an explanation of coverage of medically necessary supplies for the effective use of NMES).

Use for Walking in Patients with Spinal Cord Injury (SCI)

The type of NMES that is used to enhance the ability to walk of SCI patients is commonly referred to as functional electrical stimulation (FES). These devices are surface units that use electrical impulses to activate paralyzed or weak muscles in precise sequence. Coverage for the use of NMES/FES is limited to SCI patients, for walking, who have completed a training program, which consists of at least 32 physical therapy sessions with the device over a period of 3 months. The trial period of physical therapy will enable the physician treating the patient for his or her spinal cord injury to properly evaluate the person's ability to use these devices frequently and for the long term. Physical therapy sessions are only covered in the inpatient hospital, outpatient hospital, comprehensive outpatient rehabilitation facilities, and outpatient rehabilitation facilities. The physical therapy necessary to perform this training must be directly performed by the physical therapist as part of a one-on-one training program; this service cannot be done unattended.

The goal of physical therapy must be to train SCI patients on the use of NMES/FES devices to achieve walking, not to reverse or retard muscle atrophy.

Coverage for NMES/FES for walking will be limited to SCI patients with all of the following characteristics:

1) persons with intact lower motor units (L1 and below) (both muscle and peripheral nerve);
2) persons with muscle and joint stability for weight bearing at upper and lower extremities that can demonstrate balance and control to maintain an upright support posture independently;
3) persons that demonstrate brisk muscle contraction to NMES and have sensory perception of electrical stimulation sufficient for muscle contraction;
4) persons that possess high motivation, commitment and cognitive ability to use such devices for walking;
5) persons that can transfer independently and can demonstrate independent standing tolerance for at least 3 minutes;
6) persons that can demonstrate hand and finger function to manipulate controls;
7) persons with at least 6-month post recovery spinal cord injury and restorative surgery;
8) persons without hip and knee degenerative disease and no history of long bone fracture secondary to osteoporosis; and
9) persons who have demonstrated a willingness to use the device long-term.

NMES/FES for walking will not be covered in SCI patients with any of the following:

1) persons with cardiac pacemakers;
2) severe scoliosis or severe osteoporosis;
3) skin disease or cancer at area of stimulation;
4) irreversible contracture; or
5) autonomic dysreflexia.

The only settings where therapists with the sufficient skills to provide these services are employed, are inpatient hospitals, outpatient hospitals, comprehensive outpatient rehabilitation facilities and outpatient rehabilitation facilities. The physical therapy necessary to perform this training must be part of a one-on-one training program.

Additional therapy after the purchase of the DME would be limited by our general policies on coverage of skilled physical therapy.

All other uses of NMES remain non-covered.

(Also reference Medicare Carriers' Manual, Part 3, Claims-§2210 and Medicare Intermediary Manual, Part 3, Claims-§3653 - See - Maintenance Program 271.1)

35-98 ELECTRICAL STIMULATION FOR THE TREATMENT OF WOUNDS

Electrical stimulation (ES) has been used or studied for many different applications, one of which is accelerating wound healing. The types of ES used for healing chronic venous and arterial wound and pressure ulcers are direct current (DC), alternating current (AC), pulsed current (PC), pulsed electromagnetic induction (PEMI), and spinal cord stimulation (SCS). An example of AC is transcutaneous electrical stimulation (TENS). The PEMI includes Pulsed Electromagnetic Field (PEMF) and Pulsed Electromagnetic Energy (PEE) using pulsed radio frequency energy, both of which are nonthermal i.e., they do not produce heat. Some ES use generators to create energy in the means such as coils, rather than by leads or surface electrodes.

There is insufficient evidence to determine any clinically significant differences in healing rates. Therefore, ES cannot be covered by Medicare because its effectiveness has not been adequately demonstrated.

35-102 ELECTRICAL STIMULATION FOR THE TREATMENT OF WOUNDS
(Effective for services on and after April 1, 2003)

Electrical stimulation (ES) has been used or studied for many different applications, one of which is accelerating wound healing. Electrical stimulation for the treatment of wounds is the application of electrical current through electrodes placed directly on the skin in close proximity to the wound. Electrical stimulation for the treatment of wounds will only be covered for chronic Stage III or Stage IV pressure ulcers, arterial ulcers, diabetic ulcers and venous stasis ulcers. All other uses of electrical stimulation for the treatment of wounds are noncovered. Chronic ulcers are defined as ulcers that have not healed within 30 days of occurrence. Electrical stimulation will not be covered as an initial treatment modality.

The use of electrical stimulation for the treatment of wounds is considered an adjunctive therapy. Electrical stimulation will be covered only after appropriate standard wound therapy has been tried for at least 30-days and there are no measurable signs of healing. This 30-day period can begin while the wound is acute. Measurable signs of improved healing include a decrease in wound size, either surface area or volume, decrease in amount of exudates and decrease in amount of necrotic tissue. Standard wound care includes: optimization of nutritional status; debridement by any means to remove devitalized tissue; maintenance of a clean, moist bed of granulation tissue with appropriate moist dressings; and necessary treatment to resolve any infection that may be present. Standard wound care based on the specific type of wound includes: frequent repositioning of a patient with pressure ulcers (usually every 2 hours); off-loading of pressure and good glucose control for diabetic ulcers; establishment of adequate circulation for arterial ulcers; and the use of a compression system for patients with venous ulcers. Continued treatment with electrical stimulation is not covered if measurable signs of healing have not been demonstrated within any 30-day period of treatment. Electrical stimulation must be discontinued when the wound demonstrates 100 per-cent epithelialized wound bed. Any form of electromagnetic therapy for the treatment of chronic wounds will not be covered.

This service can only be covered when performed by a physician, physical therapist, or incident to a physician service. Evaluation of the wound is an integral part of wound therapy. When a physician, physical therapist, or a clinician incident to a physician, performs electrical stimulation, that practitioner must evaluate the wound and contact the treating physician if the wound worsens. If electrical stimulation is being used, wounds must be evaluated at least monthly by the treating physician.

Unsupervised use of electrical stimulation for wound therapy will not be covered, as this use has not been found to be medically reasonable and necessary.

45-3 INSULIN SYRINGE

Medical supplies are covered under §1861(s)(2)(A) of the Act only when they are furnished incident to a physician's professional services. To be covered under this provision an insulin syringe must have been used by the physician or under his/her direct personal supervision, and the insulin injection must have been given in an emergency situation (e.g., diabetic coma).

The use of an insulin syringe by a diabetic would not meet the requirements of §1861(s)(2)(A) of the Act.

See Intermediary Manual, §3112.4B and Carriers Manual, §2050.

45-4 VITAMIN B12 INJECTIONS TO STRENGTHEN TENDONS, LIGAMENTS, ETC., OF THE FOOT--NOT COVERED

Vitamin B12 injections to strengthen tendons, ligaments, etc., of the foot are not covered under Medicare because (1) there is no evidence that vitamin B12 injections are effective for the purpose of strengthening weakened tendons and ligaments, and (2) this is nonsurgical treatment under the subluxation exclusion. Accordingly, vitamin B12 injections are not considered reasonable and necessary within the meaning of §1862(a)(1) of the Act.

See Intermediary Manual, §§3101.3 and 3158 and Carriers Manual, §§2050.5 and 2323.

45-7 HYDROPHILIC CONTACT LENS FOR CORNEAL BANDAGE

Some hydrophilic contact lenses are used as moist corneal bandages for the treatment of acute or chronic corneal pathology, such as bullous keratopathy, dry eyes, corneal ulcers and erosion, keratitis, corneal edema, descemetocele, corneal ectasis, Mooren's ulcer, anterior corneal dystrophy, neurotrophic keratoconjunctivitis, and for other therapeutic reasons.

Payment may be made under §1861(s)(2) of the Act for a hydrophilic contact lens approved by the Food and Drug Administration (FDA) and used as a supply incident to a physician's service.

Payment for the lens is included in the payment for the physician's service to which the lens is incident. Contractors are authorized to accept an FDA letter of approval or other FDA published material as evidence of FDA approval. *(See §65-1 for coverage of a hydrophilic contact lens as a prosthetic device.) See Intermediary Manual, §3112.4 and Carriers Manual, §§2050.1 and 15010.*

45-12 PORCINE SKIN AND GRADIENT PRESSURE DRESSINGS

Porcine (pig) skin dressings are covered, if reasonable and necessary for the individual patient as an occlusive dressing for burns, donor sites of a homograft, and decubiti and other ulcers.

Gradient pressure dressings are Jobst elasticized heavy duty dressings used to reduce hypertrophic scarring and joint contractures following burn injury. They are covered when used for that purpose.

45-15 PHYSICIAN'S OFFICE WITHIN AN INSTITUTION--COVERAGE OF SERVICES AND SUPPLIES INCIDENT TO A PHYSICIAN'S SERVICES

Where a physician establishes an office within a nursing home or other institution, coverage of services and supplies furnished in the office must be determined in accordance with the "incident to a physician's professional service" provision (see Intermediary Manual, §3112.4A or Carriers Manual, §2050.1), as in any physician's office. A physician's office within an institution must be confined to a separately identified part of the facility which is used solely as the physician's office and cannot be construed to extend throughout the entire institution. Thus, services performed outside the "office" area would be subject to the coverage rules applicable to services furnished outside the office setting.

In order to accurately apply the criteria in §3112.4 or §2050.l, give consideration to the physical proximity of the institution and physician's office. When his office is located within a facility, a physician may not be reimbursed for services, supplies, and use of equipment which fall outside the scope of services "commonly furnished" in physician's offices generally, even though such services may be furnished in his institutional office. Additionally, make a distinction between the physician's office practice and the institution, especially when the physician is administrator or owner of the facility. Thus, for their services to be covered under the criteria in §3112.4A or §2050.l, the auxiliary medical personnel must be members of the office staff rather than of the institution's staff, and the cost of supplies must represent an expense to the physician's office practice. Finally, services performed by the employees of the physician outside the "office" area must be directly supervised by the physician; his presence in the facility as a whole would not suffice to meet this requirement. (In any setting, of course, supervision of auxiliary personnel in and of itself is not considered a "physician's professional service" to which the services of the auxiliary personnel could be an incidental part, i.e., in addition to supervision, the physician must perform or have performed a personal professional service to the patient to which the services of the auxiliary personnel could be considered an incidental part). Denials for failure to meet any of these requirements would be based on §1861(s)(2)(A) of the Act.

Establishment of an office within an institution would not modify rules otherwise applicable for determining coverage of the physician's personal professional services within the institution. However, in view of the opportunity afforded to a physician who maintains such an office for rendering services to a sizable number of patients in a short period of time or for performing frequent services for the same patient, claims for physicians. services rendered under such circumstances would require careful evaluation by the carrier to assure that payment is made only for services that are reasonable and necessary.

Cross-reference: Intermediary Manual, §3112.4A; Carriers Manual, §2050.1

45-16 CERTAIN DRUGS DISTRIBUTED BY THE NATIONAL CANCER INSTITUTE (Effective for services furnished on or after October 1, 1980.)

Under its Cancer Therapy Evaluation, the Division of Cancer Treatment of the National Cancer Institute (NCI), in cooperation with the Food and Drug Administration, approves and distributes certain drugs for use in treating terminally ill cancer patients. One group of these drugs, designated as Group C drugs, unlike other drugs distributed by the NCI, are not limited to use in clinical trials for the purpose of testing their efficacy. Drugs are classified as Group C drugs only if there is sufficient evidence demonstrating their efficacy within a tumor type and that they can be safely administered.

A physician is eligible to receive Group C drugs from the Division of Cancer Treatment only if the following requirements are met:

- A physician must be registered with the NCI as an investigator by having completed an FD-Form 1573;
- A written request for the drug, indicating the disease to be treated, must be submitted to the NCI;
- The use of the drug must be limited to indications outlined in the NCI's guidelines; and
- All adverse reactions must be reported to the Investigational Drug Branch of the Division of Cancer Treatment.

In view of these NCI controls on distribution and use of Group C drugs, intermediaries may assume, in the absence of evidence to the contrary, that a Group C drug and the related hospital stay are covered if all other applicable coverage requirements are satisfied.

If there is reason to question coverage in a particular case, the matter should be resolved with the assistance of the local PSRO, or if there is none, the assistance of your medical consultants.

Information regarding those drugs which are classified as Group C drugs may be obtained from:

Office of the Chief, Investigational Drug Branch Division of Cancer Treatment, CTEP, Landow Building Room 4C09, National Cancer Institute
Bethesda, Maryland 20205

45-19 TRANSCUTANEOUS ELECTRICAL NERVE STIMULATION (TENS) FOR ACUTE POST-OPERATIVE PAIN

The use of transcutaneous electrical nerve stimulation (TENS) for the relief of acute post-operative pain is covered under Medicare. TENS may be covered whether used as an adjunct to the use of drugs, or as an alternative to drugs, in the treatment of acute pain resulting from surgery.

TENS devices, whether durable or disposable, may be used in furnishing this service. When used for the purpose of treating acute post-operative pain, TENS devices are considered supplies. As such they may be hospital supplies furnished inpatients covered under Part A, or supplies incident to a physician's service when furnished in connection with surgery done on an outpatient basis, and covered under Part B.

It is expected that TENS, when used for acute post-operative pain, will be necessary for relatively short periods of time, usually 30 days or less. In cases when TENS is used for longer periods, contractors should attempt to ascertain whether TENS is no longer being used for acute pain but rather for chronic pain, in which case the TENS device may be covered as durable medical equipment as described in §60-20.

Cross-reference: HCFA Pub. 13-3, §§65-8, 3101.4, 3112.4, 3113; HCFA Pub. 14-3, §§65-8, 2050.1, 2100; HCFA Pub. 10, §§65-8, 210.4, 230, 235.

45-22 LYMPHOCYTE IMMUNE GLOBULIN, ANTI-THYMOCYTE GLOBULIN (EQUINE)

The lymphocyte immune globulin preparations are biologic drugs not previously approved or licensed for use in the management of renal allograft rejection. A number of other lymphocyte immune globulin products of equine, lapine, and murine origin are currently under investigation for their potential usefulness in controlling allograft rejections in human transplantation. These biologic drugs are viewed as adjunctive to traditional immunosuppressive products such as steroids and anti- metabolic drugs. At present, lymphocyte immune globulin preparations are not recommended to replace conventional immunosuppressive drugs, but to supplement them and to be used as alternatives to elevated or accelerated dosing with conventional immunosuppressive agents.

The FDA has approved one lymphocyte immune globulin preparation for marketing, lymphocyte immune globulin, anti-thymocyte globulin (equine). This drug is indicated for the management of allograft rejection episodes in renal transplantation. It is covered under Medicare when used for this purpose. Other forms of lymphocyte globulin preparation which the FDA approves for this indication in the future may be covered under Medicare.

45-22 DIMETHYL SULFOXIDE (DMSO)

DMSO is an industrial solvent produced as a chemical byproduct of paper production from wood pulp. The Food and Drug Administration has determined that the only purpose for which DMSO is safe and effective for humans is in the treatment of the bladder condition, interstitial cystitis. Therefore, the use of DMSO for all other indications is not considered to be reasonable and necessary. Payment may be made for its use only when reasonable and necessary for a patient in the treatment of interstitial cystitis.

45-23 ANTI-INHIBITOR COAGULANT COMPLEX (AICC)

Anti-inhibitor coagulant complex, AICC, is a drug used to treat hemophilia in patients with factor VIII inhibitor antibodies. AICC has been shown to be safe and effective and has Medicare coverage when furnished to patients with hemophilia A and inhibitor antibodies to factor VIII who have major bleeding episodes and who fail to respond to other, less expensive therapies.

45-25 SUPPLIES USED IN THE DELIVERY OF TRANSCUTANEOUS ELECTRICAL NERVE STIMULATION (TENS) AND NEURO-MUSCULAR ELECTRICAL STIMULATION (NMES)—(Effective for services rendered (i.e., items rented or purchased) on or after July 14, 1988.)

Transcutaneous Electrical Nerve Stimulation (TENS) and/or Neuromuscular Electrical Stimulation (NMES) can ordinarily be delivered to patients through the use of conventional electrodes, adhesive tapes and lead wires. There may be times, however, where it might be medically necessary for certain patients receiving TENS or NMES treatment to use, as an alternative to conventional electrodes, adhesive tapes and lead wires, a form-fitting conductive garment (i.e., a garment with conductive fibers which are separated from the patients' skin by layers of fabric).

A form-fitting conductive garment (and medically necessary related supplies) may be covered under the program only when:

1. It has received permission or approval for marketing by the Food and Drug Administration;
2. It has been prescribed by a physician for use in delivering covered TENS or NMES treatment; and
3. One of the medical indications outlined below is met:

  * The patient cannot manage without the conductive garment because there is such a large area or so many sites to be stimulated and the stimulation would have to be delivered so frequently that it is not feasible to use conventional electrodes, adhesive tapes and lead wires;
  * The patient cannot manage without the conductive garment for the treatment of chronic intractable pain because the areas or sites to be stimulated are inaccessible with the use of conventional electrodes, adhesive tapes and lead wires;
  * The patient has a documented medical condition such as skin problems that preclude the application of conventional electrodes, adhesive tapes and lead wires;
  * The patient requires electrical stimulation beneath a cast either to treat disuse atrophy, where the nerve supply to the muscle is intact, or to treat chronic intractable pain; or

- The patient has a medical need for rehabilitation strengthening (pursuant to a written plan of rehabilitation) following an injury where the nerve supply to the muscle is intact.

A conductive garment is not covered for use with a TENS device during the trial period specified in §35-46 unless:

4. The patient has a documented skin problem prior to the start of the trial period; and
5. The carrier's medical consultants are satisfied that use of such an item is medically necessary for the patient.

(*See conditions for coverage of the use of TENS in the diagnosis and treatment of chronic intractable pain in §§35-46 and 60-20 and the use of NMES in the treatment of disuse atrophy in §35-77.*)

45-29 INTRAVENOUS IRON THERAPY (EFFECTIVE FOR SERVICES PERFORMED ON OR AFTER12/01/00)

Iron deficiency is a common condition in end stage renal disease (ESRD) patients undergoing hemodialysis. Iron is a critical structural component of hemoglobin, a key protein found in normal red blood cells (RBCs) which transports oxygen. Without this important building block, anemic patients experience difficulty in restoring adequate, healthy RBCs that improve hematocrit levels. Clinical management of iron deficiency involves treating patients with iron replacement products while they undergo hemodialysis. Body iron stores can be supplemented with either oral or intravenous (IV) iron products.

The evidence suggests that there is little to distinguish various forms of IV iron therapy in terms of effectiveness. Rather, the medical literature indicates that the mode of intravenous administration is perhaps the most effective treatment for iron deficiency in hemodialysis patients. Unlike oral iron products which must be absorbed through the GI tract, IV iron products are infused directly into the bloodstream in a form that is readily available to the bone marrow for RBC synthesis, resulting in an earlier correction of iron deficiency and anemia. Review of medical literature indicated that the distinction among IV iron products lies within their safety profiles. The IV iron dextran products are associated with a small incidence of severe, life-threatening anaphylaxis. These type I hypersensitivity reactions, which are not dose-related, are immunoglobulin (Ig) E-mediated and are apparently exclusively associated with the dextran forms of injectable iron. In fact, clinical evidence indicates that the dextran component itself is what triggers the severe, life-threatening anaphylactic reactions. *Sodium ferric gluconate complex in sucrose injection* has demonstrated no life-threatening anaphylaxis and a less severe adverse-reaction rate when compared to iron dextran products.

Therefore, effective December 1, 2000, Medicare covers *sodium ferric gluconate complex in sucrose injection* when used as a first line treatment of iron deficiency anemia in patients undergoing chronic hemodialysis who are receiving supplemental erythropoietin therapy.

45-30 PHOTOSENSITIVE DRUGS

Photosensitive drugs are the light-sensitive agents used in photodynamic therapy. Once introduced into the body, these drugs selectively identify and adhere to diseased tissue. The drugs remain inactive until they are exposed to a specific wavelength of light, by means of a laser, that corresponds to their absorption peak. The activation of a photosensitive drug results in a photochemical reaction which treats the diseased tissue without affecting surrounding normal tissue.

Verteporfin

Verteporfin, a benzoporphyrin derivative, is an intravenous lipophilic photosensitive drug with an absorption peak of 690 nm. This drug was first approved by the Food and Drug Administration (FDA) on April 12, 2000, and subsequently, approved for inclusion in the United States Pharmacopoeia on July 18, 2000, meeting Medicare's definition of a drug as defined under §1861(t)(1) of the Social Security Act. Effective July 1, 2001, Verteporfin (Q3013 . Injection, Verteporfin, 15 mg) is only covered when used in conjunction with ocular photodynamic therapy (see §35-100 PHOTODYNAMIC THERAPY) when furnished intravenously incident to a physician's service. For patients with age-related macular degeneration, Verteporfin is only covered with a diagnosis of neovascular age-related macular degeneration (ICD-9-CM 362.52) with predominately classic subfoveal choroidal neovascular (CNV) lesions (where the area of classic CNV occupies ≥ 50% of the area of the entire lesion) at the initial visit as determined by a fluorescein angiogram (CPT code 92235). Subsequent follow-up visits will require a fluorescein angiogram prior to treatment. There are no requirements regarding visual acuity, lesion size, and number of retreatments.

50-4 GRAVLEE JET WASHER

The Gravlee Jet Washer is a sterile, disposable, diagnostic device for detecting endometrial cancer. The use of this device is indicated where the patient exhibits clinical symptoms or signs suggestive of endometrial disease, such as irregular or heavy vaginal bleeding.

Program payment cannot be made for the washer or the related diagnostic services when furnished in connection with the examination of an asymptomatic patient. Payment for routine physical checkups is precluded under the statute.

(See §1862(a)(7) of the Act.) (See Intermediary Manual, §3157 and Carriers Manual, §2320.)

50-10 VABRA ASPIRATOR

The VABRA aspirator is a sterile, disposable, vacuum aspirator which is used to collect uterine tissue for study to detect endometrial carcinoma. The use of this device is indicated where the patient exhibits clinical symptoms or signs suggestive of endometrial disease, such as irregular or heavy vaginal bleeding.

Program payment cannot be made for the aspirator or the related diagnostic services when furnished in connection with the examination of an asymptomatic patient. Payment for routine physical checkups is precluded under the statute (§1862(a)(7) of the Act).

Cross-reference: Intermediary Manual, §3157; Carriers Manual §2320; §50-4

50-15 ELECTROCARDIOGRAPHIC SERVICES

Reimbursement may be made under Part B for electrocardiographic (EKG) services rendered by a physician or incident to his/her services or by an approved laboratory or an approved supplier of portable X-ray services. Since there is no coverage for EKG services of any type rendered on a screening basis or as part of a routine examination, the claim must indicate the signs and symptoms or other clinical reason necessitating the services.

A separate charge by an attending or consulting physician for EKG interpretation is allowed only when it is the normal practice to make such charge in addition to the regular office visit charge. No payment is made for EKG interpretations by individuals other than physicians.

On a claim involving EKG services furnished by a laboratory or a portable X-ray supplier, identify the physician ordering the service and, when the charge includes both the taking of the tracing and its interpretation, include the identity of the physician making the interpretation. No separate bill for the services of a physician is paid unless it is clear that he/she was the patient's attending physician or was acting as a consulting physician. The taking of an EKG in an emergency, i.e., when the patient is or may be experiencing what is commonly referred to as a heart attack, is covered as a laboratory service or a diagnostic service by a portable X-ray supplier only when the evidence shows that a physician was in attendance at the time the service was performed or immediately thereafter.

Where EKG services are rendered in the patient's home and the laboratory's or portable X-ray supplier's charge is higher than that imposed for the same service when performed in the laboratory or portable X-ray supplier's office, the medical need for home service should be documented. In the absence of such justification, reimbursement for the service if otherwise medically necessary should be based on the reasonable charge applicable when performed in the laboratory or X-ray supplier's office.

The documentation required in the various situations mentioned above must be furnished not only when the laboratory or portable X-ray supplier bills the patient or carrier for its service, but also when such a facility bills the attending physician who, in turn, bills the patient or carrier for the EKG services. (In addition to the evidence required to document the claim, the laboratory or portable X-ray supplier must maintain in its records the referring physician's <u>written order and the identity of the employee taking the tracing.)</u>

Long Term EKG Monitoring, also referred to as long-term EKG recording, Holter recording, or dynamic electrocardiography, is a diagnostic procedure which provides a continuous record of the electrocardiographic activity of a patient's heart while he is engaged in his daily activities.

The basic components of the long-term EKG monitoring systems are a sensing element, the design of which may provide either for the recording of electrocardiographic information on magnetic tape or for detecting significant variations in rate or rhythm as they occur, and a component for either graphically recording the electrocardiographic data or for visual or computer assisted analysis of the information recorded on magnetic tape. The long-term EKG permits the examination in the ambulant or potentially ambulant patient of as many as 70,000 heartbeats in a 12-hour recording while the standard EKG which is obtained in the recumbent position, yields information on only 50 to 60 cardiac cycles and provides only a limited data base on which diagnostic judgments may be made.

Many patients with cardiac arrhythmias are unaware of the presence of an irregularity in heart rhythm. Due to the transient nature of many arrhythmias and the short intervals in which the rhythm of the heart is observed by conventional standard EKG techniques, the offending arrhythmias can go undetected. With the extended examination provided by the long-term EKG, the physician is able not only to detect but also to classify various types of rhythm disturbances and waveform abnormalities and note the frequency of their occurrence. The knowledge of the reaction of the heart to daily activities with respect to rhythm, rate, conduction disturbances, and changes are of great assistance in directing proper therapy and this modality is valuable in both inpatient and outpatient diagnosis and therapy. Long-term monitoring of ambulant or potentially ambulant inpatients provides significant potential for reducing the length of stay for post-coronary infarct patients in the intensive care setting and may result in earlier discharge from the hospital with greater assurance of safety to the patients. The indications for the use of this technique, noted below, are similar for both inpatients and outpatients.

The long-term EKG has proven effective in detecting transient episodes of cardiac dysrhythmia and in permitting the correlation of these episodes with cardiovascular symptomatology. It is also useful for patients who have symptoms of obscure etiology suggestive of cardiac arrhythmia. Examples of such symptoms include palpitations, chest pain, dizziness, light-headedness, near syncope, syncope, transient ischemic episodes, dyspnea, and shortness of breath.

This technique would also be appropriate at the time of institution of any arrhythmic drug therapy and may be performed during the course of therapy to evaluate response. It is also appropriate for evaluating a change of dosage and may be indicated shortly before and after the discontinuation of anti-arrhythmic medication. The therapeutic response to a drug whose duration of action and peak of effectiveness is defined in hours cannot be properly assessed by examining 30-40 cycles on a standard EKG rhythm strip. The knowledge that all patients placed on anti-arrhythmic medication do not respond to therapy and the known toxicity of anti-arrhythmic agents clearly indicate that proper assessment should be made on an individual basis to determine whether medication should be continued and at what dosage level.

The long-term EKG is also valuable in the assessment of patients with coronary artery disease. It enables the documentation of etiology of such symptoms as chest pain and shortness of breath. Since the standard EKG is often normal during the intervals between the episodes of precordial pain, it is essential to obtain EKG information while the symptoms are occurring. The long-term EKG has enabled the correlation of chest symptoms with the objective evidence of ST-segment abnormalities. It is appropriate for patients who are recovering from an acute myocardial infarction or coronary insufficiency before and after discharge from the hospital, since it is impossible to predict which of these patients is subject to ventricular arrhythmias on the basis of the presence or absence of rhythm disturbances during the period of initial coronary care. The long-term EKG enables the physician to identify patients who are at a higher risk of dying suddenly in the period following an acute myocardial infarction. It may also be reasonable and necessary where the high-risk patient with known cardiovascular disease advances to a substantially higher level of activity which might trigger increased or new types of arrhythmias necessitating treatment. Such a high-risk case would be one in which there is documentation that acute phase arrhythmias have not totally disappeared during the period of convalescence.

In view of recent developments in cardiac pacemaker monitoring techniques (see CIA 50-1), the use of the long-term EKG for routine assessment of pacemaker function can no longer be justified. Its use for the patient with an internal pacemaker would be covered only when he has symptoms suggestive of arrhythmia not revealed by the standard EKG or rhythm strip.

These guidelines are intended as a general outline of the circumstances under which the use of this diagnostic procedure would be warranted. Each patient receiving a long-term EKG should be evaluated completely, prior to performance of this diagnostic study. A complete history and physical examination should be obtained and the indications for use of the long-term EKG should be reviewed by the referring physician.

The performance of a long-term EKG does not necessarily require the prior performance of a standard EKG. Nor does the demonstration of a normal standard EKG preclude the need for a long- term EKG. Finally, the demonstration of an abnormal standard EKG does not obviate the need for a long-term EKG if there is suspicion that the dysrhythmia is transient in nature.

A period of recording of up to 24 hours would normally be adequate to detect most transient arrhythmias and provide essential diagnostic information. The medical necessity for longer periods of monitoring must be documented.

Medical documentation for adjudicating claims for the use of the long-term EKG should be similar to other EKG services, X-ray services, and laboratory procedures. Generally, a statement of the diagnostic impression of the referring physician with an indication of the patient's relevant signs and symptoms should be sufficient for purposes of making a determination regarding the reasonableness and medical necessity for the use of this procedure. However, the intermediaries or carriers should require whatever additional documentation their medical consultants deem necessary to properly adjudicate the individual claim where the information submitted is not adequate.

It should be noted that the recording device furnished to the patient is simply one component of the diagnostic system and a separate charge for it will not be recognized under the durable medical equipment benefit.

Patient-Activated EKG Recorders, distributed under a variety of brand names, permit the patient to record an EKG upon manifestation of symptoms, or in response to a physician's order (e.g., immediately following strong exertion).Most such devices also permit the patient to simultaneously voice-record in order to describe symptoms and/or activity. In addition, some of these devices permit transtelephonic transmission of the recording to a physician's office, clinic, hospital, etc., having a decoder/recorder for review and analysis, thus eliminating the need to physically transport the tape. Some of these devices also permit a "time sampling" mode of operation. However, the "time sampling" mode is not covered—only the patient-activated mode of operation, when used for the indications described below, is covered at this time.

Services in connection with patient-activated EKG recorders are covered when used as an alternative to the long-term EKG monitoring (described above) for similar indications--detecting and characterizing symptomatic arrhythmias, regulation of anti-arrhythmic drug therapy, etc. Like long- term EKG monitoring, use of these devices is covered for evaluating patients with symptoms of obscure etiology suggestive of cardiac arrhythmia such as palpitations, chest pain, dizziness, lightheadedness, near syncope, syncope, transient ischemic episodes, dyspnea and shortness of breath.

As with long-term EKG monitors, patient-activated EKG recorders may be useful for both inpatient and outpatient diagnosis and therapy. While useful for assessing some post-coronary infarct patients in the hospital setting, these devices should not, however, be covered for outpatient monitoring of recently discharged post-infarct patients.

Computer Analyzed Electrocardiograms.—Computer interpretation of EKG's is recognized as a valid and effective technique which will improve the quality and availability of cardiology services. Reimbursement may be made for such computer service when furnished in the setting and under the circumstances required for coverage of other electrocardiographic services. Where either a laboratory's or a portable x-ray supplier's charge for EKG services includes the physician review and certification of the printout as well as the computer interpretation, the certifying physician must be identified on the HCFA-1490 before the entire charge can be considered a reimbursable charge. Where the laboratory's (or portable x-ray supplier's) reviewing physician is not identified, the carrier should conclude that no professional component is involved and make its charge determination accordingly. If the supplying laboratory (or portable x-ray supplier when supplied by such a facility) does not include professional review and certification of the hard copy, a charge by the patient's physician may be recognized for the service. In any case the charge for the physician component should be substantially less than that for physician interpretation of the conventional EKG tracing in view of markedly reduced demand on the physician's time where computer interpretation is involved.

Considering the unit cost reduction expected of this innovation, the total charge for the complete EKG service (taking of tracing and interpretation) when computer interpretation is employed should never exceed that considered reasonable for the service when physician interpretation is involved.

Transtelephonic Electrocardiographic Transmissions (Formerly Referred to as EKG Telephone Reporter Systems).—Effective for services furnished on and after March 1, 1980, coverage is extended to include the use of transtelephonic electrocardiographic (EKG) transmissions as a diagnostic service for the indications described below, when performed with equipment meeting the standards described below, subject to the limitations and conditions specified below. Coverage is further limited to the amounts payable with respect to the physician's service in interpreting the results of such transmissions, including charges for rental of the equipment. The device used by the beneficiary is part of a total diagnostic system and is not considered durable medical equipment.

1. Covered Uses.—The use of transtelephonic EKGs is covered for the following uses:

    a. To detect, characterize, and document symptomatic transient arrhythmias;
    b. To overcome problems in regulating antiarrhythmic drug dosage;
    c. To carry out early posthospital monitoring of patients discharged after myocardial infarction; (only if 24-hour coverage is provided, see 4. below).

Since cardiology is a rapidly changing field, some uses other than those specified above may be covered if, in the judgment of the contractor's medical consultants, such a use was justifiable in the particular case. The enumerated uses above represent uses for which a firm coverage determination has been made, and for which contractors may make payment without extensive claims development or review.

2. Specifications for Devices—The devices used by the patient are highly portable (usually pocket-sized) and detect and convert the normal EKG signal so that it can be transmitted via ordinary telephone apparatus to a receiving station. At the receiving end, the signal is decoded and transcribed into a conventional EKG. There are numerous devices available which transmit EKG readings in this fashion. For purposes of Medicare coverage, however, the transmitting devices must meet at least the following criteria:

    a. They must be capable of transmitting EKG Leads, I, II, or III;
    b. These lead transmissions must be sufficiently comparable to readings obtained by a conventional EKG to permit proper interpretation of abnormal cardiac rhythms.

3. Potential for Abuse - Need for Screening Guidelines.--While the use of these devices may often compare favorably with more costly alternatives, this is the case only where the information they contribute is actively utilized by a knowledgeable practitioner as part of overall medical management of the patient. Consequently, it is vital that contractors be aware of the potential for abuse of these devices, and adopt necessary screening and physician education policies to detect and halt potentially abusive situations. For example, use of these devices to diagnose and treat suspected arrhythmias as a routine substitute for more conventional methods of diagnosis, such as a careful history, physical

examination, and standard EKG and rhythm strip would not be appropriate. Moreover, contractors should require written justification for use of such devices in excess of 30 consecutive days in cases involving detection of transient arrhythmias.

Contractors may find it useful to review claims for these devices with a view toward detecting patterns of practice which may be useful in developing schedules which may be adopted for screening such claims in the future.

4. Twenty-four Hour Coverage.—No payment may be made for the use of these devices to carry out early posthospital monitoring of patients discharged after myocardial infarction unless provision is made for 24 hour coverage in the manner described below.

Twenty-four hour coverage means that there must be, at the monitoring site (or sites) an experienced EKG technician receiving calls; tape recording devices do not meet this requirement. Further, such technicians should have immediate access to a physician, and have been instructed in when and how to contact available facilities to assist the patient in case of emergencies.

Cross-reference: HCFA-Pub. 13-3, §§3101.5, 3110, 3112.3, HCFA-Pub. 14-3, §§2070, 2255, 2050.1

50-20 DIAGNOSTIC PAP SMEARS (Effective for services performed on and after May 15, 1978)

A diagnostic pap smear and related medically necessary services are covered under Medicare Part B when ordered by a physician under one of the following conditions:

*   Previous cancer of the cervix, uterus, or vagina that has been or is presently being treated;
*   Previous abnormal pap smear;
*   Any abnormal findings of the vagina, cervix, uterus, ovaries, or adnexa;
*   Any significant complaint by the patient referable to the female reproductive system; or
*   Any signs or symptoms that might in the physician's judgment reasonably be related to a gynecologic disorder.

In respect to the last bullet, the contractor's medical staff must determine whether in a particular case a previous malignancy at another site is an indication for a diagnostic pap smear or whether the test must be considered a screening pap smear as described in §50-20.1.

Use the following CPT codes for indicating diagnostic pap smears:

*   88150 Cytopathology, smears, cervical or vaginal (e.g., Papanicolaou), up to three smears; screening by technician under physician supervision; or
*   88151 Cytopathology, smears, cervical or vaginal (e.g., Papanicolaou), up to three smears; requiring interpretation by physician.

50-20.1 SCREENING PAP SMEARS AND PELVIC EXAMINATIONS FOR EARLY DETECTION OF CERVICAL OR VAGINAL CANCER

(For screening pap smears, effective for services performed on or after July 1, 1990. For pelvic examinations including clinical breast examination, effective for services furnished on or after January 1, 1998.)

A screening pap smear (use HCPCS code P3000 Screening Papanicolaou smear, cervical or vaginal, up to three smears; by technician under physician supervision or P3001 Screening Papanicolaou smear, cervical or vaginal, up to three smears requiring interpretation by physician). (Use HCPCS codes G0123 Screening Cytopathology, cervical or vaginal (any reporting system), collected in preservative fluid, automated thin layer preparation, screening by cytotechnologist under physician supervision or G0124 Screening Cytopathology, cervical or vaginal (any reporting system) collected in preservative fluid, automated thin layer preparation, requiring interpretation by physician) and related medically necessary services provided to a woman for the early detection of cervical cancer (including collection of the sample of cells and a physician's interpretation of the test results) and pelvic examination (including clinical breast examination) (use HCPCS code G0101 cervical or vaginal cancer screening; pelvic and clinical breast examination) are covered under Medicare Part B when ordered by a physician (or authorized practitioner) under one of the following conditions:

- She has not had such a test during the preceding 3 years or is a woman of childbearing age (§1861(nn) of the Act).
- There is evidence (on the basis of her medical history or other findings) that she is at high risk of developing cervical cancer and her physician (or authorized practitioner) recommends that she have the test performed more frequently than every 3 years.

High risk factors for cervical and vaginal cancer are:

- Early onset of sexual activity (under 16 years of age)
- Multiple sexual partners (five or more in a lifetime)
- History of sexually transmitted disease (including HIV infection)
- Fewer than three negative or any pap smears within the previous 7 years; and
- DES (diethylstilbestrol) - exposed daughters of women who took DES during pregnancy.

NOTE: Claims for pap smears must indicate the beneficiary's low or high risk status by including the appropriate ICD-9-CM on the line item (Item 24E of the HCFA-1500).

- V76.2, *special screening for malignant neoplasms of the cervix,* indicates low risk; and
- V15.89, *other specified personal history presenting hazards to health,* indicates high risk.

If pap smear or pelvic exam claims do not point to one of these diagnosis codes, the claim will reject in the Common Working File. Claims can contain up to four diagnosis codes, but the one pointed to on the line item must be either V76.2 or V15.89.

Definitions:

A woman as described in §1861(nn) of the Act is a woman who is of childbearing age and has had a pap smear test during any of the preceding 3 years that indicated the presence of cervical or vaginal cancer or other abnormality, or is at high risk of developing cervical or vaginal cancer.

A woman of childbearing age is one who is premenopausal and has been determined by a physician or other qualified practitioner to be of childbearing age, based upon the medical history or other findings.

Other qualified practitioner", as defined in 42 CFR 410.56(a) includes a certified nurse midwife (as defined in §1861(gg) of the Act), or a physician assistant, nurse practitioner, or clinical nurse specialist (as defined in §1861(aa) of the Act) who is authorized under State law to perform the examination.

Screening Pelvic Examination:

Section 4102 of the Balanced Budget Act of 1997 provides for coverage of screening pelvic examinations (including a clinical breast examination) for all female beneficiaries, effective January 1, 1998, subject to certain frequency and other limitations. A screening pelvic examination (including a clinical breast examination) should include at least seven of the following eleven elements:

- Inspection and palpation of breasts for masses or lumps, tenderness, symmetry, or nipple discharge.
- Digital rectal examination including sphincter tone, presence of hemorrhoids, and rectal masses.

Pelvic examination (with or without specimen collection for smears and cultures) including:

- External genitalia (for example, general appearance, hair distribution, or lesions).
- Urethral meatus (for example, size, location, lesions, or prolapse).
- Urethra (for example, masses, tenderness, or scarring).
- Bladder (for example, fullness, masses, or tenderness).
- Vagina (for example, general appearance, estrogen effect, discharge lesions, pelvic support, cystocele, or rectocele).
- Cervix (for example, general appearance, lesions, or discharge).
- Uterus (for example, size, contour, position, mobility, tenderness, consistency, descent, or support).
- Adnexa/parametria (for example, masses, tenderness, organomegaly, or nodularity).
- Anus and perineum.

This description is from *Documentation Guidelines for Evaluation and Management Services*, published in May 1997 and was developed by the Health Care Financing Administration and the American Medical Association.

50-42 AMBULATORY BLOOD PRESSURE MONITORING

Ambulatory blood pressure monitoring (ABPM) involves the use of a non-invasive device which is used to measure blood pressure in 24-hour cycles. These 24-hour measurements are stored in the device and are later interpreted by the physician. ABPM must be performed for at least 24 hours to meet coverage criteria.

ABPM is only covered for those patients with suspected white coat hypertension. Suspected white coat hypertension is defined as 1) office blood pressure >140/90 mm Hg on at least three separate clinic/office visits with two separate measurements made at each visit; 2) at least two documented blood pressure measurements taken outside the office which are <140/90 mm Hg; and 3) no evidence of end-organ damage. The information obtained by ABPM is necessary in order to determine the appropriate management of the patient. ABPM is not covered for any other uses. In the rare circumstance that ABPM needs to be performed more than once in a patient, the qualifying criteria described above must be met for each subsequent ABPM test.

For those patients that undergo ABPM and have an ambulatory blood pressure of <135/85 with no evidence of end-organ damage, it is likely that their cardiovascular risk is similar to that of normotensives. They should be followed over time. Patients for which ABPM demonstrates a blood pressure of >135/85 may be at increased cardiovascular risk, and a physician may wish to consider antihypertensive therapy.

50-56 HOME PROTHROMBIN TIME INTERNATIONAL NORMALIZED RATIO (INR) MONITORING FOR ANTICOAGULATION MANAGEMENT

Use of the International Normalized Ratio (INR) allows physicians to determine the level of anticoagulation in a patient independent of the laboratory reagents used. The INR is the ratio of the patient's prothrombin time compared to the mean prothrombin time for a group of normal individuals. Maintaining patients within the therapeutic range minimizes adverse events associated with inadequate or excessive anticoagulation such as serious bleeding or thromboembolic events.

Patient self-testing and self-management through the use of a home INR monitor may be used to improve the time in therapeutic rate (TTR) for select groups of patients. Increased TTR leads to improved clinical outcomes and reductions in thromboembolic and hemorrhagic events. Home prothrombin monitoring with the use of INR devices is covered only for patients with mechanical heart valves. The monitor and the home testing must be prescribed by a treating physician as provided at 42 C.F.R. 410.32 (a) and the following requirements must be met:

1. The patient must have been anticoagulated for at least three months prior to use of the home INR device;

2. The patient must undergo an educational program on anticoagulation management and the use of the device prior to its use in the home; and

3. Self-testing with the device should not occur more frequently than once a week.

55-1 WATER PURIFICATION AND SOFTENING SYSTEMS USED IN CONJUNCTION WITH HOME DIALYSIS

Water Purification Systems—Water used for home dialysis should be chemically free of heavy trace metals and/or organic contaminants which could be hazardous to the patient. It should also be as free of bacteria as possible but need not be biologically sterile. Since the characteristics of natural water supplies in most areas of the country are such that some type of water purification system is needed, such a system used in conjunction with a home dialysis (either peritoneal or hemodialysis) unit is covered under Medicare.

There are two types of water purification systems which will satisfy these requirements:

*   Deionization-The removal of organic substances, mineral salts of magnesium and calcium (causing hardness), compounds of fluoride and chloride from tap water using the process of filtration and ion exchange; or
*   Reverse Osmosis-The process used to remove impurities from tap water utilizing pressure to force water through a porous membrane.

Use of both a deionization unit and reverse osmosis unit in series, theoretically to provide the advantages of both systems, has been determined medically unnecessary since either system can provide water which is both chemically and bacteriologically pure enough for acceptable use in home dialysis. In addition, spare deionization tanks are not covered since they are essentially a precautionary supply rather than a current requirement for treatment of the patient. Activated carbon filters used as a component of water purification systems to remove unsafe concentrations of chlorine and chloramines are covered when prescribed by a physician.

Water Softening System.-Except as indicated below, a water softening system used in conjunction with home dialysis is excluded from coverage under Medicare as not being reasonable and necessary within the meaning of S1862(a)(1) of the law. Such a system, in conjunction with a home dialysis unit, does not adequately remove the hazardous heavy metal contaminants (such as arsenic) which may be present in trace amounts.

A water softening system may be covered when used to pretreat water to be purified by a reverse osmosis (RO) unit for home dialysis where:

- The manufacturer of the RO unit has set standards for the quality of water entering the RO (e.g., the water to be purified by the RO must be of a certain quality if the unit is to perform as intended);

- The patients water is demonstrated to be of a lesser quality than required; and

- The softener is used only to soften water entering the RO unit, and thus, used only for dialysis. (The softener need not actually be built into the RO unit, but must be an integral part of the dialysis system.)

- Developing Need When a Water Softening System is Replaced with a Water Purification Unit in an Existing Home Dialysis System.-The medical necessity of water purification units must be care fully developed when they replace water softening systems in existing home dialysis systems. A purification system may be ordered under these circumstances for a number of reasons. For example, changes in the medical community's opinions regarding the quality of water necessary for safe dialysis may lead the physician to decide the quality of water previously used should be improved, or the water quality itself may have deteriorated. Patients may have dialyzed using only an existing water softener previous to Medicare ESRD coverage because of inability to pay for a purification system. On the other hand, in some cases, the installation of a purification system is not medically necessary. Thus, when such a case comes to your attention, ask the physician to furnish the reason for the changes. Supporting documentation, such as the supplier's recommendations or water analysis, may be required. All such cases should be reviewed by your medical consultants.

Cross-reference: Intermediary Manual, SS3113, 3643 (item ic); Carriers Manual, SS2100, 2100.2 2130, 2105 (item ic); Hospital Manual, S235.

55-2 PERIDEX CAPD FILTER SET -- NOT COVERED

The Peridex Filter Set is used by home continuous ambulatory peritoneal dialysis (CAPD) patients. The Peridex Filter Set is designed to provide sterile filtration during infusion of the dialysis solution in a beneficiary's peritoneal cavity; included in the filter set is a bacterial filter designed to block peritonitis-causing organisms and thus reduce the incidence of peritonitis.

Based upon advice of our medical consultants, we have determined that the Peridex CAPD Filter Set cannot be covered at this time by Medicare because it has not yet been shown to be safe and effective in preventing peritonitis.

60-3   WHITE CANE FOR USE BY A BLIND PERSON—NOT COVERED

A white cane for use by a blind person is more an identifying and self-help device rather than an item which makes a meaningful contribution in the treatment of an illness or injury.

60-4 HOME USE OF OXYGEN

A. General.—Medicare coverage of home oxygen and oxygen equipment under the durable medical equipment (DME) benefit (see §1861(s)(6)of the Act) is considered reasonable and necessary only for patients with significant hypoxemia who meet the medical documentation, laboratory evidence, and health conditions specified in subsections B, C, and D. This section also includes special coverage criteria for portable oxygen systems. Finally, a statement on the absence of coverage of the professional services of a respiratory therapist under the DME benefit is included in subsection F.

B. Medical documentation.—Initial claims for oxygen services must include a completed Form HCFA-484 (Certificate of Medical Necessity: Oxygen)to establish whether coverage criteria are met and to ensure that the oxygen services provided are consistent with the physician's prescription or other medical documentation. The treating physician's prescription or other medical documentation must indicate that other forms of treatment (e.g., medical and physical therapy directed at secretions, bronchospasm and infection) have been tried, have not been sufficiently successful, and oxygen therapy is still required. While there is no substitute for oxygen therapy, each patient must receive optimum therapy before long-term home oxygen therapy is ordered. Use Form HCFA-484 for recertifications. (See Medicare Carriers Manual §3312 for completion of Form HCFA-484.)

The medical and prescription information in section B of Form HCFA-484 can be completed only by the treating physician, the physician's employee, or another clinician (e.g., nurse, respiratory therapist, etc.) as long as that person is not the DME supplier. Although hospital discharge coordinators and medical social workers may assist in arranging for physician-prescribed home oxygen, they do not have the authority to prescribe the services. Suppliers may not enter this information. While this section may be completed by nonphysician clinician or a physician employee, it must be reviewed and the form HCFA-484 signed by the attending physician.

A physician's certification of medical necessity for oxygen equipment must include the results of specific testing before coverage can be determined.

Claims for oxygen must also be supported by medical documentation in the patient's record. Separate documentation is used with electronic billing. (See Medicare Carriers Manual, Part 3, §4105.5.) This documentation may be in the form of a prescription written by the patient's attending physician who has recently examined the patient (normally within a month of the start of therapy) and must specify:

- A diagnosis of the disease requiring home use of oxygen;
- The oxygen flow rate; and

An estimate of the frequency, duration of use (e.g., 2 liters per minute, 10 minutes per hour, 12 hours per day), and duration of need (e.g., 6 months or lifetime).
NOTE: A prescription for "Oxygen PRN" or "Oxygen as needed" does not meet this last requirement. Neither provides any basis for determining if the amount of oxygen is reasonable and necessary for the patient.

A member of the carrier's medical staff should review all claims with oxygen flow rates of more than 4 liters per minute before payment can be made.

The attending physician specifies the type of oxygen delivery system to be used (i.e., gas, liquid, or concentrator) by signing the completed form HCFA-484. In addition the supplier or physician may use the space in section C for written confirmation of additional details of the physician's order. The additional order information contained in section C may include the means of oxygen delivery (mask, nasal, cannula, etc.), the specifics of varying flow rates, and/or the noncontinuous use of oxygen as appropriate. The physician confirms this order information with their signature in section D.

New medical documentation written by the patient's attending physician must be submitted to the carrier in support of revised oxygen requirements when there has been a change in the patient's condition and need for oxygen therapy.

Carriers are required to conduct periodic, continuing medical necessity reviews on patients whose conditions warrant these reviews and on patients with indefinite or extended periods of necessity as described in Medicare Carriers Manual, Part 3, §4105.5. When indicated, carriers may also request documentation of the results of a repeat arterial blood gas or oximetry study.

NOTE: Section 4152 of OBRA 1990 requires earlier recertification and retesting of oxygen patients who begin coverage with an arterial blood gas result at or above a partial pressure of 55 or an arterial oxygen saturation percentage at or above 89. (See Medicare Carriers Manual §4105.5 for certification and retesting schedules.)

C. Laboratory Evidence.—Initial claims for oxygen therapy must also include the results of a blood gas study that has been ordered and evaluated by the attending physician. This is usually in the form of a measurement of the partial pressure of oxygen (PO2) in arterial blood. (See Medicare Carriers Manual, Part 3, §2070.1 for instructions on clinical laboratory tests.) A measurement of arterial oxygen saturation obtained by ear or pulse oximetry, however, is also acceptable when ordered and evaluated by the attending physician and performed under his or her supervision or when performed by a qualified provider or supplier of laboratory services. When the arterial blood gas and the oximetry studies are both used to document the need for home oxygen therapy and the results are conflicting, the arterial blood gas study is the preferred source of documenting medical need. A DME supplier is not considered a qualified provider or supplier of laboratory services for purposes of these guidelines. This prohibition does not extend to the results of blood gas test conducted by a hospital certified to do such tests. The conditions under which the laboratory tests are performed must be specified in writing and submitted with the initial claim, i.e., at rest, during exercise, or during sleep.

The preferred sources of laboratory evidence are existing physician and/or hospital records that reflect the patient's medical condition. Since it is expected that virtually all patients who qualify for home oxygen coverage for the first time under these guidelines have recently been discharged from a hospital where they submitted to arterial blood gas tests, the carrier needs to request that such test results be submitted in support of their initial claims for home oxygen. If more than one arterial blood gas test is performed during the patient's hospital stay, the test result obtained closest to, but no earlier than 2 days prior to the hospital discharge date is required as evidence of the need for home oxygen therapy.

For those patients whose initial oxygen prescription did not originate during a hospital stay, blood gas studies should be done while the patient is in the chronic stable state, i.e., not during a period of an acute illness or an exacerbation of their underlying disease."

Carriers may accept a attending physician's statement of recent hospital test results for a particular patient, when appropriate, in lieu of copies of actual hospital records.

A repeat arterial blood gas study is appropriate when evidence indicates that an oxygen recipient has undergone a major change in their condition relevant to home use of oxygen. If the carrier has reason to believe that there has been a major change in the patient's physical condition, it may ask for documentation of the results of another blood gas or oximetry study.

D. Health Conditions.—Coverage is available for patients with significant hypoxemia in the chronic stable state if: (1) the attending physician has determined that the patient has a health condition outlined in subsection D.1, (2) the patient meets the blood gas evidence requirements specified in subsection D.3, and (3) the patient has appropriately tried other alternative treatment measures without complete success. (See subsection B.)

1. Conditions for Which Oxygen Therapy May Be Covered.—

   - A severe lung disease, such as chronic obstructive pulmonary disease, diffuse interstitial lung disease, whether of known or unknown etiology; cystic fibrosis bronchiectasis; widespread pulmonary neoplasm; or
   - Hypoxia-related symptoms or findings that might be expected to improve with oxygen therapy. Examples of these symptoms and findings are pulmonary hypertension, recurring congestive heart failure due to chronic cor pulmonale, erythrocytosis, impairment of the cognitive process, nocturnal restlessness, and morning headache.

2. Conditions for Which Oxygen Therapy Is Not Covered.—

   - Angina pectoris in the absence of hypoxemia. This condition is generally not the result of a low oxygen level in the blood, and there are other preferred treatments;
   - Breathlessness without cor pulmonale or evidence of hypoxemia. Although intermittent oxygen use is sometimes prescribed to relieve this condition, it is potentially harmful and psychologically addicting;
   - Severe peripheral vascular disease resulting in clinically evident desaturation in one or more extremities. There is no evidence that increased PO_2 improves the oxygenation of tissues with impaired circulation; or
   - Terminal illnesses that do not affect the lungs.

3. Covered Blood Gas Values.—If the patient has a condition specified in subsection D.1, the carrier must review the medical documentation and laboratory evidence that has been submitted for a particular patient (see subsections B and C) and determine if coverage is available under one of the three group categories outlined below.

   a. Group I.—Except as modified in subsection d, coverage is provided for patients with significant hypoxemia evidenced by any of the following:

      (1) An arterial PO_2 at or below 55 mm Hg, or an arterial oxygen saturation at or below 88 percent, taken at rest, breathing room air.

      (2) An arterial PO_2 at or below 55 mm Hg, or an arterial oxygen saturation at or below 88 percent, taken during sleep for a patient who demonstrates an arterial PO_2 at or above 56 mm Hg, or an arterial oxygen saturation at or above 89 percent, while awake; or a greater than normal fall in oxygen level during sleep (a decrease in arterial PO_2 more than 10 mm Hg, or decrease in arterial oxygen saturation more than 5 percent) associated with symptoms or signs reasonably attributable to hypoxemia (e.g., impairment of cognitive

processes and nocturnal restlessness or insomnia). In either of these cases, coverage is provided only for use of oxygen during sleep, and then only one type of unit will be covered. Portable oxygen, therefore, would not be covered in this situation.

(3) An arterial PO2 at or below 55 mm Hg or an arterial oxygen saturation at or below 88 percent, taken during exercise for a patient who demonstrates an arterial PO2 at or above 56 mm Hg, or an arterial oxygen saturation at or above 89 percent, during the day while at rest. In this case, supplemental oxygen is provided for during exercise if there is evidence the use of oxygen improves the hypoxemia that was demonstrated during exercise when the patient was breathing room air.

b. Group II.—Except as modified in subsection d, coverage is available for patients whose arterial PO2 is 56-59 mm Hg or whose arterial blood oxygen saturation is 89 percent, if there is evidence of:

(1) Dependent edema suggesting congestive heart failure;

(2) Pulmonary hypertension or cor pulmonale, determined by measurement of pulmonary artery pressure, gated blood pool scan, echocardiogram, or "P" pulmonale on EKG (P wave greater than 3 mm in standard leads II, III, or AVFL; or

(3) Erythrocythemia with a hematocrit greater than 56 percent.

c. Group III.—Except as modified in subsection d, carriers must apply a rebuttable presumption that a home program of oxygen use is not medically necessary for patients with arterial PO2 levels at or above 60 mm Hg, or arterial blood oxygen saturation at or above 90 percent. In order for claims in this category to be reimbursed, the carrier's reviewing physician needs to review any documentation submitted in rebuttal of this presumption and grant specific approval of the claims. HCFA expects few claims to be approved for coverage in this category.

d. Variable Factors That May Affect Blood Gas Values.—In reviewing the arterial PO2 levels and the arterial oxygen saturation percentages specified in subsections D. 3. a, b and c, the carrier's medical staff must take into account variations in oxygen measurements that may result from such factors as the patient's age, the altitude level, or the patient's decreased oxygen carrying capacity.

E. Portable Oxygen Systems.—A patient meeting the requirements specified below may qualify for coverage of a portable oxygen system either (1) by itself or (2) to use in addition to a stationary oxygen system. A portable oxygen system is covered for a particular patient if:

- The claim meets the requirements specified in subsections A-D, as appropriate; and
- The medical documentation indicates that the patient is mobile in the home and would benefit from the use of a portable oxygen system in the home. Portable oxygen systems are not covered for patients who qualify for oxygen solely based on blood gas studies obtained during sleep.

F. Respiratory Therapists.—Respiratory therapists' services are not covered under the provisions for coverage of oxygen services under the Part B durable medical equipment benefit as outlined above. This benefit provides for coverage of home use of oxygen and oxygen equipment, but does not include a professional component in the delivery of such services.

(See §60-9; Intermediary Manual, Part 3, §3113ff; and Medicare Carriers Manual, Part 3, §2100ff.)

60-5 POWER-OPERATED VEHICLES THAT MAY BE USED AS WHEELCHAIRS

Power-operated vehicles that may be appropriately used as wheelchairs are covered under the durable medical equipment provision.

These vehicles have been appropriately used in the home setting for vocational rehabilitation and to improve the ability of chronically disabled persons to cope with normal domestic, vocational and social activities. They may be covered if a wheelchair is medically necessary and the patient is unable to operate a wheelchair manually.

A specialist in physical medicine, orthopedic surgery, neurology, or rheumatology must provide an evaluation of the patient's medical and physical condition and a prescription for the vehicle to assure that the patient requires the vehicle and is capable of using it safely. When an intermediary determines that such a specialist is not reasonably accessible, e.g., more than 1 day's round trip from the beneficiary's home, or the patient's condition precludes such travel, a prescription from the beneficiary's physician is acceptable.

The intermediary's medical staff reviews all claims for a power-operated vehicle, including the specialists' or other physicians' prescriptions and evaluations of the patient's medical and physical conditions, to insure that all coverage requirements are met. (See §60-9 and Intermediary Manual, Part 3, §3629.)

60-6 SPECIALLY SIZED WHEELCHAIRS

Payment may be made for a specially sized wheelchair even though it is more expensive than a standard wheelchair. For example, a narrow wheelchair may be required because of the narrow doorways of a patient's home or because of a patient's slender build. Such difference in the size of the wheelchair from the standard model is not considered a deluxe feature.

A physician's certification or prescription that a special size is needed is not required where you can determine from the information in file or other sources that a specially sized wheelchair (rather than a standard one) is needed to accommodate the wheelchair to the place of use or the physical size of the patient.

To determine the reasonable charge in these cases, use the criteria set out in Carriers Manual, §§5022, 5022.1, 5200, and 5205, as necessary.

Cross-reference: Intermediary Manual, §§3113.2C, 3642.1, 3643 (item 3); Carriers Manual, §§2100.2c, 2105, 4105.2, 5107; Hospital Manual, §§235.2c, 420.1 (item 13).

60-7 SELF-CONTAINED PACEMAKER MONITORS

Self-contained pacemaker monitors are accepted devices for monitoring cardiac pacemakers. Accordingly, program payment may be made for the rental or purchase of either of the following pacemaker monitors when it is prescribed by a physician for a patient with a cardiac pacemaker:

A. Digital Electronic Pacemaker Monitor.—This device provides the patient with an instantaneous digital readout of his pacemaker pulse rate. Use of this device does not involve professional services until there has been a change of five pulses (or more) per minute above or below the initial rate of the pacemaker; when such change occurs, the patient contacts his physician.

B. Audible/Visible Signal Pacemaker Monitor.—This device produces an audible and visible signal which indicates the pacemaker rate. Use of this device does not involve professional services until a change occurs in these signals; at such time, the patient contacts his physician.

NOTE: The design of the self-contained pacemaker monitor makes it possible for the patient to monitor his pacemaker periodically and minimizes the need for regular visits to the outpatient department of the provider.

Therefore, documentation of the medical necessity for pacemaker evaluation in the outpatient department of the provider should be obtained where such evaluation is employed in addition to the self-contained pacemaker monitor used by the patient in his home.

Cross-reference: §50-1

60-8   SEAT LIFT

Reimbursement may be made for the rental or purchase of a medically necessary seat lift when prescribed by a physician for a patient with severe arthritis of the hip or knee and patients with muscular dystrophy or other neuromuscular diseases when it has been determined the patient can benefit therapeutically from use of the device. In establishing medical necessity for the seat lift, the evidence must show that the item is included in the physician's course of treatment, that it is likely to effect improvement, or arrest or retard deterioration in the patient's condition, and that the severity of the condition is such that the alternative would be chair or bed confinement.

Coverage of seat lifts is limited to those types which operate smoothly, can be controlled by the patient, and effectively assist a patient in standing up and sitting down without other assistance. Excluded from coverage is the type of lift which operates by a spring release mechanism with a sudden, catapult-like motion and jolts the patient from a seated to a standing position. Limit the payment for units which incorporate a recliner feature along with the seat lift to the amount payable for a seat lift without this feature.

Cross-reference: Carriers Manual, § 5107

60-8   DURABLE MEDICAL EQUIPMENT REFERENCE LIST

The durable medical equipment (DME) list which follows is designed to facilitate your processing of DME claims. This section is designed to be used as a quick reference tool for determining the coverage status of certain pieces of DME and especially for those items which are commonly referred to by both brand and generic names. The information contained herein is applicable (where appropriate) to all DME coverage determinations discussed in the DME portion of this manual. The list is organized into two columns. The first column lists alphabetically various generic categories of equipment on which national coverage decisions have been made by HCFA; and the second column notes the coverage status of each equipment category.

In the case of equipment categories that have been determined by HCFA to be covered under the DME benefit, the list outlines the conditions of coverage that must be met if payment is to be allowed for the rental or purchase of the DME by a particular patient, or cross-refers to another section of the manual where the applicable coverage criteria are described in more detail. With respect to equipment categories that cannot be covered as DME, the list includes a brief explanation of why the equipment is not covered. This DME list will be updated periodically to reflect any additional national coverage decisions that HCFA may make with regard to other categories of equipment.

When you receive a claim for an item of equipment which does not appear to fall logically into any of the generic categories listed, you have the authority and responsibility for deciding whether those items are covered under the DME benefit. These decisions must be made by each contractor based on the advice of its medical consultants, taking into account:

- The general DME coverage instructions in the Carriers Manual, §2100ff and Intermediary Manual, §3113ff (see below for brief summary);
- Whether the item has been approved for marketing by the Food and Drug Administration (FDA) (see Carriers Manual, §2303.1 and Intermediary Manual, §3151.1) and is otherwise generally considered to be safe and effective for the purpose intended; and
- Whether the item is reasonable and necessary for the individual patient.
- As provided in the Carriers Manual, § 2100.1, and Intermediary Manual,
- §3113.1, the term DME is defined as equipment which
- Can withstand repeated use; i.e., could normally be rented, and used by successive patients;
- Is primarily and customarily used to serve a medical purpose;
- Generally is not useful to a person in the absence of illness or injury; and
- Is appropriate for use in a patient's home.

Durable Medical Equipment Reference List:

Item	Coverage Status
Air Cleaners	deny--environmental control equipment; not primarily medical in nature (§1861(n) of the Act)
Air Conditioners	deny--environmental control equipment; not primarily medical in nature (§1861(n) of the Act)
Air-Fluidized Bed	(See §60-19.)
Alternating Pressure Pads, and Mattresses and Lambs Wool Pads	covered if patient has, or is highly susceptible to, decubitus ulcers and patient's physician has specified that he will be supervising its use in connection with his course of treatment.
Audible/Visible Signal Pacemaker Monitor	(See Self-Contained Pacemaker Monitor.)
Augmentative Communication Device	(See Speech Generating Devices, §60-23.)
Bathtub Lifts	deny--convenience item; not primarily medical in nature (§1861(n) of the Act)
Bathtub Seats	deny--comfort or convenience item; hygienic equipment; not primarily medical in nature (§1861(n) of the Act)
Bead Bed	(See §60-19.)
Bed Baths (home type)	deny--hygienic equipment; not primarily medical in nature (§1861(n) of the Act)
Bed Lifter (bed elevator)	deny--not primarily medical in nature (§1861(n) of the Act.

Item	Coverage Status
Bed boards	deny--not primarily medical in nature (§1861(n) of the Act)
Bed Pans (autoclavable hospital type)	covered if patient is bed confined
Bed Side Rails	(See Hospital Beds, §60-l8.)
Beds-Lounge (power or manual)	deny--not a hospital bed; comfort or convenience item; not primarily medical in nature (§l861(n) of the Act)
Beds--Oscillating	deny--institutional equipment; inappropriate for home use
Bidet Toilet Seat	(See Toilet Seats.)
Blood Glucose Analyzer Reflectance Colorimeter	deny--unsuitable for home use (See §60-11.)
Blood Glucose Monitor	covered if patient meets certain conditions (See §60-11.)
Braille Teaching Texts	deny--educational equipment; not primarily medical in nature (§1861(n) of the Act)
Canes	covered if patient's condition impairs ambulation (See §60-3.)
Carafes	deny--convenience item; not primarily medical in nature (§l861(n) of the Act)
Catheters	deny--nonreusable disposable supply (§l861(n) of the Act)
Commodes	covered if patient is confined to bed or room. NOTE: The term "room confined" means that the patient's condition is such that leaving the room is medically contraindicated. The accessibility of bathroom facilities generally would not be a factor in this determination. However, confinement of a patient to his home in a case where there are no toilet facilities in the home may be equated to room confinement. Moreover, payment may also be made if a patient's medical condition confines him to a floor of his home and there is no bathroom located on that floor (See hospital beds in §60-18 for definition of "bed confinement".)
Communicator	(See §60-23, Speech Generating Device
Continuous Passive Motion	Continuous passive motion devices are devices covered for patients who have received a total knee replacement. To qualify for coverage, use of the device must commence within 2 days following surgery. In addition, coverage is limited to that portion of the three week period following surgery during which the device is used in the patient's home. There is insufficient evidence to justify coverage of these devices for longer periods of time or for other applications.
Continuous Positive Airway Pressure (CPAP)	(See §60-17.)
Crutches	covered if patient's condition impairs Ambulation
Cushion Lift Power Seat	(See Seat Lifts.)
Dehumidifiers (room or central heating system type)	deny--environmental control equipment; not primarily medical in nature (§l861(n) of the Act
Diathermy Machines (standard pulses wave types)	deny--inappropriate for home use (See and §35-41.)
Digital Electronic Pacemaker Monitor	(See Self-Contained Pacemaker Monitor.)
Disposable Sheets and Bags	deny--nonreusable disposable supplies (§l861(n) of the Act)

Item	Coverage Status
Elastic Stockings	deny--nonreusable supply; not rental-type items (§l861(n) of the Act)
Electric Air Cleaners	deny--(See Air Cleaners.) (§l861(n) of the Act)
Electric Hospital Beds	(See Hospital Beds §60-18.)
Electrical Stimulation for Wounds	deny--inappropriate for home use
Electrostatic Machines	deny--(See Air Cleaners and Air Conditioners.) (§l861(n) of the Act)
Elevators	deny--convenience item; not primarily medical in nature (§l861(n) of the Act)
Emesis Basins	deny--convenience item; not primarily medical in nature (§l861(n) of the Act)
Esophageal Dilator	deny--physician instrument; inappropriate for patient use
Exercise Equipment	deny--not primarily medical in nature (§l861(n) of the Act)
Fabric Supports	deny--nonreusable supplies; not rental-type it (§l861(n) of the Act)
Face Masks (oxygen)	covered if oxygen is covered (See § 60-4.)
Face Masks (surgical)	deny--nonreusable disposable items (§l861(n) of the Act)
Flowmeter	(See Medical Oxygen Regulators)
Fluidic Breathing Assister	(See IPPB Machines.)
Fomentation Device	(See Heating Pads.)
Gel Flotation Pads and Mattresses	(See Alternating Pressure Pads and Mattresses.)
Grab Bars	deny--self-help device; not primarily medical in nature (§l861(n) of the Act)
Heat and Massage Foam Cushion Pad	deny--not primarily medical in nature; personal comfort item (§§ 1861(n) and l862(a)(6) of the Act)
Heating and Cooling Plants	deny--environmental control equipment; not primarily medical in nature(§l861(n) of the Act)
Heating Pads	covered if the contractor's medical staff determines patient's medical condition is one for which the application of heat in the form of a heating pad is therapeutically effective.
Heat Lamps	covered if the contractor's medical staff determines patient's medical condition is one for which the application of heat in the form of a heat lamp is therapeutically effective.
Hospital Beds	(See § 60-18.)
Hot Packs	(See Heating Pads.)
Humidifiers (oxygen)	(See Oxygen Humidifiers.)
Humidifiers (room or central heating system types)	deny--environmental control equipment; not medical in nature (§l861(n) of the Act)
Hydraulic Lift	(See Patient Lifts.)
Incontinent Pads	deny--nonreusable supply; hygienic item (§ 1861(n) of the Act.)
Infusion Pumps	For external and implantable pumps, see §60-14. If the pump is used with an enteral or parenteral malnutritional therapy system, see §§65-10 - 65.10.2 0.2 for special coverage rules.
Injectors (hypodermic jet devices for injection of insulin	deny-- noncovered self-administered drug supply, §1861(s)(2)(A) of the Act)
IPPB Machines	covered if patient's ability to breathe is severely impaired

Item	Coverage Status
Iron Lungs	(See Ventilators.)
Irrigating Kit	deny--nonreusable supply; hygienic equipment (§1861(n) of the Act)
Lambs Wool Pads	covered under same conditions as alternating pressure pads and mattresses
Leotards	deny--(See Pressure Leotards.) (§1861(n)of the Act)
Lymphedema Pumps	covered (See §60-16.)(segmental and non-segmental therapy types)
Massage Devices	deny--personal comfort items; not primarily medical in nature (§§1861(n) and 1862(a)(6) of the Act)
Mattress	covered only where hospital bed is medically necessary (Separate Charge for replacement mattresses should not be allowed where hospital bed with mattress is rented.) (See §60-18.)
Medical Oxygen Regulators	covered if patient's ability to breathe is severely impaired (See §60-4.)
Mobile Geriatric Chair	(See Rolling Chairs.)
Motorized Wheelchairs	(See Wheelchairs (power operated).)
Muscle Stimulators	Covered for certain conditions (See §35-77.)
Nebulizers	covered if patient's ability to breathe is severely impaired
Oscillating Beds	deny--institutional equipment--inappropriate for home use
Over bed Tables	deny--convenience item; not primarily medical in nature (§1861(n) of the Act)
Oxygen	covered if the oxygen has been prescribed for use in connection with medically necessary durable medical equipment (See §60-4.)
Oxygen Humidifiers	covered if a medical humidifier has been prescribed for use in connection with medically necessary durable medical equipment for purposes of moisturizing oxygen (See §60-4.)
Oxygen Regulators (Medical)	(See Medical Oxygen Regulators.)
Oxygen Tents	(See § 60-4.)
Paraffin Bath Units (Portable)	(See Portable Paraffin Bath Units.)
Paraffin Bath Units (Standard)	deny--institutional equipment; inappropriate for home use
Parallel Bars	deny--support exercise equipment; primarily for institutional use; in the home setting other devices (e.g., a walker) satisfy the patient's need
Patient Lifts	covered if contractor's medical staff determines patient's condition is such that periodic movement is necessary to effect improvement or to arrest or retard deterioration in his condition.
Percussors	covered for mobilizing respiratory tract secretions in patients with chronic obstructive lung disease, chronic bronchitis, or emphysema, when patient or operator of powered percussor has received appropriate training by a physician or therapist, and no one competent to administer manual therapy is available.
Portable Oxygen Systems	1. Regulated (adjustable --covered under conditions specified in flow rate)§60-4. Refer all claims to medical staff for this determination. 2. Preset (flow rate --deny--emergency, first-aid, or not

Item	Coverage Status
	adjustable) precautionary equipment; essentially not therapeutic in nature
Portable Paraffin Bath Units	covered when the patient has undergone a successful trial period of paraffin therapy ordered by a physician and the patient's condition is expected to be relieved by long term use of this modality.
Portable Room Heaters	deny--environmental control equipment; not primarily medical in nature (§1861(n) of the Act)
Portable Whirlpool Pumps	deny--not primarily medical in nature; personal comfort items (§§1861(n) and 1862(a)(6) of the Act)
Postural Drainage Boards	covered if patient has a chronic pulmonary condition
Preset Portable Oxygen Units	deny--emergency, first-aid, or precautionary equipment; essentially not therapeutic in nature
Pressure Leotards	deny--nonreusable supply, not rental-type item (§1861(n) of the Act)
Pulse Tachometer	deny--not reasonable or necessary for monitoring pulse of homebound patient with or without a cardiac pacemaker
Quad-Canes	(See Walkers.)
Raised Toilet Seats	deny--convenience item; hygienic equipment; not primarily medical in nature (§1861(n) of the Act)
Reflectance Colorimeters	(See Blood Glucose Analyzers.)
Respirators	(See Ventilators.)
Rolling Chairs	covered if the contractor's medical staff determines that the patient's condition is such that there is a medical need for this item and it has been prescribed by the patient's physician in lieu of a wheelchair. Coverage is limited to those rollabout chairs having casters of at least 5 inches in diameter and specifically designed to meet the needs of ill, injured, or otherwise impaired individuals. Coverage is denied for the wide range of chairs with smaller casters as are found in general use in homes, offices, and institutions for many purposes not related to the care or treatment of ill or injured persons. This type is not primarily medical in nature. (§1861(n) of the Act)
Safety Roller	(See §60-15.)
Sauna Baths	deny--not primarily medical in nature; personal comfort items (§§1861(n) and (1862(a)(6) of the Act)
Seat Lift	covered under the conditions specified in §60-8. Refer all to medical staff for this determination.
Self-Contained Pacemaker Monitor	covered when prescribed by a physician for a patient with a cardiac pacemaker (See §§50-1C and 60-7.)
Sitz Bath	covered if the contractor's medical staff determines patient has an infection or injury of the perineal area and the item has been prescribed by the patient's physician as a part of his planned regimen of treatment in the patient's home.
Spare Tanks of Oxygen	deny--convenience or precautionary supply
Speech Teaching Machine	deny--education equipment; not primarily medical in nature (§1861(n) of the Act)
Stairway Elevators	deny--(See Elevators.) (§1861(n) of the Act)

Item	Coverage Status
Standing Table	deny--convenience item; not primarily medical in nature (§1861(n) of the Act)
Steam Packs	these packs are covered under the same condition as a heating pad (See Heating Pads.)
Suction Machine	covered if the contractor's medical staff determines that the machine specified in the claim is medically required and appropriate for home use without technical or professional supervision.
Support Hose	deny (See Fabric Supports.) (§1861(n) of the Act)
Surgical Leggings	deny--nonreusable supply; not rental-type item (§1861(n) of the Act)
Telephone Alert Systems	deny--these are emergency communications systems and do not serve a diagnostic or therapeutic purpose
Telephone Arms	deny--convenience item; not medical in nature (§1861(n) of the Act)
Toilet Seats	deny--not medical equipment (§1861(n)of the Act)
Traction Equipment	covered if patient has orthopedic impairment requiring traction equipment which prevents ambulation during the period of use (Consider covering devices usable during ambulation; e.g., cervical traction collar, under the brace provision)
Trapeze Bars	covered if patient is bed confined and the patient needs a trapeze bar to sit up because of respiratory condition, to change body position for other medical reasons, or to get in and out of bed.
Treadmill Exerciser	deny--exercise equipment; not primarily medical in nature(§1861(n) of the Act)
Ultraviolet Cabinet	covered for selected patients with generalized intractable psoriasis. Using appropriate consultation, the contractor should determine whether medical and other factors justify treatment at home rather than at alternative sites, e.g., outpatient department of a hospital.
Urinals (autoclavable hospital type)	covered if patient is bed confined
Vaporizers	covered if patient has a respiratory illness
Ventilators	covered for treatment of neuromuscular diseases, thoracic restrictive diseases, and chronic respiratory failure consequent to chronic obstructive pulmonary disease. Includes both positive and negative pressure types.
Walkers	covered if patient's condition impairs ambulation (See also §60-15.)
Water and Pressure Pads and Mattresses	(See Alternating Pressure Pads and Mattresses.)
Wheelchairs	covered if patient's condition is such that without the use of a wheelchair he would otherwise be bed or chair confined. An individual may qualify for a wheelchair and still be considered bed confined.
Wheelchairs (power operated) and wheelchairs with other special features	covered if patient's condition is such and that a wheelchair is medically necessary and the patient is unable to operate the wheelchair manually. Any claim involving a power wheelchair or a wheelchair with other special features should be referred for medical consultation since payment for the special features is

Item	Coverage Status
	limited to those which are medically required because of the patient's condition. (See §60-5 for power operated and §60-6 for specially sized wheelchairs.) NOTE: A power-operated vehicle that may appropriately be used as a wheelchair can be covered. (See §60-5 for coverage details.)
Whirlpool Bath Equipment	covered if patient is homebound and has a (standard) condition for which the whirlpool bath can be expected to provide substantial therapeutic benefit justifying its cost. Where patient is not homebound but has such a condition, payment is restricted to the cost of providing the services elsewhere; e.g., an outpatient department of a participating hospital, if that alternative is less costly. In all cases, refer claim to medical staff for a determination.
Whirlpool Pumps	deny--(See Portable Whirlpool Pumps.) (§l861(n) of the Act)

60-11 HOME BLOOD GLUCOSE MONITORS

There are several different types of blood glucose monitors that use reflectance meters to determine blood glucose levels. Medicare coverage of these devices varies, both with respect to the type of device and the medical condition of the patient for whom the device is prescribed.

Reflectance colorimeter devices used for measuring blood glucose levels in clinical settings are not covered as durable medical equipment for use in the home because their need for frequent professional re-calibration makes them unsuitable for home use. However, some types of blood glucose monitors which use a reflectance meter specifically designed for home use by diabetic patients may be covered as durable medical equipment, subject to the conditions and limitations described below.

Blood glucose monitors are meter devices that read color changes produced on specially treated reagent strips by glucose concentrations in the patient's blood. The patient, using a disposable sterile lancet, draws a drop of blood, places it on a reagent strip and, following instructions which may vary with the device used, inserts it into the device to obtain a reading. Lancets, reagent strips, and other supplies necessary for the proper functioning of the device are also covered for patients for whom the device is indicated. Home blood glucose monitors enable certain patients to better control their blood glucose levels by frequently checking and appropriately contacting their attending physician for advice and treatment. Studies indicate that the patient's ability to carefully follow proper procedures is critical to obtaining satisfactory results with these devices. In addition, the cost of the devices, with their supplies, limits economical use to patients who must make frequent checks of their blood glucose levels. Accordingly, coverage of home blood glucose monitors is limited to patients meeting the following conditions:

- The patient has been diagnosed as having diabetes;
- The patient's physician states that the patient is capable of being trained to use the particular device prescribed in an appropriate manner. In some cases, the patient may not be able to perform this function, but a responsible individual can be trained to use the equipment and monitor the patient to assure that the intended effect is achieved. This is permissible if the record is properly documented by the patient's physician; and
- The device is designed for home rather than clinical use.

There is also a blood glucose monitoring system designed especially for use by those with visual impairments. The monitors used in such systems are identical in terms of reliability and sensitivity to the standard blood glucose monitors described above. They differ by having such features as voice synthesizers, automatic timers, and specially designed arrangements of supplies and materials to enable the visually impaired to use the equipment without assistance.

These special blood glucose monitoring systems are covered under Medicare if the following conditions are met:

- The patient and device meet the three conditions listed above for coverage of standard home blood glucose monitors; and
- The patient's physician certifies that he or she has a visual impairment severe enough to require use of this special monitoring system.

The additional features and equipment of these special systems justify a higher reimbursement amount than allowed for standard blood glucose monitors. Separately identify claims for such devices and establish a separate reimbursement amount for them. For those carriers using HCPCS, the procedure code and definition is: E0609--Blood Glucose Monitor--with special features (e.g., voice synthesizers, automatic timer).

60-14 INFUSION PUMPS

The following indications for treatment using infusion pumps are covered under Medicare:

A. External Infusion Pumps.—

1. Iron Poisoning (Effective for Services Performed On or After 9/26/84).—When used in the administration of deferoxamine for the treatment of acute iron poisoning and iron overload, only external infusion pumps are covered.

2. Thromboembolic Disease (Effective for Services Performed On or After 9/26/84).—When used in the administration of heparin for the treatment of thromboembolic disease and/or pulmonary embolism, only external infusion pumps used in an institutional setting are covered.

3. Chemotherapy for Liver Cancer (Effective for Services Performed On or After 1/29/85).—The external chemotherapy infusion pump is covered when used in the treatment of primary hepatocellular carcinoma or colorectal cancer where this disease is unresectable or where the patient refuses surgical excision of the tumor.

4. Morphine for Intractable Cancer Pain (Effective for Services Performed On or After 4/22/85).— Morphine infusion via an external infusion pump is covered when used in the treatment of intractable pain caused by cancer (in either an inpatient or outpatient setting, including a hospice).

5. Continuous subcutaneous insulin infusion pumps (CSII) (Effective for Services Performed On or After 4/1/2000).—

An external infusion pump and related drugs/supplies are covered as medically necessary in the home setting in the following situation:

Treatment of Diabetes

In order to be covered, patients must meet criterion A or B:

(A) The patient has completed a comprehensive diabetes education program, and has been on a program of multiple daily injections of insulin (i.e. at least 3 injections per day), with frequent self-adjustments of insulin dose for at least 6 months prior to initiation of the insulin pump, and has documented frequency of glucose self-testing an average of at least 4 times per day during the 2 months prior to initiation of the insulin pump, and meets one or more of the following criteria while on the multiple daily injection regimen:

(1) Glycosylated hemoglobin level (HbAlc) > 7.0 percent
(2) History of recurring hypoglycemia
(3) Wide fluctuations in blood glucose before mealtime
(4) Dawn phenomenon with fasting blood sugars frequently Exceeding 200 mg/dl
(5) History of severe glycemic excursions

(B) The patient with diabetes has been on a pump prior to enrollment in Medicare and has documented frequency of glucose self-testing an average of at least 4 times per day during the month prior to Medicare enrollment.

Diabetes needs to be documented by a fasting C-peptide level that is less than or equal to 110 percent of the lower limit of normal of the laboratory's measurement method. (Effective for Services Performed on or after January 1, 2002.)

Continued coverage of the insulin pump would require that the patient has been seen and evaluated the treating physician at least every 3 months.

The pump must be ordered by and follow-up care of the patient must be managed by a physician who manages multiple patients with CSII and who works closely with a team including nurses, diabetes educators, and dietitians who are knowledgeable in the use of CSII.

6. Other uses of external infusion pumps are covered if the contractor's medical staff verifies the appropriateness of the therapy and of the prescribed pump for the individual patient.

NOTE: Payment may also be made for drugs necessary for the effective use of an external infusion pump as long as the drug being used with the pump is itself reasonable and necessary for the patient's treatment.

B. Implantable Infusion Pumps.—

1. Chemotherapy for Liver Cancer (Effective for Services Performed On or After 9/26/84).—The implantable infusion pump is covered for intra-arterial infusion of 5-FUdR for the treatment of liver cancer for patients with primary hepatocellular carcinoma or Duke's Class D colorectal cancer, in whom the metastases are limited to the liver, and where (1) the disease is unresectable or (2) where the patient refuses surgical excision of the tumor.

2. Anti-Spasmodic Drugs for Severe Spasticity.—An implantable infusion pump is covered when used to administer anti-spasmodic drugs intrathecally (e.g., baclofen) to treat chronic intractable spasticity in patients who have proven unresponsive to less invasive medical therapy as determined by the following criteria:

- As indicated by at least a 6-week trial, the patient cannot be maintained on noninvasive methods of spasm control, such as oral anti-spasmodic drugs, either because these methods fail to control adequately the spasticity or produce intolerable side effects, and
- Prior to pump implantation, the patient must have responded favorably to a trial intrathecal dose of the anti-spasmodic drug.

3. Opioid Drugs for Treatment of Chronic Intractable Pain.—An implantable infusion pump is covered when used to administer opioid drugs (e.g., morphine) intrathecally or epidurally for treatment of severe chronic intractable pain of malignant or nonmalignant origin in patients who have a life expectancy of at least 3 months and who have proven unresponsive to less invasive medical therapy as determined by the following criteria:

- The patient's history must indicate that he/she would not respond adequately to non-invasive methods of pain control, such as systemic opioids (including attempts to eliminate physical and behavioral abnormalities which may cause an exaggerated reaction to pain); and
- A preliminary trial of intraspinal opioid drug administration must be undertaken with a temporary intrathecal/epidural catheter to substantiate adequately acceptable pain relief and degree of side effects (including effects on the activities of daily living) and patient acceptance.

4. Coverage of Other Uses of Implanted Infusion Pumps .—Determinations may be made on coverage of other uses of implanted infusion pumps if the contractor's medical staff verifies that:

The drug is reasonable and necessary for the treatment of the individual patient;

- It is medically necessary that the drug be administered by an implanted infusion pump; and
- The FDA approved labeling for the pump must specify that the drug being administered and the purpose for which it is administered is an indicated use for the pump.

5. Implantation of Infusion Pump Is Contraindicated.—The implantation of an infusion pump is contraindicated in the following patients:

- Patients with a known allergy or hypersensitivity to the drug being used (e.g., oral baclofen, morphine, etc.);
- Patients who have an infection;
- Patients whose body size is insufficient to support the weight and bulk of the device; and
- Patients with other implanted programmable devices since crosstalk between devices may inadvertently change the prescription.

NOTE: Payment may also be made for drugs necessary for the effective use of an implantable infusion pump as long as the drug being used with the pump is itself reasonable and necessary for the patient's treatment.

The following indications for treatment using infusion pumps are not covered under Medicare:

A. External Infusion Pumps.—

1. Vancomycin (Effective for Services Beginning On or After September 1, 1996).—Medicare coverage of vancomycin as a durable medical equipment infusion pump benefit is not covered.

There is insufficient evidence to support the necessity of using an external infusion pump, instead of a disposable elastomeric pump or the gravity drip method, to administer vancomycin in a safe and appropriate manner.

B. Implantable Infusion Pump.—

1. Thromboembolic Disease (Effective for Services Performed On or After 9/26/84).—According to the Public Health Service, there is insufficient published clinical data to support the safety and effectiveness of the heparin implantable pump. Therefore, the use of an implantable infusion pump for infusion of heparin in the treatment of recurrent thromboembolic disease is not covered.
2. Diabetes—Implanted infusion pumps for the infusion of insulin to treat diabetes is not covered. The data do not demonstrate that the pump provides effective administration of insulin.

60-15 SAFETY ROLLER (Effective for Claims Adjudicated On or After 6/3/85)

"Safety roller" is the generic name applied to devices for patients who cannot use standard wheeled walkers. They may be appropriate, and therefore covered, for some patients who are obese, have severe neurological disorders, or restricted use of one hand, which makes it impossible to use a wheeled walker that does not have the sophisticated braking system found on safety rollers.

In order to assure that payment is not made for a safety roller when a less expensive standard wheeled walker would satisfy the patient's medical needs, carriers refer safety roller claims to their medical consultants. The medical consultant determines whether some or all of the features provided in a safety roller are necessary, and therefore covered and reimbursable. If it is determined that the patient could use a standard wheeled walker, the charge for the safety roller is reduced to the charge of a standard wheeled walker.

Some obese patients who could use a standard wheeled walker if their weight did not exceed the walker's strength and stability limits can have it reinforced and its wheel base expanded. Such modifications are routine mechanical adjustments and justify a moderate surcharge. In these cases the carrier reduces the charge for the safety roller to the charge for the standard wheeled walker plus the surcharge for modifications.

In the case of patients with medical documentation showing severe neurological disorders or restricted use of one hand which makes it impossible for them to use a wheeled walker that does not have a sophisticated braking system, a reasonable charge for the safety roller may be determined without relating it to the reasonable charge for a standard wheeled walker. (Such reasonable charge should be developed in accordance with the instructions in Medicare Carriers Manual §§5010 and 5205.)

Cross-reference: Carriers Manual §§2100ff., §60-9.

60-16 PNEUMATIC COMPRESSION DEVICES

Pneumatic compression devices consist of an inflatable garment for the arm or leg and an electrical pneumatic pump that fills the garment with compressed air. The garment is intermittently inflated and deflated with cycle times and pressures that vary between devices. Pneumatic devices are covered for the treatment of lymphedema or for the treatment of chronic venous insufficiency with venous stasis ulcers.

Lymphedema

Lymphedema is the swelling of subcutaneous tissues due to the accumulation of excessive lymph fluid. The accumulation of lymph fluid results from impairment to the normal clearing function of the lymphatic system and/or from an excessive production of lymph. Lymphedema is divided into two broad classes according to etiology. Primary lymphedema is a relatively uncommon, chronic condition which may be due to such causes as Milroy's Disease or congenital anomalies. Secondary lymphedema, which is much more common, results from the destruction of or damage to formerly functioning lymphatic channels, such as surgical removal of lymph nodes or post radiation fibrosis, among other causes.

Pneumatic compression devices are covered in the home setting for the treatment of lymphedema if the patient has undergone a four-week trial of conservative therapy and the treating physician determines that there has been no significant improvement or if significant symptoms remain after the trial. The trial of conservative therapy must include use of an appropriate compression bandage system or compression garment, exercise, and elevation of the limb. The garment may be prefabricated or custom-fabricated but must provide adequate graduated compression.

Chronic Venous Insufficiency with Venous Stasis Ulcers

Chronic venous insufficiency (CVI) of the lower extremities is a condition caused by abnormalities of the venous wall and valves, leading to obstruction or reflux of blood flow in the veins. Signs of CVI include hyperpigmentation, stasis dermatitis, chronic edema, and venous ulcers.

Pneumatic compression devices are covered in the home setting for the treatment of CVI of the lower extremities only if the patient has one or more venous stasis ulcer(s) which have failed to heal after a 6 month trial of conservative therapy directed by the treating physician. The trial of conservative therapy must include a compression bandage system or compression garment, appropriate dressings for the wound, exercise, and elevation of the limb.

General Coverage Criteria

Pneumatic compression devices are covered only when prescribed by a physician and when they are used with appropriate physician oversight, i.e., physician evaluation of the patient's condition to determine medical necessity of the device, assuring suitable instruction in the operation of the machine, a treatment plan defining the pressure to be used and the frequency and duration of use, and ongoing monitoring of use and response to treatment.

The determination by the physician of the medical necessity of a pneumatic compression device must include (1) the patient's diagnosis and prognosis; (2) symptoms and objective findings, including measurements which establish the severity of the condition; (3) the reason the device is required, including the treatments which have been tried and failed; and (4) the clinical response to an initial treatment with the device. The clinical response includes the change in pre-treatment measurements, ability to tolerate the treatment session and parameters, and ability of the patient (or caregiver) to apply the device for continued use in the home.

The only time that a segmented, calibrated gradient pneumatic compression device (HCPCS code E0652) would be covered is when the individual has unique characteristics that prevent them from receiving satisfactory pneumatic compression treatment using a nonsegmented device in conjunction with a segmented appliance or a segmented compression device without manual control of pressure in each chamber.

Cross-reference: §60-9.

60-17 CONTINUOUS POSITIVE AIRWAY PRESSURE (CPAP)

CPAP is a non-invasive technique for providing single levels of air pressure from a flow generator, via a nose mask, through the nares. The purpose is to prevent the collapse of the oropharyngeal walls and the obstruction of airflow during sleep, which occurs in obstructive sleep apnea (OSA).

Effective for services furnished between and including January 12, 1987 and March 31, 2002:

The diagnosis of OSA requires documentation of at least 30 episodes of apnea, each lasting a minimum of 10 seconds, during 6-7 hours of recorded sleep. The use of CPAP is covered under Medicare when used in adult patients with moderate or severe OSA for whom surgery is a likely alternative to CPAP.

Initial claims must be supported by medical documentation (separate documentation where electronic billing is used), such as a prescription written by the patient's attending physician, that specifies:

- a diagnosis of moderate or severe obstructive sleep apnea, and
- surgery is a likely alternative.

The claim must also certify that the documentation supporting a diagnosis of OSA (described above) is available.

Effective for services furnished on or after April 1, 2002:

The use of CPAP devices are covered under Medicare when ordered and prescribed by the licensed treating physician to be used in adult patients with OSA if either of the following criteria using the Apnea-Hypopnea Index (AHI) are met:

- AHI = 15 events per hour, or
- AHI = 5 and = 14 events per hour with documented symptoms of excessive daytime sleepiness, impaired cognition, mood disorders or insomnia, or documented hypertension, ischemic heart disease or history of stroke.

The AHI is equal to the average number of episodes of apnea and hypopnea per hour and must be based on a minimum of 2 hours of sleep recorded by polysomnography using actual recorded hours of sleep (i.e., the AHI may not be extrapolated or projected).

Apnea is defined as a cessation of airflow for at least 10 seconds. Hypopnea is defined as an abnormal respiratory event lasting at least 10 seconds with at least a 30% reduction in thoracoabdominal movement or airflow as compared to baseline, and with at least a 4% oxygen desaturation.

The polysomnography must be performed in a facility - based sleep study laboratory, and not in the home or in a mobile facility.

Initial claims for CPAP devices must be supported by information contained in the medical record indicating that the patient meets Medicare's stated coverage criteria.

Cross-reference: §60-9.

60-18 HOSPITAL BEDS

A. General Requirements for Coverage of Hospital Beds.—A physician's prescription, and such additional documentation as the contractors' medical staffs may consider necessary, including medical records and physicians' reports, must establish the medical necessity for a hospital bed due to one of the following reasons:

- The patient's condition requires positioning of the body; e.g., to alleviate pain, promote good body alignment, prevent contractures, avoid respiratory infections, in ways not feasible in an ordinary bed; or
- The patient's condition requires special attachments that cannot be fixed and used on an ordinary bed.

B. Physician's Prescription.—The physician's prescription, which must accompany the initial claim, and supplementing documentation when required, must establish that a hospital bed is medically necessary. If the stated reason for the need for a hospital bed is the patient's condition requires positioning, the prescription or other documentation must describe the medical condition, e.g., cardiac disease, chronic obstructive pulmonary disease, quadriplegia or paraplegia, and also the severity and frequency of the symptoms of the condition, that necessitates a hospital bed for positioning.

If the stated reason for requiring a hospital bed is the patient's condition requires special attachments, the prescription must describe the patient's condition and specify the attachments that require a hospital bed.

C. Variable Height Feature.—In well documented cases, the contractors' medical staffs may determine that a variable height feature of a hospital bed, approved for coverage under subsection A above, is medically necessary and, therefore, covered, for one of the following conditions:

- Severe arthritis and other injuries to lower extremities; e.g., fractured hip. The condition requires the variable height feature to assist the patient to ambulate by enabling the patient to place his or her feet on the floor while sitting on the edge of the bed;
- Severe cardiac conditions. For those cardiac patients who are able to leave bed, but who must avoid the strain of "jumping" up or down;
- Spinal cord injuries, including quadriplegic and paraplegic patients, multiple limb amputee and stroke patients. For those patients who are able to transfer from bed to a wheelchair, with or without help; or
- Other severely debilitating diseases and conditions, if the variable height feature is required to assist the patient to ambulate.

D. Electric Powered Hospital Bed Adjustments.—Electric powered adjustments to lower and raise head and foot may be covered when the contractor's medical staff determines that the patient's condition requires frequent change in body position and/or there may be an immediate need for a change in body position (i.e., no delay can be tolerated) and the patient can operate the controls and cause the adjustments. Exceptions may be made to this last requirement in cases of spinal cord injury and brain damaged patients.

E. Side Rails.—If the patient's condition requires bed side rails, they can be covered when an integral part of, or an accessory to, a hospital bed.

Cross-reference: Carriers Manual, §5015.4

60-19 AIR-FLUIDIZED BED (Effective for services rendered on or after: 07/30/90)

An air-fluidized bed uses warm air under pressure to set small ceramic beads in motion which simulate the movement of fluid. When the patient is placed in the bed, his body weight is evenly distributed over a large surface area which creates a sensation of "floating." Medicare payment for home use of the air-fluidized bed for treatment of pressure sores can be made if such use is reasonable and necessary for the individual patient.

A decision that use of an air-fluidized bed is reasonable and necessary requires that:

- The patient has a stage 3 (full thickness tissue loss) or stage 4 (deep tissue destruction) pressure sore;
- The patient is bedridden or chair bound as a result of severely limited mobility;
- In the absence of an air-fluidized bed, the patient would require institutionalization;
- The air-fluidized bed is ordered in writing by the patient's attending physician based upon a comprehensive assessment and evaluation of the patient after completion of a course of conservative treatment designed to optimize conditions that promote wound healing. This course of treatment must have been at least one month in duration without progression toward wound healing. This month of prerequisite conservative treatment may include some period in an institution as long as there is documentation available to verify that the necessary conservative treatment has been rendered.
- Use of wet-to-dry dressings for wound debridement, begun during the period of conservative treatment and which continue beyond 30 days, will not preclude coverage of air-fluidized bed. Should additional debridement again become necessary, while a patient is using an air-fluidized bed (after the first 30-day course of conservative treatment) that will not cause the air-fluidized bed to become non-covered. In all instances documentation verifying the continued need for the bed must be available.
- Conservative treatment must include:

  - Frequent repositioning of the patient with particular attention to relief of pressure over bony prominences (usually every 2 hours);
  - Use of a specialized support surface (Group II) designed to reduce pressure and shear forces on healing ulcers and to prevent new ulcer
    formation;
  - Necessary treatment to resolve any wound infection;
  - Optimization of nutrition status to promote wound healing;
  - Debridement by any means (including wet to dry dressings-which does not require an occlusive covering) to remove devitalized tissue from the wound bed;
  - Maintenance of a clean, moist bed of granulation tissue with appropriate moist dressings protected by an occlusive covering, while the wound heals.

- A trained adult caregiver is available to assist the patient with activities of daily living, fluid balance, dry skin care, repositioning, recognition and management of altered mental status, dietary needs, prescribed treatments, and management and support of the air-fluidized bed system and its problems such as leakage;
- A physician directs the home treatment regimen, and reevaluates and recertifies the need for the air-fluidized bed on a monthly basis; and
- All other alternative equipment has been considered and ruled out.

Home use of the air-fluidized bed is not covered under any of the following circumstances:

- The patient has coexisting pulmonary disease (the lack of firm back support makes coughing ineffective and dry air inhalation thickens pulmonary secretions);
- The patient requires treatment with wet soaks or moist wound dressings that are not protected with an impervious covering such as plastic wrap or other occlusive material; an air-fluidized bed;
- The caregiver is unwilling or unable to provide the type of care required by the patient on an air-fluidized bed;
- Structural support is inadequate to support the weight of the air-fluidized bed system (it generally weighs 1600 pounds or more);
- Electrical system is insufficient for the anticipated increase in energy consumption; or
- Other known contraindications exist.

Coverage of an air-fluidized bed is limited to the equipment itself. Payment for this covered item may only be made if the written order from the attending physician is furnished to the supplier prior to the delivery of the equipment. Payment is not included for the caregiver or for architectural adjustments such as electrical or structural improvement.

Cross-reference: Carriers Manual, §5102.2.

60-20 TRANSCUTANEOUS ELECTRICAL NERVE STIMULATORS (TENS)

TENS is a type of electrical nerve stimulator that is employed to treat chronic intractable pain. This stimulator is attached to the surface of the patient's skin over the peripheral nerve to be stimulated. It may be applied in a variety of settings (in the patient's home, a physician's office, or in an outpatient clinic). Payment for TENS may be made under the durable medical equipment benefit. (See §45-25 for an explanation of coverage of medically necessary supplies for the effective use of TENS and §45-19 for an explanation of coverage of TENS for acute post-operative pain.)

60-23 SPEECH GENERATING DEVICES

Effective January 1, 2001, augmentative and alternative communication devices or communicators, which are hereafter referred to as "speech generating devices" are now considered to fall within the DME benefit category established by §1861(n) of the Social Security Act. They may be covered if the contractor's medical staff determines that the patient suffers from a severe speech impairment and that the medical condition warrants the use of a device based on the following definitions.

Definition of Speech Generating Devices

Speech generating devices are defined as speech aids that provide an individual who has a severe speech impairment with the ability to meet his functional speaking needs. Speech generating are characterized by:

- Being a dedicated speech device, used solely by the individual who has a severe speech impairment;
- May have digitized speech output, using pre-recorded messages, less than or equal to 8 minutes recording time;
- May have digitized speech output, using pre-recorded messages, greater than 8 minutes recording time;

- May have synthesized speech output, which requires message formulation by spelling and device access by physical contact with the device-direct selection techniques;
- May have synthesized speech output, which permits multiple methods of message formulation and multiple methods of device access; or
- May be software that allows a laptop computer, desktop computer or personal digital assistant (PDA) to function as a speech generating device.

Devices that would not meet the definition of speech generating devices and therefore, do not fall within the scope of §1861(n) are characterized by:

- Devices that are not dedicated speech devices, but are devices that are capable of running software for purposes other than for speech generation, e.g., devices that can also run a word processing package, an accounting program, or perform other non-medical function.
- Laptop computers, desktop computers, or PDAs, which may be programmed to perform the same function as a speech generating device, are non-covered since they are not primarily medical in nature and do not meet the definition of DME. For this reason, they cannot be considered speech generating devices for Medicare coverage purposes.
- A device that is useful to someone without severe speech impairment is not considered a speech generating device for Medicare coverage purposes.

60-24 NON-IMPLANTABLE PELVIC FLOOR ELECTRICAL STIMULATOR

Non-implantable pelvic floor electrical stimulators provide neuromuscular electrical stimulation through the pelvic floor with the intent of strengthening and exercising pelvic floor musculature. Stimulation is generally delivered by vaginal or anal probes connected to an external pulse generator.

The methods of pelvic floor electrical stimulation vary in location, stimulus frequency (Hz), stimulus intensity or amplitude (mA), pulse duration (duty cycle), treatments per day, number of treatment days per week, length of time for each treatment session, overall time period for device use and between clinic and home settings. In general, the stimulus frequency and other parameters are chosen based on the patient's clinical diagnosis.

Pelvic floor electrical stimulation with a non-implantable stimulator is covered for the treatment of stress and/or urge urinary incontinence in cognitively intact patients who have failed a documented trial of pelvic muscle exercise (PME) training.

A failed trial of PME training is defined as no clinically significant improvement in urinary continence after completing 4 weeks of an ordered plan of pelvic muscle exercises designed to increase periurethral muscle strength.

65-1 HYDROPHILIC CONTACT LENSES

Hydrophilic contact lenses are eyeglasses within the meaning of the exclusion in §1862(a)(7) of the law and are not covered when used in the treatment of nondiseased eyes with spherical ametropia, refractive astigmatism, and/or corneal astigmatism. Payment may be made under the prosthetic device benefit, however, for hydrophilic contact lenses when prescribed for an aphakic patient.

Contractors are authorized to accept an FDA letter of approval or other FDA published material as evidence of FDA approval.

(See §45-7 for coverage of a hydrophilic lens as a corneal bandage.)

Cross-reference: Intermediary Manual, §§3110.3, 3110.4, 3151, and 3157; Carriers Manual, §§2130, 2320; Hospital Manual, §§228.3, 228.4, 260.1 and 260.7.

65-2 ELECTRICAL CONTINENCE AID--NOT COVERED

An electrical continence aid is a device consisting of a plastic plug, molded into the shape of the patient's anal canal, which contains two implanted electrodes that are connected by a wire to a small portable generator. An electrical current is produced which stimulates the anal musculature to cause a contraction sufficient to hold the plug in while allowing the patient to ambulate without incontinence.

Electrical continence aids are in the experimental stage of development and there is no valid scientific documentation of their effectiveness and safety. Therefore, they are not covered under Medicare since they cannot be considered to be reasonable and necessary for the treatment of an illness or injury or to improve the functioning of a malformed body member as required by §1862(a)(1) of the law.

65-3 SCLERAL SHELL

Scleral shell (or shield) is a catchall term for different types of hard scleral contact lenses.

A scleral shell fits over the entire exposed surface of the eye as opposed to a corneal contact lens which covers only the central non-white area encompassing the pupil and iris. Where an eye has been rendered sightless and shrunken by inflammatory disease, a scleral shell may, among other things, obviate the need for surgical enucleation and prosthetic implant and act to support the surrounding orbital tissue.

In such a case, the device serves essentially as an artificial eye. In this situation, payment may be made for a scleral shell under §1861(s)(8) of the law.

Scleral shells are occasionally used in combination with artificial tears in the treatment of "dry eye" of diverse etiology. Tears ordinarily dry at a rapid rate, and are continually replaced by the lacrimal gland. When the lacrimal gland fails, the half-life of artificial tears may be greatly prolonged by the use of the scleral contact lens as a protective barrier against the drying action of the atmosphere. Thus, the difficult and sometimes hazardous process of frequent installation of artificial tears may be avoided. The lens acts in this instance to substitute, in part, for the functioning of the diseased lacrimal gland and would be covered as a prosthetic device in the rare case when it is used in the treatment of "dry eye."

Cross-reference: HCFA-Pub. 13-3, §§3110.4, 3110.5; HCFA-Pub. 14-3, §§2130, 2133; HCFA- Pub. 10, §§210.4, 211

65-5 ELECTRONIC SPEECH AIDS

Electronic speech aids are covered under Part B as prosthetic devices when the patient has had a laryngectomy or his larynx is permanently inoperative. There are two types of speech aids. One operates by placing a vibrating head against the throat; the other amplifies sound waves through a tube which is inserted into the user's mouth. A patient who has had radical neck surgery and/or extensive radiation to the anterior part of the neck would generally be able to use only the "oral tube" model or one of the more sensitive and more expensive "throat contact" devices.

Cross-reference: HCFA-Pub. 13-3, §3110.4; HCFA-Pub. 14-3, §2130; HCFA-Pub. 10, §228.4

65-7 INTRAOCULAR LENSES (IOLs)

An intraocular lens, or pseudophakos, is an artificial lens which may be implanted to replace the natural lens after cataract surgery. Intraocular lens implantation services, as well as the lens itself, may be covered if reasonable and necessary for the individual. Implantation services may include hospital, surgical, and other medical services, including pre-implantation ultrasound (A-can) eye measurement of one or both eyes.

Cross-reference: HCFA Pub. 13-3, §§3110.4, 3151, and 3157; HCFA Pub.14-3, §2130; HCFA Pub. 10, §228.4

65-8 ELECTRICAL NERVE STIMULATORS

Two general classifications of electrical nerve stimulators are employed to treat chronic intractable pain: peripheral nerve stimulators and central nervous system stimulators.

A. Implanted Peripheral Nerve Stimulators.—Payment may be made under the prosthetic device benefit for implanted peripheral nerve stimulators. Use of this stimulator involves implantation of electrodes around a selected peripheral nerve. The stimulating electrode is connected by an insulated lead to a receiver unit which is implanted under the skin at a depth not greater than 1/2 inch. Stimulation is induced by a generator connected to an antenna unit which is attached to the skin surface over the receiver unit. Implantation of electrodes requires surgery and usually necessitates an operating room.

NOTE: Peripheral nerve stimulators may also be employed to assess a patient's suitability for continued treatment with an electric nerve stimulator. As explained in §35-46, such use of the stimulator is covered as part of the total diagnostic service furnished to the beneficiary rather than as a prosthesis.

B. Central Nervous System Stimulators (Dorsal Column and Depth Brain Stimulators).—The implantation of central nervous system stimulators may be covered as therapies for the relief of chronic intractable pain, subject to the following conditions:

    1. Types of Implantations.—There are two types of implantations covered by this instruction:

        a. Dorsal Column (Spinal Cord) Neurostimulation.—The surgical implantation of neurostimulator electrodes within the dura mater (endodural) or the percutaneous insertion of electrodes in the epidural space is covered.

        b. Depth Brain Neurostimulation.—The stereotactic implantation of electrodes in the deep brain (e.g., thalamus and periaqueductal gray matter) is covered.

    2. Conditions for Coverage.—No payment may be made for the implantation of dorsal column or depth brain stimulators or services and supplies related to such implantation, unless all of the conditions listed below have been met:

        a. The implantation of the stimulator is used only as a late resort (if not a last resort) for patients with chronic intractable pain;

b. With respect to item a, other treatment modalities (pharmacological, surgical, physical, or psychological therapies) have been tried and did not prove satisfactory, or are judged to be unsuitable or contraindicated for the given patient;

c. Patients have undergone careful screening, evaluation and diagnosis by a multidisciplinary team prior to implantation. (Such screening must include psychological, as well as physical evaluation);

d. All the facilities, equipment, and professional and support personnel required for the proper diagnosis, treatment training, and followup of the patient (including that required to satisfy item c) must be available; and

e. Demonstration of pain relief with a temporarily implanted electrode precedes permanent implantation.

Contractors may find it helpful to work with PROs to obtain the information needed to apply these conditions to claims.

See Intermediary Manual, §3110.4 and §§35-20 and 35-27.

65-9   INCONTINENCE CONTROL DEVICE

A. Mechanical/Hydraulic Incontinence Control Devices. Mechanical/ hydraulic incontinence control devices are accepted as safe and effective in the management of urinary incontinence in patients with permanent anatomic and neurologic dysfunctions of the bladder. This class of devices achieves control of urination by compression of the urethra. The materials used and the success rate may vary somewhat from device to device. Such a device is covered when its use is reasonable and necessary for the individual patient.

B. Collagen Implant.—A collagen implant, which is injected into the submucosal tissues of the urethra and/or the bladder neck and into tissues adjacent to the urethra, is a prosthetic device used in the treatment of stress urinary incontinence resulting from intrinsic sphincter deficiency (ISD). ISD is a cause of stress urinary incontinence in which the urethral sphincter is unable to contract and generate sufficient resistance in the bladder, especially during stress maneuvers.

Prior to collagen implant therapy, a skin test for collagen sensitivity must be administered and evaluated over a 4 week period.

In male patients, the evaluation must include a complete history and physical examination and a simple cystometrogram to determine that the bladder fills and stores properly. The patient then is asked to stand upright with a full bladder and to cough or otherwise exert abdominal pressure on his bladder. If the patient leaks, the diagnosis of ISD is established.

In female patients, the evaluation must include a complete history and physical examination (including a pelvic exam) and a simple cystometrogram to rule out abnormalities of bladder compliance and abnormalities of urethral support. Following that determination, an abdominal leak point pressure (ALLP) test is performed. Leak point pressure, stated in cm H2O, is defined as the intra-abdominal pressure at which leakage occurs from the bladder (around a catheter) when the bladder has been filled with a minimum of 150 cc fluid. If the patient has an ALLP of less than 100 cm H2O, the diagnosis of ISD is established.

To use a collagen implant, physicians must have urology training in the use of a cystoscope and must complete a collagen implant training program.

Coverage of a collagen implant, and the procedure to inject it, is limited to the following types of patients with stress urinary incontinence due to ISD:

- Male or female patients with congenital sphincter weakness secondary to conditions such as myelomeningocele or epispadias;
- Male or female patients with acquired sphincter weakness secondary to spinal cord lesions;
- Male patients following trauma, including prostatectomy and/or radiation; and
- Female patients without urethral hypermobility and with abdominal leak point pressures of 100 cm H2O or less.

Patients whose incontinence does not improve with 5 injection procedures (5 separate treatment sessions) are considered treatment failures, and no further treatment of urinary incontinence by collagen implant is covered. Patients who have a reoccurrence of incontinence following successful treatment with collagen implants in the past (e.g., 6-12 months previously) may benefit from additional treatment sessions. Coverage of additional sessions may be allowed but must be supported by medical justification.

See Intermediary Manual, §3110.4.

65-10 ENTERAL AND PARENTERAL NUTRITIONAL THERAPY COVERED AS PROSTHETIC DEVICE
(Effective for items and services furnished on or after 07-11-84.)

There are patients who, because of chronic illness or trauma, cannot be sustained through oral feeding. These people must rely on either enteral or parenteral nutritional therapy, depending upon the particular nature of their medical condition.

Coverage of nutritional therapy as a Part B benefit is provided under the prosthetic device benefit provision, which requires that the patient must have a permanently inoperative internal body organ or function thereof. (See Intermediary Manual, §3110.4.) Therefore, enteral and parenteral nutritional therapy are not covered under Part B in situations involving temporary impairments. Coverage of such therapy, however, does not require a medical judgment that the impairment giving rise to the therapy will persist throughout the patient's remaining years. If the medical record, including the judgment of the attending physician, indicates that the impairment will be of long and indefinite duration, the test of permanence is considered met.

If the coverage requirements for enteral or parenteral nutritional therapy are met under the prosthetic device benefit provision, related supplies, equipment and nutrients are also covered under the conditions in the following paragraphs and the Intermediary Manual, §3110.4.

65-10.1 Parenteral Nutrition Therapy.—Daily parenteral nutrition is considered reasonable and necessary for a patient with severe pathology of the alimentary tract which does not allow absorption of sufficient nutrients to maintain weight and strength commensurate with the patient's general condition.

Since the alimentary tract of such a patient does not function adequately, an indwelling catheter is placed percutaneously in the subclavian vein and then advanced into the superior vena cava where intravenous infusion of nutrients is given for part of the day. The catheter is then plugged by the patient until the next infusion. Following a period of hospitalization, which is required to initiate parenteral nutrition and to train the patient in catheter care, solution preparation, and infusion technique, the parenteral nutrition can be provided safely and effectively in the patient's home by nonprofessional persons who have undergone special training. However, such persons cannot be paid for their services, nor is payment available for any services furnished by nonphysician professionals except as services furnished incident to a physician's service.

For parenteral nutrition therapy to be covered under Part B, the claim must contain a physician's written order or prescription and sufficient medical documentation to permit an independent conclusion that the requirements of the prosthetic device benefit are met and that parenteral nutrition therapy is medically necessary. An example of a condition that typically qualifies for coverage is a massive small bowel resection resulting in severe nutritional deficiency in spite of adequate oral intake. However, coverage of parenteral nutrition therapy for this and any other condition must be approved on an individual, case-by-case basis initially and at periodic intervals of no more than 3 months by the carrier's medical consultant or specially trained staff, relying on such medical and other documentation as the carrier may require. If the claim involves an infusion pump, sufficient evidence must be provided to support a determination of medical necessity for the pump. Program payment for the pump is based on the reasonable charge for the simplest model that meets the medical needs of the patient as established by medical documentation.

Nutrient solutions for parenteral therapy are routinely covered. However, Medicare pays for no more than one month's supply of nutrients at any one time. Payment for the nutrients is based on the reasonable charge for the solution components unless the medical record, including a signed statement from the attending physician, establishes that the beneficiary, due to his/her physical or mental state, is unable to safely or effectively mix the solution and there is no family member or other person who can do so. Payment will be on the basis of the reasonable charge for more expensive pre-mixed solutions only under the latter circumstances.

65-10.2 Enteral Nutrition Therapy.—Enteral nutrition is considered reasonable and necessary for a patient with a functioning gastrointestinal tract who, due to pathology to or nonfunction of the structures that normally permit food to reach the digestive tract, cannot maintain weight and strength commensurate with his or her general condition. Enteral therapy may be given by nasogastric, jejunostomy, or gastrostomy tubes and can be provided safely and effectively in the home by nonprofessional persons who have undergone special training. However, such persons cannot be paid for their services, nor is payment available for any services furnished by nonphysician professionals except as services furnished incident to a physician's service.

Typical examples of conditions that qualify for coverage are head and neck cancer with reconstructive surgery and central nervous system disease leading to interference with the neuromuscular mechanisms of ingestion of such severity that the beneficiary cannot be maintained with oral feeding. However, claims for Part B coverage of enteral nutrition therapy for these and any other conditions must be approved on an individual, case-by-case basis. Each claim must contain a physician's written order or prescription and sufficient medical documentation (e.g., hospital records, clinical findings from the attending physician) to permit an independent conclusion that the patient's condition meets the requirements of the prosthetic device benefit and that enteral nutrition therapy is medically necessary. Allowed claims are to be reviewed at periodic intervals of no more than 3 months by the contractor's medical consultant or specially trained staff, and additional medical documentation considered necessary is to be obtained as part of this review.

Medicare pays for no more than one month's supply of enteral nutrients at any one time.

If the claim involves a pump, it must be supported by sufficient medical documentation to establish that the pump is medically necessary, i.e., gravity feeding is not satisfactory due to aspiration, diarrhea, dumping syndrome. Program payment for the pump is based on the reasonable charge for the simplest model that meets the medical needs of the patient as established by medical documentation.

65-10.3 Nutritional Supplementation.—Some patients require supplementation of their daily protein and caloric intake. Nutritional supplements are often given as a medicine between meals to boost protein-caloric intake or the mainstay of a daily nutritional plan. Nutritional supplementation is not covered under Medicare Part B.

65-14 COCHLEAR IMPLANTATION

A cochlear implant device is an electronic instrument, part of which is implanted surgically to stimulate auditory nerve fibers, and part of which is worn or carried by the individual to capture, analyze and code sound. Cochlear implant devices are available in single channel and multi-channel models. The purpose of implanting the device is to provide an awareness and identification of sounds and to facilitate communication for persons who are profoundly hearing impaired.

Medicare coverage is provided only for those patients who meet all of the following selection guidelines.

A. General.—

- Diagnosis of bilateral severe-to-profound sensorineural hearing impairment with limited benefit from appropriate hearing (or vibrotactile) aids;
- Cognitive ability to use auditory clues and a willingness to undergo an extended program of rehabilitation;
- Freedom from middle ear infection, an accessible cochlear lumen that is structurally suited to implantation, and freedom from lesions in the auditory nerve and acoustic areas of the central nervous system;
- No contraindications to surgery; and
- The device must be used in accordance with the FDA-approved labeling.

B. Adults.—Cochlear implants may be covered for adults (over age 18) for prelinguistically, perilinguistically, and post linguistically deafened adults. Post linguistically deafened adults must demonstrate test scores of 30 percent or less on sentence recognition scores from tape recorded tests in the patient's best listening condition.

C. Children.—Cochlear implants may be covered for prelinguistically and post linguistically deafened children aged 2 through 17. Bilateral profound sensorineural deafness must be demonstrated by the inability to improve on age appropriate closed-set word identification tasks with amplification.

65-16 TRACHEOSTOMY SPEAKING VALVE

A trachea tube has been determined to satisfy the definition of a prosthetic device, and the tracheostomy speaking valve is an add on to the trachea tube which may be considered a medically necessary accessory that enhances the function of the tube. In other words, it makes the system a better prosthesis. As such, a tracheostomy speaking valve is covered as an element of the trachea tube which makes the tube more effective.

65-17 URINARY DRAINAGE BAGS

Urinary collection and retention system are covered as prosthetic devices that replace bladder function in the case of permanent urinary incontinence. Urinary drainage bags that can be used either as bedside or leg drainage bags may be either multi-use or single use systems. Both the multi-use and the single use bags have a system that prevents urine backflow. However, the single use system is non-drainable. There is insufficient evidence to support the medical necessity of a single use system bag rather than the multi-use bag. Therefore, a single use drainage system is subject to the same coverage parameters as the multi-use drainage bags.

70-1   CORSET USED AS HERNIA SUPPORT

A hernia support (whether in the form of a corset or truss) which meets the definition of a brace is covered under Part B under §1861(s)(9) of the Act.

See Intermediary Manual, §3110.5; Medicare Carriers Manual, §2133; and Hospital Manual, §228.5.

70-2   SYKES HERNIA CONTROL

Based on professional advice, it has been determined that the Sykes hernia control (a spring-type, U-shaped, strapless truss) is not functionally more beneficial than a conventional truss. Make program reimbursement for this device only when an ordinary truss would be covered. (Like all trusses, it is only of benefit when dealing with a reducible hernia). Thus, when a charge for this item is substantially in excess of that which would be reasonable for a conventional truss used for the same condition, base reimbursement on the reasonable charges for the conventional truss.

See Intermediary Manual, §3110.5; Medicare Carriers Manual, §2133; and Hospital Manual, §228.5.

MEDICARE CARRIERS MANUAL (MCM) REFERENCES

The following Medicare references refer to policy issues identified in the main body of the HCPCS code section. Medicare Carriers Manual references are identified with the term MCM: followed by the reference number(s). .

2000 COVERED MEDICAL AND OTHER HEALTH SERVICES

The supplementary medical insurance plan covers expenses incurred for the following medical and other health services:

1. Physician's services, including surgery, consultation, and office, and institutional calls, and services and supplies furnished incident to a physician's professional service;
2. Outpatient hospital services furnished incident to physicians services;
3. Outpatient diagnostic services furnished by a hospital;
4. Outpatient physical therapy; outpatient speech pathology services;
5. Diagnostic X-ray tests, laboratory tests, and other diagnostic tests;
6. X-ray, radium, and radioactive isotope therapy;

7. Surgical dressings, and splints, casts, and other devices used for reduction of fractures and dislocations;
8. Rental or purchase of durable medical equipment for use in the patient's home;
9. Ambulance service;
10. Prosthetic devices which replace all or part of an internal body organ;
11. Leg, arm, back and neck braces and artificial legs, arms, and eyes;
12. Certain medical supplies used in connection with home dialysis delivery systems;
13. Rural health clinic (RHC) services.
14. Ambulatory surgical center (ASC) services.

(See §2255 for provisions regarding supplementary medical insurance coverage of certain of these services when furnished to hospital and SNF inpatients.)

Supplementary medical insurance also provides coverage for home health visits for which the intermediary makes payment on the basis of the reasonable cost. Outpatient hospital services are also reimbursed by the intermediary.

Some medical services may be considered for coverage under more than one of the above enumerated categories. For example, EKGs can be covered as physician's services, services incident to a physician's service or as other diagnostic tests. It is sufficient to determine that the requirements for coverage under one category are met to permit payment.

Payment for physician services and medical and other health services rendered to beneficiaries is made on a reasonable charge basis. Make payment to the beneficiary, or the physician or supplier who renders the service, depending on whether the itemized bill or assignment method is used. Payment for medical services performed by a provider-based physician is made to the physician or beneficiary or, when the physician authorizes it, to the provider. When covered medical and other health services are furnished by a nonparticipating skilled nursing facility, make payment to the SNF or to the beneficiary on the basis of the reasonable charge.

An organization which furnishes medical and other health services on a prepayment basis may elect to be paid on the basis of reasonable costs in lieu of reasonable charges.

Payment may not be made under Part B for services furnished an individual if he is entitled to have payment made for those services under Part A. An individual is considered entitled to have payment made under Part A if the expenses incurred were used to satisfy a Part A deductible or coinsurance amount, or if payment would be made under Part A except for the lack of a request for payment or physician certification.

When covered Part B services are furnished by a participating hospital, skilled nursing facility, or home health agency, the intermediary makes payment on a reasonable cost basis to the provider only. Outpatient physical therapy or speech pathology providers are reimbursed on a reasonable cost basis by the designated intermediary or carrier.

Where covered Part B services are furnished by a nonparticipating hospital, the emergency intermediary makes payment on the basis of reasonable charges to the hospital or to the patient.

Membership dues, subscription fees, charges for service policies, insurance premium and other payments analogous to premiums which entitle enrollees to services or to repairs or replacement of devices or equipment or parts therefore without charge or at a reduced charge, are not considered expenses incurred for covered items or services furnished under such contracts or undertakings. Examples of such arrangements are memberships in ambulance companies, insurance for replacement of prosthetic lenses, and service contracts for durable medical equipment.

2005.1 Physicians' Expense for Surgery, Childbirth, and Treatment for Infertility

A. Surgery and Childbirth.—Skilled medical management is appropriate throughout the events of pregnancy, beginning with diagnosis, continuing through delivery and ending after the necessary postnatal care. Similarly, in the event of termination of pregnancy, regardless of whether terminated spontaneously or for therapeutic reasons (i.e., where the life of the mother would be endangered if the fetus were brought to term), the need for skilled medical management and/or medical services is equally important as in those cases carried to full term. After the infant is delivered and is a separate individual, items and services furnished to the infant are not covered on the basis of the mother's eligibility.

Most surgeons and obstetricians bill patients an all inclusive package charge intended to cover all services associated with the surgical procedure or delivery of the child. All expenses for surgical and obstetrical care, including preoperative/prenatal examinations and tests and postoperative/postnatal services are considered incurred on the date of surgery or delivery, as appropriate. This policy applies whether the physician bills on a package charge basis, or itemizes his/her bill separately for these items.

Occasionally, a physician's bill may include charges for additional services not directly related to the surgical procedure or the delivery. Such charges are considered incurred on the date the additional services are furnished.

The above policy applies only where the charges are imposed by one physician or by a clinic on behalf of a group of physicians. Where charges are imposed by more than one physician for surgical or obstetrical services, all preoperative/prenatal and postoperative/postnatal services performed by the physician who performed the surgery or delivery are considered incurred on the date of the surgery or delivery. Expenses for services rendered by other physicians are considered incurred on the date they were performed. for services rendered by other physicians are considered incurred on the date they were performed.

B. Treatment for Infertility.—Reasonable and necessary services associated with treatment for infertility are covered under Medicare. Infertility is a condition sufficiently at variance with the usual state of health to make it appropriate for   a person who normally   is expected to be fertile to seek medical consultation and treatment. Coordinate with PROs to see that utilization guidelines are established for this treatment if inappropriate utilization or abuse is suspected.

2049 DRUGS AND BIOLOGICALS

The Medicare program provides limited benefits for outpatient drugs. The program covers drugs that are furnished "incident to" a physician's service provided that the drugs are not usually self-administered by the patients who take them.

Generally, drugs and biologicals are covered only if all of the following requirements are met:

- They meet the definition of drugs or biologicals (see §2049.1);

- They are of the type that are not usually self-administered by the patients who take them. (See §2049.2);
- They meet all the general requirements for coverage of items as incident to a physician's services (see § §2050.1 and 2050.3);
- They are reasonable and necessary for the diagnosis or treatment of the illness or injury for which they are administered according to accepted standards of medical practice (see §2049.4);
- They are not excluded as immunizations (see §2049.4.B); and
- They have not been determined by the FDA to be less than effective. (See §2049.4 D.)

Drugs that are usually self-administered by the patient, such as those in pill form, or are used for self-injection, are generally not covered by Part B. However, there are a limited number of self-administered drugs that are covered because the Medicare statute explicitly provides coverage. Examples of self-administered drugs that are covered include blood clotting factors, drugs used in immunosuppressive therapy, erythropoietin for dialysis patients, osteoporosis drugs for certain homebound patients, and certain oral cancer drugs.

(See §§2100.5 and 2130.D for coverage of drugs which are necessary to the effective use of DME or prosthetic devices.)

Definition of Drug or Biological.--Drugs and biologicals must be determined to meet the statutory definition.

Section 1861(t)(1) provides that the terms "drugs" and "biologicals" "include only such drugs (including contrast agents) and biologicals, respectively, as are included (or approved for inclusion) in one of several pharmacopoeias (except for any drugs and biologicals unfavorably evaluated therein), or as are approved by the pharmacy and drug therapeutics committee (or equivalent committee) of the medical staff of the hospital furnishing such drugs and biologicals for use in such hospital." One such pharmacopeia is the United States Pharmacopeia, Drug Indications (USP DI). The inclusion of an item in the USP DI does not necessarily mean that the item is a drug or biological. The USP DI is a database of drug information developed by the U.S. Pharmacopeia but maintained by Micromedex, which contains medically accepted uses for generic and brand name drug products. Inclusion in such reference (or approval by a hospital committee) is a necessary condition for a product to be considered a drug or biological under the Medicare program, however, it is not enough. Rather, the product must also meet all other program requirements to be determined to be a drug or biological.

Determining Self-Administration of Drug or Biological.—Whether a drug or biological is of a type which cannot be self-administered is based on the usual method of administration of the form of that drug or biological as furnished by the physician.

Whole blood is a biological which cannot be self-administered and is covered when furnished incident to a physician's services. Payment may also be made for blood fractions if all coverage requirements are satisfied. (See §2455 on Part B blood deductible.)

Medicare carriers have discretion in applying the criteria in this instruction in determining whether drugs are subject to this exclusion in their local areas. Carriers are to follow the instructions below when applying the exclusion for drugs that are usually self-administered by the patient. Each individual contractor must make its own individual determination on each drug. Contractors must continue to apply the policy that not only the drug is medically reasonable and necessary for any individual claim, but also that the route of administration is medically reasonable and necessary. That is, if a drug is available in both oral and injectable forms, the injectable form of the drug must be medically reasonable and necessary as compared to using the oral form. (See §2049.4.2)

For certain injectable drugs, it will be apparent due to the nature of the condition(s) for which they are administered or the usual course of treatment for those conditions, they are, or are not, usually self-administered. For example, an injectable drug used to treat migraine headaches is usually self-administered. On the other hand, an injectable drug, administered at the same time as chemotherapy, used to treat anemia secondary to chemotherapy is not usually self-administered.

Administered—The term "administered" refers only to the physical process by which the drug enters the patient's body. It does not refer to whether the process is supervised by a medical professional (for example, to observe proper technique or side-effects of the drug). Only injectable (including intravenous) drugs are eligible for inclusion under the "incident to" benefit. Other routes of administration including, but not limited to, oral drugs, suppositories, topical medications are all considered to be usually self-administered by the patient.

Usually—In arriving at a single determination as to whether a drug is usually self-administered, contractors should make a separate determination for each indication for a drug as to whether that drug is usually self-administered.

After determining whether a drug is usually self-administered for each indication, contractors should determine the relative contribution of each indication to total use of the drug (i.e., weighted average) in order to make an overall determination as to whether the drug is usually self-administered. For example, if a drug has three indications, is not self-administered for the first indication, but is self-administered for the second and third indications, and the first indication makes up 40% of total usage, the second indication makes up 30% of total usage, and the third indication makes up 30% of total usage, then the drug would be considered usually self-administered.

Reliable statistical information on the extent of self-administration by the patient may not always be available. Consequently, we offer the following guidance for each contractor's consideration in making this determination in the absence of such data:

1. Absent evidence to the contrary, drugs delivered intravenously should be presumed to be not usually self-administered by the patient.

2. Absent evidence to the contrary, drugs delivered by intramuscular injection should be presumed to be not usually self-administered by the patient. (For example, interferon beta-1a, trade name Avonex, when delivered by intramuscular injection is not usually self administered by the patient.) The contractor may consider the depth and nature of the particular intramuscular injection in applying this presumption.

3. Absent evidence to the contrary, drugs delivered by subcutaneous injection should be presumed to be self-administered by the patient.

In applying these presumptions, contractors should examine the use of the particular drug and consider the following factors:

A. Acute condition.—For the purposes of determining whether a drug is usually self-administered, an acute condition means a condition that begins over a short time period, is likely to be of short duration and/or the expected course of treatment is for a short, finite interval. A course of treatment consisting of scheduled injections lasting less than two weeks, regardless of frequency or route of administration, is considered acute. Evidence to support this may include Food and Drug administration (FDA) approval language, package inserts, drug compendia, and other information.

B. Frequency of administration.—How often is the injection given? For example, if the drug is administered once per month, it is less likely to be self-administered by the patient. However, if it is administered once or more per week, it is likely that the drug is self-administered by the patient.

C. By the patient—The term "by the patient" means Medicare beneficiaries as a collective whole. Include only the patients themselves and not other individuals (that is, do not include spouses, friends, or other care-givers). Base your determination on whether the drug is self-administered by the patient a majority of the time that the drug is used on an outpatient basis by Medicare beneficiaries for medically necessary indications. Ignore all instances when the drug is administered on an inpatient basis. Make this determination on a drug-by-drug basis, not on a beneficiary-by-beneficiary basis. In evaluating whether beneficiaries as a collective whole self-administer, do not consider individual beneficiaries who do not have the capacity to self-administer any drug due to a condition other than the condition for which they are taking the drug in question. For example, an individual afflicted with paraplegia or advanced dementia would not have the capacity to self-administer any injectable drug, so such individuals would not be included in the population upon which the determination for self-administration by the patient was based. Note that some individuals afflicted with a less severe stage of an otherwise debilitating condition would be included in the population upon which the determination for "self-administered by the patient" was based; for example, an early onset of dementia.

D. Evidentiary Criteria —In making a self-administration determination, contractors are only required to consider the following types of evidence: peer reviewed medical literature, standards of medical practice, evidence-based practice guidelines, FDA approved label, and package inserts. Contractors may also consider other evidence submitted by interested individuals or groups subject to their judgment.

Contractors should also use these evidentiary criteria when reviewing requests for making a determination as to whether a drug is usually self-administered, and requests for reconsideration of a pending or published determination.

Please note that prior to August 1, 2002, one of the principal factors used to determine whether a drug was subject to the self-administered exclusion was whether the FDA label contained instructions for self-administration. However, we note that under the standard in effect after August 1, 2002, the fact that the FDA label includes instructions for self-administration is not, by itself, a determining factor that a drug is subject to this exclusion.

E. Provider Notice of Non-Covered Drugs—Contractors must describe the process they will use to determine whether a drug is usually self-administered and thus does not meet the "incident to" benefit category. Contractors must place a description of the process on their Web site. Contractors must publish a list of the injectable drugs that are subject to the self-administered exclusion on their Web site, including the data and rationale that led to the determination. Contractors will report the workload associated with developing new coverage statements in CAFM 21208.

Contractors must provide notice 45 days prior to the date that these drugs will not be covered. During the 45-day time period, contractors will maintain existing medical review and payment procedures. After the 45-day notice, contractors may deny payment for the drugs subject to the notice.

Contractors must not develop local medical review policies (LMRPs) for this purpose because further elaboration to describe drugs that do not meet the 'incident to' and the 'not usually self-administered' provisions of the statute are unnecessary. Current LMRPs based solely on these provisions must be withdrawn. LMRPs that address the self-administered exclusion and other information may be reissued absent the self-administered drug exclusion material. Contractors will report this workload in CAFM 21206. However, contractors may continue to use and write LMRPs to describe reasonable and necessary uses of drugs that are not usually self-administered.

F. Conferences Between Contractors—Contractors' Medical Directors may meet and discuss whether a drug is usually self-administered without reaching a formal consensus. Each contractor uses its discretion as to whether or not it will participate in such discussions. Each contractor must make its own individual determinations, except that fiscal intermediaries may, at their discretion, follow the determinations of the local carrier with respect to the self-administered exclusion.

G. Beneficiary Appeals—If a beneficiary's claim for a particular drug is denied because the drug is subject to the "self-administered drug" exclusion, the beneficiary may appeal the denial. Because it is a "benefit category" denial and not a denial based on medical necessity, an Advance Beneficiary Notice (ABN) is not applicable. A "benefit category" denial (i.e., a denial based on the fact that there is no benefit category under which the drug may be covered) does not trigger the financial liability protection provisions of Limitation On Liability [under §1879 of the Act]. Therefore, physicians or providers may charge the beneficiary for an excluded drug. See Chapter XV of the Medicare Carrier Manual for more detail on the appeals process.

H. Provider and Physician Appeals—A physician accepting assignment may appeal a denial under the provisions found in §12000 of the Medicare Carriers Manual. See Chapter XV of the Medicare Carrier Manual for more detail on the appeals process.

Reporting Requirements—Each carrier must report to CMS, every September 1 and March 1, its complete list of injectable drugs that the contractor has determined are excluded when furnished incident to a physician's service on the basis that the drug is usually self-administered. We anticipate that contractors will review injectable drugs on a rolling basis and publish their list of excluded drugs as it is developed. For example, contractors should not wait to publish this list until every drug has been reviewed.

Incident-to Requirements.—In order for Medicare payment to be made for a drug, the "incident to" requirements are met. "Incident to" a physician's professional service means that the services are furnished as an integral, although incidental, part of the physician's personal professional services in the course of diagnosis or treatment of an illness or injury. See §2050.1 for more detail on incident-to requirements.

In order to meet all the general requirements for coverage under the incident-to provision, an FDA approved drug or biological must be furnished by a physician and administered by him/her or by auxiliary personnel employed by him/her under his/her personal supervision. The charge, if any, for the drug or biological must be included in the physician's bill, and the cost of the drug or biological must represent an expense to the physician. Drugs and biologicals furnished by other health professionals may also meet these requirements. (See §§2154, 2156, 2158 and 2160 for specific instructions.)

Reasonableness and Necessity.—Use of the drug or biological must be safe and effective and otherwise reasonable and necessary. (See §2303.) Drugs or biologicals approved for marketing by the Food and Drug Administration (FDA) are considered safe and effective for purposes of this requirement when used for indications specified on the labeling. Therefore, you may pay for the use of an FDA approved drug or biological, if:

- It was injected on or after the date of the FDA's approval;
- It is reasonable and necessary for the individual patient; and
- All other applicable coverage requirements are met.

Deny coverage for drugs and biologicals which have not received final marketing approval by the FDA unless you receive instructions from CMS to the contrary. For specific guidelines on coverage of Group C cancer drugs, see the Coverage Issues Manual.

If there is reason to question whether the FDA has approved a drug or biological for marketing, obtain satisfactory evidence of FDA's approval. Acceptable evidence includes a copy of the FDA's letter to the drug's manufacturer approving the new drug application (NDA); or listing of the drug or biological in the FDA's Approved Drug Products or FDA Drug and Device Product Approvals; or a copy of the manufacturer's package insert, approved by the FDA as part of the labeling of the drug, containing its recommended uses and dosage, as well as possible adverse reactions and recommended precautions in using it. When necessary, the RO may be able to help in obtaining information.

An unlabeled use of a drug is a use that is not included as an indication on the drug's label as approved by the FDA. FDA approved drugs used for indications other than what is indicated on the official label may be covered under Medicare if the carrier determines the use to be medically accepted, taking into consideration the major drug compendia, authoritative medical literature and/or accepted standards of medical practice. In the case of drugs used in an anti-cancer chemotherapeutic regimen, unlabeled uses are covered for a medically accepted indication as defined in §2049.4.C.

Determinations as to whether medication is reasonable and necessary for an individual patient should be made on the same basis as all other such determinations (i.e., with the advice of medical consultants and with reference to accepted standards of medical practice and the medical circumstances of the individual case). The following guidelines identify three categories with specific examples of situations in which medications would not be reasonable and necessary according to accepted standards of medical practice.

1. Not for Particular Illness.—Medications given for a purpose other than the treatment of a particular condition, illness, or injury are not covered (except for certain immunizations).

    Exclude the charge for medications, e.g., vitamins, given simply for the general good and welfare of the patient and not as accepted therapy for a particular illness.

2. Medication given by injection (parenterally) is not covered if standard medical practice indicates that the administration of the medication by mouth(orally) is effective and is an accepted or preferred method of administration. For example, the accepted standards of medical practice for the treatment of certain diseases is to initiate therapy with parenteral penicillin and to complete therapy with oral penicillin.

Exclude the entire charge for penicillin injections given after the initiation of therapy if oral penicillin is indicated unless there are special medical circumstances which justify additional injections.

3.   Excessive Medications.—Medications administered for treatment of a disease which exceed the frequency or duration of injections indicated by accepted standards of medical practice are not covered. For example, the accepted standard of medical practice in the maintenance treatment of pernicious anemia is one vitamin B-12 injection per month. Exclude the entire charge for injections given in excess of this frequency unless there are special medical circumstances which   justify additional injections.

Supplement the guidelines as necessary with guidelines concerning appropriate use of specific injections in other situations. Use the guidelines to screen out questionable cases for special review, further development or denial when the injection billed for would not be reasonable and necessary. Coordinate any type of drug treatment review with the PRO.

If a medication is determined not to be reasonable and necessary for diagnosis or treatment of an illness or injury according to these guidelines, exclude the entire charge (i.e., for both the drug and its administration). Also exclude from payment any charges for other services (such as office visits) which were primarily for the purpose of administering a noncovered injection (i.e., an injection that is not reasonable and necessary for the diagnosis or treatment of an illness or injury).

A.   Antigens.—Payment may be made for a reasonable supply of antigens that have been prepared for a particular patient if: (1) the antigens are prepared by a physician who is a doctor of medicine or osteopathy, and (2) the physician who prepared the antigens has examined the patient and has determined a plan of treatment and a dosage regimen. Antigens must be administered in accordance with the plan of treatment and by a doctor of medicine or osteopathy or by a properly instructed person (who could be the patient) under the supervision of the doctor. he associations of allergists that HCFA consulted advised that a reasonable supply of antigens is considered to be not more than a 12-week supply of antigens that has been prepared for a particular patient at any one time. The purpose of the reasonable supply limitation is to assure that the antigens retain their potency and effectiveness over the period in which they are to be administered to the patient. (See §§2005.2 and 2050.2.)

B.   Immunizations.—Vaccinations or inoculations are excluded as immunizations unless they are directly related to the treatment of an injury or direct exposure to a disease or condition, such as anti-rabies treatment, tetanus antitoxin or booster vaccine, botulin antitoxin, antivenin sera, or immune globulin. In the absence of injury or direct exposure, preventive immunization (vaccination or inoculation) against such diseases as smallpox, polio, diphtheria, etc., is not covered. However, pneumococcal, hepatitis B, and influenza virus vaccines are exceptions to this rule. (See items 1, 2, and 3.) In cases where a vaccination or inoculation is excluded from coverage, deny the entire charge.

1.   Pneumococcal Pneumonia Vaccinations.—Furnished on or after May 1, 1981, the Medicare Part B program covers pneumococcal pneumonia vaccine and its administration when furnished in compliance with any applicable State law by any provider of services or any entity or individual with a supplier number. This includes revaccination of patients at highest risk of pneumococcal infection. Typically, these vaccines are administered once in a lifetime except for persons at highest risk. Effective July 1, 2000, Medicare does not require for coverage purposes that the vaccine must be ordered by a doctor of medicine or osteopathy. Therefore, the beneficiary may receive the vaccine upon request without a physician's order and without physician supervision.

An initial vaccine may be administered only to persons at high risk (see below) of pneumococcal disease. Revaccination may be administered only to persons at highest risk of serious Pneumococcal Pneumonia Vaccinations.—Effective for services pneumococcal infection and those likely to have a rapid decline in pneumococcal antibody levels, provided that at least 5 years have passed since receipt of a previous dose of pneumococcal vaccine.

Persons at high risk for whom an initial vaccine may be administered include all people age 65 and older; immunocompetent adults who are at increased risk of pneumococcal disease or its complications because of chronic illness (e.g., cardiovascular disease, pulmonary disease, diabetes mellitus, alcoholism, cirrhosis, or cerebrospinal fluid leaks); and individuals with compromised immune systems (e.g., splenic dysfunction or anatomic asplenia, Hodgkin's disease, lymphoma, multiple myeloma, chronic renal failure, HIV infection, nephrotic syndrome, sickle cell disease, or organ transplantation).

Persons at highest risk and those most likely to have rapid declines in antibody levels are those for whom revaccination may be appropriate. This group includes persons with functional or anatomic asplenia (e.g., sickle cell disease, splenectomy), HIV infection, leukemia, lymphoma, Hodgkin's disease, multiple myeloma, generalized malignancy, chronic renal failure, nephrotic syndrome, or other conditions associated with immunosuppression such as organ or bone marrow transplantation, and those receiving immuno-suppressive chemotherapy. Routine revaccination of people age 65 or older who are not at highest risk is not appropriate.

Those administering the vaccine should not require the patient to present an immunization record prior to administering the pneumococcal vaccine, nor should they feel compelled to review the patient's complete medical record if it is not available. Instead, provided that the patient is competent, it is acceptable for them to rely on the patient's verbal history to determine prior vaccination status. If the patient is uncertain about their vaccination history in the past 5 years, the vaccine should be given. However, if the patient is certain he/she was vaccinated in the last 5 years, the vaccine should not be given. If the patient is certain that the vaccine was given and that more than 5 years have passed since receipt of the previous dose, revaccination is not appropriate unless the patient is at highest risk.

2. Hepatitis B Vaccine.—With the enactment of P.L. 98-369, coverage under Part B was extended to hepatitis B vaccine and its administration, furnished to a Medicare beneficiary who is at high or intermediate risk of contracting hepatitis B. This coverage is effective for services furnished on or after September 1, 1984.

High-risk groups currently identified include (see exception below):

- End stage renal disease (ESRD) patients;
- Hemophiliacs who receive Factor VIII or IX concentrates; Clients of institutions for the mentally retarded;
- Persons who live in the same household as an Hepatitis B Virus (HBV) carrier; Homosexual men; and
- Illicit injectable drug abusers.
- Intermediate risk groups currently identified include:
- Staff in institutions for the mentally retarded; and

- Workers in health care professions who have frequent contact with blood or blood-derived body fluids during routine work.

EXCEPTION: Persons in the above-listed groups would not be considered at high or intermediate risk of contracting hepatitis B, however, if there is laboratory evidence positive for antibodies to hepatitis B. (ESRD patients are routinely tested for hepatitis B antibodies as part of their continuing monitoring and therapy.)

For Medicare program purposes, the vaccine may be administered upon the order of a doctor of medicine or osteopathy by home health agencies, skilled nursing facilities, ESRD facilities, hospital outpatient departments, persons recognized under the incident to physicians' services provision of law, and doctors of medicine and osteopathy.

A charge separate from the ESRD composite rate will be recognized and paid for administration of the vaccine to ESRD patients.

For ESRD laboratory tests, see Coverage Issues Manual, §50-17.

3. Influenza Virus Vaccine.—Effective for services furnished on or after May 1, 1993, the Medicare Part B program covers influenza virus vaccine and its administration when furnished in compliance with any applicable State law by any provider of services or any entity or individual with a supplier number. Typically, these vaccines are administered once a year in the fall or winter. Medicare does not require for coverage purposes that the vaccine must be ordered by a doctor of medicine or osteopathy. Therefore, the beneficiary may receive the vaccine upon request without a physician's order and without physician supervision.

C. Unlabeled Use For Anti-Cancer Drugs.—Effective January 1, 1994, unlabeled uses of FDA approved drugs and biologicals used in an anti-cancer chemotherapeutic regimen for a medically accepted indication are evaluated under the conditions described in this paragraph. A regimen is a combination of anti-cancer agents which has been clinically recognized for the treatment of a specific type of cancer. An example of a drug regimen is: Cyclophosphamide + vincristine + prednisone (CVP) for non-Hodgkin's lymphoma.

In addition to listing the combination of drugs for a type of cancer, there may be a different regimen or combinations which are used at different times in the history of the cancer (induction, prophylaxis of CNS involvement, post remission, and relapsed or refractory disease). A protocol may specify the combination of drugs, doses, and schedules for administration of the drugs. For purposes of this provision, a cancer treatment regimen includes drugs used to treat toxicities or side effects of the cancer treatment regimen when the drug is administered incident to a chemotherapy treatment. Contractors must not deny coverage based solely on the absence of FDA approved labeling for the use, if the use is supported by one of the following and the use is not listed as "not indicated" in any of the three compendia. (See note at the end of this subsection.)

1. American Hospital Formulary Service Drug Information.—Drug monographs are arranged in alphabetical order within therapeutic classifications. Within the text of the monograph, information concerning indications is provided, including both labeled and unlabeled uses. Unlabeled uses are identified with daggers. The text must be analyzed to make a determination whether a particular use is supported.

2. American Medical Association Drug Evaluations.—Drug evaluations are organized into sections and chapters that are based on therapeutic classifications. The evaluation of a drug provides information concerning indications, including both labeled and unlabeled uses. Unlabeled uses are not specifically identified as such. The text must be analyzed to make a determination whether a particular use is supported. In making these determinations, also refer to the AMA Drug Evaluations Subscription, Volume III, section 17 (Oncolytic Drugs), chapter 1 (Principles of Cancer Chemotherapy), tables 1 and 2.

Table 1, Specific Agents Used In Cancer Chemotherapy, lists the anti-neoplastic agents which are currently available for use in various cancers. The indications presented in this table for a particular anti- cancer drug include labeled and unlabeled uses (although they are not identified as such). Any indication appearing in this table is considered to be a medically accepted use.

Table 2, Clinical Responses To Chemotherapy, lists some of the currently preferred regimens for various cancers. The table headings include (1) type of cancer, (2) drugs or regimens currently preferred, (3) alternative or secondary drugs or regimens, and (4) other drugs or regimens with reported activity.

A regimen appearing under the preferred or alternative/secondary headings is considered to be a medically accepted use.

A regimen appearing under the heading "Other Drugs or Regimens With Reported Activity" is considered to be for a medically accepted use provided:

- The preferred and alternative/secondary drugs or regimens are contraindicated; or
- A preferred and/or alternative/secondary drug or regimen was used but was not tolerated or was ineffective; or
- here was tumor progression or recurrence after an initial response.

3. United States Pharmacopoeia Drug Information (USPDI).— Monographs are arranged in alphabetic order by generic or family name. Indications for use appear as accepted, unaccepted, or insufficient data. An indication is considered to be a medically accepted use only if the indication is listed as accepted. Unlabeled uses are identified with brackets. A separate indications index lists all indications included in USPDI along with the medically accepted drugs used in treatment or diagnosis.

4. A Use Supported by Clinical Research That Appears in Peer Reviewed Medical Literature.—This applies only when an unlabeled use does not appear in any of the compendia or is listed as insufficient data or investigational. If an unlabeled use of a drug meets these criteria, contact the compendia to see if a report regarding this use is forthcoming. If a report is forthcoming, use this information as a basis for your decision making. The compendium process for making decisions concerning unlabeled uses is very thorough and continuously updated. Peer reviewed medical literature includes scientific, medical, and pharmaceutical publications in which original manuscripts are published, only after having been critically reviewed for scientific accuracy, validity, and reliability by unbiased independent experts. This does not include in-house publications of pharmaceutical manufacturing companies or abstracts (including meeting abstracts)

In determining whether there is supportive clinical evidence for a particular use of a drug, your medical staff (in consultation with local medical specialty groups) must evaluate the quality of the evidence in published peer reviewed medical literature. When evaluating this literature, consider (among other things) the following:

- The prevalence and life history of the disease when evaluating the adequacy of the number of subjects and the response rate. While a 20 percent response rate may be adequate for highly prevalent disease states, a lower rate may be adequate for rare diseases or highly unresponsive conditions.
- The effect on the patient's well-being and other responses to therapy that indicate effectiveness, e.g., a significant increase in survival rate or life expectancy or an objective and significant decrease in the size of the tumor or a reduction in symptoms related to the tumor. Stabilization is not considered a response to therapy.
- The appropriateness of the study design. Consider:

1. Whether the experimental design in light of the drugs and conditions under investigation is appropriate to address the investigative question. (For example, in some clinical studies, it may be unnecessary or not feasible to use randomization, double blind trials, placebos, or crossover.);
2. That nonrandomized clinical trials with a significant number of subjects may be a basis for supportive clinical evidence for determining accepted uses of drugs; and
3. That case reports are generally considered uncontrolled and anecdotal information and do not provide adequate supportive clinical evidence for determining accepted uses of drugs.

Use peer reviewed medical literature appearing in the following publications:

- *American Journal of Medicine;*
- *Annals of Internal Medicine;*
- *The Journal of the American Medical Association;*
- *Journal of Clinical Oncology;*
- *Blood;*
- *Journal of the National Cancer Institute;*
- *The New England Journal of Medicine;*
- *British Journal of Cancer;*
- *British Journal of Hematology;*
- *British Medical Journal;*
- *Cancer;*
- *Drugs;*
- *European Journal of Cancer* (formerly *European Journal of Cancer and Clinical Oncology)*;
- *Lancet;* or
- *Leukemia.*

You are not required to maintain copies of these publications. If a claim raises a question about the use of a drug for a purpose not included in the FDA approved labeling or the compendia, ask the physician to submit copies of relevant supporting literature

4. Unlabeled uses may also be considered medically accepted if determined by you to be medically accepted generally as safe and effective for the particular use.

NOTE: If a use is identified as not indicated by HCFA or the FDA or if a use is specifically identified as not indicated in one or more of the three compendia mentioned or if you determine based on peer reviewed medical literature that a particular use of a drug is not safe and effective, the off- label usage is not supported and, therefore, the drug is not covered.

5. Less Than Effective Drug.—This is a drug that has been determined by the Food and Drug Administration (FDA) to lack substantial evidence of effectiveness for all labeled indications.

Also, a drug that has been the subject of a Notice of an Opportunity for a Hearing (NOOH) published in the Federal Register before being withdrawn from the market, and for which the Secretary has not determined there is a compelling justification for its medical need, is considered less than effective. This includes any other drug product that is identical, similar, or related. Payment may not be made for a less than effective drug.

Because the FDA has not yet completed its identification of drug products that are still on the market, existing FDA efficacy decisions must be applied to all similar products once they are identified.

6. Denial of Medicare Payment for Compounded Drugs Produced in Violation of Federal Food, Drug, and Cosmetic Act.—The Food and Drug Administration (FDA) has found that, from time to time, firms established as retail pharmacies engage in mass production of compounded drugs, beyond the normal scope of pharmaceutical practice, in violation of the Federal Food, Drug, and Cosmetic Act (FFDCA). By compounding drugs on a large scale, a company may be operating as a drug manufacturer within the meaning of the FFDCA, without complying with requirements of that law. Such companies may be manufacturing drugs which are subject to the new drug application (NDA) requirements of the FFDCA, but for which FDA has not approved an NDA or which are misbranded or adulterated. If the manufacturing and processing procedures used by these facilities have not been approved by the FDA, the FDA has no assurance that the drugs these companies are producing are safe and effective. The safety and effectiveness issues pertain to such factors as chemical stability, purity, strength, bioequivalency, and bioavailability.

Section 1862(a)(1)(A) of the Act requires that drugs must be reasonable and necessary in order to by covered under Medicare. This means, in the case of drugs, they must have been approved for marketing by the FDA. Section 2049.4 instructs carriers to deny coverage for drugs that have not received final marketing approval by the FDA, unless instructed otherwise by HCFA. Section 2300.1 instructs carriers to deny coverage of services related to the use of noncovered drugs as well. Hence, if DME or a prosthetic device is used to administer a noncovered drug, coverage is denied for both the nonapproved drug and the DME or prosthetic device.

In those cases in which the FDA has determined that a company is producing compounded drugs in violation of the FFDCA, Medicare does not pay for the drugs because they do not meet the FDA approval requirements of the Medicare program. In addition, Medicare does not pay for the DME or prosthetic device used to administer such a drug if FDA determines that a required NDA has not been approved or that the drug is misbranded or adulterated.

HCFA will notify you when the FDA has determined that compounded drugs are being produced in violation of the FFDCA. Do not stop Medicare payment for such a drug unless you are notified that it is appropriate to do so through a subsequent instruction. In addition, if you or ROs become aware that other companies are possibly operating in violation of the FFDCA, notify:

Health Care Financing Administration Bureau of Policy Development Office of Physician and Ambulatory Care Policy Baltimore, MD 21244-1850

Self-Administered Drugs and Biologicals.—Drugs that are self-administered are not covered by Medicare Part B unless the statute provides for such coverage. This includes blood clotting factors, drugs used in immunosuppressive therapy, erythropoietin for dialysis patients, certain oral anti-cancer drugs, and oral anti-nausea drugs when used in certain situations.

A. Until January 1, 1995, immunosuppressive drugs are covered under Part B for a period of one year following discharge from a hospital for a Medicare covered organ transplant. HCFA interprets the 1-year period after the date of the transplant procedure to mean 365 days from the day on which an inpatient is discharged from the hospital. Beneficiaries are eligible to receive additional Part B coverage within 18 months after the discharge date for drugs furnished in 1995; within 24 months for drugs furnished in 1996; within 30 months for drugs furnished in 1997; and within 36 months for drugs furnished after 1997.

Covered drugs include those immunosuppressive drugs that have been specifically labeled as such and approved for marketing by the FDA, as well as those prescription drugs, such as prednisone, that are used in conjunction with immunosuppressive drugs as part of a therapeutic regimen reflected in FDA approved labeling for immunosuppressive drugs. Therefore, antibiotics, hypertensives, and other drugs that are not directly related to rejection are not covered. The FDA had identified and approved for marketing five specifically labeled immunosuppressive drugs. They are Sandimmune (cyclosporine),Sandoz Pharmaceutical; Imuran (azathioprine), Burroughs Wellcome; Atgam (antithymocyte globulin), Upjohn; and Orthoclone OKT3 (Muromonab-CD3), Ortho Pharmaceutical and, Prograf (tacrolimus), Fujisawa USA, Inc. You are expected to keep informed of FDA additions to the list of the immunosuppressive drugs.

B. Erythropoietin (EPO).—The statute provides that EPO is covered for the treatment of anemia for patients with chronic renal failure who are on dialysis. Coverage is available regardless of whether the drug is administered by the patient or the patient's caregiver. EPO is a biologically engineered protein which stimulates the bone marrow to make new red blood cells.

NOTE: Non-ESRD patients who are receiving EPO to treat anemia induced by other conditions such as chemotherapy or the drug zidovudine (commonly called AZT) must meet the coverage requirements in §2049.

EPO is covered for the treatment of anemia for patients with chronic renal failure who are on dialysis when:

- It is administered in the renal dialysis facility; or
- It is self-administered in the home by any dialysis patient (or patient caregiver) who is determined competent to use the drug and meets the other conditions detailed below.

NOTE: Payment may not be made for EPO under the incident to provision when EPO is administered in the renal dialysis facility. (See §5202.4.)

Medicare covers EPO and items related to its administration for dialysis patients who use EPO in the home when the following conditions are met.

1. Patient Care Plan.—A dialysis patient who uses EPO in the home must have a current care plan (a copy of which must be maintained by the designated back-up facility for Method II patients) for monitoring home use of EPO which includes the following:

    a. Review of diet and fluid intake for aberrations as indicated by hyperkalemia and elevated blood pressure secondary to volume overload;
    b. Review of medications to ensure adequate provision of supplemental iron;
    c. Ongoing evaluations of hematocrit and iron stores;
    d. Reevaluation of the dialysis prescription taking into account the patient's increased appetite and red blood cell volume;
    e. Method for physician and facility (including back-up facility for Method II patients) follow-up on blood tests and a mechanism (such as a patient log) for keeping the physician informed of the results;
    f. Training of the patient to identify the signs and symptoms of hypotension and hypertension; and
    g. The decrease or discontinuance of EPO if hypertension is uncontrollable.

2. Patient Selection.—The dialysis facility, or the physician responsible for all dialysis-related services furnished to the patient, must make a comprehensive assessment that includes the following:

    a. Pre-selection monitoring. The patient's hematocrit (or hemoglobin), serum iron, transferrin saturation, serum ferritin, and blood pressure must be measured.
    b. Conditions the patient must meet. The assessment must find that the patient meets the following conditions:

        (1) Is a dialysis patient;
        (2) Has a hematocrit (or comparable hemoglobin level) that is as follows:
            (a) For a patient who is initiating EPO treatment, no higher than 30 percent unless there is medical documentation showing the need for EPO despite a hematocrit (or comparable hemoglobin level) higher than 30 percent. Patients with severe angina, severe pulmonary distress, or severe hypotension may require EPO to prevent adverse symptoms even if they have higher hematocrit or hemoglobin levels.
            (b) For a patient who has been receiving EPO from the facility or the physician, between 30 and 36 percent; and

3. Is under the care of:

    a. A physician who is responsible for all dialysis-related services and who prescribes the EPO and follows the drug labeling instructions when monitoring the EPO home therapy; and

b. A renal dialysis facility that establishes the plan of care and monitors the progress of the home EPO therapy.

c. The assessment must find that the patient or a caregiver meets the following conditions:

(1) Is trained by the facility to inject EPO and is capable of carrying out the procedure;

(2) Is capable of reading and understanding the drug labeling; and

(3) Is trained in, and capable of observing, aseptic techniques.

d. Care and storage of drug. The assessment must find that EPO can be stored in the patient's residence under refrigeration and that the patient is aware of the potential hazard of a child's having access to the drug and syringes.

4. Responsibilities of Physician or Dialysis Facility.—The patient's physician or dialysis facility must:

a. Develop a protocol that follows the drug label instructions;

b. Make the protocol available to the patient to ensure safe and effective home use of EPO;

c. Through the amounts prescribed, ensure that the drug on hand at any time does not exceed a 2-month supply; and

d. Maintain adequate records to allow quality assurance for review by the network and State survey agencies. For Method II patients, current records must be provided to and maintained by the designated back-up facility.

See §5202.4 for information on EPO payment.

Submit claims for EPO in accordance with §§4273.1 and 4273.2.

C. Oral Anti-Cancer Drugs.—Effective January 1, 1994, Medicare Part B coverage is extended to include oral anti-cancer drugs that are prescribed as anti-cancer chemotherapeutic agents providing they have the same active ingredients and are used for the same indications as anti-cancer chemotherapeutic agents which would be covered if they were not self administered and they were furnished incident to a physician's service as drugs and biologicals.

This provision applies only to the coverage of anti-neoplastic chemotherapeutic agents. It does not apply to oral drugs and/or biologicals used to treat toxicity or side effects such as nausea or bone marrow depression. Medicare will cover anti-neoplastic chemotherapeutic agents, the primary drugs which directly fight the cancer, and self-administered antiemetics which are necessary for the administration and absorption of the anti-neoplastic chemotherapeutic agents when a high likelihood of vomiting exists. The substitution of an oral form of an anti-neoplastic drug requires that the drug be retained for absorption. The antiemetics drug is covered as a necessary means for administration of the oral drug (similar to a syringe and needle necessary for injectable administration).

Oral drugs prescribed for use with the primary drug which enhance the anti-neoplastic effect of the primary drug or permit the patient to tolerate the primary anti-neoplastic drug in higher doses for longer periods are not covered. Self-administered antiemetics to reduce the side effects of nausea and vomiting brought on by the primary drug are not included beyond the administration necessary to achieve drug absorption.

In order to assure uniform coverage policy, regional carriers and FIs must be apprised of local carriers' anti-cancer drug medical review policies which may impact on future medical review policy development. Local carrier's current and proposed anti-cancer drug medical review polices should be provided by local carrier medical directors to regional carrier or FI medical directors, upon request.

For an oral anti-cancer drug to be covered under Part B, it must:

- Be prescribed by a physician or other practitioner licensed under State law to prescribe such drugs as anti-cancer chemotherapeutic agents;
- Be a drug or biological that has been approved by the Food and Drug Administration (FDA);
- Have the same active ingredients as a non-self-administrable anti-cancer chemotherapeutic drug or biological that is covered when furnished incident to a physician's service. The oral anti-cancer drug and the non-self-administrable drug must have the same chemical/generic name as indicated by the FDA's Approved Drug Products (Orange Book), Physician's Desk Reference (PDR), or an authoritative drug compendium; —or, effective January 1, 1999, be a prodrug—an oral drug ingested into the body that metabolizes into the same active ingredient that is found in the non-self-administrable form of the drug;
- Be used for the same indications, including unlabeled uses, as the non-self-administrable version of the drug; and
- Be reasonable and necessary for the individual patient.

D. Oral Anti-Nausea Drugs—Section 4557 of the Balanced Budget Act of 1997 amends §1861(s)(2) by extending the coverage of oral anti-emetic drugs under the following conditions:

- Coverage is provided only for oral drugs approved by FDA for use as anti-emetics; the oral anti-emetic(s) must either be administered by the treating physician or in accordance with a written order from the physician as part of a cancer chemotherapy regimen;
- Oral anti-emetic drug(s) administered with a particular chemotherapy treatment must be initiated within 2 hours of the administration of the chemotherapeutic agent and may be continued for a period not to exceed 48 hours from that time.
- The oral anti-emetic drug(s) provided must be used as a full therapeutic replacement for the intravenous anti-emetic drugs that would have otherwise been administered at the time of the chemotherapy treatment.

Only drugs pursuant to a physician's order at the time of the chemotherapy treatment qualify for this benefit. The dispensed number of dosage units may not exceed a loading dose administered within 2 hours of that treatment, plus a supply of additional dosage units not to exceed 48 hours of therapy. However, more than one oral anti-emetic drug may be prescribed and will be covered for concurrent usage within these parameters if more than one oral drug is needed to fully replace the intravenous drugs that would otherwise have been given.

Oral drugs that are not approved by the FDA for use as anti-emetics and which are used by treating physicians adjunctively in a manner incidental to cancer chemotherapy are not covered by this benefit and are not reimbursable within the scope of this benefit.

It is recognized that a limited number of patients will fail on oral anti-emetic drugs. Intravenous anti-emetics may be covered (subject to the rules of medical necessity) when furnished to patients who fail on oral anti-emetic therapy.

This coverage, effective for services on or after January 1, 1998, is subject to regular Medicare Part B coinsurance and deductible provisions.

NOTE: Existing coverage policies authorizing the administration of suppositories to prevent vomiting when oral cancer drugs are used are unchanged by this new coverage.

E. Hemophilia Clotting Factors.—Section 1861(s)(2)(I) of the Act provides Medicare coverage of blood clotting factors for hemophilia patients competent to use such factors to control bleeding without medical supervision, and items related to the administration of such factors. Hemophilia, a blood disorder characterized by prolonged coagulation time, Is caused by deficiency of a factor in plasma necessary for blood to clot. (The discovery in 1964 of a cryoprecipitate rich in antihemophilic factor activity facilitated management of acute bleeding episodes.) For purposes of Medicare Part B coverage, hemophilia encompasses the following conditions:

- Factor VIII deficiency (classic hemophilia);
- Factor IX deficiency (also termed plasma thromboplastin component (PTC) or Christmas factor deficiency); and
- Von Willebrand's disease.

Claims for blood clotting factors for hemophilia patients with these diagnoses may be covered if the patient is competent to use such factors without medical supervision.

The amount of clotting factors determined to be necessary to have on hand and thus covered under this provision is based on the historical utilization pattern or profile developed by the carrier for each patient. It is expected that the treating source; e.g., a family physician or comprehensive hemophilia diagnostic and treatment center, has such information. From this data, the contractor is able to make reasonable projections concerning the quantity of clotting factors anticipated to be needed by the patient over a specific period of time. Unanticipated occurrences involving extraordinary events, such as automobile accidents of inpatient hospital stays, will change this base line data and should be appropriately considered. In addition, changes in a patient's medical needs over a period of time require adjustments in the profile. (See §5245 for payment policies.)

2070.4 Coverage of Portable X-ray Services Not Under the Direct Supervision of a Physician.-

A. Diagnostic X-ray Tests.—Diagnostic x-ray services furnished by a portable x-ray supplier are covered under Part B when furnished in a place or residence used as the patient's home and in nonparticipating institutions. These services must be performed under the general supervision of a physician and certain conditions relating to health and safety (as prescribed by the Secretary) must be met.

Diagnostic portable x-ray services are also covered under Part B when provided in participating SNFs and hospitals, under circumstances in which they cannot be covered under hospital insurance, i.e., the services are not furnished by the participating institution either directly or under arrangements that provide for the institution to bill for the services. (See §2255 for reimbursement for Part B services furnished to inpatients of participating and nonparticipating institutions.)

B. Applicability of Health and Safety Standards.—The health and safety standards apply to all suppliers of portable x-ray services, except physicians who provide immediate personal supervision during the administration of diagnostic x-ray services. Payment is made only for services of approved suppliers who have been found to meet the standards. Notice of the coverage dates for services of approved suppliers are given to carriers by the RO.

When the services of a supplier of portable x-ray services no longer meet the conditions of coverage, physicians having an interest in the supplier's certification status must be notified. The notification action regarding suppliers of portable x-ray equipment is the same as required for decertification of independent laboratories, and the procedures explained in §2070.1C should be followed.

C. Scope of Portable X-Ray Benefit.—In order to avoid payment for services which are inadequate or hazardous to the patient, the scope of the covered portable x-ray benefit is defined as:

- Skeletal films involving arms and legs, pelvis, vertebral column, and skull;
- Chest films which do not involve the use of contrast media (except routine screening procedures and tests in connection with routine physical examinations); and
- Abdominal films which do not involve the use of contrast media.

D. Exclusions From Coverage as Portable X-Ray Services.— Procedures and examinations which are not covered under the portable x-ray provision include the following:

- Procedures involving fluoroscopy;
- Procedures involving the use of contrast media;
- Procedures requiring the administration of a substance to the patient or injection of a substance into the patient and/or special manipulation of the patient;
- Procedures which require special medical skill or knowledge possessed by a doctor of medicine or doctor of osteopathy or which require that medical judgment be exercised;
- Procedures requiring special technical competency and/or special equipment or materials;
- Routine screening procedures; and
- Procedures which are not of a diagnostic nature.

E. Reimbursement Procedure.

1. Name of Ordering Physician. — Assure that portable x-ray tests have been provided on the written order of a physician. Accordingly, if a bill does not include the name of the physician who ordered the service, that information must be obtained before payment may be made.

2. Reason Chest X-Ray Ordered. — Because all routine screening procedures and tests in connection with routine physical examinations are excluded from coverage under Medicare, all bills for portable x-ray services involving the chest contain, in addition to the name of the physician who ordered the service, the reason an x-ray test was required.

If this information is not shown, it is obtained from either the supplier or the physician. If the test was for an excluded routine service, no payment may be made.

See also §§4110 ff. for additional instructions on reviewing bills involving portable x-ray.

F. Electrocardiograms.—The taking of an electrocardiogram tracing by an approved supplier of portable x-ray services may be covered as an "other diagnostic test." The health and safety standards referred to in §2070.4B are thus also applicable to such diagnostic EKG services, e.g., the technician must meet the personnel qualification requirements in the Conditions for Coverage of Portable x-ray Services. (See §50-15 (Electrocardiographic Services) in the Coverage Issues Manual.)

2079 SURGICAL DRESSINGS, AND SPLINTS, CASTS, AND OTHER DEVICES USED FOR REDUCTIONS OF FRACTURES AND DISLOCATIONS

Surgical dressings are limited to primary and secondary dressings required for the treatment of a wound caused by, or treated by, a surgical procedure that has been performed by a physician or other health care professional to the extent permissible under State law. In addition, surgical dressings required after debridement of a wound are also covered, irrespective of the type of debridement, as long as the debridement was reasonable and necessary and was performed by a health care professional who was acting within the scope of his or her legal authority when performing this function. Surgical dressings are covered for as long as they are medically necessary.

Primary dressings are therapeutic or protective coverings applied directly to wounds or lesions either on the skin or caused by an opening to the skin. Secondary dressing materials that serve a therapeutic or protective function and that are needed to secure a primary dressing are also covered. Items such as adhesive tape, roll gauze, bandages, and disposable compression material are examples of secondary dressings. Elastic stockings, support hose, foot coverings, leotards, knee supports, surgical leggings, gauntlets, and pressure garments for the arms and hands are examples of items that are not ordinarily covered as surgical dressings. Some items, such as transparent film, may be used as a primary or secondary dressing.

If a physician, certified nurse midwife, physician assistant, nurse practitioner, or clinical nurse specialist applies surgical dressings as part of a professional service that is billed to Medicare, the surgical dressings are considered incident to the professional services of the health care practitioner. (See sections 2050.1, 2154, 2156, 2158, and 2160.) When surgical dressings are not covered incident to the services of a health care practitioner and are obtained by the patient from a supplier (e.g., a drugstore, physician, or other health care practitioner that qualifies as a supplier) on an order from a physician or other health care professional authorized under State law or regulation to make such an order, the surgical dressings are covered separately under Part B.

2100 DURABLE MEDICAL EQUIPMENT - GENERAL

Expenses incurred by a beneficiary for the rental or purchase of durable medical equipment (DME) are reimbursable if the following three requirements are met. The decision whether to rent or purchase an item of equipment resides with the beneficiary.

A. The equipment meets the definition of DME (§2100.1); and
B. The equipment is necessary and reasonable for the treatment of the patient's illness or injury or to improve the functioning of his malformed body member (§2100.2); and
C. The equipment is used in the patient's home (§2100.3).

Payment may also be made under this provision for repairs, maintenance, and delivery of equipment as well as for expendable and nonreusable items essential to the effective use of the equipment subject to the conditions in §2100.4.

See §2105 and its appendix for coverage guidelines and screening list of DME. See §4105.3 for models of payment: decisions as to rental or purchase, lump sum and periodic payments, etc. Where covered DME is furnished to a beneficiary by a supplier of services other than a provider of services, reimbursement is made by the carrier on the basis of the reasonable charge. If the equipment is furnished by a provider of services, reimbursement is made to the provider by the intermediary on a reasonable cost basis; see Coverage Issues Appendix 25-1 for hemodialysis equipment and supplies.

2100.1 Definition of Durable Medical Equipment.—Durable medical equipment is equipment which a) can withstand repeated use, and b) is primarily and customarily used to serve a medical purpose, and c) generally is not useful to a person in the absence of an illness or injury; and d) is appropriate for use in the home.

All requirements of the definition must be met before an item can be considered to be durable medical equipment.

A. Durability.—An item is considered durable if it can withstand repeated use, i.e., the type of item which could normally be rented. Medical supplies of an expendable nature such as, incontinent pads, lambs wool pads, catheters, ace bandages, elastic stockings, surgical face masks, irrigating kits, sheets and bags are not considered "durable" within the meaning of the definition. There are other items which, although durable in nature, may fall into other coverage categories such as braces, prosthetic devices, artificial arms, legs, and eyes.

B. Medical Equipment.—Medical equipment is equipment which is primarily and customarily used for medical purposes and is not generally useful in the absence of illness or injury. In most instances, no development will be needed to determine whether a specific item of equipment is medical in nature. However, some cases will require development to determine whether the item constitutes medical equipment. This development would include the advice of local medical organizations (hospitals, medical schools, medical societies) and specialists in the field of physical medicine and rehabilitation. If the equipment is new on the market, it may be necessary, prior to seeking professional advice, to obtain information from the supplier or manufacturer explaining the design, purpose, effectiveness and method of using the equipment in the home as well as the results of any tests or clinical studies that have been conducted.

1. Equipment Presumptively Medical.—Items such as hospital beds, wheelchairs, hemodialysis equipment, iron lungs, respirators, intermittent positive pressure breathing machines, medical regulators, oxygen tents, crutches, canes, trapeze bars, walkers, inhalators, nebulizers, commodes, suction machines and traction equipment presumptively constitute medical equipment. (Although hemodialysis equipment is a prosthetic device (§ 2130), it also meets the definition of DME, and reimbursement for the rental or purchase of such equipment for use in the beneficiary's home will be made only under the provisions for payment applicable to DME. See 25-1 and 25-2 of the Coverage Issues Appendix for coverage of home use of hemodialysis.)

NOTE: There is a wide variety in type of respirators and suction machines. The carrier's medical staff should determine whether the apparatus specified in the claim is appropriate for home use.

2. Equipment Presumptively Nonmedical.—Equipment which is primarily and customarily used for a nonmedical purpose may not be considered "medical" equipment for which payment can be made under the medical insurance program. This is true even though the item has some remote medically related use. For example, in the case of a cardiac patient, an air conditioner might possibly be used to lower room temperature to reduce fluid loss in the patient and to restore an environment conducive to maintenance of the proper fluid balance. Nevertheless, because the primary and customary use of an air conditioner is a nonmedical one, the air conditioner cannot be deemed to be medical equipment for which payment can be made.

Other devices and equipment used for environmental control or to enhance the environmental setting in which the beneficiary is placed are not considered covered DME. These include, for example, room heaters, humidifiers, dehumidifiers, and electric air cleaners. Equipment which basically serves comfort or convenience functions or is primarily for the convenience of a person caring for the patient, such as elevators, stairway elevators, and posture chairs do not constitute medical equipment. Similarly, physical fitness equipment, e.g., an exercycle; first-aid or precautionary-type equipment, e.g., present portable oxygen units; self-help devices, e.g., safety grab bars; and training equipment, e.g., speech teaching machines and braille training texts, are considered nonmedical in nature.

3. Special Exception Items.—Specified items of equipment may be covered under certain conditions even though they do not meet the definition of DME because they are not primarily and customarily used to serve a medical purpose and/or are generally useful in the absence of illness or injury. These items would be covered when it is clearly established that they serve a therapeutic purpose in an individual case and would include:

   a. Gel pads and pressure and water mattresses (which generally serve a preventive purpose) when prescribed for a patient who had bed sores or there is medical evidence indicating that he is highly susceptible to such ulceration; and

   b. Heat lamps for a medical rather than a soothing or cosmetic purpose, e.g., where the need for heat therapy has been established.

In establishing medical necessity (§2100.2) for the above items, the evidence must show that the item is included in the physician's course of treatment and a physician is supervising its use. (See also Appendix to § 2105.)

NOTE: The above items represent special exceptions and no extension of coverage to other items should be inferred.

Repairs, Maintenance, Replacement, and Delivery.—Under the circumstances specified below, payment may be made for repair, maintenance, and replacement of medically required DME, including equipment which had been in use before the user enrolled in Part B of the program. However, do not pay for repair, maintenance, or replacement of equipment in the frequent and substantial servicing or oxygen equipment payment categories. In addition, payments for repair and maintenance may not include payment for parts and labor covered under a manufacturer's or supplier's warranty.

A. Repairs.— To repair means to fix or mend and to put the equipment back in good condition after damage or wear. Repairs to equipment which a beneficiary owns are covered when necessary to make the equipment serviceable. However, do not pay for repair of previously denied equipment or equipment in the frequent and substantial servicing or oxygen equipment payment categories. If the expense for repairs exceeds the estimated expense of purchasing or renting another item of equipment for the remaining period of medical need, no payment can be made for the amount of the excess. (See subsection C where claims for repairs suggest malicious damage or culpable neglect.)

Since renters of equipment recover from the rental charge the expenses they incur in maintaining in working order the equipment they rent out, separately itemized charges for repair of rented equipment are not covered. This includes items in the frequent and substantial servicing, oxygen equipment, capped rental, and inexpensive or routinely purchased payment categories which are being rented.

A new Certificate of Medical Necessity (CMN) and/or physician's order is not needed for repairs. For replacement items, see Subsection C below.

B. Maintenance.—Routine periodic maintenance, such as testing, cleaning, regulating and checking of the beneficiary's equipment is not covered. Such routine maintenance is generally expected to be done by the owner rather than by a retailer or some other person who charges the beneficiary. Normally, purchasers of DME are given operating manuals which describe the type of servicing an owner may perform to properly maintain the equipment. It is reasonable to expect that beneficiaries will perform this maintenance. Thus, hiring a third party to do such work is for the convenience of the beneficiary and is not covered.

However, more extensive maintenance which, based on the manufacturers' recommendations, is to be performed by authorized technicians, is covered as repairs for medically necessary equipment which a beneficiary owns. This might include, for example, breaking down sealed components and performing tests which require specialized testing equipment not available to the beneficiary. Do not pay for maintenance of purchased items that require frequent and substantial servicing or oxygen equipment. See §5102.2.G.

Since renters of equipment recover from the rental charge the expenses they incur in maintaining in working order the equipment they rent out, separately itemized charges for maintenance of rented equipment are generally not covered. Payment may not be made for maintenance of rented equipment other than the maintenance and servicing fee established for capped rental items in §5102.1.E.4.

A new CMN and/or physician's order is not needed for covered maintenance.

C. Replacement.—Replacement refers to the provision of an identical or nearly identical item. Situations involving the provision of a different item because of a change in medical condition are not addressed in this section.

Equipment which the beneficiary owns or is a capped rental item may be replaced in cases of loss or irreparable damage. Irreparable damage refers to a specific accident or to a natural disaster (e.g., fire, flood, etc.). A physician's order and/or new Certificate of Medical Necessity (CMN), when required, is needed to reaffirm the medical necessity of the item.

Irreparable wear refers to deterioration sustained from day-to-day usage over time and a specific event cannot be identified. Replacement of equipment due to irreparable wear takes into consideration the reasonable useful lifetime of the equipment. If the item of equipment has been in continuous use by the patient on either a rental or purchase basis for the equipment's useful lifetime, the beneficiary may elect to obtain a new piece of equipment. Replacement may be reimbursed when a new physician order and/or new CMN, when required, is needed to reaffirm the medical necessity of the item.

The reasonable useful lifetime of durable medical equipment is determined through program instructions. In the absence of program instructions, carriers may determine the reasonable useful lifetime of equipment, but in no case can it be less than 5 years. Computation of the useful lifetime is based on when the equipment is delivered to the beneficiary, not the age of the equipment. Replacement due to wear is not covered during the reasonable useful lifetime of the equipment. During the reasonable useful lifetime, Medicare does cover repair up to the cost of replacement (but not actual replacement) for medically necessary equipment owned by the beneficiary. (See subsection A.)

Charges for the replacement of oxygen equipment, items that require frequent and substantial servicing or inexpensive or routinely purchased items which are being rented are not covered.

Cases suggesting malicious damage, culpable neglect or wrongful disposition of equipment as discussed in §2100.6 should be investigated and denied where the DMERC/Carrier determines that it is unreasonable to make program payment under the circumstances.

D. Delivery.—Payment for delivery of DME whether rented or purchased is generally included in the fee schedule allowance for the item. See §5105 for the rules that apply to making reimbursement for exceptional cases.

E. Leased Renal Dialysis Equipment.—Generally, where renal dialysis equipment is leased directly from the manufacturer, the rental charge is closely related to the manufacturer's cost of the equipment which means it does not include a margin for recovering the cost of repairs beyond the initial warranty period.

In view of physical distance and other factors which may make it impractical for the manufacturer to perform repairs, it is not feasible to make the manufacturer responsible for all repairs and include a margin for the additional costs. Therefore, reimbursement may be made for the repair and maintenance of home dialysis equipment leased directly from the manufacturer (or other party acting essentially as an intermediary between the patient and the manufacturer for the purpose of assuming the financial risk) if the rental charge does not include a margin to recover these costs, and then only when the patient is free to secure repairs locally in the most economical manner.

Where, on the other hand, a third party is in the business of medical equipment retail supply and rental, the presumption that there is a margin in the rental charge for dialysis equipment to cover the costs of repair services will be retained. The exclusion from coverage of separately itemized repair charges will, therefore, continue to be applied in these situations, and the patient must look to the supplier to perform (or cover the cost of) necessary repairs, maintenance, and replacement of the home dialysis equipment.

In all cases, whether the dialysis equipment is being purchased, is owned outright, or is being leased, Medicare payment is to be made only after the initial warranty period has expired. Generally, reimbursement for repairs, maintenance, and replacement parts for medically necessary home dialysis equipment may be made in a lump sum payment. However, where extensive repairs are required and the charge for repairing the item represents a substantial proportion of the purchase price of a replacement system, exercise judgment with respect to a possible need to make periodic payments, instead of a lump-sum payment, for repair of such equipment.

As in the case of the maintenance of purchased DME, routine periodic servicing of leased dialysis equipment, including most testing and cleaning, is not covered. While reimbursement will be made for more extensive maintenance and necessary repairs of leased dialysis equipment, the patient or family member is expected to perform those services for which the training for home or self-dialysis would have qualified them, e.g., replacement of a light bulb.

Reasonable charges for travel expenses related to the repair of leased dialysis equipment are covered if the repairman customarily charges for travel and this is a common practice among other repairman in the area. When a repair charge includes an element for travel, however, the location of other suitably qualified repairmen will be considered in determining the allowance for travel.

NOTE: The above coverage instructions pertain to a special case and no extension of such coverage with respect to other items should be inferred.

Coverage of Supplies and Accessories.— Reimbursement may be made for supplies, e.g., oxygen (see §60-4 in the Coverage Issues Manual for the coverage of oxygen in the home), that are necessary for the effective use of durable medical equipment. Such supplies include those drugs and biologicals which must be put directly into the equipment in order to achieve the therapeutic benefit of the durable medical equipment or to assure the proper functioning of the equipment, e.g., tumor chemotherapy agents used with an infusion pump or heparin used with a home dialysis system. However, the coverage of such drugs or biologicals does not preclude the need for a determination that the drug or biological itself is reasonable and necessary for treatment of the illness or injury or to improve the functioning of a malformed body member.

In the case of prescription drugs, other than oxygen, used in conjunction with durable medical equipment, prosthetic, orthotics, and supplies (DMEPOS) or prosthetic devices, the entity that dispenses the drug must furnish it directly to the patient for whom a prescription is written. The entity that dispenses the drugs must have a Medicare supplier number, must possess a current license to dispense prescription drugs in the State in which the drug is dispensed, and must bill and receive payment in its own name.

A supplier that is not the entity that dispenses the drugs cannot purchase the drugs used in conjunction with DME for resale to the beneficiary. Payments made for drugs provided on or after December 1, 1996 to suppliers not having a valid pharmacy license to dispense prescription drugs must be recouped.

2120.1 Vehicle and Crew Requirement

A. The Vehicle.—The vehicle must be a specially designed and equipped automobile or other vehicle (in some areas of the United States this might be a boat or plane) for transporting the sick or injured. It must have customary patient care equipment including a stretcher, clean linens, first aid supplies, oxygen equipment, and it must also have such other safety and lifesaving equipment as is required by State or local authorities.

B. The Crew.—The ambulance crew must consist of at least two members. Those crew members charged with the care or handling of the patient must include one individual with adequate first aid training, i.e., training at least equivalent to that provided by the standard and advanced Red Cross first aid courses. Training "equivalent" to the standard and advanced Red Cross first aid training courses included ambulance service training and experience acquired in military service, successful completion by the individual of a comparable first aid course furnished by or under the sponsorship of State or local authorities, an educational institution, a fire department, a hospital, a professional organization, or other such qualified organization. On-the-job training involving the administration of first aid under the supervision of or in conjunction with trained first aid personnel for a period of time sufficient to assure the trainee's proficiency in handling the wide range of patient care services that may have to be performed by a qualified attendant can also be considered as "equivalent training."

C.   Verification of Compliance.—In determining whether the vehicles and personnel of each supplier meet all of the above requirements, carriers may accept the supplier's statement (absent information to the contrary) that its vehicles and personnel meet all of the requirements if (1) the statement describes the first aid, safety, and other patient care items with which the vehicles are equipped, (2) the statement shows the extent of first aid training acquired by the personnel assigned to those vehicles, (3) the statement contains the supplier's agreement to notify the carrier of any change in operation which could affect the coverage of his ambulance services, and (4) the information provided indicates that the requirements are met. The statement must be accompanied by documentary evidence that the ambulance has the equipment required by State and local authorities. Documentary evidence could include a letter from such authorities, a copy of a license, permit certificate, etc., issued by the authorities. The statement and supporting documentation would be kept on file by the carrier.

When a supplier does not submit such a statement or whenever there is a question about a supplier's compliance with any of the above requirements for vehicle and crew (including suppliers who have completed the statement), carriers should take appropriate action including, where necessary, on-site inspection of the vehicles and verification of the qualifications of personnel to determine whether the ambulance service qualifies for reimbursement under Medicare. Since the requirements described above for coverage of ambulance services are applicable to the overall operation of the ambulance supplier's service, it is not required that information regarding personnel and vehicles be obtained on an individual trip basis.

D.   Ambulance of Providers of Services.—The Part A intermediary is responsible for the processing of claims for ambulance service furnished by participating hospitals, skilled nursing facilities and home health agencies and has the responsibility to determine the compliance of provider's ambulance and crew. Since provider ambulance services furnished "under arrangements" with suppliers can be covered only if the supplier meets the above requirements, the Part A intermediary may ask the carrier to identify those suppliers who meet the requirements.

E.   Equipment and Supplies.—As mentioned above, the ambulance must have customary patient care equipment and first aid supplies. Reusable devices and equipment such as backboards, neck boards and inflatable leg and arm splints are considered part of the general ambulance service and would be included in the charge for the trip. On the other hand, separate reasonable charge based on actual quantities used may be recognized for nonreusable items and disposable supplies such as oxygen, gauze and dressings required in the care of the patient during his trip.

2125 COVERAGE GUIDELINES FOR AMBULANCE SERVICE CLAIMS

Reimbursement may be made for expenses incurred by a patient for ambulance service provided the following conditions have been met:

A. Patient was transported by an approved supplier of ambulance services.

B. The patient was suffering from an illness or injury which contraindicated transportation by other means. (section 2120.2A)

C. The patient was transported from and to points listed below.(section 2120.3)

1. From patient's residence (or other place where need arose) to hospital or skilled nursing home.

2. Skilled nursing home to a hospital or hospital to a skilled nursing home.

3. Hospital to hospital or skilled nursing home to skilled nursing home.

4. From a hospital or skilled nursing home to patient's residence.

5. Round trip for hospital or participating skilled nursing facility inpatients to the nearest hospital or nonhospital treatment facility

A patient's residence is the place where he makes his home and dwells permanently, or for an extended period of time. A skilled nursing home is one which is listed in the Directory of Medical Facilities as a participating SNF or as an institution which meets section 1861(j)(1) of the law. Ambulance service to a physician's office or a physician-directed clinic is not covered. (See section 2120.3G where a stop is made at a physician's office enroute to a hospital and 2120.3C for additional exceptions.)

2130 PROSTHETIC DEVICES

A. General.—Prosthetic devices (other than dental) which replace all or part of an internal body organ (including contiguous tissue), or replace all or part of the function of a permanently inoperative or malfunctioning internal body organ are covered when furnished on a physician's order. This does not require a determination that there is no possibility that the patient's condition may improve sometime in the future. If the medical record, including the judgment of the attending physician, indicates the condition is of long and indefinite duration, the test of permanence is considered met. (Such a device may also be covered under §2050.l as a supply when furnished incident to a physician's service.)

Examples of prosthetic devices include cardiac pacemakers, prosthetic lenses (see subsection B), breast prostheses (including a surgical brassiere) for postmastectomy patients, maxillofacial devices and devices which replace all or part of the ear or nose. A urinary collection and retention system with or without a tube is a prosthetic device replacing bladder function in case of permanent urinary incontinence. The Foley catheter is also considered a prosthetic device when ordered for a patient with permanent urinary incontinence. However, chucks, diapers, rubber sheets, etc., are supplies that are not covered under this provision. (Although hemodialysis equipment is a prosthetic device, payment for the rental or purchase of such equipment for use in the home is made only under the provisions for payment applicable to durable medical equipment (see §4105ff) or the special rules that apply to the ESRD program.)

NOTE: Medicare does not cover a prosthetic device dispensed to a patient prior to the time at which the patient undergoes the procedure that makes necessary the use of the device. For example, do not make a separate Part B payment for an intraocular lens (IOL) or pacemaker that a physician, during an office visit prior to the actual surgery, dispenses to the patient for his/her use. Dispensing a prosthetic device in this manner raises health and safety issues. Moreover, the need for the device cannot be clearly established until the procedure that makes its use possible is successfully performed.

Therefore, dispensing a prosthetic device in this manner is not considered reasonable and necessary for the treatment of the patient's condition.

Colostomy (and other ostomy) bags and necessary accouterments required for attachment are covered as prosthetic devices. This coverage also includes irrigation and flushing equipment and other items and supplies directly related to ostomy care, whether the attachment of a bag is required.

Accessories and/or supplies which are used directly with an enteral or parenteral device to achieve the therapeutic benefit of the prosthesis or to assure the proper functioning of the device are covered under the prosthetic device benefit subject to the additional guidelines in the Coverage Issues Manual §§65-10 - 65-10.3.

Covered items include catheters, filters, extension tubing, infusion bottles, pumps (either food or infusion), intravenous (I.V) pole, needles, syringes, dressings, tape, Heparin Sodium (parenteral only), volumetric monitors (parenteral only), and parenteral and enteral nutrient solutions. Baby food and other regular grocery products that can be blenderized and used with the enteral system are not covered. Note that some of these items, e.g., a food pump and an I.V. pole, qualify as DME. Although coverage of the enteral and parenteral nutritional therapy systems is provided on the basis of the prosthetic device benefit, the payment rules relating to rental or purchase of DME apply of such items. (See §4105.3.) Code claims in accordance with the HCFA Common procedure Coding System (HCPCS).

The coverage of prosthetic devices includes replacement of and repairs to such devices as explained in subsection D.

B. Prosthetic Lenses.—The term "internal body organ" includes the lens of an eye. Prostheses replacing the lens of an eye include post-surgical lenses customarily used during convalescence from eye surgery in which the lens of the eye was removed. In addition, permanent lenses are also covered when required by an individual lacking the organic lens of the eye because of surgical removal or congenital absence. Prosthetic lenses obtained on or after the beneficiary's date of entitlement to supplementary medical insurance benefits may be covered even though the surgical removal of the crystalline lens occurred before entitlement.

1. Prosthetic Cataract Lenses.—Make payment for one of the following prosthetic lenses or combinations of prosthetic lenses when determined to be medically necessary by a physician (see §2020.25 for coverage of prosthetic lenses prescribed by a doctor of optometry) to restore essentially the vision provided by the crystalline lens of the eye:

    *   prosthetic bifocal lenses in frames;
    *   prosthetic lenses in frames for far vision, and prosthetic lenses in frames for near vision; or
    *   when a prosthetic contact lens(es) for far vision is prescribed (including cases of binocular and monocular aphakia), make payment for the contact lens(es) and prosthetic lenses in frames for near vision to be worn at the same time as the contact lens(es), and prosthetic lenses in frames to be worn when the contacts have been removed.

    Make payment for lenses which have ultraviolet absorbing or reflecting properties, in lieu of payment for regular (untinted) lenses, if it has been determined that such lenses are medically reasonable and necessary for the individual patient.

Do not make payment for cataract sunglasses obtained in addition to the regular (untinted) prosthetic lenses since the sunglasses duplicate the restoration of vision function performed by the regular prosthetic lenses.

2. Payment for IOLs Furnished in Ambulatory Surgical Centers (ASCs). Effective for services furnished on or after March 12, 1990, payment for IOLs inserted during or subsequent to cataract surgery in a Medicare certified ASC is included with the payment for facility services that are furnished in connection with the covered surgery. Section 5243.3 explains payment procedures for ASC facility services and the IOL allowance.

3. Limitation on Coverage of Conventional Lenses.—Make payment for no more than one pair of conventional eyeglasses or conventional contact lenses furnished after each cataract surgery with insertion of an IOL.

C. Dentures.—Dentures are excluded from coverage. However, when a denture or a portion thereof is an integral part (built-in) of a covered prosthesis (e.g., an obturator to fill an opening in the palate), it is covered as part of that prosthesis.

D. Supplies, Repairs, Adjustments, and Replacement.—Make payment for supplies that are necessary for the effective use of a prosthetic device (e.g., the batteries needed to operate an artificial larynx). Adjustment of prosthetic devices required by wear or by a change in the patient's condition is covered when ordered by a physician. To the extent applicable, follow the provisions relating to the repair and replacement of durable medical equipment in §2100.4 for the repair and replacement of prosthetic devices. (See §2306.D in regard to payment for devices replaced under a warranty.) Regardless of the date that the original eyewear was furnished (i.e., whether before, on, or after January 1, 1991), do not pay for replacement of conventional eyeglasses or contact lenses covered under subsection B.3.

Necessary supplies, adjustments, repairs, and replacements are covered even when the device had been in use before the user enrolled in Part B of the program, so long as the device continues to be medically required.

2133 LEG, ARM, BACK, AND NECK BRACES, TRUSSES, AND ARTIFICIAL LEGS, ARMS, AND EYES

These appliances are covered when furnished incident to physicians' services or on a physician's order. A brace includes rigid and semi-rigid devices which are used for the purpose of supporting a weak or deformed body member or restricting or eliminating motion in a diseased or injured part of the body. Elastic stockings, garter belts, and similar devices do not come within the scope of the definition of a brace. Back braces include, but are not limited to, special corsets, e.g., sacroiliac, sacrolumbar, dorsolumbar corsets and belts. A terminal device (e.g., hand or hook) is covered under this provision whether an artificial limb is required by the patient. (See §2323.) Stump stockings and harnesses (including replacements) are also covered when these appliances are essential to the effective use of the artificial limb.

Adjustments to an artificial limb or other appliance required by wear or by a change in the patient's condition are covered when ordered by a physician. To the extent applicable, follow the provisions in §2100.4 relating to the repair and replacement of durable medical equipment for the repair and replacement of artificial limbs, braces, etc. Adjustments, repairs and replacements are covered even when the item had been in use before the user enrolled in Part B of the program so long as the device continues to be medically required.

2134 THERAPEUTIC SHOES FOR INDIVIDUALS WITH DIABETES

Coverage of therapeutic shoes (depth or custom-molded) along with inserts for individuals with diabetes is available as of May 1, 1993. These diabetic shoes are covered if the requirements as specified in this section concerning certification and prescription are fulfilled. In addition, this benefit provides for a pair of diabetic shoes even if only one foot suffers from diabetic foot disease. Each shoe is equally equipped so that the affected limb, as well as the remaining limb, is protected.

Claims for therapeutic shoes for diabetics are processed by the Durable Medical Equipment Regional Carriers (DMERCs.)

A. Definitions.—The following items may be covered under the diabetic shoe benefit:

    1. Custom-Molded Shoes.—Custom-molded shoes are shoes that are:

- Constructed over a positive model of the patient's foot; Made from leather or other suitable material of equal quality;
- Have removable inserts that can be altered or replaced as the patient's condition warrants; and
- Have some form of shoe closure.

    2. Depth Shoes.—Depth shoes are shoes that:

- Have a full length, heel-to-toe filler that, when removed, provides a minimum of 3/16 inch of additional depth used to accommodate custom-molded or customized inserts;
- Are made from leather or other suitable material of equal quality;
- Have some form of shoe closure; and
- Are available in full and half sizes with a minimum of 3 widths so that the sole is graded to the size and width of the upper portions of the shoes according to the American standard last sizing schedule or its equivalent. (The American standard last sizing schedule is the numerical shoe sizing system used for shoes sold in the United States.)

    3. Inserts.—Inserts are total contact, multiple density, removable inlays that are directly molded to the patient's foot or a model of the patient's foot and that are made of a suitable material with regard to the patient's condition.

B. Coverage.—

    1. Limitations.—For each individual, coverage of the footwear and inserts is limited to one of the following within one calendar year:

- No more than one pair of custom-molded shoes (including inserts provided with such shoes) and two additional pairs of inserts; or
- No more than one pair of depth shoes and three pairs of inserts (not including the non-customized removable inserts provided with such shoes).

2. Coverage of Diabetic Shoes and Brace.—Orthopedic shoes, as stated in §2323.D, generally are not covered. This exclusion does not apply to orthopedic shoes that are an integral part of a leg brace. In situations in which an individual qualifies for both diabetic shoes and a leg brace, these items are covered separately. Thus, the diabetic shoes may be covered if the requirements for this section are met, while the brace may be covered if the requirements of section 2133 are met.

3. Substitution of Modifications for Inserts.—An individual may substitute modification(s) of custom-molded or depth shoes instead of obtaining a pair(s) of inserts in any combination. Payment for the modification(s) may not exceed the limit set for the inserts for which the individual is entitled. The following is a list of the most common shoe modifications available, but it is not meant as an exhaustive list of the modifications available for diabetic shoes:

- Rigid Rocker Bottoms. These are exterior elevations with apex positions for 51 percent to 75 percent distance measured from the back end of the heel. The apex is a narrowed or pointed end of an anatomical structure. The apex must be positioned behind the metatarsal heads and tapering off sharply to the front tip of the sole. Apex height helps to eliminate pressure at the metatarsal heads.

  Rigidity is ensured by the steel in the shoe. The heel of the shoe tapers off in the back in order to cause the heel to strike in the middle of the heel.

- Roller Bottoms (Sole or Bar). These are the same as rocker bottoms, but the heel is tapered from the apex to the front tip of the sole.
- Metatarsal Bars.—An exterior bar is placed behind the metatarsal heads in order to remove pressure from the metatarsal heads. The bars are of various shapes, heights, and construction depending on the exact purpose.
- Wedges (Posting). Wedges are either of hind foot, fore foot, or both and may be in the middle or to the side. The function is to shift or transfer weight bearing upon standing or during ambulation to the opposite side for added support, stabilization, equalized weight distribution, or balance.
- Offset Heels. This is a heel flanged at its base either in the middle, to the side, or a combination, that is then extended upward to the shoe in order to stabilize extreme positions of the hind foot.
- Other modifications to diabetic shoes include, but are not limited to:

  - Flared heels;
  - Velcro closures; and Inserts for missing toes.

4. Separate Inserts. Inserts may be covered and dispensed independently of diabetic shoes if the supplier of the shoes verifies in writing that the patient has appropriate footwear into which the insert can be placed. This footwear must meet the definitions found above for depth shoes and custom-molded shoes.

C. Certification. The need for diabetic shoes must be certified by a physician who is a doctor of medicine or a doctor of osteopathy and who is responsible for diagnosing and treating the patient's diabetic systemic condition through a comprehensive plan of care. This managing physician must:

- Document in the patient's medical record that the patient has diabetes;

- Certify that the patient is being treated under a comprehensive plan of care for his or her diabetes, and that he or she needs diabetic shoes; and
- Document in the patient's record that the patient has one or more of the following conditions:

  - Peripheral neuropathy with evidence of callus formation;
  - History of pre-ulcerative calluses;
  - History of previous ulceration;
  - Foot deformity;
  - Previous amputation of the foot or part of the foot; or
  - Poor circulation.

D. Prescription. Following certification by the physician managing the patient's systemic diabetic condition, a podiatrist or other qualified physician who is knowledgeable in the fitting of diabetic shoes and inserts may prescribe the particular type of footwear necessary.

E. Furnishing Footwear. The footwear must be fitted and furnished by a podiatrist or other qualified individual such as a pedorthist, an orthotist, or a prosthetist. The certifying physician may not furnish the diabetic shoes unless he or she is the only qualified individual in the area. It is left to the discretion of each carrier to determine the meaning of "in the area."

F. Payment. For 1994, payment for diabetic shoes and inserts is limited to 80 percent of the reasonable charge, up to a limit of $348 for one pair of custom-molded shoes including any initial inserts, $59 for each additional pair of custom-molded shoe inserts, $116 for one pair of depth shoes, and $59 for each pair of depth shoe inserts. These limits are based on 1988 amounts that were set forth in §1833(o) of the Act and then adjusted by the same percentage increases allowed for DME for fee screen limits by applying the same update factor that is applied to DME fees, except that if the updated limit is not a multiple of $1, it is rounded to the nearest multiple of $1.

Although percentage increase in payment for diabetic shoes are the same percentage increases that are used for payment of DME through the DME fee schedule, the shoes are not subject to DME coverage rules or the DME fee schedule. In addition, diabetic shoes are neither considered DME nor orthotics, but a separate category of coverage under Medicare Part B. (See §1861(s)(12) and §1833(o) of the Act.)

Payment for the certification of diabetic shoes and for the prescription of the shoes is considered to be included in the payment for the visit or consultation during which these services are provided. If the sole purpose of an encounter with the beneficiary is to dispense or fit the shoes, then no payment may be made for a visit or consultation provided on the same day by the same physician. Thus, a separate payment is not made for certification of the need for diabetic shoes, the prescribing of diabetic shoes, or the fitting of diabetic shoes unless the physician documents that these services were not the sole purpose of the visit or consultation.

2303 SERVICES NOT REASONABLE AND NECESSARY

Items and services which are not reasonable and necessary for the diagnosis or treatment of illness or injury, or to improve the functioning of a malformed body member; e.g., payment cannot be made for the rental of a special hospital bed to be used by the patient in his home unless it was a reasonable and necessary part of the patient's treatment. See also §2318.

2320 ROUTINE SERVICES AND APPLIANCES

Routine physical checkups; eyeglasses, contact lenses, and eye examinations for the purpose of prescribing, fitting or changing eyeglasses; eye refractions; hearing aids and examinations for hearing aids; and immunizations are not covered.

The routine physical checkup exclusion applies to (a) examinations performed without relationship to treatment or diagnosis for a specific illness, symptom, complaint, or injury, and (b) examinations required by third parties such as insurance companies, business establishments, or Government agencies.

(If the claim is for a diagnostic test or examination performed solely for the purpose of establishing a claim under title IV of Public Law 91-173 (Black Lung Benefits), advise the claimant to contact his/her Social Security office regarding the filing of a claim for reimbursement under that program.)

The exclusions apply to eyeglasses or contact lenses and eye examinations for the purpose of prescribing, fitting, or changing eyeglasses or contact lenses for refractive errors. The exclusions do not apply to physician services (and services incident to a physician's service) performed in conjunction with an eye disease (e.g., glaucoma or cataracts) or to postsurgical prosthetic lenses which are customarily used during convalescence from eye surgery in which the lens of the eye was removed or to permanent prosthetic lenses required by an individual lacking the organic lens of the eye, whether by surgical removal or congenital disease. Such prosthetic lens is a replacement for an internal body organ (the lens of the eye). (See §2130.)

The coverage of services rendered by an ophthalmologist is dependent on the purpose of the examination rather than on the ultimate diagnosis of the patient's condition. When a beneficiary goes to an ophthalmologist with a complaint or symptoms of an eye disease or injury, the ophthalmologist's services (except for eye refractions) are covered regardless of the fact that only eyeglasses were prescribed. However, when a beneficiary goes to his/her ophthalmologist for an eye examination with no specific complaint, the expenses for the examination are not covered even though as a result of such examination the doctor discovered a pathologic condition.

In the absence of evidence to the contrary, you may carrier may assume that an eye examination performed by an ophthalmologist on the basis of a complaint by the beneficiary or symptoms of an eye disease was not for the purpose of prescribing, fitting, or changing eyeglasses.

Expenses for all refractive procedures, whether performed by an ophthalmologist (or any other physician) or an optometrist and without regard to the reason for performance of the refraction, are excluded from coverage. (See
§§4125 and 5217 for claims review and reimbursement instructions concerning refractive services.)

With the exception of vaccinations for pneumococcal pneumonia, hepatitis B, and influenza, which are specifically covered under the law, vaccinations or inoculations are generally excluded as immunizations unless they are directly related to the treatment of an injury or direct exposure such as antirabies treatment, tetanus antitoxin or booster vaccine, botulin antitoxin, antivenin, or immune globulin.

2323 FOOT CARE AND SUPPORTIVE DEVICES FOR FEET

NOTE: See §4281 for the relationship between foot care and the coverage and billing of the diagnosis and treatment of peripheral neuropathy with loss of protective sensation (LOPS) in people with diabetes.

A. Exclusion of Coverage.—The following foot care services are generally excluded from coverage under both Part A and Part B. Exceptions to this general exclusion for limited treatment of routine foot care services are described in subsections A.2 and B. (See §4120 for procedural instructions in applying foot care exclusions.)

    1. Treatment of Flat Foot.—The term "flat foot" is defined as a condition in which one or more arches of the foot have flattened out. Services or devices directed toward the care or correction of such conditions, including the prescription of supportive devices, are not covered.

    2. Treatment of Subluxation of Foot.—Subluxations of the foot are defined as partial dislocations or displacements of joint surfaces, tendons ligaments, or muscles of the foot. Surgical or nonsurgical treatments undertaken for the sole purpose of correcting a subluxated structure in the foot as an isolated entity are not covered.

    This exclusion does not apply to medical or surgical treatment of subluxation of the ankle joint (talo-crural joint). In addition, reasonable and necessary medical or surgical services, diagnosis, or treatment for medical conditions that have resulted from or are associated with partial displacement of structures is covered. For example, if a patient has osteoarthritis that has resulted in a partial displacement of joints in the foot, and the primary treatment is for the osteoarthritis, coverage is provided.

    3. Routine Foot Care.—Except as provided in subsection B, routine foot care is excluded from coverage. Services that normally are considered routine and not covered by Medicare include the following:

- The cutting or removal of corns and calluses;
- The trimming, cutting, clipping, or debriding of nails; and
- Other hygienic and preventive maintenance care, such as cleaning and soaking the feet, the use of skin creams to maintain skin tone of either ambulatory or bedfast patients, and any other service performed in the absence of localized illness, injury, or symptoms involving the foot.

B. Exceptions to Routine Foot Care Exclusion.—

    1. Necessary and Integral Part of Otherwise Covered Services.—In certain circumstances, services ordinarily considered to be routine may be covered if they are performed as a necessary and integral part of otherwise covered services, such as diagnosis and treatment of ulcers, wounds, or infections.

    2. Treatment of Warts on Foot.—The treatment of warts (including plantar warts) on the foot is covered to the same extent as services provided for the treatment of warts located elsewhere on the body.

    3. Presence of Systemic Condition.—The presence of a systemic condition such ametabolic, neurologic, or peripheral vascular disease may require scrupulous foot care by a professional that in the absence of such condition(s) would be considered routine (and, therefore, excluded from coverage). Accordingly, foot care that would otherwise be considered routine may be covered

when systemic condition(s) result in severe circulatory embarrassment or areas of diminished sensation in the individual's legs or feet. (See subsection C.)

In these instances, certain foot care procedures that otherwise are considered routine (e.g., cutting or removing corns and calluses, or trimming, cutting, clipping, or debriding nails) may pose a hazard when performed by a nonprofessional person on patients with such systemic conditions. (See §4120 for procedural instructions.)

4. Mycotic Nails.—In the absence of a systemic condition, treatment of mycotic nails may be covered.

The treatment of mycotic nails for an ambulatory patient is covered only when the physician attending the patient's mycotic condition documents that (1) there is clinical evidence of mycosis of the toenail, and (2) the patient has marked limitation of ambulation, pain, or secondary infection resulting from the thickening and dystrophy of the infected toenail plate.

The treatment of mycotic nails for a nonambulatory patient is covered only when the physician attending the patient's mycotic condition documents that (1) there is clinical evidence of mycosis of the toenail, and (2) the patient suffers from pain or secondary infection resulting from the thickening and dystrophy of the infected toenail plate.

For the purpose of these requirements, documentation means any written information that is required by the carrier in order for services to be covered. Thus, the information submitted with claims must be substantiated by information found in the patient's medical record. Any information, including that contained in a form letter, used for documentation purposes is subject to carrier verification in order to ensure that the information adequately justifies coverage of the treatment of mycotic nails. (See §4120 for claims processing criteria.)

C. Systemic Conditions.—Although not intended as a comprehensive list, the following metabolic, neurologic, and peripheral vascular diseases (with synonyms in parentheses) most commonly represent the underlying conditions that might justify coverage for routine foot care.

- Diabetes mellitus
- Arteriosclerosis obliterans (A.S.O., arteriosclerosis of the extremities, occlusive peripheral arteriosclerosis)
- Buerger's disease (thromboangiitis obliterans)
- Chronic thrombophlebitis
- Peripheral neuropathies involving the feet
- Associated with malnutrition and vitamin deficiency
- Malnutrition (general, pellagra)
- Alcoholism
- Malabsorption (celiac disease, tropical sprue)
- Pernicious anemia
- Associated with carcinoma
- Associated with diabetes mellitus
- Associated with drugs and toxins
- Associated with multiple sclerosis
- Associated with uremia (chronic renal disease)
- Associated with traumatic injury

- Associated with leprosy or neurosyphilis
- Associated with hereditary disorders
- Hereditary sensory radicular neuropathy
- Angiokeratoma corporis diffusum (Fabry's)
- Amyloid neuropathy

When the patient's condition is one of those designated by an asterisk (*), routine procedures are covered only if the patient is under the active care of a doctor of medicine or osteopathy who documents the condition.

D. Supportive Devices for Feet.—Orthopedic shoes and other supportive devices for the feet generally are not covered. However, this exclusion does not apply to such a shoe if it is an integral part of a leg brace (see §2133), and its expense is included as part of the cost of the brace. Also, this exclusion does not apply to therapeutic shoes furnished to diabetics. (See §2134.)

E. Coding.—You are responsible for informing all medical specialties that codes and policies for routine foot care and supportive devices for the feet are not exclusively for the use of podiatrists. These codes must be used to report foot care services regardless of the specialty of the physician who furnishes the services. Instruct physicians to use the most appropriate code available when billing for routine foot care.

4107 DURABLE MEDICAL EQUIPMENT - BILLING AND PAYMENT CONSIDERATIONS UNDER THE FEE SCHEDULE

The Omnibus Budget Reconciliation Act of 1987 requires that payment for DME, prosthetics and orthotics be made under fee schedules effective January 1, 1989. The allowable charge is limited to the lower of the actual charge for the equipment, or the fee schedule amount. The equipment is categorized into one of six classes:

- Inexpensive or other routinely purchased DME;
- Items requiring frequent and substantial servicing;
- Customized items;
- Prosthetic and orthotic devices;
- Capped rental items; or
- Oxygen and oxygen equipment.

The fee schedule allowances for each class are determined in accord with §§5102ff

4107.6 Written Order Prior to Delivery.--Ensure that your system will pay for the equipment listed below only when the supplier has a written order in hand prior to delivery. Otherwise, do not pay for that item even if a written order is subsequently furnished. However, you can pay for a similar item if it is subsequently provided by an unrelated supplier which has a written order in hand prior to delivery. The HCPCS codes for the equipment requiring a written order are:

B0180 B0181 B0182 B0183 B0184 B0185 B0188 B0189 B0190 B0192 B0195 B0620 B0720 B0730 B1230

EOMB Messages.--The following EOMB messages are suggested: (See §§7012ff. for other applicable messages.)

A. General.—

- "This is the maximum approved amount for this item." (Use when payment is reduced for a line item.)

B. Inexpensive/Frequently Purchased Equipment.—

- "The total approved amount for this item is_____whether this item is purchased or rented." (Use in first month.)
- "This is your next to last rental payment."
- "This is your last rental payment."
- "This item has been rented up to the Medicare payment limit."
- "The approved amount has been reduced by the previously approved rental amounts."

C. Items Requiring Frequent and Substantial Servicing.—Use the general rental messages in §4107.8A, if applicable. If the beneficiary has purchased the item prior to June 1, 1989, follow §7014.6. If the beneficiary purchase an item in this category on or after June 1, 1989, use the following message:

- "This equipment can only be paid for on a rental basis."

D. Customized Items and Other Prosthetic and Orthotic Devices.—

- "The total approved amount for this item is_____."

E. Capped Rental Items.—

- "Under a provision of Medicare law, monthly rental payments for this item can continue for up to 15 months from the first rental month or until the equipment is no longer needed, whichever comes first."
- "If you no longer are using this equipment or have recently moved and will rent this item from a different supplier, please contact our office." (Use on beneficiary's EOMB.)
- "This is your next to last rental payment."
- "This is your last rental payment."
- "This item has been rented up to the 15 month Medicare payment limit."
- "Your equipment supplier must supply and service this item for as long as you continue to need it."
- "Medicare cannot pay for maintenance and/or servicing of this item until 6 months have elapsed since the end of the 15th paid rental month."
- If the beneficiary purchased a capped rental item prior to June 1, 1989, follow §7014.6.

If the beneficiary purchased a capped rental item on or after June 1, 1989, use the following denial message:

- "This equipment can only be paid for on a rental basis."

F. Oxygen and Oxygen Equipment.—

- "The monthly allowance includes payment for all covered oxygen contents and supplies." "Payment for the amount of oxygen supplied has been reduced or denied based on the patient's medical condition." (To supplier after medical review.)
- "The approved amount has been reduced to the amount allowable for medically necessary oxygen therapy." (To beneficiary.)
- "Payment denied because the allowance for this item is included in the monthly payment amount."
- "Payment denied because Medicare oxygen coverage requirements are not met." If the beneficiary purchased an oxygen system prior to June 1, 1989, follow §7014.6. If the beneficiary purchased an oxygen system on or after June 1, 1989, use the following denial message:
- "This item can only be paid for on a rental basis."

G. Items Requiring a Written Order Prior to Delivery.—

- "Payment is denied because the supplier did not obtain a written order from your doctor prior to the delivery of this item."

Oxygen HCPCS Codes Effective 1/1/89.--

NEW	OLD	DEFINITION
Q0036 notes (1) and (8)	E1377-E1385, E1397	Oxygen concentrator, See High humidity
Q0038 See note (2)	E0400, E0405	Oxygen contents, gaseous, per unit (for use with owned gaseous stationary systems or when both a stationary and portable gaseous system are owned; 1 unit = 50 cubic ft.)
Q0039 See note (2)	E0410, E0415O	Oxygen contents, liquid, per unit, (for use with owned stationary liquid systems or when both a stationary and portable liquid system are owned; 1 unit = 10 lbs.)
Q0040 See note (2)	E0416	Portable oxygen contents, per unit (for use only with portable gaseous systems when no stationary gas system is used; 1 unit = 5 cubic ft.)
Q0041 See note (2)	None	Portable oxygen contents, liquid, per unit (for use only with portable liquid systems when no stationary liquid system is used; 1 unit = 1 lb.)

NEW	OLD	DEFINITION
Q0042	E0425	Stationary compressed See note (3)gas system rental, includes contents (per unit), regulator with flow gauge, humidifier, nebulizer, cannula or mask & tubing; 1 unit = 50 cubic ft.
E0425 See notes (4) and (8)	Same	No change
E0430 See notes (8) and (9)	Same	No change
E0435 See notes (7) and 8	Same	No change in terminology, but and (8)see note (7).
Q0043	E0440	Stationary liquid (see note (3) oxygen system rental), includes contents (per unit), use of reservoir, contents indicator, flowmeter, humidifier, nebulizer, cannula or mask and tubing; 1 unit of contents = 10 lbs.
B0440 See note (4)	Same	No change
E0455	Same	No change See note (6)
E0555 See note (6)	Same	No change
E0580	Same	No change See note (6)
E1351	Same	No change See note (6)
E1352 See note (6)	Same	No change
E1353	Same See notes (6) and (8)	No change
E1354 See note (6)	Same	No change
E1371	Same See note (6)	No change
E1374 See note (6)	Same	No change
E1400 See note (1) and (8)	E1388-E1396	Same as Q0014
E1401 See notes (1) and (8)	E1388-E1396	Same as Q0015
E1402	Same	No change
E1403	Same	No change
E1404	Same	No change
E1405	Q0037	Combine the fee See note (10)schedule amounts for the stationary oxygen system and the nebulizer with a compressor and heater (code E0585) to determine the fee schedule amount to apply to oxygen enrichers with a heater (code E1405)

NEW	OLD	DEFINITION
E1406	Q0037	Combine the fee schedule amounts for the stationary oxygen system and the nebulizer with only a compressor (i.e., without a heater, code E0570) to determine the fee schedule amount to apply to oxygen enrichers without a heater (code E1406)

4120 FOOT CARE

NOTE: See §4281 for the relationship between foot care and the coverage and billing of the diagnosis and treatment of peripheral neuropathy with loss of protective sensation (LOPS) in people with diabetes.

4120.1 Application of Foot Care Exclusions to Physicians' Services.--The exclusion of foot care is determined by the nature of the service (§2323). Thus, reimbursement for an excluded service should be denied whether performed by a podiatrist, osteopath, or a doctor of medicine, and without regard to the difficulty or complexity of the procedure.

When an itemized bill shows both covered services and noncovered services not integrally related to the covered service, the portion of charges attributable to the noncovered services should be denied. (For example, if an itemized bill shows surgery for an ingrown toenail and also removal of calluses not necessary for the performance of toe surgery, any additional charge attributable to removal of the calluses should be denied.)

In reviewing claims involving foot care, the carrier should be alert to the following exceptional situations:

1. Payment may be made for incidental noncovered services performed as a necessary and integral part of, and secondary to, a covered procedure. For example, if trimming of toenails is required for application of a cast to a fractured foot, the carrier need not allocate and deny a portion of the charge for the trimming of the nails. However, a separately itemized charge for such excluded service should be disallowed. When the primary procedure is covered the administration of anesthesia necessary for the performance of such procedure is also covered.

2. Payment may be made for initial diagnostic services performed in connection with a specific symptom or complaint if it seems likely that its treatment would be covered even though the resulting diagnosis may be one requiring only noncovered care.

4273 CLAIMS FOR PAYMENT FOR EPOETIN ALFA (EPO)

Effective June 1, 1989, the drug EPO is covered under Part B if administered incident to a physician's services. EPO is used to treat anemia associated with chronic renal failure, including patients on dialysis and those who are not on dialysis.

Completion of Initial Claim for EPO.—The following information is required. Due to space limitations, some items must be documented on a separate form. Therefore, initial claims are generally submitted on paper unless your electronic billers are able to submit supplemental documentation with EMC claims. Return incomplete assigned claims in accordance with §3311.

Develop incomplete unassigned claims.

A. Diagnoses.—The diagnoses must be submitted according to ICD-9-CM and correlated to the procedure. This information is in Items 23A and 24D, of the Form HCFA-1500.

B. Hematocrit (HCT)/Hemoglobin (Hgb).—There are special HCPCS codes for reporting the injection of EPO. These allow the simultaneous reporting of the patient's latest HCT or Hgb reading before administration of EPO.

Instruct the physician and/or staff to enter a separate line item for injections of EPO at different HCT/Hgb levels. The Q code for each line items is entered in Item 24C.

1. Code Q9920 - Injection of EPO, per 1,000 units, at patient HCT of 20 or less/Hgb of 6.8 or less.

2. Codes Q9921 through Q9939 - Injection of EPO, per 1,000 units, at patient HCT of 21 to 39/Hgb of 6.9 to 13.1.

   For HCT levels of 21 or more, up to a HCT of 39/Hgb of 6.9 to 13.1, a Q code that includes the actual HCT levels is used. To convert actual Hgb to corresponding HCT values for Q code reporting, multiply the Hgb value by 3 and round to the nearest whole number. Use the whole number to determine the appropriate Q code.

   EXAMPLES: If the patient's HCT is 25/Hgb is 8.2-8.4, Q9925 must be entered on the claim. If the patient's HCT is 39/Hgb is 12.9-13.1, Q9939 is entered.

3. Code Q9940 - Injection of EPO, per 1,000 units at patient HCT of 40 or above. A single line item may include multiple doses of EPO administered while th patient's HCT level remained the same.

C. Units Administered.—The standard unit of EPO is 1,000. The number of 1,000 units administered per line item is included on the claim. The physician's office enters 1 in the units field for each multiple of 1,000 units. For example, if 12,000 units are administered, 12 is entered. This information is shown in Item 24F (Days/Units) on Form HCFA-1500.

In some cases, the dosage for a single line item does not total an even multiple of 1,000. If this occurs, the physician's office rounds down supplemental dosages of 0 to 499 units to the prior 1,000 units. Supplemental dosages of 500 to 999 are rounded up to the next 1,000 units.

EXAMPLES: A patient's HCT reading on August 6 was 22/Hgb was 7.3.The patient received 5,000 units of EPO on August 7, August 9 and August 11, for a total of 15,000 units. The first line of Item 24 of Form HCFA-1500 shows:

Dates of Service	Procedure Code	Days or Units
8/7-8/11	Q9922	15

On September 13, the patient's HCT reading increased to 27/Hgb increased to 9. The patient received 5,100 units of EPO on September 13, September 15, and September 17, for a total of 15,300 units.

Since less than 15,500 units were given, the figure is rounded down to 15,000. This line on the claim form shows:

Dates of Service	Procedure Code	Days or Units
9/13-9/17	Q9927	15

On October 16, the HCT level increased to 33/Hgb increased to 11. The patient received doses of 4,850 units on October 16, October 18, and October 20 for a total of 14,550 units. Since more than 14,500 units were administered, the figure is rounded up to 15,000. Form HCFA-1500 shows:

Dates of Service	Procedure Code	Days or Units
10/16-10/20	Q9933	15

D. Date of the patient's most recent HCT or Hgb.

E. Most recent HCT or Hgb level prior to initiation of EPO therapy.

F. Date of most recent HCT or Hgb level prior to initiation of EPO therapy.

G Patient's most recent serum creatinine, within the last month, prior to initiation of EPO therapy.
H. Date of most recent serum creatinine prior to initiation of EPO therapy.

I. Patient's weight in kilograms.

J. Patient's starting dose per kilogram. (The usual starting dose is 50-100 units per kilogram.) When a claim is submitted on Form HCFA-1500, these items are submitted on a separate document. It is not necessary to enter them into your claims processing system. This information is used in utilization review.

Completion of Subsequent Claims for EPO.--Subsequent claims include the following:

A. Diagnoses.

B. Hematocrit or Hemoglobin.—This is indicated by the appropriate Q code. Claims include a EJ modifier to the Q code. This allows you to identify subsequent claims which do not require as much information as initial claims and prevent unnecessary development.

C. Number of units administered.—See §4273.1 for a description of these items. Subsequent claims may be submitted electronically. See §3023.7 for including the number of units in standard format EMC claims.

4450. PARENTERAL AND ENTERAL NUTRITION (PEN)

PEN coverage is determined by information provided by the attending physician and the PEN supplier. A certification of medical necessity (CMN) contains pertinent information needed to ensure consistent coverage and payment determinations nationally. A completed CMN must accompany and support the claims for PEN to establish whether coverage criteria are met and to ensure that the PEN provided is consistent with the attending physician's prescription.

The medical and prescription information on a PEN CMN can be completed most appropriately by the attending physician, or from information in the patient's records by an employee of the physician for the physician's review and signature. Although PEN suppliers may assist in providing PEN items they cannot complete the CMN since they do not have the same access to patient information needed to properly enter medical or prescription information.

A. Scheduling and Documenting Certifications and Recertifications of Medical Necessity for PEN.--A PEN CMN must accompany the initial claim submitted. The initial certification is valid for three months. Establish the schedule on a case-by-case basis for recertifying the need for PEN therapy. A change in prescription for a beneficiary past the initial certification period does not restart the certification process. A period of medical necessity ends when PEN is not medically required for two consecutive months. The entire certification process, if required, begins after the period of two consecutive months have elapsed.

B. Initial Certifications.--In reviewing the claim and the supporting data on the CMN, compare certain items, especially pertinent dates of treatment. For example, the start date of PEN coverage cannot precede the date of physician certification. The estimated duration of therapy must be contained on the CMN. Use this information to verify that the test of permanence is met. Once coverage is established, the estimated length of need at the start of PEN services will determine the recertification schedule. (See §4450 A.)

Verify that the information shown on the certification supports the need for PEN supplies as billed. A diagnosis must show a functional impairment that precludes the enteral patient from swallowing and the parenteral patient from absorbing nutrients.

The attending physician and/or his/her designated employee are in a position to accurately complete the patient's medical information including:

-   The patient's general condition, estimated duration of therapy, and other treatments or therapies (see §3329 B.2.);
-   The patient's clinical assessment relating to the need for PEN therapy (see §3329 B.3.); and
-   The nutritional support therapy (i.e., the enteral or parenteral formulation). (See §3329 B.4.)

Initial assigned claims with the following conditions can be denied without development:

-   Inappropriate or missing diagnosis or functional impairment;
-   Estimated duration of therapy is less than 90 consecutive days;
-   Duration of therapy is not listed;
-   Supplies have not been provided;
-   Supplies were provided prior to onset date of therapy; and
-   Stamped physician's signature.

Develop unassigned claims for missing or incomplete information. (See §3329 C.)

Review all claims with initial certifications and recertifications before payment is authorized.

C. Revised Certifications/Change in Prescription.--Remind suppliers to submit revised certifications if the attending physician changes the PEN prescription. A revised certification is appropriate when:

- There is a change in the attending physician's orders in the category of nutrients and/or calories prescribed;
- There is a change by more than one liter in the daily volume of parenteral solutions;
- There is a change from home-mix to pre-mix or pre-mix to home-mix parenteral solutions;
- There is a change from enteral to parenteral or parenteral to enteral therapy; or
- There is a change in the method of infusion (e.g., from gravity-fed to pump-fed).

Do not adjust payments on PEN claims unless a revised or renewed certification documents the necessity for the change. Adjust payments timely, if necessary, for supplies since the PEN prescription was changed.

Do not exceed payment levels for the most current certification or recertification if a prescription change is not documented by a new recertification.

Adjust your diary for scheduled recertifications. When the revised certification has been considered, reschedule the next recertification according to the recertification schedule. (See § 4450 A.)

D. Items Requiring Special Attention.--

1. Nutrients.--Category IB of enteral nutrients contains products that are natural intact protein/protein isolates commonly known as blenderized nutrients. Additional documentation is required to justify the necessity of Category IB nutrients. The attending physician must provide sufficient information to indicate that the patient:

   - Has an intolerance to nutritionally equivalent (semi-synthetic) products;
   - Had a severe allergic reaction to a nutritionally equivalent (semi-synthetic) product; or
   - Was changed to a blenderized nutrient to alleviate adverse symptoms expected to be of permanent duration with continued use of semi-synthetic products.

   Also, enteral nutrient categories III through VI require additional medical justification for coverage.

   Parenteral nutrition may be either "self-mixed" (i.e., the patient is taught to prepare the nutrient solution aseptically) or "pre-mixed" (i.e., the nutrient solution is prepared by trained professionals employed or contracted by the PEN supplier). The attending physician must provide information to justify the reason for "pre-mixed" parenteral nutrient solutions.

2. Prospective Billing.--Pay for no more than a one-month supply of parenteral or enteral nutrients for any one prospective billing period. Claims submitted retroactively may include multiple months.

3. Pumps.--Enteral nutrition may be administered by syringe, gravity, or pump. The attending physician must specify the reason that necessitates the use of an enteral feeding pump. Ensure that the equipment for which payment is claimed is consistent with that prescribed (e.g., expect a claim for an I.V. pole, if a pump is used).

   Effective April 1, 1990, claims for parenteral and enteral pumps are limited to rental payments for a total of 15 months during a period of medical need. A period of medical need ends when enteral or parenteral nutrients are not medically necessary for two consecutive months.

Do not allow additional rental payments once the 15-month limit is reached, unless the attending physician changes the prescription between parenteral and enteral nutrients.

Do not continue rental payments after a pump is purchased unless the attending physician changes the prescription between parenteral and enteral nutrients.

Do not begin a new 15-month rental period when a patient changes suppliers. The new supplier is entitled to the balance remaining on the 15-month rental period.

Effective October 1, 1990, necessary maintenance and servicing of pumps after the 15-month rental limit is reached, includes repairs and extensive maintenance that involves the breaking down of sealed components or performing tests that require specialized testing equipment not available to the beneficiary or nursing home.

4. Supplies.--Enteral care kits contain all the necessary supplies for the enteral patient using the syringe, gravity, or pump method of nutrient administration. Parenteral nutrition care kits and their components are considered all inclusive items necessary to administer therapy during a monthly period.

Compare the enteral feeding care kits on the claim with the method of administration indicated on the CMN.

- Reduce the allowance to the amount paid for a gravity-fed care kit when billed for a pump feeding kit in the absence of documentation or unacceptable documentation for a pump.
- Limit payment to a one-month supply.
- Deny payment for additional components included as part of the PEN supply kit.

5. Attending Physician Identification.--A CMN must contain the attending physician's Unique Physician Identification Number (UPIN) and be signed and dated by the attending physician. A stamped signature is unacceptable.

Deny certifications and recertifications altered by "whiting out" or "pasting over" and entering new data. Consider suppliers that show a pattern of altering CMNs for educational contact and/or audit.

Be alert to certifications from suppliers who have questionable utilization or billing practices or who are under sanction. Consider an audit of any such situations.

4471 PAYMENT FOR IMMUNOSUPPRESSIVE DRUGS

Beginning January 1, 1987, Medicare pays for FDA approved immunosuppressive drugs and for drugs used in immunosuppressive therapy.(See §2050.5.)Generally, pay for self-administered immuno-suppressive drugs that are specifically labeled and approved for marketing as such by the FDA, or identified in FDA-approved labeling for use in conjunction with immunosuppressive drug therapy. This benefit is subject to the Part B deductible and coinsurance provision and is limited to the 1-year period after the date of the transplant. Pay for immunosuppressive drugs which are provided outside the 1-year period if they are covered under another provision of the law (e.g., as inpatient hospital services or are furnished incident to a physician's service).

"One-year period after the date of the transplant" means 365 days from the day on which an inpatient is discharged from the hospital. From surgery until hospital discharge, payment for these drugs is included in Medicare's Part A payment to the hospital. If the same patient receives a subsequent transplant operation within 365 days, the period begins anew.

Prescriptions generally should be nonrefillable and limited to a 30 day supply. The 30 day guideline is necessary because dosage frequently diminishes over a period of time, and further, it is not uncommon for the physician to change the prescription from one drug to another. Also, these drugs are expensive and the coinsurance liability on unused drugs could be a financial burden to the beneficiary. Unless there are special circumstances, do not consider a supply of drugs in excess of 30 days to be reasonable and necessary.

Routing Claims

Route claims for immunosuppressive drugs and any supporting documentation to one of two specialty carriers. Process your part of the claim and notify the beneficiary, and if needed, the physician and supplier of the transfer. The specialty carrier to which to route the claim is based upon the drug supplier's home office.

If the supplier's home office is west of the Mississippi river or in Minnesota:

Transamerica Occidental Life Insurance Company
Medicare Immuno Drug Claims
P.O. Box 60549
Los Angeles, CA 90060-0549

If the supplier's home office is east of the Mississippi river, excluding Minnesota:

Blue Cross and Blue Shield of South Carolina Medicare Immunosuppressive Drug Unit PEN Claims
P.O. Box 102401
Columbia, SC29224

Notify all suppliers regularly of the billing address for the specialty carriers for submission of immunosuppressive drug claims.

Determination of Eligibility

Benefit eligibility is limited to the l-year period following the date of the beneficiary's discharge from a hospital or transplant center after a Medicare covered kidney, heart or liver transplant.(See §5249.)The specialty carrier consults one of three alternative sources of information to determine the date of kidney transplant:

HCFA compiles and furnishes in hardcopy or tape format to specialty carriers a monthly listing of beneficiaries who have received kidney transplants. HCFA's system is not yet equipped to handle heart and liver transplant data. The initial listing included all beneficiaries who had received a kidney transplant since January 1, 1986.It is updated monthly. The listing includes:

- HICN under which benefits are paid.
- Last name, first name, and middle initial of person receiving benefits.

- Month, day, and year of beneficiary's most recent kidney transplant (MMDDYY).
- Month, day, and year that beneficiary died (MMDDYY)
- Month, day, and year of kidney transplant failure (MMDDYY).
- Intermediaries send copies of the Part A Medicare Benefit Notice which contains the date of transplant to the specialty carriers. The specialty carriers maintain the data and release it to area carriers upon request.

If you are unable to locate the beneficiary's transplant information above, refer to the discharge date listed on the prescription form. The prescription form, or facsimile thereof, should accompany the initial claim and indicate the date of discharge. You may contact the prescribing physician for substantiation of the discharge date. If you do not have any eligibility information other than the prescription regarding the discharge date, you may pay for 1 month's supply of immunosuppressive drugs based upon the discharge date listed. If the information obtained indicates transplant failure, do not approve payment for drugs in subsequent periods.

Reasonable Charge Determinations

For purposes of establishing customary and prevailing charges, the United States is considered a single locality structure.

Since immunosuppressive drugs have not been previously covered, there is no existing charge data base for determining customary or prevailing charges. Therefore, the normal gap filling techniques in §5022 are not appropriate.

To establish reimbursement for the initial 3 month coverage period; i.e., January 1, 1987 through March 31, 1987, use available drug pricing data. Sources for pricing ingredient costs may include the Drug Topics Red Book, the American Druggist Blue Book, or manufacturers price lists. Also consider the appropriateness of an additional charge for administration.

During the initial 3 month interim coverage period, gather charge data and use it to establish customary and prevailing charges. Establish and maintain reasonable charge screens until a general revision is made to the reasonable charge screens at the beginning of the new fee screen year, i.e., January 1, 1988.Then use the charge data for the period January 1 through June 30, 1987 as the base year to calculate reasonable charges.

Adjust prevailing charges if they are grossly deficient or excessive in comparison to data from other sources.(See §5246 for determining appropriateness of charges.)For example, prevailing charges may be adjusted where they appear grossly excessive in relation to charge data from mail order pharmacies reflecting substantial discounts over published prices.

HCPCS Codes

The following HCPCS codes are assigned:

Code	Definition
Q0004	Azathioprine (e.g., Imuran) - oral, tab, 50 mg., 100s ea.
Q0005	Azathioprine (e.g., Imuran) - parenteral, vial, 100 mg., 20 ml. ea.
Q0006	Cyclosporine (e.g., Sandimmune) - oral, sol; 100 mg/ml., 50 ml., ea.
Q0007	Cyclosporine (e.g., Sandimmune) - parenteral amp, I.V, 250 mg., 5 ml., 10s ea UD

Q0008	Lymphocyte Immune Globulin, Antithymocyte Globulin (e.g., Atgam) - parenteral, amp, 50 mg./ml., 5 lea.
Q0009	Monoclonal Antibodies (eg Muromonab C D3; Orthoclone) -parenteral, amp, 5 mg./5 ml., 5 ml. ea.

5102.3 Transition to Fee Schedule-Relationship to Prior Rules.—

A. Comparability and Inherent Reasonableness Limitations.—Effective January 1, 1989, until further notice, you may no longer apply the comparable circumstances provision contained in §5026. Between January 1, 1989 and December 31, 1990, you may not apply the special limitations provision contained in §5246.

B. Purchase of Items Requiring Frequent and Substantial Servicing or Capped Rental Items.-

1. Purchase Prior to January 1, 1989.—If the beneficiary purchased an item of equipment in either of these two categories (see §5102.1.B or E) prior to January 1, 1989, pay the reasonable and necessary charges for maintenance and servicing of this equipment. In the event the item of equipment needs to be replaced on or after June 1, 1989, pay on a rental basis according to the instructions in §5102.1.B. or E.

   If the beneficiary purchased the equipment even though you determined that rental was more economical under the rent/purchase guidelines, or if the beneficiary made an approved purchase on an installment plan, make payment on an installment basis until the purchase price has been reached or medical necessity terminated. If the purchase price has not been reached by January 1, 1989, continue paying on an installment basis but at the monthly fee schedule amount until the purchase price is reached, the purchase price fee schedule calculated under prior instructions is reached, or the medical necessity ends, whichever occurs first. The limitation on total payments to 15 months rental (as described in §5102.1.E) does not apply.

2. Purchase On Or After June 1, 1989.—If a beneficiary purchased an item of equipment that requires frequent and substantial servicing on or after June 1, 1989, do not make payment. Also, do not make payment for maintenance and servicing or for replacement of items in either category that are purchased on or after June 1, 1989.

   If a beneficiary purchased an item of equipment in the capped rental category between June 1, 1989 and April 30, 1991, do not make payment. Also, do not make payment for maintenance and servicing. However, see §5102.1.E.5 or 6 for payment of purchase options after April 30, 1991 and for payment of replacement of items purchased between June 1, 1989 and April 30, 1991.

3. Purchase Between January 1, 1989 and June 1, 1989.—If a beneficiary purchased an item of equipment in either category after December 31, 1988, but before June 1, 1989, pay monthly installments equivalent to the rental fee schedule amounts until the medical necessity ends, the purchase price fee schedule calculated under prior instructions is reached, or the actual purchase charge has been reached, whichever occurs first. Pay the reasonable and necessary charges for maintenance and servicing of this equipment. In the event the item of equipment needs to be replaced on or after June 1, 1989, pay on a rental basis according to the instructions in §5102.1.B. or E. Payment may be made for purchase even if the purchase was preceded by a period of rental.

However, total payments for rental plus purchase of capped rental items may not exceed the amount that would have been paid had the equipment been continuously rented for 15 months. (Therefore, if a purchase occurs during a period of continuous use after 15 months of rentals have been paid, no payment may be made other than the reasonable and necessary charges for servicing as described in §5102.1.E.4.)

C. Purchase of Oxygen Equipment.—

1. Purchase Prior to June 1, 1989.—If the beneficiary purchased stationary or portable oxygen equipment (see §5102.1.F) prior to June 1, 1989, pay the reasonable and necessary charges for maintenance and servicing of this equipment. In the event the item of equipment needs to be replaced on or after June 1, 1989, pay on a rental basis according to the instructions in §5102.1.F. If the beneficiary purchased the equipment even though you determined that rental was more economical under the rent/purchase guidelines, or if the beneficiary made an approved purchase on an installment plan, make payment on an installment basis until the purchase price had been reached or medical necessity terminated. If the purchase price has not been reached by June 1, 1989, continue paying on an installment basis (see §5102.1.F.9) but at the monthly fee schedule amount until the purchase price is reached or the medical necessity ends, whichever occurs first.

2. Purchase On Or After June 1, 1989.—If a beneficiary purchased stationary or portable oxygen equipment on or after June 1, 1989, do not make payment for the equipment. However, make payment for the contents in accordance with §5102.1.F.4 or 5. Also, do not make payment for maintenance and servicing or for replacement of oxygen equipment that is purchased on or after June 1, 1989.

D. 15-Month Ceiling.—For purposes of computing the 10-month purchase option or the 15-month period for capped rental items, begin counting the first month that the beneficiary continuously rented the equipment. For example, if the beneficiary began renting the equipment in July 1988, the rental month which begins in January 1989 is counted as the beneficiary's 7th month of rental. Therefore, if the equipment has been continuously rented prior to October 2, 1987, no further rental payments are made since the 15-month period is terminated before January 1, 1989. The maintenance and service provision in §5102.1.E.4 begins July 1, 1989.

If the beneficiary has reached (on a date of service prior to January 1989) the purchase price limitation on a rental claim, do not make any further purchase or rental payments until the useful life has elapsed according to the instructions in §5102.1.E.7. However, for capped rental items previously rented that have reached the purchase cap under the rent/purchase rules, pay claims for maintenance and servicing fees in accordance with §5102.1.E.4 effective July 1, 1989.

E. Oxygen.—Claims for oxygen contents provided after May 31, 1989, but prior to the start of the June equipment rental month, may be paid in either of the following two ways. Either continue paying the reasonable charge payment amount for contents through the end of the May monthly rental period; or pay the reasonable charge payment amount for contents through the end of May and pay the actual charge for contents up to the fee schedule allowance for oxygen contents only, as prorated for the period June 1 through the end of the May rental period. Begin paying the appropriate full fee schedule amount at the beginning of the new rental period. For example, a beneficiary's rental period began May 15, 1989. Pay on a reasonable charge basis from May 15 through June 14; or pay on a reasonable charge basis from May 15 through May 31, 1989 and pay the actual charge up to 14/31 of the oxygen contents fee (established in §5102.1.F.4) from June 1 through June 14, 1989. Pay the lesser of the full fee schedule amount or actual charge beginning June 15, 1989.

F. Purchase Options For Capped Rental Items.—

    1. Electric Wheelchairs.—If the beneficiary purchases an electric wheelchair prior to May 1, 1991, pay for the wheelchair as a routinely purchased item in accordance with §5102.1.A. If the beneficiary elects to rent an electric wheelchair prior to May 1, 1991, pay the rental fee schedule amount not to exceed the purchase price in accordance with §5102.1.A. If, on May 1,1991, the purchase price has not been reached, convert the monthly fee schedule amount from routinely purchased to capped rental. As such, each month's rental before and after conversion must be counted toward the 10 month purchase option in §5102.1.E.6 and the 15 month rental cap in §5102.1.E.2.

    2. All Other Capped Rental Items.—If the beneficiary purchased a capped rental item prior to May 1, 1991, do not make payment. If the beneficiary rented a capped rental item prior to May 1, 1991, pay the rental fee schedule amount not to exceed the 15 month rental cap in accordance with §5102.1.E.2.Each month's rental must be counted toward the 10 month purchase option in §5102.1.E.6 and the 15 month rental cap in §5102.1.E.2.

15030 SUPPLIES

Make a separate payment for supplies furnished in connection with a procedure only when one of the two following conditions exists:

A. HCPCS codes A4550, A4200, and A4263 are billed in conjunction with the appropriate procedure in the Medicare Physician Fee Schedule Data Base (place of service is physician's office); or

B. The supply is a pharmaceutical or radiopharmaceutical diagnostic imaging agent (including codes A4641 through A4647); pharmacologic stressing agent (code J1245); or therapeutic radionuclide (CPT code 79900). The procedures performed are:

- Diagnostic radiologic procedures (including diagnostic nuclear medicine) requiring pharmaceutical or radiopharmaceutical contrast media and/or pharmacological stressing agent,
- Other diagnostic tests requiring a pharmacological stressing agent,
- Clinical brachytherapy procedures (other than remote afterloading high intensity brachytherapy procedures (CPT codes 77781 through 77784) for which the expendable source is included in the TC RVUs), or
- Therapeutic nuclear medicine procedures.

15360 ECHOCARDIOGRAPHY SERVICES
(CODES 93303 - 93350)

Separate Payment for Contrast Media.—Effective October 1, 2000, physicians may separately bill for contrast agents used in echocardiography. Physicians should use HCPCS Code A9700 (Supply of injectable contrast material for use in echocardiography, per study). The type of service code is 9. This code will be carrier-priced.

APPENDIX E: HCPCS MACR & MIPS CROSS-REFERENCES

Terminology

Term/Acronym	Definition
APC	Ambulatory Payment Classification
CCS Category	Clinical Classifications Software Services and Procedures category created by the Agency for Healthcare Research and Quality (AHRQ)
CMS-HCC V22	Centers for Medicare & Medicaid Services Hierarchical Condition Category Risk Adjustment Model, Version 22
CPT	Current Procedural Terminology
DGN	Diagnosis as detailed in International Classification of Disease, Tenth Revision, Clinical Modification (ICD-10-CM)
DME	Durable Medical Equipment, Prosthetics, Orthotics, and Supplies
DRG	Diagnosis-Related Group
E&M	Evaluation and Management
ER	Emergency Room (Emergency Department)
HCPCS	Healthcare Common Procedure Coding System
HH	Home Health
ICD-10-CM	International Classification of Disease, Tenth Revision, Clinical Modification
ICD-10 PCS	International Classification of Disease, Tenth Revision, Procedure Coding System
IP	Inpatient
ISO	Initial sort order; this is the header for the first column (Column A) in every table and refers to the original order of the rows in the table, in the event that a user manipulates the information in a table by using a filter drop-down.
MACRA	Medicare Access and CHIP (Children's Health Insurance Program) Reauthorization Act of 2015
MIPS	Merit-based Incentive Payment System
MS-DRG	Medicare Severity Diagnosis-Related Group
OP	Outpatient
PAC	Post-Acute Care
PB	Part B Physician/Supplier (Carrier)
RA	Risk adjustment
RIC	Rehabilitation Impairment Category
SA	Service assignment
SNF	Skilled Nursing Facility

What is MACRA?

MACRA is the Medicare Access and CHIP Reauthorization Act. MACRA replaces the current Medicare reimbursement schedule with a new pay-for-performance program that's focused on quality, value, and accountability. The Centers for Medicare and Medicaid Services (CMS) stated that MACRA enacts a new payment framework that rewards health care providers for giving better care instead of more service.

MACRA combines parts of the <u>Physician Quality Reporting System</u> (PQRS), <u>Value-based Payment Modifier</u> (VBM), and the <u>Medicare Electronic Health Record</u> (EHR) incentive program into one single program called the Merit-based Incentive Payment System, or "MIPS".

What is MIPS?

MIPS is the Merit-based Incentive Payment System Episode-Based Cost Measure. The Medicare Access and CHIP Reauthorization Act of 2015 (MACRA) established the Quality Payment Program, a new way to pay clinicians. Under the Quality Payment Program, clinicians are rewarded for giving high-quality and high value care through Advanced Alternate Payment Models (APMs) or the Merit-based Incentive Payment System (MIPS). Clinicians participating in MIPS will earn a performance-based payment adjustment to their Medicare payment.

This payment adjustment is based on a MIPS final score that assesses evidence-based and practice-specific quality data in the following categories:

1. Quality
2. Improvement activities
3. Advancing care information
4. Cost

The MIPS cost performance category will be calculated in 2017, but will not be used to determine payment adjustment. That is, the cost performance category of the MIPS final score is weighted at zero percent for the 2017 performance year; it also is proposed to continue to be weighted at zero percent of the MIPS final score for the 2018 performance year.

As required by MACRA, the MIPS cost performance category will be weighted at 30 percent of the MIPS final score for the 2019 performance year meaning that it will affect payment in the 2021 payment year.

How do episode-based cost measures relate to the Quality Payment Program?

MACRA established a process to enhance the infrastructure for resource use measurement, including for the purpose of developing cost measures for the MIPS cost performance category. MACRA requires cost measures implemented in MIPS to include consideration of patient condition groups and care episode groups (referred to as "episode groups"). As a result, eight episode-based cost measures are currently under development and are being field tested.

These 8 measures are being developed with extensive input from 7 Clinical Subcommittees (CS), a Technical Expert Panel, and public comment:

- Elective Outpatient Percutaneous Coronary Intervention (PCI)
- Knee Arthroplasty
- Revascularization for Lower Extremity Chronic Critical Limb Ischemia
- Routine Cataract Removal with Intraocular Lens (IOL) Implantation
- Screening/Surveillance Colonoscopy
- Intracranial Hemorrhage or Cerebral Infarction
- Simple Pneumonia with Hospitalization
- ST-Elevation Myocardial Infarction (STEMI) with PCI

When will these episode-based measures be used in MIPS?

The eight episode-based measures currently being field tested and are not included in the 2017 or 2018 MIPS performance years. These measures are being field tested before consideration of their potential use in the MIPS cost performance category in a future year. As part of this field testing, CMS and Acumen are now seeking stakeholder feedback on the draft measure specifications for the eight measures in their current stage of development, the Field Test Report template, and all accompanying documentation. This feedback will be considered in refining the measures and for future measure development activities.

HCPCS Trigger Codes

Episodes are defined by the codes that trigger (or open) the episode group and determine the patient cohort included in the episode group. The table below lists the trigger codes for the episode group in the "Code Type" and "Code" columns, and an episode is triggered if any of these codes below occur. For trigger codes with a logic of "DGN Check," the given trigger code in the "Code" column must occur with any of the given DGNs listed for that trigger code in order to open an episode. For trigger codes with a logic of "POS Check," the given trigger code in the "code" column must occur with any of the given place of service codes listed for that trigger code in order to open an episiode.

HCPCS Trigger Codes are marked in the code section with a ⓟ to the left of the code.

	HCPCS	Measure	Logic	Logic Code	Logic code description	Logic Notes
ⓟ	C9600	Elective Outpatient Percutaneous Coronary Intervention (PCI)	Place of service check	11	Office	An episode will only be triggered when it happens under certain outpatient setting
ⓟ	C9600		Place of service check	19	Off campus-outpatient hosptial	An episode will only be triggered when it happens under certain outpatient setting
ⓟ	C9600		Place of service check	22	Outpatient hospital	An episode will only be triggered when it happens under certain outpatient setting
ⓟ	C9600		Place of service check	24	Ambulatory surgical center	An episode will only be triggered when it happens under certain outpatient setting
ⓟ	C9601		Place of service check	11	Office	An episode will only be triggered when it happens under certain outpatient setting
ⓟ	C9601		Place of service check	19	Off campus-outpatient hosptial	An episode will only be triggered when it happens under certain outpatient setting
ⓟ	C9601		Place of service check	22	Outpatient hospital	An episode will only be triggered when it happens under certain outpatient setting

	HCPCS	Measure	Logic	Logic Code	Logic code description	Logic Notes
Ⓟ	C9601		Place of service check	24	Ambulatory surgical center	An episode will only be triggered when it happens under certain outpatient setting
Ⓟ	C9602		Place of service check	11	Office	An episode will only be triggered when it happens under certain outpatient setting
Ⓟ	C9602		Place of service check	19	Off campus-outpatient hosptial	An episode will only be triggered when it happens under certain outpatient setting
Ⓟ	C9602		Place of service check	22	Outpatient hospital	An episode will only be triggered when it happens under certain outpatient setting
Ⓟ	C9602		Place of service check	24	Ambulatory surgical center	An episode will only be triggered when it happens under certain outpatient setting
Ⓟ	C9603		Place of service check	11	Office	An episode will only be triggered when it happens under certain outpatient setting
Ⓟ	C9603		Place of service check	19	Off campus-outpatient hosptial	An episode will only be triggered when it happens under certain outpatient setting
Ⓟ	C9603		Place of service check	22	Outpatient hospital	An episode will only be triggered when it happens under certain outpatient setting
Ⓟ	C9603		Place of service check	24	Ambulatory surgical center	An episode will only be triggered when it happens under certain outpatient setting
Ⓟ	C9604		Place of service check	11	Office	An episode will only be triggered when it happens under certain outpatient setting
Ⓟ	C9604		Place of service check	19	Off campus-outpatient hosptial	An episode will only be triggered when it happens under certain outpatient setting
Ⓟ	C9604		Place of service check	22	Outpatient hospital	An episode will only be triggered when it happens under certain outpatient setting
Ⓟ	C9604		Place of service check	24	Ambulatory surgical center	An episode will only be triggered when it happens under certain outpatient setting
Ⓟ	C9605		Place of service check	11	Office	An episode will only be triggered when it happens under certain outpatient setting
Ⓟ	C9605		Place of service check	19	Off campus-outpatient hosptial	An episode will only be triggered when it happens under certain outpatient setting

	HCPCS	Measure	Logic	Logic Code	Logic code description	Logic Notes
℗	C9605		Place of service check	22	Outpatient hospital	An episode will only be triggered when it happens under certain outpatient setting
℗	C9605		Place of service check	24	Ambulatory surgical center	An episode will only be triggered when it happens under certain outpatient setting
℗	C9606		Place of service check	11	Office	An episode will only be triggered when it happens under certain outpatient setting
℗	C9606		Place of service check	19	Off campus-outpatient hosptial	An episode will only be triggered when it happens under certain outpatient setting
℗	C9606		Place of service check	22	Outpatient hospital	An episode will only be triggered when it happens under certain outpatient setting
℗	C9606		Place of service check	24	Ambulatory surgical center	An episode will only be triggered when it happens under certain outpatient setting
℗	C9607		Place of service check	11	Office	An episode will only be triggered when it happens under certain outpatient setting
℗	C9607		Place of service check	19	Off campus-outpatient hosptial	An episode will only be triggered when it happens under certain outpatient setting
℗	C9607		Place of service check	22	Outpatient hospital	An episode will only be triggered when it happens under certain outpatient setting
℗	C9607		Place of service check	24	Ambulatory surgical center	An episode will only be triggered when it happens under certain outpatient setting
℗	C9608		Place of service check	11	Office	An episode will only be triggered when it happens under certain outpatient setting
℗	C9608		Place of service check	19	Off campus-outpatient hosptial	An episode will only be triggered when it happens under certain outpatient setting
℗	C9608		Place of service check	22	Outpatient hospital	An episode will only be triggered when it happens under certain outpatient setting
℗	C9608		Place of service check	24	Ambulatory surgical center	An episode will only be triggered when it happens under certain outpatient setting

HCPCS Post-Trigger Services Assigned to the Episode Group for Durable Medical Equipment, Prosthetics, Orthotics, and Supplies (DME) Service Category

This table presents the services assigned to each episode group for the DME service category during the post-trigger period of the episode window. Assigned services are categorized into a Clinical Theme for the purposes of presenting metrics by Clinical Theme in the Field Test Reports.

HCPCS Post-Trigger Services are marked in the code section with a Ⓣ to the left of the code.

	HCPCS	Measure	Clinical Theme	Service Assignment Decision	Service Assignment Window
Ⓣ	A4221	Revascularization for Lower Extremity Chronic Critical Limb Ischemia	None	Assign if service is newly occuring, regardless of diagnosis	< 7 days from trigger event
Ⓣ	A4222	Elective Outpatient Percutaneous Coronary Intervention (PCI)	None	Sometimes assign, depending on diagnosis	Anytime in episode window
Ⓣ	A4256	Revascularization for Lower Extremity Chronic Critical Limb Ischemia	None	Assign if service is newly occuring, regardless of diagnosis	Anytime in episode window
Ⓣ	A4326	Intracranial Hemorrhage Or Cerebral Infarction	None	Sometimes assign, depending on diagnosis	< 90 days from trigger event
Ⓣ	A4349	Intracranial Hemorrhage Or Cerebral Infarction	None	Sometimes assign, depending on diagnosis	< 90 days from trigger event
Ⓣ	A4351	Intracranial Hemorrhage Or Cerebral Infarction	None	Sometimes assign, depending on diagnosis	< 90 days from trigger event
Ⓣ	A4352	Intracranial Hemorrhage Or Cerebral Infarction	None	Sometimes assign, depending on diagnosis	< 90 days from trigger event

	HCPCS	Measure	Clinical Theme	Service Assignment Decision	Service Assignment Window
⊤	**A4353**	Intracranial Hemorrhage Or Cerebral Infarction	None	Sometimes assign, depending on diagnosis	< 90 days from trigger event
⊤	**A4357**	Intracranial Hemorrhage Or Cerebral Infarction	None	Sometimes assign, depending on diagnosis	< 90 days from trigger event
⊤	**A4362**	Revascularization for Lower Extremity Chronic Critical Limb Ischemia	Wound Care Services	Yes, assign regardless of diagnosis	Anytime in episode window
⊤	**A4450**	Revascularization for Lower Extremity Chronic Critical Limb Ischemia	None	Yes, assign regardless of diagnosis	Anytime in episode window
⊤	**A4452**	Revascularization for Lower Extremity Chronic Critical Limb Ischemia	None	Yes, assign regardless of diagnosis	Anytime in episode window
⊤	**A4604**	Revascularization for Lower Extremity Chronic Critical Limb Ischemia	None	Assign if service is newly occuring, regardless of diagnosis	Anytime in episode window
⊤	**A4605**	Simple Pneumonia with Hospitalization	Post-Acute Care (oxygen, rehabilitation, speech/swallow, supplies/other DME)	Assign if service is newly occuring, regardless of diagnosis	Anytime in episode window
⊤	**A4623**	Simple Pneumonia with Hospitalization	Post-Acute Care (oxygen, rehabilitation, speech/swallow, supplies/other DME)	Assign if service is newly occuring, regardless of diagnosis	Anytime in episode window

	HCPCS	Measure	Clinical Theme	Service Assignment Decision	Service Assignment Window
ⓣ	A4624	Simple Pneumonia with Hospitalization	Post-Acute Care (oxygen, rehabilitation, speech/swallow, supplies/other DME)	Assign if service is newly occuring, regardless of diagnosis	Anytime in episode window
ⓣ	A4629	Simple Pneumonia with Hospitalization	Post-Acute Care (oxygen, rehabilitation, speech/swallow, supplies/other DME)	Assign if service is newly occuring, regardless of diagnosis	Anytime in episode window
ⓣ	A5500	Revascularization for Lower Extremity Chronic Critical Limb Ischemia	None	Yes, assign regardless of diagnosis	Anytime in episode window
ⓣ	A5501	Revascularization for Lower Extremity Chronic Critical Limb Ischemia	None	Yes, assign regardless of diagnosis	Anytime in episode window
ⓣ	A5512	Revascularization for Lower Extremity Chronic Critical Limb Ischemia	None	Yes, assign regardless of diagnosis	Anytime in episode window
ⓣ	A5513	Revascularization for Lower Extremity Chronic Critical Limb Ischemia	None	Yes, assign regardless of diagnosis	Anytime in episode window
ⓣ	A6010	Intracranial Hemorrhage Or Cerebral Infarction	None	Sometimes assign, depending on diagnosis	< 90 days from trigger event
ⓣ	A6021	Intracranial Hemorrhage Or Cerebral Infarction	None	Sometimes assign, depending on diagnosis	< 90 days from trigger event
ⓣ	A6022	Revascularization for Lower Extremity Chronic Critical Limb Ischemia	Wound Care Services	Yes, assign regardless of diagnosis	Anytime in episode window

	HCPCS	Measure	Clinical Theme	Service Assignment Decision	Service Assignment Window
ⓣ	A6196	Intracranial Hemorrhage Or Cerebral Infarction	None	Sometimes assign, depending on diagnosis	< 90 days from trigger event
ⓣ	A6197	Intracranial Hemorrhage Or Cerebral Infarction	None	Sometimes assign, depending on diagnosis	< 90 days from trigger event
ⓣ	A6199	Intracranial Hemorrhage Or Cerebral Infarction	None	Sometimes assign, depending on diagnosis	< 90 days from trigger event
ⓣ	A6203	Revascularization for Lower Extremity Chronic Critical Limb Ischemia	Wound Care Services	Yes, assign regardless of diagnosis	Anytime in episode window
ⓣ	A6209	Intracranial Hemorrhage Or Cerebral Infarction	None	Sometimes assign, depending on diagnosis	< 90 days from trigger event
ⓣ	A6210	Intracranial Hemorrhage Or Cerebral Infarction	None	Sometimes assign, depending on diagnosis	< 90 days from trigger event
ⓣ	A6211	Revascularization for Lower Extremity Chronic Critical Limb Ischemia	Wound Care Services	Yes, assign regardless of diagnosis	Anytime in episode window
ⓣ	A6212	Intracranial Hemorrhage Or Cerebral Infarction	None	Sometimes assign, depending on diagnosis	< 90 days from trigger event
ⓣ	A6222	Intracranial Hemorrhage Or Cerebral Infarction	None	Sometimes assign, depending on diagnosis	< 90 days from trigger event
ⓣ	A6223	Revascularization for Lower Extremity Chronic Critical Limb Ischemia	Wound Care Services	Yes, assign regardless of diagnosis	Anytime in episode window

	HCPCS	Measure	Clinical Theme	Service Assignment Decision	Service Assignment Window
Ⓣ	A6231	Intracranial Hemorrhage Or Cerebral Infarction	None	Sometimes assign, depending on diagnosis	< 90 days from trigger event
Ⓣ	A6234	Revascularization for Lower Extremity Chronic Critical Limb Ischemia	Wound Care Services	Yes, assign regardless of diagnosis	Anytime in episode window
Ⓣ	A6248	Revascularization for Lower Extremity Chronic Critical Limb Ischemia	Wound Care Services	Yes, assign regardless of diagnosis	Anytime in episode window
Ⓣ	A6252	Intracranial Hemorrhage Or Cerebral Infarction	None	Sometimes assign, depending on diagnosis	< 90 days from trigger event
Ⓣ	A6253	Revascularization for Lower Extremity Chronic Critical Limb Ischemia	Wound Care Services	Yes, assign regardless of diagnosis	Anytime in episode window
Ⓣ	A6266	Intracranial Hemorrhage Or Cerebral Infarction	None	Sometimes assign, depending on diagnosis	< 90 days from trigger event
Ⓣ	A6402	Revascularization for Lower Extremity Chronic Critical Limb Ischemia	Wound Care Services	Yes, assign regardless of diagnosis	Anytime in episode window
Ⓣ	A6446	Intracranial Hemorrhage Or Cerebral Infarction	None	Sometimes assign, depending on diagnosis	< 90 days from trigger event
Ⓣ	A6449	Intracranial Hemorrhage Or Cerebral Infarction	None	Sometimes assign, depending on diagnosis	< 90 days from trigger event
Ⓣ	A6545	Revascularization for Lower Extremity Chronic Critical Limb Ischemia	Wound Care Services	Yes, assign regardless of diagnosis	Anytime in episode window

	HCPCS	Measure	Clinical Theme	Service Assignment Decision	Service Assignment Window
ⓣ	A6550	Intracranial Hemorrhage Or Cerebral Infarction	None	Sometimes assign, depending on diagnosis	< 90 days from trigger event
ⓣ	A7000	Intracranial Hemorrhage Or Cerebral Infarction	None	Sometimes assign, depending on diagnosis	< 90 days from trigger event
ⓣ	A7003	Simple Pneumonia with Hospitalization	Post-Acute Care (oxygen, rehabilitation, speech/swallow, supplies/other DME)	Assign if service is newly occuring, regardless of diagnosis	Anytime in episode window
ⓣ	A7005	Simple Pneumonia with Hospitalization	Post-Acute Care (oxygen, rehabilitation, speech/swallow, supplies/other DME)	Assign if service is newly occuring, regardless of diagnosis	Anytime in episode window
ⓣ	A7030	Simple Pneumonia with Hospitalization	Post-Acute Care (oxygen, rehabilitation, speech/swallow, supplies/other DME)	Assign if service is newly occuring, regardless of diagnosis	Anytime in episode window
ⓣ	A7031	Simple Pneumonia with Hospitalization	Post-Acute Care (oxygen, rehabilitation, speech/swallow, supplies/other DME)	Assign if service is newly occuring, regardless of diagnosis	Anytime in episode window
ⓣ	A7032	Simple Pneumonia with Hospitalization	Post-Acute Care (oxygen, rehabilitation, speech/swallow, supplies/other DME)	Assign if service is newly occuring, regardless of diagnosis	Anytime in episode window
ⓣ	A7033	Revascularization for Lower Extremity Chronic Critical Limb Ischemia	None	Assign if service is newly occuring, regardless of diagnosis	Anytime in episode window

	HCPCS	Measure	Clinical Theme	Service Assignment Decision	Service Assignment Window
Ⓣ	**A7034**	Simple Pneumonia with Hospitalization	Post-Acute Care (oxygen, rehabilitation, speech/swallow, supplies/other DME)	Assign if service is newly occuring, regardless of diagnosis	Anytime in episode window
Ⓣ	**A7035**	Simple Pneumonia with Hospitalization	Post-Acute Care (oxygen, rehabilitation, speech/swallow, supplies/other DME)	Assign if service is newly occuring, regardless of diagnosis	Anytime in episode window
Ⓣ	**A7037**	Simple Pneumonia with Hospitalization	Post-Acute Care (oxygen, rehabilitation, speech/swallow, supplies/other DME)	Assign if service is newly occuring, regardless of diagnosis	Anytime in episode window
Ⓣ	**A7038**	Simple Pneumonia with Hospitalization	Post-Acute Care (oxygen, rehabilitation, speech/swallow, supplies/other DME)	Assign if service is newly occuring, regardless of diagnosis	Anytime in episode window
Ⓣ	**A7046**	Simple Pneumonia with Hospitalization	Post-Acute Care (oxygen, rehabilitation, speech/swallow, supplies/other DME)	Assign if service is newly occuring, regardless of diagnosis	Anytime in episode window
Ⓣ	**A7526**	Simple Pneumonia with Hospitalization	Post-Acute Care (oxygen, rehabilitation, speech/swallow, supplies/other DME)	Assign if service is newly occuring, regardless of diagnosis	Anytime in episode window
Ⓣ	**B4034**	Intracranial Hemorrhage Or Cerebral Infarction	None	Sometimes assign, depending on diagnosis	< 90 days from trigger event
Ⓣ	**B4035**	Intracranial Hemorrhage Or Cerebral Infarction	None	Sometimes assign, depending on diagnosis	< 90 days from trigger event

	HCPCS	Measure	Clinical Theme	Service Assignment Decision	Service Assignment Window
ⓣ	**B4036**	Intracranial Hemorrhage Or Cerebral Infarction	None	Sometimes assign, depending on diagnosis	< 90 days from trigger event
ⓣ	**B4150**	Intracranial Hemorrhage Or Cerebral Infarction	None	Sometimes assign, depending on diagnosis	< 90 days from trigger event
ⓣ	**B4152**	Elective Outpatient Percutaneous Coronary Intervention (PCI)	Complications (neuro, renal, vascular, infectious)	Sometimes assign, depending on diagnosis	Anytime in episode window
ⓣ	**B4153**	Intracranial Hemorrhage Or Cerebral Infarction	None	Sometimes assign, depending on diagnosis	< 90 days from trigger event
ⓣ	**B4154**	Intracranial Hemorrhage Or Cerebral Infarction	None	Sometimes assign, depending on diagnosis	< 90 days from trigger event
ⓣ	**B4185**	Revascularization for Lower Extremity Chronic Critical Limb Ischemia	None	Yes, assign regardless of diagnosis	Anytime in episode window
ⓣ	**B4189**	Revascularization for Lower Extremity Chronic Critical Limb Ischemia	None	Yes, assign regardless of diagnosis	Anytime in episode window
ⓣ	**B4193**	Revascularization for Lower Extremity Chronic Critical Limb Ischemia	None	Yes, assign regardless of diagnosis	Anytime in episode window
ⓣ	**B4199**	Revascularization for Lower Extremity Chronic Critical Limb Ischemia	None	Yes, assign regardless of diagnosis	Anytime in episode window

	HCPCS	Measure	Clinical Theme	Service Assignment Decision	Service Assignment Window
Ⓣ	B4224	Revascularization for Lower Extremity Chronic Critical Limb Ischemia	None	Yes, assign regardless of diagnosis	Anytime in episode window
Ⓣ	B9002	Intracranial Hemorrhage Or Cerebral Infarction	None	Sometimes assign, depending on diagnosis	< 90 days from trigger event
Ⓣ	E0100	Intracranial Hemorrhage Or Cerebral Infarction	None	Sometimes assign, depending on diagnosis	< 90 days from trigger event
Ⓣ	E0105	Intracranial Hemorrhage Or Cerebral Infarction	None	Sometimes assign, depending on diagnosis	< 90 days from trigger event
Ⓣ	E0110	Knee Arthroplasty	None	Sometimes assign, depending on diagnosis	Anytime in episode window
Ⓣ	E0114	Knee Arthroplasty	None	Sometimes assign, depending on diagnosis	Anytime in episode window
Ⓣ	E0135	Intracranial Hemorrhage Or Cerebral Infarction	None	Sometimes assign, depending on diagnosis	< 90 days from trigger event
Ⓣ	E0141	Knee Arthroplasty	None	Sometimes assign, depending on diagnosis	Anytime in episode window
Ⓣ	E0143	Elective Outpatient Percutaneous Coronary Intervention (PCI)	Complications (neuro, renal, vascular, infectious)	Sometimes assign, depending on diagnosis	Anytime in episode window
Ⓣ	E0149	Intracranial Hemorrhage Or Cerebral Infarction	None	Sometimes assign, depending on diagnosis	< 90 days from trigger event
Ⓣ	E0154	Intracranial Hemorrhage Or Cerebral Infarction	None	Sometimes assign, depending on diagnosis	< 90 days from trigger event
Ⓣ	E0156	Intracranial Hemorrhage Or Cerebral Infarction	None	Sometimes assign, depending on diagnosis	< 90 days from trigger event

	HCPCS	Measure	Clinical Theme	Service Assignment Decision	Service Assignment Window
ⓣ	**E0163**	Elective Outpatient Percutaneous Coronary Intervention (PCI)	Complications (neuro, renal, vascular, infectious)	Sometimes assign, depending on diagnosis	Anytime in episode window
ⓣ	**E0165**	Intracranial Hemorrhage Or Cerebral Infarction	None	Sometimes assign, depending on diagnosis	< 90 days from trigger event
ⓣ	**E0168**	Intracranial Hemorrhage Or Cerebral Infarction	None	Sometimes assign, depending on diagnosis	< 90 days from trigger event
ⓣ	**E0181**	Intracranial Hemorrhage Or Cerebral Infarction	None	Sometimes assign, depending on diagnosis	< 90 days from trigger event
ⓣ	**E0184**	Intracranial Hemorrhage Or Cerebral Infarction	None	Sometimes assign, depending on diagnosis	< 90 days from trigger event
ⓣ	**E0185**	Intracranial Hemorrhage Or Cerebral Infarction	None	Sometimes assign, depending on diagnosis	< 90 days from trigger event
ⓣ	**E0250**	Intracranial Hemorrhage Or Cerebral Infarction	None	Sometimes assign, depending on diagnosis	< 90 days from trigger event
ⓣ	**E0255**	Intracranial Hemorrhage Or Cerebral Infarction	None	Sometimes assign, depending on diagnosis	< 90 days from trigger event
ⓣ	**E0260**	Elective Outpatient Percutaneous Coronary Intervention (PCI)	Complications (neuro, renal, vascular, infectious)	Sometimes assign, depending on diagnosis	Anytime in episode window
ⓣ	**E0261**	Intracranial Hemorrhage Or Cerebral Infarction	None	Sometimes assign, depending on diagnosis	< 90 days from trigger event

	HCPCS	Measure	Clinical Theme	Service Assignment Decision	Service Assignment Window
ⓣ	E0271	Intracranial Hemorrhage Or Cerebral Infarction	None	Sometimes assign, depending on diagnosis	< 90 days from trigger event
ⓣ	E0277	Intracranial Hemorrhage Or Cerebral Infarction	None	Sometimes assign, depending on diagnosis	< 90 days from trigger event
ⓣ	E0295	Intracranial Hemorrhage Or Cerebral Infarction	None	Sometimes assign, depending on diagnosis	< 90 days from trigger event
ⓣ	E0303	Intracranial Hemorrhage Or Cerebral Infarction	None	Sometimes assign, depending on diagnosis	< 90 days from trigger event
ⓣ	E0431	Elective Outpatient Percutaneous Coronary Intervention (PCI)	None	Sometimes assign, depending on diagnosis	Anytime in episode window
ⓣ	E0439	Simple Pneumonia with Hospitalization	Post-Acute Care (oxygen, rehabilitation, speech/swallow, supplies/other DME)	Assign if service is newly occuring, regardless of diagnosis	Anytime in episode window
ⓣ	E0442	Simple Pneumonia with Hospitalization	Post-Acute Care (oxygen, rehabilitation, speech/swallow, supplies/other DME)	Assign if service is newly occuring, regardless of diagnosis	Anytime in episode window
ⓣ	E0443	Elective Outpatient Percutaneous Coronary Intervention (PCI)	None	Sometimes assign, depending on diagnosis	Anytime in episode window
ⓣ	E0444	Simple Pneumonia with Hospitalization	Post-Acute Care (oxygen, rehabilitation, speech/swallow, supplies/other DME)	Assign if service is newly occuring, regardless of diagnosis	Anytime in episode window

	HCPCS	Measure	Clinical Theme	Service Assignment Decision	Service Assignment Window
ⓣ	E0465	Simple Pneumonia with Hospitalization	Post-Acute Care (oxygen, rehabilitation, speech/swallow, supplies/other DME)	Assign if service is newly occuring, regardless of diagnosis	Anytime in episode window
ⓣ	E0466	Revascularization for Lower Extremity Chronic Critical Limb Ischemia	None	Assign if service is newly occuring, regardless of diagnosis	Anytime in episode window
ⓣ	E0470	Revascularization for Lower Extremity Chronic Critical Limb Ischemia	None	Assign if service is newly occuring, regardless of diagnosis	Anytime in episode window
ⓣ	E0471	Revascularization for Lower Extremity Chronic Critical Limb Ischemia	None	Assign if service is newly occuring, regardless of diagnosis	Anytime in episode window
ⓣ	E0482	Simple Pneumonia with Hospitalization	Post-Acute Care (oxygen, rehabilitation, speech/swallow, supplies/other DME)	Assign if service is newly occuring, regardless of diagnosis	Anytime in episode window
ⓣ	E0483	Revascularization for Lower Extremity Chronic Critical Limb Ischemia	None	Assign if service is newly occuring, regardless of diagnosis	Anytime in episode window
ⓣ	E0486	Simple Pneumonia with Hospitalization	Post-Acute Care (oxygen, rehabilitation, speech/swallow, supplies/other DME)	Assign if service is newly occuring, regardless of diagnosis	Anytime in episode window
ⓣ	E0562	Revascularization for Lower Extremity Chronic Critical Limb Ischemia	None	Assign if service is newly occuring, regardless of diagnosis	Anytime in episode window

	HCPCS	Measure	Clinical Theme	Service Assignment Decision	Service Assignment Window
ⓣ	E0570	Revascularization for Lower Extremity Chronic Critical Limb Ischemia	None	Assign if service is newly occuring, regardless of diagnosis	Anytime in episode window
ⓣ	E0600	Simple Pneumonia with Hospitalization	Post-Acute Care (oxygen, rehabilitation, speech/swallow, supplies/other DME)	Assign if service is newly occuring, regardless of diagnosis	Anytime in episode window
ⓣ	E0601	Simple Pneumonia with Hospitalization	Post-Acute Care (oxygen, rehabilitation, speech/swallow, supplies/other DME)	Assign if service is newly occuring, regardless of diagnosis	Anytime in episode window
ⓣ	E0627	Intracranial Hemorrhage Or Cerebral Infarction	None	Sometimes assign, depending on diagnosis	< 90 days from trigger event
ⓣ	E0630	Intracranial Hemorrhage Or Cerebral Infarction	None	Sometimes assign, depending on diagnosis	< 90 days from trigger event
ⓣ	E0651	Knee Arthroplasty	None	Sometimes assign, depending on diagnosis	< 30 days from trigger event
ⓣ	E0667	Knee Arthroplasty	None	Sometimes assign, depending on diagnosis	< 30 days from trigger event
ⓣ	E0705	Intracranial Hemorrhage Or Cerebral Infarction	None	Sometimes assign, depending on diagnosis	< 90 days from trigger event
ⓣ	E0730	Knee Arthroplasty	None	Sometimes assign, depending on diagnosis	Anytime in episode window
ⓣ	E0731	Knee Arthroplasty	None	Sometimes assign, depending on diagnosis	Anytime in episode window
ⓣ	E0745	Knee Arthroplasty	None	Sometimes assign, depending on diagnosis	Anytime in episode window
ⓣ	E0747	Revascularization for Lower Extremity Chronic Critical Limb Ischemia	Wound Care Services	Yes, assign regardless of diagnosis	Anytime in episode window

	HCPCS	Measure	Clinical Theme	Service Assignment Decision	Service Assignment Window
ⓣ	E0748	Revascularization for Lower Extremity Chronic Critical Limb Ischemia	Wound Care Services	Yes, assign regardless of diagnosis	Anytime in episode window
ⓣ	E0760	Knee Arthroplasty	None	Sometimes assign, depending on diagnosis	Anytime in episode window
ⓣ	E0776	Intracranial Hemorrhage Or Cerebral Infarction	None	Sometimes assign, depending on diagnosis	< 90 days from trigger event
ⓣ	E0784	Revascularization for Lower Extremity Chronic Critical Limb Ischemia	None	Assign if service is newly occuring, regardless of diagnosis	Anytime in episode window
ⓣ	E0935	Knee Arthroplasty	None	Assign if service is newly occuring, regardless of diagnosis	Anytime in episode window
ⓣ	E0950	Intracranial Hemorrhage Or Cerebral Infarction	None	Sometimes assign, depending on diagnosis	< 90 days from trigger event
ⓣ	E0951	Intracranial Hemorrhage Or Cerebral Infarction	None	Sometimes assign, depending on diagnosis	< 90 days from trigger event
ⓣ	E0955	Intracranial Hemorrhage Or Cerebral Infarction	None	Sometimes assign, depending on diagnosis	< 90 days from trigger event
ⓣ	E0961	Intracranial Hemorrhage Or Cerebral Infarction	None	Sometimes assign, depending on diagnosis	< 90 days from trigger event
ⓣ	E0971	Intracranial Hemorrhage Or Cerebral Infarction	None	Sometimes assign, depending on diagnosis	< 90 days from trigger event
ⓣ	E0973	Intracranial Hemorrhage Or Cerebral Infarction	None	Sometimes assign, depending on diagnosis	< 90 days from trigger event

	HCPCS	Measure	Clinical Theme	Service Assignment Decision	Service Assignment Window
ⓣ	E0978	Intracranial Hemorrhage Or Cerebral Infarction	None	Sometimes assign, depending on diagnosis	< 90 days from trigger event
ⓣ	E1002	Intracranial Hemorrhage Or Cerebral Infarction	None	Sometimes assign, depending on diagnosis	< 90 days from trigger event
ⓣ	E1007	Elective Outpatient Percutaneous Coronary Intervention (PCI)	Complications (neuro, renal, vascular, infectious)	Sometimes assign, depending on diagnosis	Anytime in episode window
ⓣ	E1008	Intracranial Hemorrhage Or Cerebral Infarction	None	Sometimes assign, depending on diagnosis	< 90 days from trigger event
ⓣ	E1012	Intracranial Hemorrhage Or Cerebral Infarction	None	Sometimes assign, depending on diagnosis	< 90 days from trigger event
ⓣ	E1028	Intracranial Hemorrhage Or Cerebral Infarction	None	Sometimes assign, depending on diagnosis	< 90 days from trigger event
ⓣ	E1038	Intracranial Hemorrhage Or Cerebral Infarction	None	Sometimes assign, depending on diagnosis	< 90 days from trigger event
ⓣ	E1161	Intracranial Hemorrhage Or Cerebral Infarction	None	Sometimes assign, depending on diagnosis	< 90 days from trigger event
ⓣ	E1226	Intracranial Hemorrhage Or Cerebral Infarction	None	Sometimes assign, depending on diagnosis	< 90 days from trigger event
ⓣ	E1390	Elective Outpatient Percutaneous Coronary Intervention (PCI)	None	Sometimes assign, depending on diagnosis	Anytime in episode window

	HCPCS	Measure	Clinical Theme	Service Assignment Decision	Service Assignment Window
ⓣ	E1392	Elective Outpatient Percutaneous Coronary Intervention (PCI)	None	Sometimes assign, depending on diagnosis	Anytime in episode window
ⓣ	E1810	Knee Arthroplasty	None	Sometimes assign, depending on diagnosis	Anytime in episode window
ⓣ	E1811	Knee Arthroplasty	None	Sometimes assign, depending on diagnosis	Anytime in episode window
ⓣ	E2201	Intracranial Hemorrhage Or Cerebral Infarction	None	Sometimes assign, depending on diagnosis	< 90 days from trigger event
ⓣ	E2203	Intracranial Hemorrhage Or Cerebral Infarction	None	Sometimes assign, depending on diagnosis	< 90 days from trigger event
ⓣ	E2209	Intracranial Hemorrhage Or Cerebral Infarction	None	Sometimes assign, depending on diagnosis	< 90 days from trigger event
ⓣ	E2228	Intracranial Hemorrhage Or Cerebral Infarction	None	Sometimes assign, depending on diagnosis	< 90 days from trigger event
ⓣ	E2311	Elective Outpatient Percutaneous Coronary Intervention (PCI)	Complications (neuro, renal, vascular, infectious)	Sometimes assign, depending on diagnosis	Anytime in episode window
ⓣ	E2313	Intracranial Hemorrhage Or Cerebral Infarction	None	Sometimes assign, depending on diagnosis	< 90 days from trigger event
ⓣ	E2361	Intracranial Hemorrhage Or Cerebral Infarction	None	Sometimes assign, depending on diagnosis	< 90 days from trigger event
ⓣ	E2365	Elective Outpatient Percutaneous Coronary Intervention (PCI)	None	Sometimes assign, depending on diagnosis	Anytime in episode window

	HCPCS	Measure	Clinical Theme	Service Assignment Decision	Service Assignment Window
Ⓣ	E2370	Intracranial Hemorrhage Or Cerebral Infarction	None	Sometimes assign, depending on diagnosis	< 90 days from trigger event
Ⓣ	E2374	Intracranial Hemorrhage Or Cerebral Infarction	None	Sometimes assign, depending on diagnosis	< 90 days from trigger event
Ⓣ	E2375	Elective Outpatient Percutaneous Coronary Intervention (PCI)	None	Sometimes assign, depending on diagnosis	Anytime in episode window
Ⓣ	E2377	Intracranial Hemorrhage Or Cerebral Infarction	None	Sometimes assign, depending on diagnosis	< 90 days from trigger event
Ⓣ	E2402	Intracranial Hemorrhage Or Cerebral Infarction	None	Sometimes assign, depending on diagnosis	< 90 days from trigger event
Ⓣ	E2510	Intracranial Hemorrhage Or Cerebral Infarction	None	Sometimes assign, depending on diagnosis	< 90 days from trigger event
Ⓣ	E2599	Simple Pneumonia with Hospitalization	Post-Acute Care (oxygen, rehabilitation, speech/swallow, supplies/other DME)	Assign if service is newly occuring, regardless of diagnosis	Anytime in episode window
Ⓣ	E2601	Intracranial Hemorrhage Or Cerebral Infarction	None	Sometimes assign, depending on diagnosis	< 90 days from trigger event
Ⓣ	E2603	Intracranial Hemorrhage Or Cerebral Infarction	None	Sometimes assign, depending on diagnosis	< 90 days from trigger event
Ⓣ	E2607	Intracranial Hemorrhage Or Cerebral Infarction	None	Sometimes assign, depending on diagnosis	< 90 days from trigger event

	HCPCS	Measure	Clinical Theme	Service Assignment Decision	Service Assignment Window
Ⓣ	E2611	Intracranial Hemorrhage Or Cerebral Infarction	None	Sometimes assign, depending on diagnosis	< 90 days from trigger event
Ⓣ	E2613	Intracranial Hemorrhage Or Cerebral Infarction	None	Sometimes assign, depending on diagnosis	< 90 days from trigger event
Ⓣ	E2615	Intracranial Hemorrhage Or Cerebral Infarction	None	Sometimes assign, depending on diagnosis	< 90 days from trigger event
Ⓣ	E2620	Intracranial Hemorrhage Or Cerebral Infarction	None	Sometimes assign, depending on diagnosis	< 90 days from trigger event
Ⓣ	E2622	Intracranial Hemorrhage Or Cerebral Infarction	None	Sometimes assign, depending on diagnosis	< 90 days from trigger event
Ⓣ	G0333	Revascularization for Lower Extremity Chronic Critical Limb Ischemia	None	Assign if service is newly occuring, regardless of diagnosis	Anytime in episode window
Ⓣ	J2260	Revascularization for Lower Extremity Chronic Critical Limb Ischemia	None	Assign if service is newly occuring, regardless of diagnosis	Anytime in episode window
Ⓣ	J7605	Simple Pneumonia with Hospitalization	Post-Acute Care (oxygen, rehabilitation, speech/swallow, supplies/other DME)	Assign if service is newly occuring, regardless of diagnosis	Anytime in episode window
Ⓣ	J7606	Simple Pneumonia with Hospitalization	Post-Acute Care (oxygen, rehabilitation, speech/swallow, supplies/other DME)	Assign if service is newly occuring, regardless of diagnosis	Anytime in episode window

	HCPCS	Measure	Clinical Theme	Service Assignment Decision	Service Assignment Window
ⓣ	**J7608**	Simple Pneumonia with Hospitalization	Post-Acute Care (oxygen, rehabilitation, speech/swallow, supplies/other DME)	Assign if service is newly occuring, regardless of diagnosis	Anytime in episode window
ⓣ	**J7613**	Simple Pneumonia with Hospitalization	Post-Acute Care (oxygen, rehabilitation, speech/swallow, supplies/other DME)	Assign if service is newly occuring, regardless of diagnosis	Anytime in episode window
ⓣ	**J7620**	Simple Pneumonia with Hospitalization	Post-Acute Care (oxygen, rehabilitation, speech/swallow, supplies/other DME)	Assign if service is newly occuring, regardless of diagnosis	Anytime in episode window
ⓣ	**J7626**	Simple Pneumonia with Hospitalization	Post-Acute Care (oxygen, rehabilitation, speech/swallow, supplies/other DME)	Assign if service is newly occuring, regardless of diagnosis	Anytime in episode window
ⓣ	**J7644**	Simple Pneumonia with Hospitalization	Post-Acute Care (oxygen, rehabilitation, speech/swallow, supplies/other DME)	Assign if service is newly occuring, regardless of diagnosis	Anytime in episode window
ⓣ	**J7682**	Simple Pneumonia with Hospitalization	Post-Acute Care (oxygen, rehabilitation, speech/swallow, supplies/other DME)	Assign if service is newly occuring, regardless of diagnosis	Anytime in episode window
ⓣ	**J7686**	Simple Pneumonia with Hospitalization	Post-Acute Care (oxygen, rehabilitation, speech/swallow, supplies/other DME)	Assign if service is newly occuring, regardless of diagnosis	Anytime in episode window

	HCPCS	Measure	Clinical Theme	Service Assignment Decision	Service Assignment Window
Ⓣ	**K0001**	Elective Outpatient Percutaneous Coronary Intervention (PCI)	None	Sometimes assign, depending on diagnosis	Anytime in episode window
Ⓣ	**K0002**	Intracranial Hemorrhage Or Cerebral Infarction	None	Sometimes assign, depending on diagnosis	< 90 days from trigger event
Ⓣ	**K0003**	Elective Outpatient Percutaneous Coronary Intervention (PCI)	None	Sometimes assign, depending on diagnosis	Anytime in episode window
Ⓣ	**K0004**	Intracranial Hemorrhage Or Cerebral Infarction	None	Sometimes assign, depending on diagnosis	< 90 days from trigger event
Ⓣ	**K0005**	Intracranial Hemorrhage Or Cerebral Infarction	None	Sometimes assign, depending on diagnosis	< 90 days from trigger event
Ⓣ	**K0006**	Intracranial Hemorrhage Or Cerebral Infarction	None	Sometimes assign, depending on diagnosis	< 90 days from trigger event
Ⓣ	**K0007**	Intracranial Hemorrhage Or Cerebral Infarction	None	Sometimes assign, depending on diagnosis	< 90 days from trigger event
Ⓣ	**K0108**	Intracranial Hemorrhage Or Cerebral Infarction	None	Sometimes assign, depending on diagnosis	< 90 days from trigger event
Ⓣ	**K0195**	Intracranial Hemorrhage Or Cerebral Infarction	None	Sometimes assign, depending on diagnosis	< 90 days from trigger event
Ⓣ	**K0462**	Intracranial Hemorrhage Or Cerebral Infarction	None	Sometimes assign, depending on diagnosis	< 90 days from trigger event

	HCPCS	Measure	Clinical Theme	Service Assignment Decision	Service Assignment Window
ⓣ	**K0552**	Revascularization for Lower Extremity Chronic Critical Limb Ischemia	None	Assign if service is newly occuring, regardless of diagnosis	Anytime in episode window
ⓣ	**K0606**	Elective Outpatient Percutaneous Coronary Intervention (PCI)	None	Sometimes assign, depending on diagnosis	Anytime in episode window
ⓣ	**K0738**	Elective Outpatient Percutaneous Coronary Intervention (PCI)	None	Sometimes assign, depending on diagnosis	Anytime in episode window
ⓣ	**K0739**	Intracranial Hemorrhage Or Cerebral Infarction	None	Sometimes assign, depending on diagnosis	< 90 days from trigger event
ⓣ	**K0800**	Revascularization for Lower Extremity Chronic Critical Limb Ischemia	None	Yes, assign regardless of diagnosis	Anytime in episode window
ⓣ	**K0816**	Intracranial Hemorrhage Or Cerebral Infarction	None	Sometimes assign, depending on diagnosis	< 90 days from trigger event
ⓣ	**K0821**	Simple Pneumonia with Hospitalization	Post-Acute Care (oxygen, rehabilitation, speech/swallow, supplies/other DME)	Assign if service is newly occuring, regardless of diagnosis	< 15 days from trigger event
ⓣ	**K0822**	Intracranial Hemorrhage Or Cerebral Infarction	None	Sometimes assign, depending on diagnosis	< 90 days from trigger event
ⓣ	**K0823**	Elective Outpatient Percutaneous Coronary Intervention (PCI)	None	Sometimes assign, depending on diagnosis	Anytime in episode window

	HCPCS	Measure	Clinical Theme	Service Assignment Decision	Service Assignment Window
ⓣ	**K0825**	Elective Outpatient Percutaneous Coronary Intervention (PCI)	Complications (neuro, renal, vascular, infectious)	Sometimes assign, depending on diagnosis	Anytime in episode window
ⓣ	**K0835**	Revascularization for Lower Extremity Chronic Critical Limb Ischemia	None	Yes, assign regardless of diagnosis	Anytime in episode window
ⓣ	**K0848**	Intracranial Hemorrhage Or Cerebral Infarction	None	Sometimes assign, depending on diagnosis	< 90 days from trigger event
ⓣ	**K0849**	Intracranial Hemorrhage Or Cerebral Infarction	None	Sometimes assign, depending on diagnosis	< 90 days from trigger event
ⓣ	**K0856**	Intracranial Hemorrhage Or Cerebral Infarction	None	Sometimes assign, depending on diagnosis	< 90 days from trigger event
ⓣ	**K0858**	Intracranial Hemorrhage Or Cerebral Infarction	None	Sometimes assign, depending on diagnosis	< 90 days from trigger event
ⓣ	**K0861**	Intracranial Hemorrhage Or Cerebral Infarction	None	Sometimes assign, depending on diagnosis	< 90 days from trigger event
ⓣ	**K0862**	Elective Outpatient Percutaneous Coronary Intervention (PCI)	Complications (neuro, renal, vascular, infectious)	Sometimes assign, depending on diagnosis	Anytime in episode window
ⓣ	**K0902**	Knee Arthroplasty	None	Sometimes assign, depending on diagnosis	Anytime in episode window
ⓣ	**L1810**	Knee Arthroplasty	None	Sometimes assign, depending on diagnosis	Anytime in episode window
ⓣ	**L1812**	Knee Arthroplasty	None	Sometimes assign, depending on diagnosis	Anytime in episode window
ⓣ	**L1820**	Knee Arthroplasty	None	Sometimes assign, depending on diagnosis	Anytime in episode window

	HCPCS	Measure	Clinical Theme	Service Assignment Decision	Service Assignment Window
⊤	L1830	Knee Arthroplasty	None	Sometimes assign, depending on diagnosis	Anytime in episode window
⊤	L1832	Knee Arthroplasty	None	Sometimes assign, depending on diagnosis	Anytime in episode window
⊤	L1833	Knee Arthroplasty	None	Sometimes assign, depending on diagnosis	Anytime in episode window
⊤	L1843	Knee Arthroplasty	None	Sometimes assign, depending on diagnosis	Anytime in episode window
⊤	L1845	Knee Arthroplasty	None	Sometimes assign, depending on diagnosis	Anytime in episode window
⊤	L1930	Intracranial Hemorrhage Or Cerebral Infarction	None	Sometimes assign, depending on diagnosis	< 90 days from trigger event
⊤	L1932	Intracranial Hemorrhage Or Cerebral Infarction	None	Sometimes assign, depending on diagnosis	< 90 days from trigger event
⊤	L1940	Intracranial Hemorrhage Or Cerebral Infarction	None	Sometimes assign, depending on diagnosis	< 90 days from trigger event
⊤	L1945	Intracranial Hemorrhage Or Cerebral Infarction	None	Sometimes assign, depending on diagnosis	< 90 days from trigger event
⊤	L1950	Intracranial Hemorrhage Or Cerebral Infarction	None	Sometimes assign, depending on diagnosis	< 90 days from trigger event
⊤	L1951	Intracranial Hemorrhage Or Cerebral Infarction	None	Sometimes assign, depending on diagnosis	< 90 days from trigger event
⊤	L1960	Intracranial Hemorrhage Or Cerebral Infarction	None	Sometimes assign, depending on diagnosis	< 90 days from trigger event
⊤	L1970	Intracranial Hemorrhage Or Cerebral Infarction	None	Sometimes assign, depending on diagnosis	< 90 days from trigger event

	HCPCS	Measure	Clinical Theme	Service Assignment Decision	Service Assignment Window
⊤	**L1971**	Intracranial Hemorrhage Or Cerebral Infarction	None	Sometimes assign, depending on diagnosis	< 90 days from trigger event
⊤	**L1990**	Intracranial Hemorrhage Or Cerebral Infarction	None	Sometimes assign, depending on diagnosis	< 90 days from trigger event
⊤	**L2005**	Intracranial Hemorrhage Or Cerebral Infarction	None	Sometimes assign, depending on diagnosis	< 90 days from trigger event
⊤	**L2020**	Intracranial Hemorrhage Or Cerebral Infarction	None	Sometimes assign, depending on diagnosis	< 90 days from trigger event
⊤	**L2036**	Intracranial Hemorrhage Or Cerebral Infarction	None	Sometimes assign, depending on diagnosis	< 90 days from trigger event
⊤	**L2200**	Intracranial Hemorrhage Or Cerebral Infarction	None	Sometimes assign, depending on diagnosis	< 90 days from trigger event
⊤	**L2210**	Intracranial Hemorrhage Or Cerebral Infarction	None	Sometimes assign, depending on diagnosis	< 90 days from trigger event
⊤	**L2220**	Intracranial Hemorrhage Or Cerebral Infarction	None	Sometimes assign, depending on diagnosis	< 90 days from trigger event
⊤	**L2275**	Intracranial Hemorrhage Or Cerebral Infarction	None	Sometimes assign, depending on diagnosis	< 90 days from trigger event
⊤	**L2280**	Intracranial Hemorrhage Or Cerebral Infarction	None	Sometimes assign, depending on diagnosis	< 90 days from trigger event
⊤	**L2330**	Intracranial Hemorrhage Or Cerebral Infarction	None	Sometimes assign, depending on diagnosis	< 90 days from trigger event

	HCPCS	Measure	Clinical Theme	Service Assignment Decision	Service Assignment Window
ⓣ	**L2340**	Intracranial Hemorrhage Or Cerebral Infarction	None	Sometimes assign, depending on diagnosis	< 90 days from trigger event
ⓣ	**L2397**	Knee Arthroplasty	None	Sometimes assign, depending on diagnosis	Anytime in episode window
ⓣ	**L2755**	Intracranial Hemorrhage Or Cerebral Infarction	None	Sometimes assign, depending on diagnosis	< 90 days from trigger event
ⓣ	**L2780**	Intracranial Hemorrhage Or Cerebral Infarction	None	Sometimes assign, depending on diagnosis	< 90 days from trigger event
ⓣ	**L2820**	Intracranial Hemorrhage Or Cerebral Infarction	None	Sometimes assign, depending on diagnosis	< 90 days from trigger event
ⓣ	**L3670**	Intracranial Hemorrhage Or Cerebral Infarction	None	Sometimes assign, depending on diagnosis	< 90 days from trigger event
ⓣ	**L3760**	Intracranial Hemorrhage Or Cerebral Infarction	None	Sometimes assign, depending on diagnosis	< 90 days from trigger event
ⓣ	**L3807**	Intracranial Hemorrhage Or Cerebral Infarction	None	Sometimes assign, depending on diagnosis	< 90 days from trigger event
ⓣ	**L3809**	Intracranial Hemorrhage Or Cerebral Infarction	None	Sometimes assign, depending on diagnosis	< 90 days from trigger event
ⓣ	**L3908**	Intracranial Hemorrhage Or Cerebral Infarction	None	Sometimes assign, depending on diagnosis	< 90 days from trigger event
ⓣ	**L4360**	Revascularization for Lower Extremity Chronic Critical Limb Ischemia	None	Yes, assign regardless of diagnosis	Anytime in episode window

	HCPCS	Measure	Clinical Theme	Service Assignment Decision	Service Assignment Window
Ⓣ	**L4361**	Revascularization for Lower Extremity Chronic Critical Limb Ischemia	None	Yes, assign regardless of diagnosis	Anytime in episode window
Ⓣ	**L4631**	Revascularization for Lower Extremity Chronic Critical Limb Ischemia	None	Yes, assign regardless of diagnosis	Anytime in episode window
Ⓣ	**L5210**	Revascularization for Lower Extremity Chronic Critical Limb Ischemia	Amputation-Related Services	Yes, assign regardless of diagnosis	Anytime in episode window
Ⓣ	**L5301**	Revascularization for Lower Extremity Chronic Critical Limb Ischemia	Amputation-Related Services	Yes, assign regardless of diagnosis	Anytime in episode window
Ⓣ	**L5321**	Revascularization for Lower Extremity Chronic Critical Limb Ischemia	Amputation-Related Services	Yes, assign regardless of diagnosis	Anytime in episode window
Ⓣ	**L5450**	Revascularization for Lower Extremity Chronic Critical Limb Ischemia	None	Yes, assign regardless of diagnosis	Anytime in episode window
Ⓣ	**L5530**	Revascularization for Lower Extremity Chronic Critical Limb Ischemia	None	Yes, assign regardless of diagnosis	Anytime in episode window
Ⓣ	**L5540**	Revascularization for Lower Extremity Chronic Critical Limb Ischemia	None	Yes, assign regardless of diagnosis	Anytime in episode window
Ⓣ	**L5580**	Revascularization for Lower Extremity Chronic Critical Limb Ischemia	None	Yes, assign regardless of diagnosis	Anytime in episode window

	HCPCS	Measure	Clinical Theme	Service Assignment Decision	Service Assignment Window
Ⓣ	**L5590**	Revascularization for Lower Extremity Chronic Critical Limb Ischemia	None	Yes, assign regardless of diagnosis	Anytime in episode window
Ⓣ	**L5611**	Revascularization for Lower Extremity Chronic Critical Limb Ischemia	Amputation-Related Services	Yes, assign regardless of diagnosis	Anytime in episode window
Ⓣ	**L5620**	Revascularization for Lower Extremity Chronic Critical Limb Ischemia	Amputation-Related Services	Yes, assign regardless of diagnosis	Anytime in episode window
Ⓣ	**L5624**	Revascularization for Lower Extremity Chronic Critical Limb Ischemia	Amputation-Related Services	Yes, assign regardless of diagnosis	Anytime in episode window
Ⓣ	**L5629**	Revascularization for Lower Extremity Chronic Critical Limb Ischemia	Amputation-Related Services	Yes, assign regardless of diagnosis	Anytime in episode window
Ⓣ	**L5631**	Revascularization for Lower Extremity Chronic Critical Limb Ischemia	Amputation-Related Services	Yes, assign regardless of diagnosis	Anytime in episode window
Ⓣ	**L5637**	Revascularization for Lower Extremity Chronic Critical Limb Ischemia	Amputation-Related Services	Yes, assign regardless of diagnosis	Anytime in episode window
Ⓣ	**L5645**	Revascularization for Lower Extremity Chronic Critical Limb Ischemia	Amputation-Related Services	Yes, assign regardless of diagnosis	Anytime in episode window
Ⓣ	**L5647**	Revascularization for Lower Extremity Chronic Critical Limb Ischemia	Amputation-Related Services	Yes, assign regardless of diagnosis	Anytime in episode window

	HCPCS	Measure	Clinical Theme	Service Assignment Decision	Service Assignment Window
ⓣ	L5649	Revascularization for Lower Extremity Chronic Critical Limb Ischemia	Amputation-Related Services	Yes, assign regardless of diagnosis	Anytime in episode window
ⓣ	L5650	Revascularization for Lower Extremity Chronic Critical Limb Ischemia	Amputation-Related Services	Yes, assign regardless of diagnosis	Anytime in episode window
ⓣ	L5651	Revascularization for Lower Extremity Chronic Critical Limb Ischemia	Amputation-Related Services	Yes, assign regardless of diagnosis	Anytime in episode window
ⓣ	L5652	Revascularization for Lower Extremity Chronic Critical Limb Ischemia	Amputation-Related Services	Yes, assign regardless of diagnosis	Anytime in episode window
ⓣ	L5671	Revascularization for Lower Extremity Chronic Critical Limb Ischemia	Amputation-Related Services	Yes, assign regardless of diagnosis	Anytime in episode window
ⓣ	L5673	Revascularization for Lower Extremity Chronic Critical Limb Ischemia	Amputation-Related Services	Yes, assign regardless of diagnosis	Anytime in episode window
ⓣ	L5679	Revascularization for Lower Extremity Chronic Critical Limb Ischemia	Amputation-Related Services	Yes, assign regardless of diagnosis	Anytime in episode window
ⓣ	L5683	Revascularization for Lower Extremity Chronic Critical Limb Ischemia	Amputation-Related Services	Yes, assign regardless of diagnosis	Anytime in episode window
ⓣ	L5685	Revascularization for Lower Extremity Chronic Critical Limb Ischemia	Amputation-Related Services	Yes, assign regardless of diagnosis	Anytime in episode window

	HCPCS	Measure	Clinical Theme	Service Assignment Decision	Service Assignment Window
Ⓣ	**L5700**	Revascularization for Lower Extremity Chronic Critical Limb Ischemia	Amputation-Related Services	Yes, assign regardless of diagnosis	Anytime in episode window
Ⓣ	**L5701**	Revascularization for Lower Extremity Chronic Critical Limb Ischemia	Amputation-Related Services	Yes, assign regardless of diagnosis	Anytime in episode window
Ⓣ	**L5704**	Revascularization for Lower Extremity Chronic Critical Limb Ischemia	None	Yes, assign regardless of diagnosis	Anytime in episode window
Ⓣ	**L5705**	Revascularization for Lower Extremity Chronic Critical Limb Ischemia	None	Yes, assign regardless of diagnosis	Anytime in episode window
Ⓣ	**L5781**	Revascularization for Lower Extremity Chronic Critical Limb Ischemia	Amputation-Related Services	Yes, assign regardless of diagnosis	Anytime in episode window
Ⓣ	**L5812**	Revascularization for Lower Extremity Chronic Critical Limb Ischemia	Amputation-Related Services	Yes, assign regardless of diagnosis	Anytime in episode window
Ⓣ	**L5828**	Revascularization for Lower Extremity Chronic Critical Limb Ischemia	Amputation-Related Services	Yes, assign regardless of diagnosis	Anytime in episode window
Ⓣ	**L5845**	Revascularization for Lower Extremity Chronic Critical Limb Ischemia	Amputation-Related Services	Yes, assign regardless of diagnosis	Anytime in episode window
Ⓣ	**L5848**	Revascularization for Lower Extremity Chronic Critical Limb Ischemia	Amputation-Related Services	Yes, assign regardless of diagnosis	Anytime in episode window

	HCPCS	Measure	Clinical Theme	Service Assignment Decision	Service Assignment Window
ⓣ	**L5850**	Revascularization for Lower Extremity Chronic Critical Limb Ischemia	Amputation-Related Services	Yes, assign regardless of diagnosis	Anytime in episode window
ⓣ	**L5856**	Revascularization for Lower Extremity Chronic Critical Limb Ischemia	Amputation-Related Services	Yes, assign regardless of diagnosis	Anytime in episode window
ⓣ	**L5858**	Revascularization for Lower Extremity Chronic Critical Limb Ischemia	Amputation-Related Services	Yes, assign regardless of diagnosis	Anytime in episode window
ⓣ	**L5859**	Revascularization for Lower Extremity Chronic Critical Limb Ischemia	Amputation-Related Services	Yes, assign regardless of diagnosis	Anytime in episode window
ⓣ	**L5910**	Revascularization for Lower Extremity Chronic Critical Limb Ischemia	Amputation-Related Services	Yes, assign regardless of diagnosis	Anytime in episode window
ⓣ	**L5920**	Revascularization for Lower Extremity Chronic Critical Limb Ischemia	Amputation-Related Services	Yes, assign regardless of diagnosis	Anytime in episode window
ⓣ	**L5925**	Revascularization for Lower Extremity Chronic Critical Limb Ischemia	Amputation-Related Services	Yes, assign regardless of diagnosis	Anytime in episode window
ⓣ	**L5940**	Revascularization for Lower Extremity Chronic Critical Limb Ischemia	Amputation-Related Services	Yes, assign regardless of diagnosis	Anytime in episode window
ⓣ	**L5950**	Revascularization for Lower Extremity Chronic Critical Limb Ischemia	Amputation-Related Services	Yes, assign regardless of diagnosis	Anytime in episode window

	HCPCS	Measure	Clinical Theme	Service Assignment Decision	Service Assignment Window
ⓣ	L5962	Revascularization for Lower Extremity Chronic Critical Limb Ischemia	Amputation-Related Services	Yes, assign regardless of diagnosis	Anytime in episode window
ⓣ	L5964	Revascularization for Lower Extremity Chronic Critical Limb Ischemia	Amputation-Related Services	Yes, assign regardless of diagnosis	Anytime in episode window
ⓣ	L5968	Revascularization for Lower Extremity Chronic Critical Limb Ischemia	Amputation-Related Services	Yes, assign regardless of diagnosis	Anytime in episode window
ⓣ	L5972	Revascularization for Lower Extremity Chronic Critical Limb Ischemia	Amputation-Related Services	Yes, assign regardless of diagnosis	Anytime in episode window
ⓣ	L5973	Revascularization for Lower Extremity Chronic Critical Limb Ischemia	None	Yes, assign regardless of diagnosis	Anytime in episode window
ⓣ	L5980	Revascularization for Lower Extremity Chronic Critical Limb Ischemia	Amputation-Related Services	Yes, assign regardless of diagnosis	Anytime in episode window
ⓣ	L5981	Revascularization for Lower Extremity Chronic Critical Limb Ischemia	Amputation-Related Services	Yes, assign regardless of diagnosis	Anytime in episode window
ⓣ	L5986	Revascularization for Lower Extremity Chronic Critical Limb Ischemia	Amputation-Related Services	Yes, assign regardless of diagnosis	Anytime in episode window
ⓣ	L5987	Revascularization for Lower Extremity Chronic Critical Limb Ischemia	Amputation-Related Services	Yes, assign regardless of diagnosis	Anytime in episode window

	HCPCS	Measure	Clinical Theme	Service Assignment Decision	Service Assignment Window
Ⓣ	**L6935**	Revascularization for Lower Extremity Chronic Critical Limb Ischemia	None	Yes, assign regardless of diagnosis	Anytime in episode window
Ⓣ	**L8400**	Revascularization for Lower Extremity Chronic Critical Limb Ischemia	Amputation-Related Services	Yes, assign regardless of diagnosis	Anytime in episode window
Ⓣ	**L8420**	Revascularization for Lower Extremity Chronic Critical Limb Ischemia	Amputation-Related Services	Yes, assign regardless of diagnosis	Anytime in episode window
Ⓣ	**L8430**	Revascularization for Lower Extremity Chronic Critical Limb Ischemia	Amputation-Related Services	Yes, assign regardless of diagnosis	Anytime in episode window
Ⓣ	**L8440**	Revascularization for Lower Extremity Chronic Critical Limb Ischemia	Amputation-Related Services	Yes, assign regardless of diagnosis	Anytime in episode window
Ⓣ	**L8460**	Revascularization for Lower Extremity Chronic Critical Limb Ischemia	Amputation-Related Services	Yes, assign regardless of diagnosis	Anytime in episode window
Ⓣ	**L8470**	Revascularization for Lower Extremity Chronic Critical Limb Ischemia	Amputation-Related Services	Yes, assign regardless of diagnosis	Anytime in episode window
Ⓣ	**Q0513**	Simple Pneumonia with Hospitalization	Post-Acute Care (oxygen, rehabilitation, speech/swallow, supplies/other DME)	Assign if service is newly occuring, regardless of diagnosis	Anytime in episode window

	HCPCS	Measure	Clinical Theme	Service Assignment Decision	Service Assignment Window
Ⓣ	**Q0514**	Simple Pneumonia with Hospitalization	Post-Acute Care (oxygen, rehabilitation, speech/swallow, supplies/other DME)	Assign if service is newly occuring, regardless of diagnosis	Anytime in episode window

APPENDIX F: HCPCS TO NDC DRUG NAME CROSS-WALK

The HCPCS cross-walk to NDC drug name is intended to help providers who bill for drugs understand which drug products (identified by drug name) are assigned to which HCPCS billing codes. The crosswalks are not intended to be a comprehensive list of all drugs/NDCs available in the United States. The NDC to HCPCS Crosswalk also includes information on the NDC dose and package size.

COLUMN DEFINITIONS

HCPCS: Five (5) digit HCPCS code

Drug Name: Product Name (brand or generic name may appear)

Dose: The dosage descriptor assigned to the HCPCS code

Pkg Size: The amount of the drug in one item. (ex., For a product that is 100mcg/0.5 ml in one vial, the package size would be 0.5.)

Labeler Name: Manufacturer Name

HCPCS	DRUG NAME	DOSE	PKG SIZE	LABELER NAME
A9515	Choline C 11	Per study dose	30	Zevacor Molecular
A9543	Zevalin Y-90	Up to 40 millicuries	1	Spectrum Pharmaceuticals
A9575	Dotarem	0.1 ml	10	Guerbet LLC
		0.1 ml	15	
		0.1 ml	20	
		0.1 ml	100	
A9576	Prohance Multipack	1 ml	50	Bracco Diagnostics
A9577	Multihance	1 ml	5	
		1 ml	10	
		1 ml	15	
		1 ml	20	
	Multihance 5 x 15 ml Syringe	1 ml	15	
A9578	Multihance Multipack	1 ml	50	
		1 ml	100	
A9579	Magnevist 46.9%	1 ml	5	Bayer Healthcare Pharmaceuticals Inc.
		1 ml	10	
		1 ml	15	
		1 ml	20	
		1 ml	50	
		1 ml	100	
	Novaplus® Omniscan	1 ml	10	Ge Healthcare
		1 ml	15	

HCPCS	DRUG NAME	DOSE	PKG SIZE	LABELER NAME
		1 ml	20	
	Omniscan	1 ml	5	
		1 ml	10	
		1 ml	15	
		1 ml	20	
		1 ml	100	
	Optimark	1 ml	5	Liebel Flarsheim
		1 ml	10	
		1 ml	15	
		1 ml	20	
		1 ml	30	
		1 ml	50	
	Prohance	1 ml	5	Bracco Diagnostics
		1 ml	10	
		1 ml	15	
		1 ml	20	
	Prohance Prefilled Syringes	1 ml	10	
		1 ml	17	
A9581	Eovist	1 ml	15	Bayer Healthcare Pharmaceuticals Inc.
	Gadoxetate Disodium	1 ml	10	
A9585	Gadavist	0.1 ml	2	
		0.1 ml	7.5	
		0.1 ml	10	
		0.1 ml	15	
		0.1 ml	30	
		0.1 ml	65	
A9587	Netspot	0.1 mCi	1	Advanced Accelerator Applications
A9588	Axumin	1 mCi	5	Blue Earth Diagnostics
A9600	Metastron	per millicurie	4	Ge Healthcare
A9604	Quadramet	Up to 150 millicuries	3	Lantheus Medical Imaging, Inc.
A9606	Xofigo	1 mCi	6	Bayer Healthcare Pharmaceuticals Inc.
C9132	Kcentra	1 iu	1	Csl Behring gmbh
C9140	Afstyla	1 iu	1	Csl Behring LLC
C9248	Cleviprex	1 mg	50	The Medicines Company
		1 mg	100	Chiesi Usa, Inc.
C9250	Artiss	2 ml	1	Baxter Healthcare Corporation
C9257	Avastin	0.25 mg	4	Genentech, Inc.
		0.25 mg	16	

HCPCS	DRUG NAME	DOSE	PKG SIZE	LABELER NAME
C9293	Voraxaze	10 units	1	Btg International
C9447	Omidria (Phenylephrine + Ketorolac Irrigation)	4 ml	4	Omeros
C9460	Kengreal	1 mg	1	The Medicines Company
C9482	Sotalol	1 mg	10	Altathera Pharmaceuticals LLC
C9483	Tecentriq (Atezolizumab)	10 mg	20	Genentech, Inc.
C9484	Exondys 51	10 mg	2	Sarepta Therapeutics
	Exondys 51 10 ml	10 mg	10	
C9485	Lartruvo	10 mg	19	Eli Lilly and Company
		10 mg	50	
C9486	Sustol	0.1 mg	0.4	Heron Therapeutics
C9488	Vaprisol	1 mg	100	Cumberland Pharmaceuticals, Inc.
C9489	Spinraza	0.1 mg	5	Biogen
C9490	Zinplava	10 mg	40	Merck Sharp & Dohme Corp.
C9491	Bavencio	10 mg	10	Serono
C9492	Imfinzi	10 mg	2.4	Astrazeneca Pharmaceuticals, Lp
		10 mg	10	
C9493	Radicava	1 mg	100	Mt Pharma America, Inc.
C9494	Ocrevus	1 mg	10	Genentech
C9497	Adasuve	10 mg	1	Gate Pharmaceuticals
J0129	Abatacept	10 mg	1	Bristol-Myers Squibb Company
	Orencia	10 mg	1	
		10 mg	0.4	
		10 mg	0.7	
	Orencia Clickject	10 mg	1	Bristol-Myers Squibb Co.
J0130	Reopro	10 mg	5	Eli Lilly and Company
J0132	Acetadote	100 mg	30	Cumberland Pharmaceuticals Inc
	Acetylcysteine	100 mg	30	Perrigo Pharmaceuticals
	Acetylcysteine Injection	100 mg	30	Akorn
		100 mg	30	Perrigo Pharmaceuticals
J0133	Acyclovir Sodium	5 mg	10	Fresenius Kabi Usa LLC
		5 mg	20	
J0153	Adenocard	1 mg	2	Astellas Pharma Us, Inc.
		1 mg	4	
	Adenoscan	1 mg	20	
		1 mg	30	
	Adenosine	1 mg	2	Akorn

HCPCS	DRUG NAME	DOSE	PKG SIZE	LABELER NAME
		1 mg	4	Sagent Pharmaceuticals Inc
		1 mg	20	Hospira, Inc
		1 mg	30	
J0171	Adrenalin	0.1 mg	1	Par Sterile Products LLC
	Epinephrine HCl	0.1 mg	1	Hospira, Inc
		0.1 mg	10	A-S Medication Solutions
		0.1 mg	30	Par Sterile Products LLC
J0178	Eylea	1 mg	0.05	Regeneron Pharmaceuticals, Inc.
J0180	Fabrazyme	1 mg	1	Genzyme Corporation
J0202	Lemtrada	1 mg	1.2	
J0207	Amifostine For Injection	500 mg	1	Sun Pharmaceutical Global Fze.
	Ethyol	500 mg	1	Cumberland Pharmaceuticals Inc
J0221	Lumizyme	10 mg	1	Genzyme Corporation
J0256	Aralast Np	10 mg	1	Baxalta Us Inc.
	Prolastin-C	10 mg	1	Grifols Usa, LLC.
	Zemaira	10 mg	1	Csl Behring
J0257	Glassia	10 mg	1	Baxalta Us Inc.
J0278	Amikacin Sulfate	100 mg	2	West-Ward Pharmaceuticals Corp
		100 mg	4	
J0280	Aminophylline	250 mg	10	Hospira, Inc
		250 mg	20	
	Novaplus Aminophylline	250 mg	10	
J0285	Amphotericin B	50 mg	1	X-Gen Pharmaceuticals, Inc.
J0287	Abelcet	10 mg	20	Si gma-Tau Pharmaceuticals
J0289	Ambisome	10 mg	1	Astellas Pharma Us, Inc.
J0290	Ampicillin For Injection	500 mg	1	Wg Critical Care
	Ampicillin Sodium	500 mg	1	Sandoz, Inc.
		500 mg	10	Fresenius Kabi Usa LLC
J0295	Ampicillin-Sulbactam	1.5 gm	1	West-Ward Pharmaceuticals Corp
		1.5 gm	30	Sagent Pharmaceuticals Inc
	Unasyn 1.5 gm	1.5 gm	1	Pfizer Inc.
	Unasyn 15 gm	1.5 gm	1	
	Unasyn 3 gm	1.5 gm	1	
J0348	Eraxis	1 mg	1	
J0360	Hydralazine HCl	20 mg	1	Akorn
J0401	Abilify Maintena	1 mg	1	Otsuka America Pharmaceutical, Inc.
J0456	Azithromycin	500 mg	1	Pfizer Inc.

HCPCS	DRUG NAME	DOSE	PKG SIZE	LABELER NAME
	Zithromax	500 mg	1	
J0461	Atropine Sulfate	0.01 mg	1	American Regent
		0.01 mg	5	Hospira, Inc
		0.01 mg	10	
		0.01 mg	20	West-Ward Pharmaceuticals Corp
J0470	Bal In Oil	100 mg	3	Akorn
J0475	Gablofen	10 mg	20	Mallinckrodt
	Lioresal	10 mg	10	Saol Therapeutics
		10 mg	20	
		10 mg	40	
J0476	Gablofen	50 mcg	1	Mallinckrodt
	Lioresal	50 mcg	1	Saol Therapeutics
J0480	Simulect	20 mg	1	Novartis Pharmaceuticals Corporation
J0485	Nulojix	1 mg	1	Bristol-Myers Squibb Company
J0490	Benlysta	10 mg	5	Glaxosmithkline
		10 mg	20	
J0500	Bentyl	20 mg	2	Aptalis Pharmaceuticals
J0515	Benztropine	1 mg	2	Akorn
	Cogentin	1 mg	2	West-Ward Pharmaceuticals Corp
J0558	Bicillin C-R	100,000 units	2	A-S Medication Solutions
	Bicillin C-R Pediatric	100,000 units	2	Pfizer Inc.
J0561	Bicillin L-A	100,000 units	1	A-S Medication Solutions
		100,000 units	2	
		100,000 units	4	Pfizer Inc.
J0570	Probuphine System Kit	74.2 mg	1	Braeburn Pharmaceuticals
J0583	Angiomax	1 mg	1	The Medicines Company
	BIValirudin	1 mg	1	Hospira, Inc
J0585	Botox	1 unit	1	Allergan Sales, LLC
	Botox Cosmetic	1 unit	1	
J0586	Dysport	5 unit	1	Ipsen Biopharmaceuticals, Inc
		5 units	1	Galderma Laboratories, L.P.
J0587	Myobloc	100 units	0.5	Solstice Neurosciences, LLC
		100 units	1	
		100 units	2	
J0588	Xeomin	1 unit	1	Merz Pharmaceuticals, LLC
J0592	Buprenorphine HCl	0.1 mg	1	Hospira, Inc
	Buprenorphine HCl Injection	0.1 mg	1	Par Sterile Products LLC

HCPCS	DRUG NAME	DOSE	PKG SIZE	LABELER NAME
J0594	Busulfan	1 mg	10	Sagent Pharmaceuticals, Inc.
J0595	Butorphanol Tartrate	1 mg	1	Hospira, Inc
		1 mg	2	
J0596	Ruconest	10 units	1	Santarus Pharmaceuticals, Inc.
J0597	Berinert	10 units	1	Csl Behring gmbh
J0598	Cinryze	10 units	1	Shire Viropharma, Inc.
J0600	Calcium Disodium Versenate	1000 mg	5	Medicis Pharmaceuticals, Inc.
J0610	Calcium Gluconate	10 ml	10	Fresenius Kabi Usa LLC
		10 ml	50	
		10 ml	100	American Regent
J0630	Miacalcin	400 units	2	Novartis Pharmaceuticals Corporation
J0636	Calcitriol	0.1 mcg	1	Akorn
J0637	Cancidas	5 mg	1	Merck Sharp & Dohme Corp.
J0638	Ilaris	1 mg	150	Novartis Pharmaceuticals Corp.
		1 mg	180	Novartis Pharmaceuticals Corporation
J0640	Leucovorin Calcium	50 mg	1	West-Ward
J0641	Levoleucovorin Calcium	0.5 mg	1	West-Ward Pharmaceutical Corp.
		0.5 mg	17.5	Sandoz, Inc.
J0670	Polocaine	10 ml	50	Fresenius Kabi Usa LLC
	Polocaine-Mpf	10 ml	20	
		10 ml	30	
J0690	Cefazolin Sodium	500 mg	1	West-Ward Pharmaceuticals Corp
		500 mg	10	Sandoz, Inc.
		500 mg	50	Baxter Healthcare Corporation
		500 mg	100	
	Cefazolin Sodium In Dextrose	500 mg	50	B. Braun Medical Inc.
J0692	Cefepime	500 mg	1	Sagent Pharmaceuticals Inc
	Cefepime HCl	500 mg	1	Sandoz, Inc.
		500 mg	50	Baxter Healthcare Corporation
		500 mg	100	
	Cefepime HCl In Dextrose	500 mg	1	B. Braun Medical Inc.
	Maxipime	500 mg	1	Hospira, Inc
J0694	Cefoxitin Sodium	1 gm	1	West-Ward Pharmaceuticals Corp
		1 gm	10	

HCPCS	DRUG NAME	DOSE	PKG SIZE	LABELER NAME
	Premierpro Rx Cefoxitin Sodium	1 gm	1	Fresenius Kabi Usa LLC
J0696	Ceftriaxone	250 mg	1	West-Ward Pharmaceuticals Corp
		250 mg	1	Sandoz, Inc.
	Ceftriaxone In D5W	250 mg	1	B. Braun Medical Inc.
		250 mg	50	Baxter Healthcare Corporation
	Ceftriaxone Sodium	250 mg	1	Sagent Pharmaceuticals Inc
J0697	Cefuroxime Sodium	750 mg	1	West-Ward Pharmaceuticals Corp
	Zinacef	750 mg	1	
	Zinacef (Frozen)	750 mg	50	Teligent
J0702	Celestone SolUSPan	3 mg & 3 mg	5	Schering Corporation
J0712	Teflaro	10 mg	1	Forest Laboratories
J0713	Ceftazidime	500 mg	1	B. Braun Medical Inc.
	Fortaz	500 mg	1	Teligent
	Fortaz (Add-V)	500 mg	1	
	Fortaz (Frozen)	500 mg	50	
	Fortaz Add-V)	500 mg	1	
	Tazicef	500 mg	1	Hospira, Inc
J0717	Cimzia	1 mg	1	Ucb, Inc.
J0720	Chloramphenicol Sod Succinate	1 gm	1	Fresenius Kabi Usa LLC
J0725	Chorionic Gonadotropin	1000 units	1	
	Novarel	1000 units	1	Ferring Pharmaceuticals Inc.
J0735	Clonidine Hydrochloride	1 mg	10	West-Ward Pharmaceuticals Corp
	Clonidine Hydrochloride Injection	1 mg	10	
	Duraclon	1 mg	10	Mylan Institutional
J0740	Cidofovir	375 mg	5	Heritage Pharmaceuticals, Inc.
J0743	Imipenem and Cilastatin	250 mg	1	Hospira, Inc
	Primaxin IV	250 mg	1	Merck Sharp & Dohme Corp.
J0744	Ciprofloxacin	200 mg	20	Hospira, Inc
		200 mg	100	
		200 mg	200	
J0770	Colistimethate Sodium	Up to 150 mg	1	Perrigo Pharmaceuticals
	Coly-Mycin M Parenteral	Up to 150 mg	1	Par Sterile Products LLC
J0775	Xiaflex (Collagenase Clostridium Histolyticum)	0.01 mg	1	Auxilium Pharmaceuticals
J0780	Prochlorperazine Edisylate	10 mg	2	West-Ward Pharmaceutical Corp.
J0795	Acthrel	1 mcg	1	Ferring Pharmaceuticals Inc.

HCPCS	DRUG NAME	DOSE	PKG SIZE	LABELER NAME
J0800	H.P. Acthar	40 units	5	Mallinckrodt
J0834	Cortrosyn	0.25 mg	1	Amphastar Pharmaceuticals, Inc.
	Cosyntropin	0.25 mg	1	Sandoz, Inc.
	Cosyntropin (Cortrosyn Generic)	0.25 mg	1	Mylan Institutional
	Cosyntropin Novaplus (Cortrosyn Generic)	0.25 mg	1	
J0840	Crofab Powder For Solution	Up to 1 gm	1	Btg International
J0850	Cytogam	Per vial	50	Csl Behring Ag
J0875	Dalvance	5 mg	1	Durata Pharmaceuticals
J0878	Cubicin	1 mg	1	Cubist Pharmaceuticals
	Daptomycin	1 mg	1	Hospira
J0881	Aranesp	1 mcg	0.3	A mgen Usa, Inc.
		1 mcg	0.4	
		1 mcg	0.42	
		1 mcg	0.5	
		1 mcg	0.6	
		1 mcg	0.75	
		1 mcg	1	
J0882		1 mcg	0.3	
		1 mcg	0.4	
		1 mcg	0.42	
		1 mcg	0.5	
		1 mcg	0.6	
		1 mcg	0.75	
		1 mcg	1	
J0885	Epogen	1000 units	1	
		1000 units	2	
	Procrit	1000 units	1	Janssen Products, Lp
		1000 units	2	
J0887	Mircera	1 mcg	0.3	Vifor (International) Ltd.
J0888		1 mcg	0.3	
J0894	Dacogen	1 mg	1	Otsuka America Pharmaceutical, Inc.
	Decitabine	1 mg	1	Sandoz, Inc.
J0895	Deferoxamine Mesylate	500 mg	1	Hospira, Inc
	Desferal	500 mg	1	Novartis Pharmaceuticals Corporation
		500 mg	4	
J0897	Prolia	1 mg	1	A mgen Usa, Inc.
	Xgeva	1 mg	1	
J1000	Depo-Estradiol	5 mg	5	Pfizer Inc.

HCPCS	DRUG NAME	DOSE	PKG SIZE	LABELER NAME
J1020	Depo-Medrol	20 mg	5	
	Methylprednisolone Acetate USP	20 mg	1	Sicor Pharmaceuticals, Inc.
J1030	Depo-Medrol	40 mg	1	Pfizer Inc.
		40 mg	5	
		40 mg	10	
	Methylprednisolone Acetate USP	40 mg	1	Sicor Pharmaceuticals, Inc.
		40 mg	5	
		40 mg	10	
J1040	Depo-Medrol	80 mg	1	Pfizer Inc.
		80 mg	5	
	Methylprednisolone Acetate	80 mg	1	Sicor Pharmaceuticals, Inc.
		80 mg	5	
J1050	Depo-Provera	1 mg	2.5	Pfizer Inc.
J1071	Depo-Testosterone	1 mg	1	
		1 mg	10	
	Testosterone Cypionate	1 mg	1	
		1 mg	10	
	Testosterone Cypionate USP/Nf	1 mg	10	A-S Medication Solutions
J1100	Dexamethasone Sodium Phosphate	1 mg	1	Pfizer Inc.
		1 mg	5	
		1 mg	10	Mylan Institutional
		1 mg	30	
J1110	D.H.E. 45	1 mg	1	Valeant Pharmaceuticals International
	Dihydroergotamine Mesylate	1 mg	1	Perrigo Pharmaceuticals
J1120	Acetazolamide Sodium	500 mg	1	West-Ward Pharmaceuticals Corp
J1160	Digoxin	0.5 mg	2	
	Lanoxin	0.5 mg	1	Covis Pharmaceuticals
	Lanoxin Inj	0.5 mg	1	
J1162	Digifab	Per vial	1	Btg International
J1165	Phenytoin	50 mg	2	X-Gen Pharmaceuticals, Inc.
		50 mg	5	
	Phenytoin Sodium	50 mg	2	West-Ward Pharmaceuticals Corp
		50 mg	5	
J1170	Dilaudid (Pfsyr)	4 mg	0.5	Fresenius Kabi Usa, LLC
		4 mg	1	
	Hydromorphone	4 mg	1	Akorn
		4 mg	5	
		4 mg	50	

HCPCS	DRUG NAME	DOSE	PKG SIZE	LABELER NAME
	Hydromorphone HCl	4 mg	0.5	Hospira, Inc
		4 mg	1	
		4 mg	2	Purdue Pharma Lp
		4 mg	5	Hospira, Inc
		4 mg	20	West-Ward Pharmaceuticals Corp
		4 mg	50	Hospira, Inc
	Hydromorphone Hydrochloride	4 mg	1	
		4 mg	5	Sicor Pharmaceuticals, Inc.
		4 mg	50	
J1190	Dexrazoxane	250 mg	1	Mylan Institutional
	Zinecard	250 mg	1	Pfizer Inc.
J1200	Benadryl	50 mg	10	Mylan Institutional
	Diphenhydramine HCl	50 mg	1	Hospira, Inc
J1205	Chlorothiazide Sodium	500 mg	1	Akorn
	Diuril IV	500 mg	1	Oak
J1212	Rimso-50	50 ml	50	Mylan Institutional
J1230	Methadone HCl	10 mg	20	
J1240	Dimenhydrinate	50 mg	1	Fresenius Kabi Usa LLC
J1245	Dipyridamole	10 mg	10	West-Ward Pharmaceuticals Corp
J1250	Dobutamine HCl	250 mg	20	Hospira, Inc
		250 mg	40	
		250 mg	250	Baxter Healthcare Corporation
J1265	Dopamine	40 mg	10	Hospira, Inc
	Dopamine 200 mg/5 ml	40 mg	5	
	Dopamine HCl 200 mg in 5% Dextrose Lifecare 250 ml	40 mg	250	
	Dopamine HCl 400 mg in 5% Dextrose Lifecare 250 ml	40 mg	250	
	Dopamine HCl 400 mg in 5% Dextrose Lifecare 500 ml	40 mg	500	
	Dopamine HCl 800 mg in 5% Dextrose Lifecare 250 ml	40 mg	250	
	Dopamine In D5W	40 mg	250	Baxter Healthcare Corporation
		40 mg	500	
J1267	Doribax	10 mg	1	Shionogi Inc
J1270	Doxercalciferol	1 mcg	2	Akorn
	Hectorol	1 mcg	1	Genzyme Corporation
		1 mcg	2	
J1290	Kalbitor®	1 mg	1	Dyax Corp.

HCPCS	DRUG NAME	DOSE	PKG SIZE	LABELER NAME
J1300	Soliris	10 mg	1	Alexion Pharmaceuticals
J1325	Epoprostenol	0.5 mg	1	Sicor Pharmaceuticals, Inc.
	Epoprostenol (Veletri)	0.5 mg	1	Actelion Pharmaceuticals U.S, Inc
	Flolan	0.5 mg	1	Glaxosmithkline
J1335	Invanz	500 mg	1	Merck Sharp & Dohme Corp.
J1364	Erythromycin	500 mg	10	Hospira, Inc
	Erythromycin Lactobionate	500 mg	1	
J1380	Delestrogen	10 mg	5	Par Sterile Products LLC
	Estradiol Valerate	10 mg	5	Perrigo Pharmaceuticals
J1410	Premarin	25 mg	1	Pfizer Inc.
J1430	Ethanolamine Oleate	100 mg	2	Qol Medical
J1439	Injectafer	1 mg	15	American Regent
J1442	Neupogen	1 mcg	0.5	A mgen Usa, Inc.
		1 mcg	0.8	
		1 mcg	1	
		1 mcg	1.6	
J1447	Granix	1 mcg	0.5	Cephalon Inc.
		1 mcg	0.8	
J1450	Diflucan	200 mg	100	West-Ward Pharmaceuticals Corp
	Fluconazole In Dextrose	200 mg	100	
		200 mg	200	
	Fluconazole In Sodium Chloride	200 mg	100	
		200 mg	200	
	Fluconazole Injection	200 mg	100	Pfizer Inc.
		200 mg	200	
	Novaplus Fluconazole	200 mg	200	Hospira, Inc
J1453	Emend For Injection 150 mg	1 mg	1	Merck Sharp & Dohme
J1458	Naglazyme	1 mg	1	Biomarin Pharmaceutical, Inc.
J1459	PrIVigen	500 mg	50	Csl Behring Ag
		500 mg	110	
		500 mg	200	
		500 mg	400	
J1460	Gamastan S/D	1 CC	2	Grifols Usa, LLC.
		1 CC	10	
J1556	BIVigam	500 mg	50	Biotest Pharmaceuticals Corporation
		500 mg	100	
J1557	Gammaplex	500 mg	100	Bio Products Laboratory
		500 mg	200	

HCPCS	DRUG NAME	DOSE	PKG SIZE	LABELER NAME
J1559	Hizentra	100 mg	5	Csl Behring Ag
		100 mg	10	
		100 mg	20	
		100 mg	50	
J1560	Gamastan S/D	10 CC	2	Grifols Usa, LLC.
		10 CC	10	
J1561	Gammaked	500 mg	10	Kedrion Biopharma, Inc.
		500 mg	50	
		500 mg	100	
		500 mg	200	
	Gamunex-C	500 mg	10	Grifols Usa, LLC.
		500 mg	25	
		500 mg	50	
		500 mg	100	
		500 mg	200	
		500 mg	400	
J1566	Carimune Nf	500 mg	1	Csl Behring Ag
	Gammagard S/D	500 mg	1	Baxter Healthcare Corporation
J1568	Octagam	500 mg	20	Octapharma Usa
		500 mg	50	
		500 mg	100	
		500 mg	200	
		500 mg	500	
J1569	Gammagard Liquid	500 mg	10	Baxalta Us Inc.
		500 mg	25	
		500 mg	50	
		500 mg	100	
		500 mg	200	
		500 mg	300	
J1570	Cytovene	500 mg	1	Genentech, Inc.
	Ganciclovir	500 mg	1	Par Pharmaceutical
J1571	Cbi Hepagam B 1 ml	0.5 ml	1	Cangene Biopharma Inc
	Cbi Hepagam B 5 ml	0.5 ml	5	
	Nova Hepagam B 1 ml	0.5 ml	1	
	Nova Hepagam B 5 ml	0.5 ml	5	
J1572	Flebogamma 10% Dif	500 mg	50	Grifols Usa, LLC.
		500 mg	100	
		500 mg	200	
	Flebogamma Dif	500 mg	50	
		500 mg	100	
		500 mg	200	

HCPCS	DRUG NAME	DOSE	PKG SIZE	LABELER NAME
		500 mg	400	
J1575	Hyqvia	100 mg	25	Baxalta Us Inc.
		100 mg	50	
		100 mg	100	
		100 mg	200	
		100 mg	300	
J1580	Gentamicin Sulfate	80 mg	2	Hospira, Inc
		80 mg	20	Fresenius Kabi Usa LLC
		80 mg	50	Baxter Healthcare Corporation
		80 mg	100	
J1602	Simponi Aria	1 mg	4	Janssen Biotech, Inc.
J1610	Glucagen	1 mg	1	Bedford Laboratories
	Glucagen Diagnostic Kit	1 mg	1	Boehringer Ingelheim
	Glucagen Hypokit	1 mg	1	Novo Nordisk® Inc.
	Glucagen(R)	1 mg	1	Boehringer Ingelheim
	Glucagon Emergency	1 mg	1	Eli Lilly and Company
	Glucagon Hydrochloride	1 mg	1	Novo Nordisk® Inc.
	Glucagon Hydrochloride Kit	1 mg	1	Fresenius Kabi Usa LLC
J1626	Granisetron HCl	100 mcg	1	West-Ward Pharmaceuticals Corp
		100 mcg	4	
J1630	Haldol	5 mg	1	Janssen Pharmaceuticals, Inc.
	Haloperidol Lactate	5 mg	1	West-Ward
		5 mg	10	
J1631	Haldol Decanoate	50 mg	1	Janssen Pharmaceuticals, Inc.
	Haloperidol Decanoate	50 mg	1	Patriot Pharmaceuticals, LLC
		50 mg	5	Amneal Pharmaceuticals, LLC
J1640	Panhematin	1 mg	1	Recordati Rare Diseases
J1642	Heparin (Porcine) Lock Flush	10 units	1	Medefil, Inc.
		10 units	3	
		10 units	5	
	Heparin Lock Flush	10 units	2	Becton Dickinson & Co.
		10 units	3	
		10 units	5	
		10 units	6	
	Heparin Sodium Flush	10 units	5	
J1644	Heparin (Porcine) In D5W	1000 units	250	B. Braun Medical Inc.
		1000 units	500	
	Heparin (Porcine) In Nacl	1000 units	250	Hospira, Inc

HCPCS	DRUG NAME	DOSE	PKG SIZE	LABELER NAME
		1000 units	500	B. Braun Medical Inc.
		1000 units	1000	Baxter Healthcare Corporation
	Heparin Sodium	1000 units	1	Hospira, Inc
	Heparin Sodium (Porcine)	1000 units	0.5	
		1000 units	1	Pfizer Inc.
		1000 units	2	
		1000 units	4	Sagent Pharmaceuticals Inc
		1000 units	5	Fresenius Kabi Usa LLC
		1000 units	10	Pfizer Inc.
		1000 units	30	
	Heparin Sodium In Nacl	1000 units	1000	Hospira, Inc
J1645	Fra gmin	2500 iu	0.2	Pfizer Inc.
		2500 iu	0.3	
		2500 iu	0.5	
		2500 iu	0.6	
		2500 iu	0.72	
		2500 iu	1	
J1650	Enoxaparin Sodium	10 mg	0.3	Amphastar Pharmaceuticals, Inc.
		10 mg	0.4	
		10 mg	0.6	
		10 mg	0.8	
		10 mg	1	
		10 mg	3	Sandoz, Inc.
	Lovenox	10 mg	0.3	Sanofi-Aventis
		10 mg	0.4	
		10 mg	0.6	
		10 mg	0.8	
		10 mg	1	
		10 mg	3	
J1652	Arixtra	0.5 mg	0.4	Mylan Institutional
		0.5 mg	0.5	
		0.5 mg	0.6	
		0.5 mg	0.8	
	Fondaparinux Sodium	0.5 mg	0.4	Dr. Reddy'S Laboratories, Inc.
		0.5 mg	0.5	
		0.5 mg	0.6	
		0.5 mg	0.8	
J1670	Hypertet S/D	250 units	1	Grifols Usa, LLC.
J1720	Solu-Cortef	100 mg	1	Pfizer Inc.

HCPCS	DRUG NAME	DOSE	PKG SIZE	LABELER NAME
	Solu-Cortef 500 mg 4 ml	100 mg	1	
J1740	BonIVa	1 mg	3	Genentech, Inc.
	Ibandronate Sodium	1 mg	3	Sagent Pharmaceuticals Inc
J1742	Corvert	1 mg	10	Pfizer Inc.
	Ibutilide Fumarate	1 mg	10	Mylan Institutional
J1743	Elaprase	1 mg	3	Shire Us, Inc.
J1745	Remicade	10 mg	1	Janssen Biotech, Inc.
J1750	Infed	50 mg	2	Watson Pharmaceuticals
J1756	Venofer	1 mg	2.5	American Regent
		1 mg	5	
		1 mg	10	
J1786	Cerezyme	10 units	1	Genzyme Corporation
J1800	Propranolol	1 mg	1	West-Ward Pharmaceuticals Corp
	Propranolol HCl	1 mg	1	Fresenius Kabi Usa LLC
J1815	Humalog	5 units	3	Eli Lilly and Company
		5 units	10	
	Humalog Mix 50/50	5 units	10	
	Humulin N	5 units	3	
		5 units	10	A-S Medication Solutions
	Humulin R	5 units	3	Eli Lilly and Company
		5 units	10	
	Humulin R U-500	5 units	20	
	Novolin 70/30	5 units	10	Novo Nordisk® Inc.
	Novolin N	5 units	10	
	Novolin R	5 units	10	
	Novolog	5 units	10	
	Novolog Flexpen	5 units	3	
	Novolog Mix 70/30	5 units	10	
	Novolog Mix 70/30 Flexpen	5 units	3	
	Novolog Penfill	5 units	3	
J1817	Humalog	50 units	3	Eli Lilly and Company
		50 units	10	
	Humulin N	50 units	10	A-S Medication Solutions
	Humulin R	50 units	3	Eli Lilly and Company
		50 units	10	
		50 units	20	
	Novolin 70/30	50 units	10	Novo Nordisk® Inc.
	Novolin N	50 units	10	
	Novolin R	50 units	10	
	Novolog	50 units	10	

HCPCS	DRUG NAME	DOSE	PKG SIZE	LABELER NAME
	Novolog Flexpen	50 units	3	
	Novolog Mix 70/30	50 units	10	
	Novolog Mix 70/30 Flexpen	50 units	3	
	Novolog Penfill	50 units	3	
J1885	Ketorolac Tromethamine	15 mg	1	Hospira, Inc
		15 mg	2	
J1930	Somatuline Depot	1 mg	0.2	Ipsen Biopharmaceuticals, Inc
		1 mg	0.3	
		1 mg	0.5	
J1931	Aldurazyme	0.1 mg	5	Genzyme Corporation
J1940	Furosemide	20 mg	2	Heritage Pharmaceuticals, Inc.
		20 mg	4	Hospira, Inc
		20 mg	10	
J1942	Aristada	1 mg	1.6	Alkermes, Inc.
		1 mg	2.4	
		1 mg	3.2	
		1 mg	3.9	
J1950	Lupron Depot 3.75 mg	3.75 mg	1	Abbvie Us, LLC
	Lupron Depot 3-Month, 11.25 mg	3.75 mg	1	
	Lupron Depot-Ped 11.25 mg	3.75 mg	1	
	Lupron Depot-Ped 3-Month, 11.25 mg	3.75 mg	1	
	Lupron Depot-Ped 3-Month, 30 mg	3.75 mg	1	
J1953	Levetiracetam	10 mg	5	West-Ward Pharmaceuticals Corp
		10 mg	100	Mylan Institutional
	Levetiracetam (Keppra)	10 mg	5	Ucb, Inc.
J1955	Carnitor	1 gm	5	Si gma-Tau Pharmaceuticals
J1956	Levaquin	250 mg	50	Sandoz, Inc.
		250 mg	100	
		250 mg	150	
	Levofloxacin	250 mg	20	Akorn
		250 mg	30	
		250 mg	50	West-Ward Pharmaceuticals Corp
		250 mg	100	
		250 mg	150	
J1980	Levsin Injection .5 mg/ ml	0.25 mg	5	Meda Pharmaceuticals
J2001	Lidocaine In D5W	10 mg	250	B. Braun Medical Inc.

HCPCS	DRUG NAME	DOSE	PKG SIZE	LABELER NAME
		10 mg	500	
J2010	Lincocin	300 mg	2	Pfizer Inc.
		300 mg	10	
J2020	Linezolid	200 mg	300	Hospira, Inc
	Zyvox	200 mg	100	Pfizer Inc.
		200 mg	300	
J2060	AtIVan	2 mg	1	West-Ward Pharmaceuticals Corp
		2 mg	10	
	Lorazepam	2 mg	1	Hospira, Inc
		2 mg	10	
J2150	Mannitol	50 ml	50	
J2175	Demerol	100 mg	0.5	
		100 mg	1	
		100 mg	1.5	
		100 mg	2	
		100 mg	20	
		100 mg	30	
	Meperidine HCl	100 mg	1	West-Ward Pharmaceuticals Corp
		100 mg	30	Hospira, Inc
J2185	Meropenem	100 mg	1	B. Braun Medical Inc.
	Merrem	100 mg	1	Astrazeneca Pharmaceuticals Lp
J2210	Methylergonovine Maleate	0.2 mg	1	American Regent
J2248	Micafungin Sodium (Mycamine)	1 mg	1	Astellas Pharma Us, Inc.
J2250	Midazolam HCl	1 mg	1	Hospira, Inc
		1 mg	2	
		1 mg	5	
		1 mg	10	
J2260	Milrinone In Dextrose	5 mg	100	Baxter Healthcare Corporation
		5 mg	200	
	Milrinone Lactate	5 mg	10	Hospira, Inc
		5 mg	20	
		5 mg	50	
J2270	Morphine Sulfate	10 mg	1	
		10 mg	10	
		10 mg	20	
		10 mg	30	
		10 mg	50	
		10 mg	30	

HCPCS	DRUG NAME	DOSE	PKG SIZE	LABELER NAME
J2274	Duramorph	10 mg	10	West-Ward Pharmaceuticals Corp
	Infumorph 200	10 mg	20	
	Infumorph 500	10 mg	20	
	Morphine Sulfate	10 mg	10	Hospira, Inc
J2278	Prialt	1 mcg	1	Jazz Pharmaceuticals, Inc.
		1 mcg	5	
		1 mcg	20	
J2280	Avelox	100 mg	250	Schering Corporation
	Moxifloxacin HCl	100 mg	250	Fresenius Kabi Usa LLC
J2300	Nalbuphine HCl	10 mg	1	Hospira, Inc
		10 mg	10	
J2310	Naloxone HCl	1 mg	1	
		1 mg	10	
J2315	VIVitrol	1 mg	1	Alkermes, Inc.
J2323	Tysabri	1 mg	15	Biogen
J2353	Sandostatin Lar Depot	1 mg	1	Novartis Pharmaceuticals Corporation
J2354	Octreotide Acetate	25 mcg	1	Sicor Pharmaceuticals, Inc.
		25 mcg	5	
	Sandostatin	25 mcg	1	Novartis Pharmaceuticals Corporation
		25 mcg	5	
J2355	Neumega	5 mg	1	Pfizer Inc.
J2357	Xolair	5 mg	1	Genentech, Inc.
J2358	Zyprexa Relprevv	1 mg	1	Eli Lilly and Company
J2360	Orphenadrine Citrate	60 mg	2	Watson Pharmaceuticals
	Orphenadrine Citrate Injection	60 mg	2	Akorn
J2400	Nesacaine	30 ml	30	Fresenius Kabi Usa LLC
	Nesacaine-Mpf	30 ml	20	
J2405	Ondansetron HCl	1 mg	2	Hospira, Inc
		1 mg	20	West-Ward Pharmaceutical Corp.
	Zofran	1 mg	20	West-Ward Pharmaceuticals Corp
J2407	OrbactIV	10 mg	1	The Medicines Company
J2410	Opana	1 mg	1	Endo Pharmaceuticals Inc
J2425	KepIVance	50 mcg	1	Sobi
	KepIVance/Palifermin	50 mcg	1	
J2426	Invega Sustenna	1 mg	0.25	Janssen Pharmaceuticals, Inc.
		1 mg	0.5	
		1 mg	0.75	
		1 mg	1	

HCPCS	DRUG NAME	DOSE	PKG SIZE	LABELER NAME
		1 mg	1.5	
J2430	Pamidronate Disodium	30 mg	1	Sagent Pharmaceuticals Inc
		30 mg	10	Mylan Institutional
J2469	Aloxi	25 mcg	5	Eisai Inc.
J2501	Paricalcitol	1 mcg	1	West-Ward Pharmaceuticals Corp
		1 mcg	2	
	Zemplar	1 mcg	1	Abbvie Us, LLC
		1 mcg	2	
J2503	Macugen	0.3 mg	0.09	Eyetech, Inc.
J2504	Adagen	25 iu	1.5	Si gma-Tau Pharmaceuticals
J2505	Neulasta	6 mg	0.6	A mgen Usa, Inc.
	Neulasta Delivery Kit	6 mg	0.6	
J2507	Krystexxa	1 mg	1	Crealta
J2510	Penicillin G Procaine	Up to 600000 units	1	Pfizer Inc.
		Up to 600000 units	2	
J2515	Nembutal	50 mg	20	Oak
		50 mg	50	
	Pentobarbital	50 mg	20	Sagent Pharmaceutical
J2540	Penicillin G Pot In Dextrose	600000 units	50	Baxter Healthcare Corporation
	Penicillin G Potassium	600000 units	1	Sandoz, Inc.
	Pfizerpen-G	600000 units	1	Pfizer Inc.
J2543	Novaplus Zosyn	1.125 gm	50	
		1.125 gm	100	
	Piperacillin and Tazobactam	1.125 gm	1	Hospira, Inc
	Piperacillin Sodium/ Tazo	1.125 gm	1	
	Piperacillin Sodium/ Tazo (Add-Vantage)	1.125 gm	1	
	Piperacillin Sodium-Tazobactam Sodium	1.125 gm	1	Pfizer Inc.
		1.125 gm	50	
		1.125 gm	100	
	Zosyn	1.125 gm	1	
J2545	Nebupent	300 mg	1	Fresenius Kabi Usa LLC
J2550	Phenergan	50 mg	1	West-Ward Pharmaceuticals Corp
	Promethazine	50 mg	1	
	Promethazine HCl	50 mg	1	
J2560	Phenobarbital Sodium	120 mg	1	

HCPCS	DRUG NAME	DOSE	PKG SIZE	LABELER NAME
J2562	Mozobil (Plerixafor)	1 mg	1.2	Sanofi-Aventis
J2597	Ddavp	1 mcg	1	Ferring Pharmaceuticals Inc.
		1 mcg	10	
	Desmopressin Acetate	1 mcg	1	
		1 mcg	10	
J2675	Progesterone	50 mg	10	West-Ward Pharmaceuticals Corp
J2680	Fluphenazine Decanoate	25 mg	5	West-Ward Pharmaceutical Corp.
J2690	Procainamide HCl	1 gm	2	Hospira, Inc
		1 gm	10	
J2700	Bactocill In Dextrose	250 mg	50	Baxter Healthcare Corporation
	Oxacillin	250 mg	1	Sagent Pharmaceuticals Inc
	Oxacillin Sodium	250 mg	1	Sandoz, Inc.
J2704	DiprIVan	10 mg	10	Fresenius Kabi Usa LLC
		10 mg	20	
		10 mg	50	
		10 mg	100	
	Propofol	10 mg	20	Hospira, Inc
		10 mg	50	
		10 mg	100	
J2720	Protamine Sulfate	10 mg	5	Fresenius Kabi Usa LLC
		10 mg	25	
J2724	Ceprotin	10 units	1	Baxalta Us Inc.
J2765	Metoclopramide HCl	10 mg	2	Hospira, Inc
J2770	Synercid	500 mg	1	Pfizer Inc.
J2778	Lucentis	0.1 mg	0.05	Genentech, Inc.
J2780	Ranitidine	25 mg	2	Zydus Pharmaceuticals Usa Inc
		25 mg	6	Teligent
	Zantac	25 mg	2	
		25 mg	40	
J2783	Elitek	0.5 mg	1	Sanofi-Aventis
		0.5 mg	7.5	
J2785	Regadenoson	0.1 mg	5	Astellas Pharma Us, Inc.
J2788	Hyperrho S/D	50 mcg	1	Grifols Usa, LLC.
	Micrhogam	50 mcg (250 iu)	1	Kedrion Biopharma, Inc.
	Micrhogam Uf Plus	50 mcg (250 iu)	1	
J2790	Hyperrho S/D	300 mcg (1500 iu)	1	Grifols Usa, LLC.

HCPCS	DRUG NAME	DOSE	PKG SIZE	LABELER NAME
	Rhogam Ultra-Filtered Plus	300 mcg (1500 iu)	1	Kedrion Biopharma, Inc.
J2791	Rhophylac	100 units	2	Csl Behring Ag
J2792	Winrho Sdf	100 iu	1.3	Cangene Biopharma Inc
		100 iu	2.2	
		100 iu	4.4	
		100 iu	13	
J2794	Risperdal Consta	0.5 mg	1	Janssen Pharmaceuticals, Inc.
J2795	Naropin	1 mg	10	Fresenius Kabi Usa LLC
		1 mg	20	
		1 mg	30	
		1 mg	100	
		1 mg	200	
		1 mg	20	
		1 mg	30	
	RopIVacaine	1 mg	10	Hospira, Inc
		1 mg	20	
		1 mg	30	Sandoz, Inc.
	RopIVacaine Hydrochloride	1 mg	10	Hospira, Inc
		1 mg	20	
		1 mg	30	
J2796	Nplate	10 mcg	1	A mgen Usa, Inc.
J2800	Methocarbamol	10 ml	10	Mylan Institutional
	Robaxin	10 ml	10	West-Ward Pharmaceuticals Corp
J2805	Sincalide Inj	5 mcg	1	Bracco Diagnostics
J2810	Theophylline In D5W	40 mg	500	B. Braun Medical Inc.
J2820	Leukine (Lyo Pwd)	50 mcg	1	Sanofi-Aventis
J2850	Chirhostim	1 mcg	1	Chirhoclin, Inc.
J2916	Ferrlecit	12.5 mg	5	Sanofi-Aventis
	Sodium Ferric Gluconate	12.5 mg	5	West-Ward Pharmaceuticals Corp
	Sodium Ferric Gluconate Complex In Sucrose	12.5 mg	5	Watson Pharmaceuticals
J2920	Methylprednisolone Sodium Succ	40 mg	1	Sagent Pharmaceuticals, Inc.
		40 mg	3	Fresenius Kabi Usa LLC
	Solu-Medrol	40 mg	1	Pfizer Inc.
J2930	Methylprednisolone Sodium Succ	125 mg	1	Sagent Pharmaceuticals, Inc.
	Solu-Medrol	125 mg	1	Pfizer Inc.
J2997	ActIVase	1 mg	1	Genentech, Inc.

HCPCS	DRUG NAME	DOSE	PKG SIZE	LABELER NAME
	Cathflo ActIVase	1 mg	1	
J3000	Streptomycin Sulfate	1 gm	1	X-Gen Pharmaceuticals, Inc.
J3010	Fentanyl Citrate	0.1 mg	2	Hospira, Inc
		0.1 mg	5	
		0.1 mg	10	
		0.1 mg	20	
		0.1 mg	50	
	Sublimaze	0.1 mg	2	Akorn
		0.1 mg	5	
		0.1 mg	20	
J3060	Elelyso	10 units	1	Pfizer Inc.
J3070	Talwin Lactate	30 mg	1	Hospira, Inc
J3090	SIVextro	1 mg	1	Cubist Pharmaceuticals
J3095	VibatIV	10 mg	1	Astellas Pharma Us, Inc.
J3101	Tnkase	1 mg	1	Genentech, Inc.
J3105	Terbutaline	1 mg	1	West-Ward Pharmaceuticals Corp
	Terbutaline Sulfate	1 mg	1	Fresenius Kabi Usa LLC
J3121	Testosterone Enanthate	1 mg	5	West-Ward Pharmaceuticals Corp
J3230	Chlorpromazine HCl	50 mg	1	
		50 mg	2	
J3240	Thyrogen	0.9 mg	1	Genzyme Corporation
J3243	Tigecycline	1 mg	1	Pfizer Inc.
J3250	Tigan	200 mg	2	Par Sterile Products LLC
		200 mg	20	
J3260	Tobramycin Injection	80 mg	2	Pfizer Inc.
		80 mg	30	Mylan Institutional
	Tobramycin Sulfate	80 mg	1	X-Gen Pharmaceuticals, Inc.
		80 mg	2	Hospira, Inc
		80 mg	30	Akorn
		80 mg	50	Fresenius Kabi Usa LLC
J3262	Actemra	1 mg	80	Genentech, Inc.
		1 mg	200	
		1 mg	400	
J3285	Remodulin	1 mg	20	united Therapeutics
J3300	Triamcinolone Acetonide, PreservatIVe Free	1 mg	1	Alcon Laboratories, Inc.
J3301	Kenalog	10 mg	1	Bristol-Myers Squibb Company
		10 mg	5	
		10 mg	10	

HCPCS	DRUG NAME	DOSE	PKG SIZE	LABELER NAME
	Kenalog-40	10 mg	5	A-S Medication Solutions
		10 mg	10	
J3315	Trelstar	3.75 mg	1	Allergan Sales, LLC
J3357	Stelara	1 mg	0.5	Janssen Biotech, Inc.
		1 mg	1	
J3360	Diazepam	5 mg	2	Hospira, Inc
		5 mg	10	
J3370	Vancocin HCl	500 mg	200	Baxter Healthcare Corporation
	Vancomycin	500 mg	100	
		500 mg	150	
		500 mg	200	
	Vancomycin HCl	500 mg	1	Pfizer Inc.
		500 mg	100	Baxter Healthcare Corporation
		500 mg	150	
	Vancomycin Hydrochloride	500 mg	1	Hospira, Inc
J3380	Entyvio	1 mg	1	Takeda Pharmaceuticals America, Inc.
J3385	VprIV	100 units	1	Shire Us, Inc.
J3396	Visudyne	0.1 mg	1	Valeant Pharmaceuticals International
J3410	Hydroxyzine HCl	25 mg	1	American Regent
		25 mg	2	
		25 mg	10	
J3411	Thiamine HCl	100 mg	2	Fresenius Kabi Usa LLC
J3415	Pyridoxine HCl	100 mg	1	
J3420	Cyanocobalamin	1000 mcg	1	West-Ward Pharmaceuticals Corp
		1000 mcg	10	
		1000 mcg	30	
J3430	Vitamin K1	1 mg	0.5	Hospira, Inc
		1 mg	1	
J3465	Vfend IV	10 mg	1	Pfizer Inc.
	Voriconazole	10 mg	1	Sandoz, Inc.
J3471	Vitrase	1 unit	1.2	Bausch & Lomb
J3473	Hylenex	1 USP unit	1	Halozyme Therapeutics, Inc.
J3475	Magnesium Sulfate	500 mg	2	Fresenius Kabi Usa LLC
		500 mg	10	Hospira, Inc
		500 mg	20	
		500 mg	50	Fresenius Kabi Usa LLC
		500 mg	100	Fresenius Kabi Usa

HCPCS	DRUG NAME	DOSE	PKG SIZE	LABELER NAME
		500 mg	500	
		500 mg	1000	
	Magnesium Sulfate In 5% Dextrose	500 mg	100	Wg Critical Care
J3480	Potassium Chloride	2 MEQ	5	Hospira, Inc
		2 MEQ	10	
		2 MEQ	20	
		2 MEQ	30	Fresenius Kabi Usa LLC
		2 MEQ	50	Baxter Healthcare Corporation
		2 MEQ	100	
		2 MEQ	250	B. Braun Medical Inc.
		2 MEQ	1000	
	Potassium Chloride/Dextrose	2 MEQ	1000	Baxter Healthcare Corporation
	Potassium Chloride/Sodium Chloride	2 MEQ	1000	
J3485	Retrovir	10 mg	20	Glaxosmithkline
J3486	Geodon	10 mg	1	Pfizer Inc.
J3489	Reclast	1 mg	100	Novartis Pharmaceuticals Corporation
	Zoledronic Acid	1 mg	1	Sun Pharmaceutical Global Fze.
		1 mg	5	West-Ward Pharmaceuticals Corp
		1 mg	100	Heritage Pharmaceuticals, Inc.
	Zometa	1 mg	5	Novartis Pharmaceuticals Corporation
		1 mg	100	
J7030	Sodium Chloride	1000 ml	250	B. Braun Medical Inc.
		1000 ml	500	
		1000 ml	1000	
	Sodium Chloride (FDA Ok'D Import)	1000 ml	250	Baxter Healthcare Corporation
		1000 ml	500	B. Braun Medical Inc.
		1000 ml	1000	Baxter Healthcare Corporation
J7040	Sodium Chloride	500 ml	250	B. Braun Medical Inc.
		500 ml	500	
		500 ml	1000	
	Sodium Chloride (FDA Ok'D Import)	500 ml	250	Baxter Healthcare Corporation
		500 ml	500	B. Braun Medical Inc.

HCPCS	DRUG NAME	DOSE	PKG SIZE	LABELER NAME
		500 ml	1000	Baxter Healthcare Corporation
J7042	Dextrose-Nacl	500 ml	500	B. Braun Medical Inc.
		500 ml	1000	
J7050	Sodium Chloride	250 ml	250	
		250 ml	500	
		250 ml	1000	
	Sodium Chloride (FDA Ok'D Import)	250 ml	250	Baxter Healthcare Corporation
		250 ml	500	
		250 ml	1000	
J7060	Dextrose	500 ml	250	B. Braun Medical Inc.
		500 ml	500	
		500 ml	1000	
	Dextrose 5%	500 ml	250	Hospira, Inc
J7070	Dextrose	1000 CC	250	B. Braun Medical Inc.
		1000 CC	500	
		1000 CC	1000	
J7120	Lactated Ringers	1000 CC	250	
		1000 CC	500	
		1000 CC	1000	
		1000 CC	3000	
J7180	Corifact	1 iu	1	Csl Behring gmbh
J7182	Novoeight	1 iu	1	Novo Nordisk® Inc.
J7183	Wilate	1 I.U. VWF:RCO	1	Octapharma Usa
J7185	Xyntha	1 iu	1	Pfizer Inc.
J7186	Alphanate /Von Willebrand Factor Complex	PER FACTOR VIII iu	1	Grifols Usa, LLC.
J7187	Humate-P Low Diluent	1 iu	1	Csl Behring gmbh
J7189	Novoseven Rt	1 mcg	1	Novo Nordisk® Inc.
J7190	Alphanate /Von Willebrand Factor Complex	1 iu	1	Grifols Usa, LLC.
	Hemofil M	1 iu	1	Baxalta Us Inc.
	Koate-Dvi	1 iu	1	Kedrion Biopharma, Inc.
	Monoclate-P	1 iu	1	Csl Behring
J7192	Advate	1 iu	1	Baxalta Us Inc.
	Helixate Fs	1 iu	1	Csl Behring
	Helixate Fs 3000	1 iu	1	
	Kogenate Fs	1 iu	1	Bayer Healthcare Pharmaceuticals Inc.

HCPCS	DRUG NAME	DOSE	PKG SIZE	LABELER NAME
	Kogenate Fs 3000 Bio-Set	1 iu	1	
	Kogenate Fs Bio-Set	1 iu	1	
	Kogenate Fs Fixed Poly Bio-Set	1 iu	1	
	Recombinate	1 iu	1	Baxalta Us Inc.
J7193	Alphanine®Sd Vf 1000 iu M2V Usa	1 iu	1	Grifols Usa, LLC.
	Alphanine®Sd Vf 1500 iu M2V Usa	1 iu	1	
	Alphanine®Sd Vf 500 iu M2V Usa	1 iu	1	
	Mononine	1 iu	1	Csl Behring
J7194	Bebulin	1 iu	1	Baxalta Us Inc.
	Profilnine® Sd Fix Sd M2V(1000)	1 iu	1	Grifols Usa, LLC.
	Profilnine® Sd Fix Sd M2V(1500)	1 iu	1	
	Profilnine® Sd Fix Sd M2V(500)	1 iu	1	
J7195	Benefix	1 iu	1	Pfizer Inc.
J7197	Thrombate Iii	1 iu	1	Grifols Therapeutics, Inc.
J7198	Feiba Nf	1 iu	1	Baxter Healthcare Corporation
J7200	Rixubis	1 iu	1	Baxalta Us Inc.
J7201	Alprolix	1 iu	1	Biogen
J7205	Eloctate	1 iu	1	
J7308	Levulan Kerastick	354 mg	1	Dusa Pharmaceuticals
J7311	Fluocinolone Acetonide Implt (Retisert)	0.59 mg	1	Bausch & Lomb
J7312	Ozurdex	0.1 mg	0.7	Allergan Sales, LLC
J7313	Iluvien	0.01 mg	1	Alimera Sciences, Inc.
J7316	Jetrea	0.125 mg	0.2	Thrombogenics, Inc.
J7320	Genvisc 850	1 mg	2.5	Orthogenrx Inc.
J7321	Hyalgan	per dose	2	Fidia Pharma Usa Inc
	Supartz	per dose	2.5	Bioventus LLC
J7323	Euflexxa	per dose	2	Ferring Pharmaceuticals Inc.
J7324	Orthovisc	per dose	2	Depuy Synthes Sales, Inc.
J7325	Synvisc	1 mg	2	Genzyme Corporation
	Synviscone	1 mg	6	
J7326	Gel-One	PER DOSE	3	Zimmer Biomet, Inc. (Supplied By Seikagaku Corp.)
J7327	Monovisc	per dose	1	Depuy Synthes Sales, Inc.
J7336	Qutenza	1 SQ CM	1	Acorda Therapeutics
J7500	Azasan	50 mg	100	Salix Pharmaceuticals, Inc.
	Azathioprine	50 mg	50	Mylan Institutional

HCPCS	DRUG NAME	DOSE	PKG SIZE	LABELER NAME
		50 mg	100	Roxane Laboratories
J7502	Cyclosporine	100 mg	30	IVax Pharmaceuticals, Inc.
		100 mg	50	
	Cyclosporine Modified	100 mg	30	Teva Pharmaceuticals Usa, Inc.
	Gengraf	100 mg	30	Abbvie Us, LLC
		100 mg	50	
	Neoral	100 mg	30	Novartis Pharmaceuticals Corporation
		100 mg	50	
	Sandimmune	100 mg	30	
		100 mg	50	
J7503	Envarsus Xr	0.25 mg	30	Veloxis Pharmaceuticals
		0.25 mg	100	
J7504	Atgam	250 mg	5	Pfizer Inc.
J7507	Prograf	1 mg	100	Astellas Pharma Us, Inc.
	Tacrolimus	1 mg	100	Novartis Pharmaceuticals Corporation
	Tacrolimus, Oral	1 mg	100	Sandoz, Inc.
J7508	Astagraf Xl	0.1 mg	30	Astellas Pharma Us, Inc.
J7509	Medrol	4 mg	25	Pfizer Inc.
		4 mg	50	
		4 mg	100	
	Medrol (Pak)	4 mg	21	
	Methylprednisolone	4 mg	21	A-S Medication Solutions
		4 mg	25	Greenstone
		4 mg	50	
		4 mg	100	Sandoz, Inc.
	Methylprednisolone (Pak)	4 mg	21	
J7510	Flo-Pred	5 mg	52	Taro Pharmaceuticals
	Prednisolone	5 mg	60	A-S Medication Solutions
		5 mg	120	Hi-Tech
		5 mg	240	
		5 mg	480	
J7511	Thymoglobulin	25 mg	1	Genzyme Corporation
J7512	Prednisone	1 mg	6	A-S Medication Solutions
		1 mg	8	
		1 mg	10	
		1 mg	12	
		1 mg	14	
		1 mg	15	

HCPCS	DRUG NAME	DOSE	PKG SIZE	LABELER NAME
		1 mg	18	
		1 mg	20	
		1 mg	21	
		1 mg	30	
		1 mg	40	
		1 mg	48	
		1 mg	50	
		1 mg	60	
		1 mg	100	Roxane Laboratories
		1 mg	120	
		1 mg	500	
		1 mg	1000	
	Prednisone (Pak)	1 mg	21	A-S Medication Solutions
	Prednisone Intensol	1 mg	30	Roxane Laboratories
J7515	Cyclosporine	25 mg	30	IVax Pharmaceuticals, Inc.
	Cyclosporine Modified	25 mg	30	Teva Pharmaceuticals Usa, Inc.
	Gengraf	25 mg	30	Abbvie
	Neoral	25 mg	30	Novartis Pharmaceuticals Corporation
	Sandimmune	25 mg	30	
J7516	Cyclosporine	250 mg	5	Perrigo Pharmaceuticals
	Sandimmune	250 mg	5	Novartis Pharmaceuticals Corporation
J7517	Cellcept	250 mg	100	Genentech, Inc.
		250 mg	175	
		250 mg	500	
	Mycophenolate Mofetil	250 mg	1	Teva Pharmaceuticals Usa, Inc.
		250 mg	100	Strides Pharma Inc.
		250 mg	225	Ascend Laboratories
		250 mg	500	
J7518	Mycophenolic Acid	180 mg	30	American Health Packaging
		180 mg	120	Mylan Pharmaceuticals, Inc
	Mycophenolic Acid Dr	180 mg	30	American Health Packaging
		180 mg	100	Mylan Institutional
	Myfortic	180 mg	120	Novartis Pharmaceuticals Corporation
J7520	Rapamune	1 mg	60	Pfizer Inc.
		1 mg	100	
	Sirolimus	1 mg	30	American Health Packaging
		1 mg	100	Dr. Reddy'S Laboratories, Inc.

HCPCS	DRUG NAME	DOSE	PKG SIZE	LABELER NAME
J7525	Prograf	5 mg	1	Astellas Pharma Us, Inc.
J7527	Zortress	0.25 mg	60	Novartis Pharmaceuticals Corporation
J7605	Arformoterol	15 mcg	2	Sunovion Pharmaceuticals Inc.
J7606	Perforomist	20 mcg	2	Mylan Specialty, L.P.
J7608	Acetylcysteine	1 gm	4	American Regent
		1 gm	10	
		1 gm	30	Hospira, Inc
J7611	Albuterol Sulfate	1 mg	0.5	Nephron Pharmaceuticals Corp.
		1 mg	20	Bausch & Lomb
J7612	Levalbuterol	0.5 mg	0.5	Teva Pharmaceuticals Usa, Inc.
	Levalbuterol Inhalation Solution Concentrated	0.5 mg	0.5	Mylan Pharmaceuticals, Inc
	Xopenex	0.5 mg	0.5	Akorn
J7613	Albuterol Sulfate	1 mg	3	Mylan Pharmaceuticals, Inc
J7614	Levalbuterol	0.5 mg	3	Teva Pharmaceuticals Usa, Inc.
	Xopenex	0.5 mg	3	Akorn, Inc.
J7620	Albuterol Ipratropium	2.5 mg/0.5 mg	3	Teva Pharmaceuticals Usa, Inc.
J7626	Budesonide	Up to 0.50 mg	2	
	Pulmicort	Up to 0.50 mg	2	Astrazeneca Pharmaceuticals Lp
J7631	Cromolyn Sodium	10 mg	2	IVax Pharmaceuticals, Inc.
J7639	Pulmozyme	1 mg	2.5	Genentech, Inc.
J7644	Ipratropium Bromide	1 mg	2.5	Mylan Pharmaceuticals, Inc
J7674	Provocholine	1 mg	1	Methapharm Inc
J7682	Bethkis	300 mg	4	Chiesi Usa, Inc.
	Kitabis Pak	300 mg	5	Pari Respiratory Equipment
	Tobi	300 mg	5	Novartis Pharmaceuticals Corporation
	Tobramycin Inhalation	300 mg	5	Teva Pharmaceuticals Usa, Inc.
J7686	Tyvaso	1.74 mg	2.9	united Therapeutics
	Tyvaso (Refill Kit)	1.74 mg	2.9	
	Tyvaso (Starter Kit)	1.74 mg	2.9	
J8501	Aprepitant	5 mg	1	Sandoz, Inc.
	Aprepitant (Bi Fold)	5 mg	1	Sandoz
	Aprepitant (Tri-Fold)	5 mg	1	

HCPCS	DRUG NAME	DOSE	PKG SIZE	LABELER NAME
	Emend	5 mg	1	Merck Sharp & Dohme Corp.
	Emend Bi-Pack	5 mg	1	
	Emend Tri-Fold	5 mg	1	
J8510	Myleran	2 mg	1	Aspen
J8520	Capecitabine	150 mg	60	West-Ward
	Xeloda	150 mg	60	Genentech, Inc.
J8521	Capecitabine	500 mg	20	Mylan Institutional
		500 mg	120	West-Ward
	Xeloda	500 mg	120	Genentech, Inc.
J8530	Cyclophosphamide	25 mg	100	Roxane Laboratories
J8540	Dexamethasone	0.25 mg	28	A-S Medication Solutions
		0.25 mg	237	Morton Grove Pharm.
J8560	Etoposide	50 mg	20	Mylan Pharmaceuticals, Inc
J8600	Alkeran	2 mg	50	Apopharma Usa, Inc.
J8610	Methotrexate	2.5 mg	20	Mylan Institutional
		2.5 mg	36	Roxane Laboratories
		2.5 mg	100	
	Rheumatrex	2.5 mg	8	Par Pharmaceutical
		2.5 mg	12	
		2.5 mg	16	
		2.5 mg	20	
		2.5 mg	24	
	Trexall	2.5 mg	30	Duramed Pharmaceuticals, Inc.
J8655	Akynzeo	300 mg/0.5 mg	1	Eisai Inc.
J8700	Temodar	5 mg	1	Schering Corporation
	Temozolomide	5 mg	1	Teva Pharmaceuticals Usa, Inc.
J8705	Hycamtin, Oral	0.25 mg	1	Novartis Pharmaceuticals Corporation
J9000	Adriamycin	10 mg	5	West-Ward Pharmaceutical Corp.
		10 mg	10	
		10 mg	25	
		10 mg	100	
	Doxorubicin HCl	10 mg	1	Pfizer Inc.
		10 mg	5	
		10 mg	10	
		10 mg	25	
		10 mg	75	
		10 mg	100	
	Doxorubicin HCl (Lyo)	10 mg	1	Mylan Institutional

HCPCS	DRUG NAME	DOSE	PKG SIZE	LABELER NAME
J9017	Trisenox	1 mg	10	Cephalon Inc.
J9019	Erwinaze	1,000 iu	1	Jazz Pharmaceuticals, Inc.
J9025	Azacitidine	1 mg	1	Actavis Pharma
	Azacitidine (Vidaza)	1 mg	1	Celgene Corporation
J9027	Clofarabine	1 mg	20	Fresenius Kabi Usa, LLC
	Clolar	1 mg	20	Sanofi-Aventis
J9031	Tice Bcg	1 EA	1	Organon Usa, Inc.
J9032	Beleodaq	10 mg	1	Spectrum Pharmaceuticals
J9033	Treanda	1 mg	0.5	Cephalon Inc.
		1 mg	1	
		1 mg	2	
J9034	Bendeka	1 mg	4	
J9035	Avastin	10 mg	4	Genentech, Inc.
		10 mg	16	
J9039	Blincyto	1 mcg	1	A mgen Usa, Inc.
J9040	Bleo 15K	15 units	1	Amneal Biosciences
	Bleomycin	15 units	1	Fresenius Kabi Usa LLC
	Bleomycin Sulfate	15 units	1	Sicor Pharmaceuticals, Inc.
J9041	Velcade	0.1 mg	1	Millennium Pharmaceuticals
J9042	Adcetris	1 mg	1	Seattle Genetics
J9043	Jevtana	1 mg	1	Sanofi-Aventis
J9045	Carboplatin	50 mg	5	Sicor Pharmaceuticals, Inc.
		50 mg	15	
		50 mg	45	
		50 mg	60	
J9047	Kyprolis	1 mg	1	A mgen Usa, Inc.
J9050	Bicnu	100 mg	1	Heritage Pharmaceuticals, Inc.
J9055	Erbitux	10 mg	50	Eli Lilly and Company
		10 mg	100	
J9060	Cisplatin	10 mg	50	Sicor Pharmaceuticals, Inc.
		10 mg	100	
		10 mg	200	Wg Critical Care
J9065	Cladribine	1 mg	10	Mylan Institutional
J9070	Cyclophosphamide	100 mg	50	Sandoz, Inc.
		100 mg	75	
		100 mg	100	
J9098	Depocyt	10 mg	5	Si gma-Tau Pharmaceuticals
J9100	Cytarabine	100 mg	1	Fresenius Kabi Usa LLC
		100 mg	5	Mylan Institutional
		100 mg	20	Hospira, Inc

HCPCS	DRUG NAME	DOSE	PKG SIZE	LABELER NAME
		100 mg	25	
		100 mg	50	Pfizer Inc.
J9120	Cosmegen	0.5 mg	1	Recordati Rare Diseases
J9130	Dacarbazine	100 mg	1	Sicor Pharmaceuticals, Inc.
J9145	Darzalex	10 mg	5	Janssen Biotech, Inc.
		10 mg	20	
J9150	Daunorubicin HCl	10 mg	1	Sicor Pharmaceuticals, Inc.
		10 mg	4	
J9155	Firmagon	1 mg	1	Ferring Pharmaceuticals Inc.
J9171	Docefrez	1 mg	1	Sun Pharmaceutical Global Fze.
	Docetaxel	1 mg	1	Hospira, Inc.
		1 mg	2	Pfizer Inc.
		1 mg	4	Hospira, Inc.
		1 mg	7	Sagent Pharmaceuticals Inc
		1 mg	8	Pfizer Inc.
		1 mg	10	X-Gen Pharmaceuticals
		1 mg	16	Hospira, Inc
		1 mg	20	Pfizer Inc.
	Taxotere	1 mg	1	Sanofi-Aventis
		1 mg	4	
J9176	Empliciti	1 mg	1	Bristol-Myers Squibb Company
J9178	Ellence	2 mg	25	Pfizer Inc.
		2 mg	100	
	Epirubicin	2 mg	25	Impax Generics
		2 mg	100	
J9179	Halaven	0.1 mg	2	Eisai Inc.
J9181	Etopophos	10 mg	1	Bristol-Myers Squibb Company
	Etoposide	10 mg	5	Sicor Pharmaceuticals, Inc.
		10 mg	25	
		10 mg	50	
	Toposar	10 mg	25	
		10 mg	50	
J9185	Fludarabine Phosphate	50 mg	1	
		50 mg	2	Sagent Pharmaceutical
J9190	Adrucil	500 mg	10	Sicor Pharmaceuticals, Inc.
		500 mg	50	
		500 mg	100	
	Fluorouracil	500 mg	10	Pfizer Inc.
		500 mg	20	

HCPCS	DRUG NAME	DOSE	PKG SIZE	LABELER NAME
		500 mg	50	
		500 mg	100	
J9200	Floxuridine	500 mg	1	Fresenius Kabi Usa LLC
J9201	Gemcitabine	200 mg	1	Hospira, Inc
		200 mg	5.26	
		200 mg	26.3	
		200 mg	52.6	
	Gemcitabine HCl	200 mg	1	Heritage Pharmaceuticals, Inc.
	Gemcitabine Hydrochloride	200 mg	1	
	Gemzar	200 mg	1	Eli Lilly and Company
J9202	Zoladex	3.6 mg	1	Astrazeneca Pharmaceuticals Lp
J9205	OnIVyde 43 mg/10 ml Per Vial	1 mg	10	Merrimack Pharmaceuticals
J9206	Camptosar	20 mg	2	Pfizer Inc.
		20 mg	5	
		20 mg	15	
	Irinotecan HCl	20 mg	2	West-Ward Pharmaceuticals Corp
		20 mg	5	
		20 mg	25	Hospira, Inc
J9207	Ixabepilone	1 mg	1	R-Pharm Us
	Ixempra Kit	1 mg	1	
J9208	Ifex	1 gm	1	Baxter Healthcare Corporation
	Ifosfamide	1 gm	1	Pfizer Inc.
		1 gm	20	Mylan Institutional
		1 gm	60	Pfizer Inc.
J9209	Mesna	200 mg	10	Sicor Pharmaceuticals, Inc.
	Mesnex	200 mg	10	Baxter Healthcare Corporation
J9211	Idamycin Pfs	5 mg	5	Pfizer Inc.
		5 mg	10	
		5 mg	20	
	Idarubicin	5 mg	5	Sicor Pharmaceuticals, Inc.
		5 mg	10	
		5 mg	20	
J9214	Intron-A	1 MIL units	1	Schering Corporation
		1 MIL units	2.5	
		1 MIL units	3	
J9217	Eligard	7.5 mg	1	Tolmar
	Lupron Depot 4-Month, 30 mg	7.5 mg	1	Abbvie Us, LLC

HCPCS	DRUG NAME	DOSE	PKG SIZE	LABELER NAME
	Lupron Depot 6-Month, 45 mg	7.5 mg	1	
	Lupron Depot 7.5 mg Kit	7.5 mg	1	
	Lupron Depot-3 Month 22.5 mg Kit	7.5 mg	1	
	Lupron Depot-Ped 15 mg	7.5 mg	1	
	Lupron Depot-Ped 7.5 mg	7.5 mg	1	
J9218	Leuprolide Acetate	1 mg	2.8	Sandoz, Inc.
	Leuprolide Acetate Inj	1 mg	1	Sun Pharmaceutical Global Inc.
J9225	Vantas Implant	50 mg	1	Endo Pharmaceuticals Valera Inc.
J9226	Supprelin La Implant	50 mg	1	
J9228	Yervoy	1 mg	10	Bristol-Myers Squibb Company
		1 mg	40	
J9230	Mustargen	10 mg	1	Recordati Rare Diseases
J9245	Alkeran	50 mg	1	Apopharma Usa, Inc.
	Evomela	50 mg	1	Spectrum Pharmaceuticals
	Melphalan	50 mg	1	Sagent Pharmaceuticals, Inc.
J9250	Methotrexate	5 mg	2	Hospira, Inc
	Methotrexate Powder 1 gm In 50 ml Sd Vial (P.F.)	5 mg	1	Fresenius Kabi Usa LLC
	Methotrexate Sodium	5 mg	1	
		5 mg	2	Sicor Pharmaceuticals, Inc.
		5 mg	4	Mylan Institutional
		5 mg	8	Pfizer Inc.
		5 mg	10	
		5 mg	40	Sicor Pharmaceuticals, Inc.
J9260	Methotrexate	50 mg	2	Hospira, Inc
	Methotrexate Powder 1 gm In 50 ml Sd Vial (P.F.)	50 mg	1	Fresenius Kabi Usa LLC
	Methotrexate Sodium	50 mg	1	
		50 mg	2	Sicor Pharmaceuticals, Inc.
		50 mg	4	Mylan Institutional
		50 mg	8	Pfizer Inc.
		50 mg	10	
		50 mg	40	Sicor Pharmaceuticals, Inc.
J9261	Arranon	50 mg	50	Novartis Pharmaceuticals Corporation
J9263	Eloxatin	0.5 mg	10	Sanofi-Aventis
		0.5 mg	20	
	Oxaliplatin	0.5 mg	1	Pfizer Inc.
		0.5 mg	10	

HCPCS	DRUG NAME	DOSE	PKG SIZE	LABELER NAME
		0.5 mg	20	
J9264	Abraxane	1 mg	50	Celgene Corporation
J9266	Oncaspar	1 EA	5	Baxalta Incorporated
J9267	Paclitaxel	1 mg	5	Mylan Institutional
		1 mg	16.7	
		1 mg	25	Sicor Pharmaceuticals, Inc.
		1 mg	50	Mylan Institutional
J9268	Nipent	10 mg	1	Hospira, Inc
J9271	Keytruda	1 mg	4	Merck Sharp & Dohme Corp.
		1 mg	50	
J9280	Mitomycin	5 mg	1	Accord Healthcare Inc.
J9293	Mitoxantrone Hydrochloride	5 mg	10	Sicor Pharmaceuticals, Inc.
		5 mg	12.5	
		5 mg	15	
J9295	Portrazza	1 mg	50	Eli Lilly and Company
J9299	OpdIVo	1 mg	4	Bristol-Myers Squibb Company
		1 mg	10	
J9301	Gazyva	10 mg	40	Genentech, Inc.
J9302	Arzerra	10 mg	5	Novartis Pharmaceuticals Corporation
		10 mg	50	
J9303	Panitumumab	10 mg	5	A mgen Usa, Inc.
		10 mg	20	
J9305	Alimta	10 mg	1	Eli Lilly and Company
J9306	Perjeta	1 mg	14	Genentech, Inc.
J9307	Folotyn	1 mg	1	Spectrum Pharmaceuticals
		1 mg	2	
J9308	Cyramza	5 mg	10	Eli Lilly and Company
		5 mg	50	
J9310	Rituxan	100 mg	10	Genentech, Inc.
		100 mg	50	
J9315	Istodax (Romidepsin)	1 mg	1	Celgene Corporation
J9320	Zanosar	1 gm	1	Sicor Pharmaceuticals, Inc.
J9325	I mlygic	1 million PFU	1	A mgen Usa, Inc.
J9328	Temodar IV	1 mg	1	Schering Corporation
J9330	Temsirolimus	1 mg	1	Pfizer Inc.
J9351	Hycamtin	0.1 mg	1	Novartis Pharmaceuticals Corporation
	Topotecan	0.1 mg	1	Pfizer Inc.
	Topotecan HCl	0.1 mg	1	Sagent Pharmaceuticals Inc

HCPCS	DRUG NAME	DOSE	PKG SIZE	LABELER NAME
J9352	Yondelis	0.1 mg	1	Janssen Products, Lp
J9354	Kadcyla	1 mg	1	Genentech, Inc.
J9355	Herceptin	10 mg	1	
J9357	Valstar	200 mg	5	Endo Pharmaceuticals Valera Inc.
J9360	Vinblastine Sulfate	1 mg	10	Fresenius Kabi Usa LLC
J9370	Vincristine Sulfate	1 mg	1	Sicor Pharmaceuticals, Inc.
		1 mg	2	
J9371		1 mg	1	Spectrum Pharmaceuticals
J9390	Navelbine	10 mg	1	Pierre Fabre Pharmaceuticals
		10 mg	5	
	Vinorelbine Tartrate	10 mg	1	Mylan Institutional
		10 mg	5	Pfizer Inc.
J9395	Faslodex	25 mg	5	Astrazeneca Pharmaceuticals Lp
J9400	Zaltrap	1 mg	4	Sanofi-Aventis
		1 mg	8	
P9041	Albuked 5	50 ml	50	Kedrion Biopharma
		50 ml	250	
	Albumin	50 ml	100	Octapharma Usa
	Albumin (Human)	50 ml	100	
		50 ml	250	Grifols
		50 ml	500	
	Albumin 5%, 12.5 G In 250 ml	50 ml	250	Octapharma Usa
	Albumin 5%, 25 G In 500 ml	50 ml	500	
	Albumin 5%, 25Gr	50 ml	500	
	Albumin 5%, 5 G In 100 ml	50 ml	100	
	Albumin, 12.5Gr	50 ml	250	
	Albuminar-5	50 ml	250	Csl Behring
		50 ml	500	
	Albumin-Zlb	50 ml	250	Alpine Biologics
		50 ml	500	
	Alburx	50 ml	250	Csl Behring
		50 ml	500	
	Albutein 5%	50 ml	50	Grifols
	Albutein®	50 ml	250	
	Albutein® 5% Albumin 500 ml	50 ml	500	
	Buminate	50 ml	250	Baxter
		50 ml	500	
	Plasbumin-5	50 ml	50	Talecris
		50 ml	250	
P9045	Albuked 5	250 ml	250	Kedrion Biopharma

HCPCS	DRUG NAME	DOSE	PKG SIZE	LABELER NAME
	Albumin	250 ml	100	Octapharma Usa
	Albumin (Human)	250 ml	250	Grifols
		250 ml	500	
	Albumin 5%, 12.5 G In 250 ml	250 ml	250	Octapharma Usa
	Albumin 5%, 25 G In 500 ml	250 ml	500	
	Albumin 5%, 25Gr	250 ml	500	
	Albumin 5%, 5 G In 100 ml	250 ml	100	
	Albumin, 12.5Gr	250 ml	250	
	Albuminar-5	250 ml	250	Csl Behring
		250 ml	500	
		250 ml	1000	
	Albumin-Zlb	250 ml	250	Alpine Biologics
		250 ml	500	
	Alburx	250 ml	250	Csl Behring
		250 ml	500	
	Albutein® 5%	250 ml	250	Grifols
	Albutein® 5% Albumin 500 ml	250 ml	500	
	Buminate	250 ml	250	Baxter
		250 ml	500	
	Plasbumin-5	250 ml	50	Talecris
		250 ml	250	
P9046	Albuked 25	20 ml	50	Kedrion Biopharma
		20 ml	100	
	Albumin	20 ml	50	Octapharma Usa
		20 ml	100	
	Albumin (Human)	20 ml	50	
		20 ml	100	
	Albumin 25%, 12.5 G In 50 ml	20 ml	50	
	Albumin 25%, 25 G In 100 ml	20 ml	100	
	Albumin-Alpine	20 ml	50	Alpine Biologics
		25 ml	100	
	Albuminar-25	20 ml	20	Csl Behring
		20 ml	50	
		20 ml	100	
	Alburx	20 ml	50	
		20 ml	100	
	Albutein 25%	20 ml	20	Grifols
	Albutein®	20 ml	50	
		20 ml	100	
	Albutein® 25% Albumin 100 ml	20 ml	100	

HCPCS	DRUG NAME	DOSE	PKG SIZE	LABELER NAME
	Buminate	20 ml	20	Baxter
		20 ml	50	
		20 ml	100	
	Flexbumin	20 ml	50	
		20 ml	100	
	Kedbumin	20 ml	50	Kedrion Biopharma
	Plasbumin-25	20 ml	20	Talecris
		20 ml	50	
		20 ml	100	
P9047	Albuked 25	50 ml	50	Kedrion Biopharma
		50 ml	100	
	Albumin	50 ml	50	Octapharma Usa
	Albumin (Human)	50 ml	50	
		50 ml	100	
	Albumin (Human) 25%	50 ml	100	
	Albumin 25%, 12.5 G In 50 ml	50 ml	50	
	Albumin 25%, 25 G In 100 ml	50 ml	100	
	Albuminar-25	50 ml	50	Csl Behring
		50 ml	100	
	Albumin-Zlb	50 ml	50	Alpine Biologics
		50 ml	100	
	Alburx	50 ml	50	Csl Behring
		50 ml	100	
	Albutein® 25%	50 ml	50	Grifols
	Albutein® 25% Albumin 100 ml	50 ml	100	
	Buminate	50 ml	20	Baxter
		50 ml	50	
		50 ml	100	
	Flexbumin	50 ml	50	
		50 ml	100	
	Human Albumin Grifols	50 ml	50	Grifols
		50 ml	100	
	Kedbumin	50 ml	50	Kedrion Biopharma
	Plasbumin-25	50 ml	20	Talecris
		50 ml	50	
		50 ml	100	
Q0138	Feraheme	1 mg	1	Amag Pharmaceuticals
Q0139		1 mg	1	
Q0162	Ondansetron	1 mg	1	Mylan Pharmaceuticals, Inc
		1 mg	10	Glenmark Pharmaceuticals, Usa
		1 mg	30	

HCPCS	DRUG NAME	DOSE	PKG SIZE	LABELER NAME
		1 mg	50	Northstar Rx LLC
	Ondansetron HCl	1 mg	1	Teva Pharmaceuticals Usa, Inc.
	Ondansetron Odt	1 mg	1	Mylan Pharmaceuticals, Inc
		1 mg	10	American Health Packaging
		1 mg	30	
	Zofran	1 mg	1	Novartis Pharmaceuticals Corporation
		1 mg	50	
	Zofran Odt	1 mg	1	
Q0163	Diphenhydramine HCl	50 mg	6	A-S Medication Solutions
		50 mg	10	
		50 mg	15	
		50 mg	20	
		50 mg	24	
		50 mg	30	
Q0164	Prochlorperazine Maleate	5 mg	6	
		5 mg	10	
		5 mg	30	
		5 mg	100	Teva Pharmaceuticals Usa, Inc.
Q0166	Granisetron HCl	1 mg	1	
		1 mg	20	Taro Pharmaceuticals
Q0167	Dronabinol	2.5 mg	1	Mylan Pharmaceuticals, Inc
		2.5 mg	30	American Health Packaging
		2.5 mg	60	Mylan Pharmaceuticals, Inc
	Marinol	2.5 mg	60	Abbvie Us, LLC
		2.5 mg	100	American Health Packaging
Q0169	Promethazine HCl	12.5 mg	5	A-S Medication Solutions
		12.5 mg	8	
		12.5 mg	10	
		12.5 mg	12	
		12.5 mg	20	
		12.5 mg	30	
		12.5 mg	60	
		12.5 mg	100	Sandoz, Inc.
		12.5 mg	120	A-S Medication Solutions
		12.5 mg	473	Hi-Tech
		12.5 mg	1000	Sandoz, Inc.
Q2035	Afluria 2016/2017	0.5 ml	5	Seqirus
	Afluria 2017/2018	0.5 ml	5	

HCPCS	DRUG NAME	DOSE	PKG SIZE	LABELER NAME
Q2037	Fluvirin 2016/2017	0.5 ml	5	
	Fluvirin 2017/2018	0.5 ml	5	
Q2043	Provenge®	Per infusion (minimum 50 million cells)	250	Dendreon
Q2050	Doxil	10 mg	10	Janssen Products, Lp
		10 mg	25	
	Doxorubicin HCl, Liposomal,	10 mg	10	Dr.Reddy'S Laboratories
		10 mg	25	
Q3027	Avonex	1 mcg	1	Biogen
	Avonex Pen	1 mcg	1	
Q4074	Ventavis	Up to 20 mcg	1	Actelion Pharmaceuticals U.S, Inc
Q4081	Epogen	100 units	1	A mgen Usa, Inc.
		100 units	2	
	Procrit	100 units	1	Janssen Products, Lp
		100 units	2	
Q4101	Apligraf	1 SQ CM	1	Organogenesis, Inc.
Q4102	Oasis Wound Matrix	1 SQ CM	1	Cook (Smith & Nephew, Inc.)
Q4106	Dermagraft	1 SQ CM	1	Organogenesis, Inc.
Q4107	Graftjacket Std	1 SQ CM	1	Kinetic Concepts Incorporated
Q4111	Gammagraft	1 SQ CM	2.25	Promethean Lifesciences, Inc.
		1 SQ CM	7.5	
		1 SQ CM	18	
		1 SQ CM	56	
Q4112	Cymetra	1 CC	2	Lifecell Corporation
Q4113	Graftjacket Xpress	1 CC	1	Kinetic Concepts Incorporated
Q4115	Alloskin	1 SQ CM	25	Allosource
		1 SQ CM	80	
		1 SQ CM	120	
Q4116	Alloderm	1 SQ CM	1	Lifecell Corporation
		1 SQ CM	2	
		1 SQ CM	4	
		1 SQ CM	8	
		1 SQ CM	21	
		1 SQ CM	28	
		1 SQ CM	48	
		1 SQ CM	50	
		1 SQ CM	64	

HCPCS	DRUG NAME	DOSE	PKG SIZE	LABELER NAME
		1 SQ CM	72	
		1 SQ CM	77	
		1 SQ CM	96	
		1 SQ CM	108	
		1 SQ CM	128	
		1 SQ CM	132	
		1 SQ CM	144	
		1 SQ CM	160	
		1 SQ CM	164	
		1 SQ CM	192	
		1 SQ CM	200	
		1 SQ CM	240	
		1 SQ CM	320	
	Alloderm Select	1 SQ CM	160	
	Alloderm Select Contour	1 SQ CM	77	
Q4121	Theraskin	1 SQ CM	1	Skin and Wound Allograft Institute
		1 SQ CM	12.9	
		1 SQ CM	38.71	
Q4123	Alloskin Rt	1 SQ CM	25	Allosource
		1 SQ CM	80	
Q4131	Epicord	1 SQ CM	6	Mimedx Group, Inc.
		1 SQ CM	15	
	Epifix	1 SQ CM	10.1	
	Epifix Amniotic Membrane Allograft	1 SQ CM	1	
		1 sq cm	2	
		1 SQ CM	4	
		1 sq cm	6	
		1 sq cm	9.5	
		1 sq cm	16	
		1 sq cm	16.9	
		1 sq cm	49	
Q4132	Grafix Core	1 SQ CM	1	Osiris Therapeutics
Q4133	Grafix Prime	1 SQ CM	1	
Q5101	Zarxio™ (Filgrastim-Sndz)	1 mcg	0.5	Sandoz, Inc.
		1 mcg	0.8	
Q5102	Inflectra	10 mg	1	Pfizer
Q9950	Lumason	1 ml	5	Bracco Diagnostics
Q9956	Optison	1 ml	3	Ge Healthcare

HCPCS	DRUG NAME	DOSE	PKG SIZE	LABELER NAME
Q9957	Definity	1 ml	2	Lantheus Medical Imaging, Inc.
Q9958	Conray 30	1 ml	150	Liebel Flarsheim
	Cysto-Conray Ii	1 ml	250	
	Cystografin	1 ml	100	Bracco Diagnostics
		1 ml	300	
	Cystografin-Dilute	1 ml	300	
Q9960	Conray 43	1 ml	50	Liebel Flarsheim
		1 ml	250	
Q9961	Cholografin Meglumine	1 ml	20	Bracco Diagnostics
	Conray	1 ml	30	Liebel Flarsheim
		1 ml	50	
		1 ml	100	
		1 ml	150	
Q9963	Gastrografin	1 ml	30	Bracco Diagnostics
		1 ml	120	
	Md Gastroview	1 ml	30	Liebel Flarsheim
	Md-76R	1 ml	50	
		1 ml	100	
		1 ml	200	
	Sinografin	1 ml	10	Bracco Diagnostics
Q9965	Omnipaque 140	1 ml	50	Ge Healthcare
	Omnipaque 180	1 ml	10	
		1 ml	20	
Q9966	Isovue-200	1 ml	50	Bracco Diagnostics
		1 ml	200	
	Isovue-250	1 ml	50	
		1 ml	100	
		1 ml	150	
	Isovue-250 Multipack	1 ml	200	
	Isovue-M-200	1 ml	10	
		1 ml	20	
	Omnipaque	1 ml	50	Ge Healthcare
	Omnipaque 240	1 ml	10	
		1 ml	20	
		1 ml	50	
		1 ml	100	
		1 ml	150	
		1 ml	200	
	Optiray 240	1 ml	50	Liebel Flarsheim
		1 ml	100	
		1 ml	125	

HCPCS	DRUG NAME	DOSE	PKG SIZE	LABELER NAME
		1 ml	200	
	Ultravist 240	1 ml	100	Bayer Healthcare Pharmaceuticals Inc.
		1 ml	200	
	Visipaque 270	1 ml	50	Ge Healthcare
		1 ml	100	
		1 ml	150	
		1 ml	200	
Q9967	Hexabrix 320	1 ml	20	Liebel Flarsheim
		1 ml	50	
		1 ml	100	
		1 ml	200	
	Hexabrix 320 mgI/ ml, 100 ml Volume	1 ml	100	Guerbet LLC
	Hexabrix 320 mgI/ ml, 200 ml Volume	1 ml	200	
	Hexabrix 320 mgI/ ml, 50 ml Volume	1 ml	50	
	Isovue-300	1 ml	30	Bracco Diagnostics
		1 ml	50	
		1 ml	75	
		1 ml	100	
		1 ml	150	
		1 ml	200	
		1 ml	500	
	Isovue-300 Multi Pack	1 ml	200	
		1 ml	500	
	Isovue-370	1 ml	50	
		1 ml	75	
		1 ml	100	
		1 ml	125	
		1 ml	150	
		1 ml	200	
		1 ml	500	
	Isovue-370 Multi Pack	1 ml	200	
		1 ml	500	
	Isovue-M-300	1 ml	15	
	Omnipaque	1 ml	50	Ge Healthcare
		1 ml	100	
		1 ml	150	
		1 ml	500	
	Omnipaque 300	1 ml	10	

HCPCS	DRUG NAME	DOSE	PKG SIZE	LABELER NAME
		1 ml	30	
		1 ml	50	
		1 ml	75	
		1 ml	100	
		1 ml	125	
		1 ml	150	
		1 ml	200	
		1 ml	500	
	Omnipaque 350	1 ml	50	
		1 ml	75	
		1 ml	100	
		1 ml	125	
		1 ml	150	
		1 ml	200	
		1 ml	500	
	Optiray 300	1 ml	50	Liebel Flarsheim
		1 ml	100	
		1 ml	150	
		1 ml	200	
		1 ml	500	
	Optiray 320	1 ml	20	
		1 ml	30	
		1 ml	50	
		1 ml	75	
		1 ml	100	
		1 ml	125	
		1 ml	150	
		1 ml	200	
		1 ml	500	
	Optiray 350	1 ml	50	
		1 ml	75	
		1 ml	100	
		1 ml	125	
		1 ml	150	
		1 ml	200	
		1 ml	500	
	Oxilan 300	1 ml	50	Guerbet LLC
		1 ml	100	
		1 ml	150	
		1 ml	500	
	Oxilan 350	1 ml	50	Mallinckrodt

HCPCS	DRUG NAME	DOSE	PKG SIZE	LABELER NAME
		1 ml	100	Liebel Flarsheim
		1 ml	125	
		1 ml	150	Guerbet LLC
		1 ml	200	
	Ultravist 300	1 ml	50	Bayer Healthcare Pharmaceuticals Inc.
		1 ml	100	
		1 ml	125	
		1 ml	150	
		1 ml	200	
		1 ml	500	
	Ultravist 370	1 ml	50	
		1 ml	100	
		1 ml	125	
		1 ml	150	
		1 ml	200	
		1 ml	250	
		1 ml	500	
	Visipaque	1 ml	50	Ge Healthcare
		1 ml	100	
		1 ml	150	
		1 ml	200	
	Visipaque 320	1 ml	50	
		1 ml	100	
		1 ml	150	
		1 ml	200	
		1 ml	500	
Q9989	Stelara (IV Infusion)	1 mg	26	Janssen Biotech, Inc.

HCPCS	DRUG NAME	DOSE	PKG SIZE	LABELER NAME

APPENDIX G: NDC DRUG NAME CROSS-WALK TO HCPCS

The NDC Drug Name to HCPCS cross-walk is intended to help providers who bill for drugs understand which drug products (identified by drug name) are assigned to which HCPCS billing codes. The crosswalks are not intended to be a comprehensive list of all drugs/NDCs available in the United States. The NDC to HCPCS Crosswalk also includes information on the NDC dose and package size.

COLUMN DEFINITIONS

Drug Name: Product Name (brand or generic name may appear)

HCPCS: Five (5) digit HCPCS code

Dose: The dosage descriptor assigned to the HCPCS code

Pkg Size: The amount of the drug in one item. (ex., For a product that is 100mcg/0.5 ml in one vial, the package size would be 0.5.)

Labeler Name: Manufacturer Name

Drug Name	HCPCS	Dose	Pkg Size	Labeler Name
Choline C 11	A9515	Per study dose	30	Zevacor Molecular
Abatacept	J0129	10 mg	1	Bristol-Myers Squibb Company
Abelcet	J0287	10 mg	20	Sigma-Tau Pharmaceuticals
Abilify Maintena	J0401	1 mg	1	Otsuka America Pharmaceutical, Inc.
Abraxane	J9264	1 mg	50	Celgene Corporation
Acetadote	J0132	100 mg	30	Cumberland Pharmaceuticals Inc
Acetazolamide Sodium	J1120	500 mg	1	West-Ward Pharmaceuticals Corp
Acetylcysteine	J0132	100 mg	30	Perrigo Pharmaceuticals
	J7608	1 gm	4	American Regent
		1 gm	10	
		1 gm	30	Hospira, Inc
Acetylcysteine Inj	J0132	100 mg	30	Akorn
Acetylcysteine Injection		100 mg	30	Perrigo Pharmaceuticals
Actemra	J3262	1 mg	80	Genentech, Inc.
		1 mg	200	
		1 mg	400	
Acthrel	J0795	1 mcg	1	Ferring Pharmaceuticals Inc.
Activase	J2997	1 mg	1	Genentech, Inc.
Acyclovir Sodium	J0133	5 mg	10	Fresenius Kabi USA LLC
		5 mg	20	
Adagen	J2504	25 iu	1.5	Sigma-Tau Pharmaceuticals

Drug Name	HCPCS	Dose	Pkg Size	Labeler Name
Adasuve	C9497	10 mg	1	Gate Pharmaceuticals
Adcetris	J9042	1mg	1	Seattle Genetics
Adenocard	J0153	1 mg	2	Astellas Pharma Us, Inc.
		1 mg	4	
Adenoscan		1 mg	20	
		1 mg	30	
Adenosine		1 mg	2	Akorn
		1 mg	4	Sagent Pharmaceuticals Inc
		1 mg	20	Hospira, Inc
		1 mg	30	
Adrenalin	J0171	0.1 mg	1	Par Sterile Products LLC
Adriamycin	J9000	10 mg	5	West-Ward Pharmaceutical Corp.
		10 mg	10	
		10 mg	25	
		10 mg	100	
Adrucil	J9190	500 mg	10	SICOR Pharmaceuticals, Inc.
		500 mg	50	
		500 mg	100	
Advate	J7192	1 iu	1	Baxalta Us Inc.
Afluria 2016/2017	Q2035	0.5 ml	5	Seqirus
Afluria 2017/2018		0.5 ml	5	
Afstyla	C9140	1 iu	1	Csl Behring LLC
Akynzeo	J8655	300 mg/0.5 mg	1	Eisai Inc.
Albuked 25	P9046	20 ml	50	Kedrion Biopharma
		20 ml	100	
	P9047	50 ml	50	
		50 ml	100	
Albuked 5	P9041	50 ml	50	
		50 ml	250	
	P9045	250 ml	250	
Albumin	P9041	50 ml	100	Octapharma USA
	P9045	250 ml	100	
	P9046	20 ml	50	
		20 ml	100	
	P9047	50 ml	50	
Albumin (Human)	P9041	50 ml	100	
		50 ml	250	Grifols
		50 ml	500	
	P9045	250 ml	250	
		250 ml	500	

Drug Name	HCPCS	Dose	Pkg Size	Labeler Name
	P9046	20 ml	50	Octapharma USA
		20 ml	100	
	P9047	50 ml	50	
		50 ml	100	
Albumin (Human) 25%		50 ml	100	
Albumin 25%, 12.5 G In 50 ml	P9046	20 ml	50	
	P9047	50 ml	50	
Albumin 25%, 25 G In 100 ml	P9046	20 ml	100	
	P9047	50 ml	100	
Albumin 5%, 12.5 G In 250 ml	P9041	50 ml	250	
	P9045	250 ml	250	
Albumin 5%, 25 G In 500 ml	P9041	50 ml	500	
	P9045	250 ml	500	
Albumin 5%, 25Gr	P9041	50 ml	500	
	P9045	250 ml	500	
Albumin 5%, 5 G In 100 ml	P9041	50 ml	100	
	P9045	250 ml	100	
Albumin, 12.5Gr	P9041	50 ml	250	
	P9045	250 ml	250	
Albumin-Alpine	P9046	20 ml	50	Alpine Biologics
		25 ml	100	
Albuminar-25		20 ml	20	Csl Behring
		20 ml	50	
		20 ml	100	
	P9047	50 ml	50	
		50 ml	100	
Albuminar-5	P9041	50 ml	250	
		50 ml	500	
	P9045	250 ml	250	
		250 ml	500	
		250 ml	1000	
Albumin-Zlb	P9041	50 ml	250	Alpine Biologics
		50 ml	500	
	P9045	250 ml	250	
		250 ml	500	
	P9047	50 ml	50	
		50 ml	100	
Alburx	P9041	50 ml	250	Csl Behring
		50 ml	500	

Drug Name	HCPCS	Dose	Pkg Size	Labeler Name
	P9045	250 ml	250	
		250 ml	500	
	P9046	20 ml	50	
		20 ml	100	
	P9047	50 ml	50	
		50 ml	100	
Albutein 25%	P9046	20 ml	20	Grifols
Albutein 5%	P9041	50 ml	50	
Albutein®		50 ml	250	
	P9046	20 ml	50	
		20 ml	100	
Albutein® 25%	P9047	50 ml	50	
Albutein® 25% Albumin 100 ml	P9046	20 ml	100	
	P9047	50 ml	100	
Albutein® 5%	P9045	250 ml	250	
Albutein® 5% Albumin 500 ml	P9041	50 ml	500	
	P9045	250 ml	500	
Albuterol Ipratropium	J7620	2.5 mg/0.5 mg	3	Teva Pharmaceuticals USA, Inc.
Albuterol Sulfate	J7611	1 mg	0.5	Nephron Pharmaceuticals Corp.
		1 mg	20	Bausch & Lomb
	J7613	1 mg	3	Mylan Pharmaceuticals, Inc
Aldurazyme	J1931	0.1 mg	5	Genzyme Corporation
Alimta	J9305	10 mg	1	Eli Lilly And Company
Alkeran	J8600	2 mg	50	Apopharma USA, Inc.
	J9245	50 mg	1	
Alloderm	Q4116	1 cm2	1	LifeCell Corporation
		1 cm2	2	
		1 cm2	4	
		1 cm2	8	
		1 cm2	21	
		1 cm2	28	
		1 cm2	48	
		1 cm2	50	
		1 cm2	64	
		1 cm2	72	
		1 cm2	77	
		1 cm2	96	
		1 cm2	108	

Drug Name	HCPCS	Dose	Pkg Size	Labeler Name
		1 cm2	128	
		1 cm2	132	
		1 cm2	144	
		1 cm2	160	
		1 cm2	164	
		1 cm2	192	
		1 cm2	200	
		1 cm2	240	
		1 cm2	320	
Alloderm Select		1 cm2	160	
Alloderm Select Contour		1 cm2	77	
Alloskin	**Q4115**	1 cm2	25	Allosource
		1 cm2	80	
		1 cm2	120	
Alloskin Rt	**Q4123**	1 cm2	25	
		1 cm2	80	
Aloxi	**J2469**	25 mcg	5	Eisai Inc.
Alphanate /Von Willebrand Factor Complex	**J7186**	per factor VIII iu	1	Grifols USA, LLC.
	J7190	1 iu	1	
AlphaNine SD Vf 1000 Iu M2V USA	**J7193**	1 iu	1	
AlphaNine SD Vf 1500 Iu M2V USA		1 iu	1	
AlphaNine SD Vf 500 Iu M2V USA		1 iu	1	
Alprolix	**J7201**	1 iu	1	Biogen
AmBisome	**J0289**	10 mg	1	Astellas Pharma Us, Inc.
Amifostine For Injection	**J0207**	500 mg	1	Sun Pharmaceutical Global Fze.
Amikacin Sulfate	**J0278**	100 mg	2	West-Ward Pharmaceuticals Corp
		100 mg	4	
Aminophylline	**J0280**	250 mg	10	Hospira, Inc
		250 mg	20	
Amphotericin B	**J0285**	50 mg	1	X-Gen Pharmaceuticals, Inc.
Ampicillin For Injection	**J0290**	500 mg	1	Wg Critical Care
Ampicillin Sodium		500 mg	1	Sandoz, Inc.
		500 mg	10	Fresenius Kabi USA LLC
Ampicillin-Sulbactam	**J0295**	1.5 gm	1	West-Ward Pharmaceuticals Corp
		1.5 gm	30	Sagent Pharmaceuticals Inc
Angiomax	**J0583**	1 mg	1	The Medicines Company

Drug Name	HCPCS	Dose	Pkg Size	Labeler Name
Apligraf	**Q4101**	1 cm2	1	Organogenesis, Inc.
Aprepitant	**J8501**	5 mg	1	Sandoz, Inc.
Aprepitant (Bi Fold)		5 mg	1	Sandoz
Aprepitant (Tri-Fold)		5 mg	1	
Aralast Np	**J0256**	10 mg	1	Baxalta Us Inc.
Aranesp	**J0881**	1 mcg	0.3	Amgen USA, Inc.
		1 mcg	0.4	
		1 mcg	0.42	
		1 mcg	0.5	
		1 mcg	0.6	
		1 mcg	0.75	
		1 mcg	1	
	J0882	1 mcg	0.3	
		1 mcg	0.4	
		1 mcg	0.42	
		1 mcg	0.5	
		1 mcg	0.6	
		1 mcg	0.75	
		1 mcg	1	
Arformoterol	**J7605**	15 mcg	2	Sunovion Pharmaceuticals Inc.
Aristada	**J1942**	1 mg	1.6	Alkermes, Inc.
		1 mg	2.4	
		1 mg	3.2	
		1 mg	3.9	
Arixtra	**J1652**	0.5 mg	0.4	Mylan Institutional
		0.5 mg	0.5	
		0.5 mg	0.6	
		0.5 mg	0.8	
Arranon	**J9261**	50 mg	50	Novartis Pharmaceuticals Corporation
Artiss	**C9250**	2 ml	1	Baxter Healthcare Corporation
Arzerra	**J9302**	10 mg	5	Novartis Pharmaceuticals Corporation
		10 mg	50	
Astagraf Xl	**J7508**	0.1 mg	30	Astellas Pharma Us, Inc.
Atgam	**J7504**	250 mg	5	Pfizer Inc.
Ativan	**J2060**	2 mg	1	West-Ward Pharmaceuticals Corp
		2 mg	10	
Atropine Sulfate	**J0461**	0.01 mg	1	American Regent
		0.01 mg	5	Hospira, Inc
		0.01 mg	10	

Drug Name	HCPCS	Dose	Pkg Size	Labeler Name
		0.01 mg	20	West-Ward Pharmaceuticals Corp
Avastin	**C9257**	0.25 mg	4	Genentech, Inc.
		0.25 mg	16	
	J9035	10 mg	4	
		10 mg	16	
Avelox	**J2280**	100 mg	250	Schering Corporation
Avonex	**Q3027**	1 mcg	1	Biogen
Avonex Pen		1 mcg	1	
Axumin	**A9588**	1 mCi	5	Blue Earth Diagnostics
Azacitidine	**J9025**	1 mg	1	Actavis Pharma
Azacitidine (Vidaza)		1 mg	1	Celgene Corporation
Azasan	**J7500**	50 mg	100	Salix Pharmaceuticals, Inc.
Azathioprine		50 mg	50	Mylan Institutional
		50 mg	100	Roxane Laboratories
Azithromycin	**J0456**	500 mg	1	Pfizer Inc.
Bactocill In Dextrose	**J2700**	250 mg	50	Baxter Healthcare Corporation
Bal In Oil	**J0470**	100 mg	3	Akorn
Bavencio	**C9491**	10 mg	10	Serono
Bebulin	**J7194**	1 iu	1	Baxalta Us Inc.
Beleodaq	**J9032**	10 mg	1	Spectrum Pharmaceuticals
Benadryl	**J1200**	50 mg	10	Mylan Institutional
Bendeka	**J9034**	1 mg	4	Cephalon Inc.
BeneFIX	**J7195**	1 iu	1	Pfizer Inc.
Benlysta	**J0490**	10 mg	5	GlaxoSmithKline
		10 mg	20	
Bentyl	**J0500**	20 mg	2	Aptalis Pharmaceuticals
Benztropine	**J0515**	1 mg	2	Akorn
Berinert	**J0597**	10 units	1	Csl Behring Gmbh
Bethkis	**J7682**	300 mg	4	Chiesi USA, Inc.
Bicillin C-R	**J0558**	100,000 units	2	A-S Medication Solutions
Bicillin Cr Pediatric		100,000 units	2	Pfizer Inc.
Bicillin L-A	**J0561**	100,000 units	1	A-S Medication Solutions
		100,000 units	2	
		100,000 units	4	Pfizer Inc.
BiCNU	**J9050**	100 mg	1	Heritage Pharmaceuticals, Inc.
Bivalirudin	**J0583**	1 mg	1	Hospira, Inc
Bivigam	**J1556**	500 mg	50	Biotest Pharmaceuticals Corporation
		500 mg	100	
Bleo 15K	**J9040**	15 units	1	Amneal Biosciences
Bleomycin		15 units	1	Fresenius Kabi USA LLC

Drug Name	HCPCS	Dose	Pkg Size	Labeler Name
Bleomycin Sulfate		15 units	1	SICOR Pharmaceuticals, Inc.
Blincyto	J9039	1 mcg	1	Amgen USA, Inc.
Boniva	J1740	1 mg	3	Genentech, Inc.
Botox	J0585	1 unit	1	Allergan Sales, LLC
Botox Cosmetic		1 unit	1	
Budesonide	J7626	Up to 0.50 mg	2	Teva Pharmaceuticals USA, Inc.
Buminate	P9041	50 ml	250	Baxter
		50 ml	500	
	P9045	250 ml	250	
		250 ml	500	
	P9046	20 ml	20	
		20 ml	50	
		20 ml	100	
	P9047	50 ml	20	
		50 ml	50	
		50 ml	100	
Buprenorphine Hcl	J0592	0.1 mg	1	Hospira, Inc
Buprenorphine Hcl Injection		0.1 mg	1	Par Sterile Products LLC
Busulfan	J0594	1 mg	10	Sagent Pharmaceuticals, Inc.
Butorphanol Tartrate	J0595	1 mg	1	Hospira, Inc
		1 mg	2	
Calcitriol	J0636	0.1 mcg	1	Akorn
Calcium Disodium Versenate	J0600	1000 mg	5	Medicis Pharmaceuticals, Inc.
Calcium Gluconate	J0610	10 ml	10	Fresenius Kabi USA LLC
		10 ml	50	
		10 ml	100	American Regent
Camptosar	J9206	20 mg	2	Pfizer Inc.
		20 mg	5	
		20 mg	15	
Cancidas	J0637	5 mg	1	Merck Sharp & Dohme Corp.
Capecitabine	J8520	150 mg	60	West-Ward
	J8521	500 mg	20	Mylan Institutional
		500 mg	120	West-Ward
Carboplatin	J9045	50 mg	5	SICOR Pharmaceuticals, Inc.
		50 mg	15	
		50 mg	45	
		50 mg	60	
Carimune Nf	J1566	500 mg	1	Csl Behring Ag
Carnitor	J1955	1 gm	5	Sigma-Tau Pharmaceuticals
Cathflo Activase	J2997	1 mg	1	Genentech, Inc.
Cbi HepaGam B 1 ml	J1571	0.5 ml	1	Cangene Biopharma Inc

Drug Name	HCPCS	Dose	Pkg Size	Labeler Name
Cbi HepaGam B 5 ml		0.5 ml	5	
Cefazolin Sodium	J0690	500 mg	1	West-Ward Pharmaceuticals Corp
		500 mg	10	Sandoz, Inc.
		500 mg	50	Baxter Healthcare Corporation
		500 mg	100	
Cefazolin Sodium In Dextrose		500 mg	50	B. Braun Medical Inc.
Cefepime	J0692	500 mg	1	Sagent Pharmaceuticals Inc
Cefepime Hcl		500 mg	1	Sandoz, Inc.
		500 mg	50	Baxter Healthcare Corporation
		500 mg	100	
Cefepime Hcl In Dextrose		500 mg	1	B. Braun Medical Inc.
Cefoxitin Sodium	J0694	1 gm	1	West-Ward Pharmaceuticals Corp
		1 gm	10	
Ceftazidime	J0713	500 mg	1	B. Braun Medical Inc.
Ceftriaxone	J0696	250 mg	1	West-Ward Pharmaceuticals Corp
		250 mg	1	Sandoz, Inc.
Ceftriaxone In D5W		250 mg	1	B. Braun Medical Inc.
		250 mg	50	Baxter Healthcare Corporation
Ceftriaxone Sodium		250 mg	1	Sagent Pharmaceuticals Inc
Cefuroxime Sodium	J0697	750 mg	1	West-Ward Pharmaceuticals Corp
Celestone Soluspan	J0702	3 mg & 3 mg	5	Schering Corporation
CellCept	J7517	250 mg	100	Genentech, Inc.
		250 mg	175	
		250 mg	500	
Ceprotin	J2724	10 units	1	Baxalta Us Inc.
Cerezyme	J1786	10 units	1	Genzyme Corporation
ChiRhoStim	J2850	1 mcg	1	Chirhoclin, Inc.
Chloramphenicol Sod Succinate	J0720	1 gm	1	Fresenius Kabi USA LLC
Chlorothiazide Sodium	J1205	500 mg	1	Akorn
Chlorpromazine Hcl	J3230	50 mg	1	West-Ward Pharmaceuticals Corp
		50 mg	2	
Choline C 11	A9515	Per Study Dose	30	Zevacor Molecular
Cholografin Meglumine	Q9961	1 ml	20	Bracco Diagnostics
Chorionic Gonadotropin	J0725	1000 units	1	Fresenius Kabi USA LLC
Cidofovir	J0740	375 mg	5	Heritage Pharmaceuticals, Inc.

Drug Name	HCPCS	Dose	Pkg Size	Labeler Name
Cimzia	J0717	1 mg	1	UCB, Inc.
Cinryze	J0598	10 units	1	Shire Viropharma, Inc.
Ciprofloxacin	J0744	200 mg	20	Hospira, Inc
		200 mg	100	
		200 mg	200	
Cisplatin	J9060	10 mg	50	SICOR Pharmaceuticals, Inc.
		10 mg	100	
		10 mg	200	Wg Critical Care
Cladribine	J9065	1 mg	10	Mylan Institutional
Cleviprex	C9248	1 mg	50	The Medicines Company
		1 mg	100	Chiesi USA, Inc.
Clofarabine	J9027	1 mg	20	Fresenius Kabi USA, LLC
Clolar		1 mg	20	Sanofi-Aventis
Clonidine Hydrochloride	J0735	1 mg	10	West-Ward Pharmaceuticals Corp
Clonidine Hydrochloride Injection		1 mg	10	
Cogentin	J0515	1 mg	2	
Colistimethate Sodium	J0770	Up to 150 mg	1	Perrigo Pharmaceuticals
Coly-Mycin M Parenteral		Up to 150 mg	1	Par Sterile Products LLC
Conray	Q9961	1 ml	30	Liebel Flarsheim
		1 ml	50	
		1 ml	100	
		1 ml	150	
Conray 30	Q9958	1 ml	150	
Conray 43	Q9960	1 ml	50	
		1 ml	250	
Corifact	J7180	1 iu	1	Csl Behring Gmbh
Cortrosyn	J0834	0.25 mg	1	Amphastar Pharmaceuticals, Inc.
Corvert	J1742	1 mg	10	Pfizer Inc.
Cosmegen	J9120	0.5 mg	1	Recordati Rare Diseases
Cosyntropin	J0834	0.25 mg	1	Sandoz, Inc.
Cosyntropin (Cortrosyn Generic)		0.25 mg	1	Mylan Institutional
Cosyntropin Novaplus (Cortrosyn Generic)		0.25 mg	1	
CroFab Powder For Solution	J0840	Up to 1 gm	1	Btg International
Cromolyn Sodium	J7631	10 mg	2	Ivax Pharmaceuticals, Inc.
Cubicin	J0878	1 mg	1	Cubist Pharmaceuticals
Cyanocobalamin	J3420	1000 mcg	1	West-Ward Pharmaceuticals Corp
		1000 mcg	10	

Drug Name	HCPCS	Dose	Pkg Size	Labeler Name
		1000 mcg	30	
Cyclophosphamide	J8530	25 mg	100	Roxane Laboratories
	J9070	100 mg	50	Sandoz, Inc.
		100 mg	75	
		100 mg	100	
Cyclosporine	J7502	100 mg	30	Ivax Pharmaceuticals, Inc.
		100 mg	50	
	J7515	25 mg	30	
	J7516	250 mg	5	Perrigo Pharmaceuticals
Cyclosporine Modified	J7502	100 mg	30	Teva Pharmaceuticals USA, Inc.
	J7515	25 mg	30	
Cymetra	Q4112	1 CC	2	LifeCell Corporation
Cyramza	J9308	5 mg	10	Eli Lilly And Company
		5 mg	50	
Cysto-Conray Ii	Q9958	1 ml	250	Liebel Flarsheim
Cystografin		1 ml	100	Bracco Diagnostics
		1 ml	300	
Cystografin-Dilute		1 ml	300	
Cytarabine	J9100	100 mg	1	Fresenius Kabi USA LLC
		100 mg	5	Mylan Institutional
		100 mg	20	Hospira, Inc
		100 mg	25	
		100 mg	50	Pfizer Inc.
CytoGam	J0850	Per vial	50	Csl Behring Ag
Cytovene	J1570	500 mg	1	Genentech, Inc.
D.H.E. 45	J1110	1 mg	1	Valeant Pharmaceuticals International
Dacarbazine	J9130	100 mg	1	SICOR Pharmaceuticals, Inc.
Dacogen	J0894	1 mg	1	Otsuka America Pharmaceutical, Inc.
Dalvance	J0875	5 mg	1	Durata Pharmaceuticals
Daptomycin	J0878	1 mg	1	Hospira
Darzalex	J9145	10 mg	5	Janssen Biotech, Inc.
		10 mg	20	
Daunorubicin Hcl	J9150	10 mg	1	SICOR Pharmaceuticals, Inc.
		10 mg	4	
DDAVP	J2597	1 mcg	1	Ferring Pharmaceuticals Inc.
		1 mcg	10	
Decitabine	J0894	1 mg	1	Sandoz, Inc.
Deferoxamine Mesylate	J0895	500 mg	1	Hospira, Inc

Drug Name	HCPCS	Dose	Pkg Size	Labeler Name
Definity	Q9957	1 ml	2	Lantheus Medical Imaging, Inc.
Delestrogen	J1380	10 mg	5	Par Sterile Products LLC
Demerol	J2175	100 mg	0.5	Hospira, Inc
		100 mg	1	
		100 mg	1.5	
		100 mg	2	
		100 mg	20	
		100 mg	30	
DepoCyt	J9098	10 mg	5	Sigma-Tau Pharmaceuticals
Depo-Estradiol	J1000	5 mg	5	Pfizer Inc.
Depo-Medrol	J1020	20 mg	5	
	J1030	40 mg	1	
		40 mg	5	
		40 mg	10	
	J1040	80 mg	1	
		80 mg	5	
Depo-Provera	J1050	1 mg	2.5	
Depo-Testosterone	J1071	1 mg	1	
		1 mg	10	
Dermagraft	Q4106	1 cm2	1	Organogenesis, Inc.
Desferal	J0895	500 mg	1	Novartis Pharmaceuticals Corporation
		500 mg	4	
Desmopressin Acetate	J2597	1 mcg	1	Ferring Pharmaceuticals Inc.
		1 mcg	10	
Dexamethasone	J8540	0.25 mg	28	A-S Medication Solutions
		0.25 mg	237	Morton Grove Pharm.
Dexamethasone Sodium Phosphate	J1100	1 mg	1	Pfizer Inc.
		1 mg	5	
		1 mg	10	Mylan Institutional
		1 mg	30	
Dexrazoxane	J1190	250 mg	1	
Dextrose	J7060	500 ml	250	B. Braun Medical Inc.
		500 ml	500	
		500 ml	1000	
	J7070	1000 CC	250	
		1000 CC	500	
		1000 CC	1000	
Dextrose 5%	J7060	500 ml	250	Hospira, Inc
Dextrose-NaCl	J7042	500 ml	500	B. Braun Medical Inc.

Drug Name	HCPCS	Dose	Pkg Size	Labeler Name
		500 ml	1000	
Diazepam	J3360	5 mg	2	Hospira, Inc
		5 mg	10	
Diflucan	J1450	200 mg	100	West-Ward Pharmaceuticals Corp
DigiFab	J1162	Per vial	1	Btg International
Digoxin	J1160	0.5 mg	2	West-Ward Pharmaceuticals Corp
Dihydroergotamine Mesylate	J1110	1 mg	1	Perrigo Pharmaceuticals
Dilaudid (Pfsyr)	J1170	4 mg	0.5	Fresenius Kabi USA, LLC
		4 mg	1	
Dimenhydrinate	J1240	50 mg	1	Fresenius Kabi USA LLC
Diphenhydramine Hcl	J1200	50 mg	1	Hospira, Inc
	Q0163	50 mg	6	A-S Medication Solutions
		50 mg	10	
		50 mg	15	
		50 mg	20	
		50 mg	24	
		50 mg	30	
Diprivan	J2704	10 mg	10	Fresenius Kabi USA LLC
		10 mg	20	
		10 mg	50	
		10 mg	100	
Dipyridamole	J1245	10 mg	10	West-Ward Pharmaceuticals Corp
Diuril Iv	J1205	500 mg	1	Oak
Dobutamine Hcl	J1250	250 mg	20	Hospira, Inc
		250 mg	40	
		250 mg	250	Baxter Healthcare Corporation
Docefrez	J9171	1 mg	1	Sun Pharmaceutical Global Fze.
Docetaxel		1 mg	1	Hospira, Inc.
		1 mg	2	Pfizer Inc.
		1 mg	4	Hospira, Inc.
		1 mg	7	Sagent Pharmaceuticals Inc
		1 mg	8	Pfizer Inc.
		1 mg	10	X-Gen Pharmaceuticals
		1 mg	16	Hospira, Inc
		1 mg	20	Pfizer Inc.
Dopamine	J1265	40 mg	10	Hospira, Inc
Dopamine 200Mg/5 ml		40 mg	5	
Dopamine Hcl 200Mgin 5% Dextrose LifeCare 250 ml		40 mg	250	

Drug Name	HCPCS	Dose	Pkg Size	Labeler Name
Dopamine Hcl 400Mgin 5% Dextrose LifeCare 250 ml		40 mg	250	
Dopamine Hcl 400Mgin 5% Dextrose LifeCare 500 ml		40 mg	500	
Dopamine Hcl 800Mgin 5% Dextrose LifeCare 250 ml		40 mg	250	
Dopamine In D5W		40 mg	250	Baxter Healthcare Corporation
		40 mg	500	
Doribax	J1267	10 mg	1	Shionogi Inc
Dotarem	A9575	0.1 ml	10	Guerbet LLC
		0.1 ml	15	
		0.1 ml	20	
		0.1 ml	100	
Doxercalciferol	J1270	1 mcg	2	Akorn
Doxil	Q2050	10 mg	10	Janssen Products, Lp
		10 mg	25	
Doxorubicin Hcl	J9000	10 mg	1	Pfizer Inc.
		10 mg	5	
		10 mg	10	
		10 mg	25	
		10 mg	75	
		10 mg	100	
Doxorubicin Hcl (Lyo)		10 mg	1	Mylan Institutional
Doxorubicin Hcl, Liposomal,	Q2050	10 mg	10	Dr.Reddy's Laboratories
		10 mg	25	
Dronabinol	Q0167	2.5 mg	1	Mylan Pharmaceuticals, Inc
		2.5 mg	30	American Health Packaging
		2.5 mg	60	Mylan Pharmaceuticals, Inc
Duraclon	J0735	1 mg	10	Mylan Institutional
Duramorph	J2274	10 mg	10	West-Ward Pharmaceuticals Corp
Dysport	J0586	5 unit	1	Ipsen Biopharmaceuticals, Inc
		5 units	1	Galderma Laboratories, L.P.
Elaprase	J1743	1 mg	3	Shire Us, Inc.
Elelyso	J3060	10 units	1	Pfizer Inc.
Eligard	J9217	7.5 mg	1	Tolmar
Elitek	J2783	0.5 mg	1	Sanofi-Aventis
		0.5 mg	7.5	
Ellence	J9178	2 mg	25	Pfizer Inc.
		2 mg	100	
Eloctate	J7205	1 iu	1	Biogen
Eloxatin	J9263	0.5 mg	10	Sanofi-Aventis

Drug Name	HCPCS	Dose	Pkg Size	Labeler Name
		0.5 mg	20	
Emend	**J8501**	5 mg	1	Merck Sharp & Dohme Corp.
Emend Bi-Pack		5 mg	1	
Emend For Injection 150Mg	**J1453**	1 mg	1	Merck Sharp & Dohme
Emend Tri-Fold	**J8501**	5 mg	1	Merck Sharp & Dohme Corp.
Empliciti	**J9176**	1 mg	1	Bristol-Myers Squibb Company
Enoxaparin Sodium	**J1650**	10 mg	0.3	Amphastar Pharmaceuticals, Inc.
		10 mg	0.4	
		10 mg	0.6	
		10 mg	0.8	
		10 mg	1	
		10 mg	3	Sandoz, Inc.
Entyvio	**J3380**	1 mg	1	Takeda Pharmaceuticals America, Inc.
Envarsus XR	**J7503**	0.25 mg	30	Veloxis Pharmaceuticals
		0.25 mg	100	
Eovist	**A9581**	1 ml	15	Bayer Healthcare Pharmaceuticals Inc.
Epicord	**Q4131**	1 cm2	6	Mimedx Group, Inc.
		1 cm2	15	
Epifix		1 cm2	10.1	
Epifix Amniotic Membrane Allograft		1 cm2	1	
		1 sq cm	2	
		1 cm2	4	
		1 sq cm	6	
		1 sq cm	9.5	
		1 sq cm	16	
		1 sq cm	16.9	
		1 sq cm	49	
Epinephrine Hcl	**J0171**	0.1 mg	1	Hospira, Inc
		0.1 mg	10	A-S Medication Solutions
		0.1 mg	30	Par Sterile Products LLC
Epirubicin	**J9178**	2 mg	25	Impax Generics
		2 mg	100	
Epogen	**J0885**	1000 units	1	Amgen USA, Inc.
		1000 units	2	
	Q4081	100 units	1	
		100 units	2	
Epoprostenol	**J1325**	0.5 mg	1	SICOR Pharmaceuticals, Inc.

Drug Name	HCPCS	Dose	Pkg Size	Labeler Name
Epoprostenol (Veletri)		0.5 mg	1	Actelion Pharmaceuticals U.S, Inc
Eraxis	J0348	1 mg	1	Pfizer Inc.
Erbitux	J9055	10 mg	50	Eli Lilly And Company
		10 mg	100	
Erwinase	J9019	1,000 iu	1	Jazz Pharmaceuticals, Inc.
Erythromycin	J1364	500 mg	10	Hospira, Inc
Erythromycin Lactobionate		500 mg	1	
Estradiol Valerate	J1380	10 mg	5	Perrigo Pharmaceuticals
Ethanolamine Oleate	J1430	100 mg	2	QoL Medical
Ethyol	J0207	500 mg	1	Cumberland Pharmaceuticals Inc
Etopophos	J9181	10 mg	1	Bristol-Myers Squibb Company
Etoposide	J8560	50 mg	20	Mylan Pharmaceuticals, Inc
	J9181	10 mg	5	SICOR Pharmaceuticals, Inc.
		10 mg	25	
		10 mg	50	
Euflexxa	J7323	per dose	2	Ferring Pharmaceuticals Inc.
Evomela	J9245	50 mg	1	Spectrum Pharmaceuticals
Exondys 51	C9484	10 mg	2	Sarepta Therapeutics
Exondys 51 10 ml		10 mg	10	
Eylea	J0178	1 mg	0.05	Regeneron Pharmaceuticals, Inc.
Fabrazyme	J0180	1 mg	1	Genzyme Corporation
Faslodex	J9395	25 mg	5	AstraZeneca Pharmaceuticals Lp
Feiba Nf	J7198	1 iu	1	Baxter Healthcare Corporation
Fentanyl Citrate	J3010	0.1 mg	2	Hospira, Inc
		0.1 mg	5	
		0.1 mg	10	
		0.1 mg	20	
		0.1 mg	50	
Feraheme	Q0138	1 mg	1	Amag Pharmaceuticals
	Q0139	1 mg	1	
Ferrlecit	J2916	12.5 mg	5	Sanofi-Aventis
Firmagon	J9155	1 mg	1	Ferring Pharmaceuticals Inc.
Flebogamma 10% Dif	J1572	500 mg	50	Grifols USA, LLC.
		500 mg	100	
		500 mg	200	
Flebogamma Dif		500 mg	50	
		500 mg	100	
		500 mg	200	

Drug Name	HCPCS	Dose	Pkg Size	Labeler Name
		500 mg	400	
Flexbumin	**P9046**	20 ml	50	Baxter
		20 ml	100	
	P9047	50 ml	50	
		50 ml	100	
Flolan	**J1325**	0.5 mg	1	GlaxoSmithKline
Flo-Pred	**J7510**	5 mg	52	Taro Pharmaceuticals
Floxuridine	**J9200**	500 mg	1	Fresenius Kabi USA LLC
Fluconazole In Dextrose	**J1450**	200 mg	100	West-Ward Pharmaceuticals Corp
		200 mg	200	
Fluconazole In Sodium Chloride		200 mg	100	
		200 mg	200	
Fluconazole Injection		200 mg	100	Pfizer Inc.
		200 mg	200	
Fludarabine Phosphate	**J9185**	50 mg	1	SICOR Pharmaceuticals, Inc.
		50 mg	2	Sagent Pharmaceutical
Fluocinolone Acetonide Implant (Retisert)	**J7311**	0.59 mg	1	Bausch & Lomb
Fluorouracil	**J9190**	500 mg	10	Pfizer Inc.
		500 mg	20	
		500 mg	50	
		500 mg	100	
Fluphenazine Decanoate	**J2680**	25 mg	5	West-Ward Pharmaceutical Corp.
Fluvirin 2016/2017	**Q2037**	0.5 ml	5	Seqirus
Fluvirin 2017/2018		0.5 ml	5	
Folotyn	**J9307**	1 mg	1	Spectrum Pharmaceuticals
		1 mg	2	
Fondaparinux Sodium	**J1652**	0.5 mg	0.4	Dr. Reddy's Laboratories, Inc.
		0.5 mg	0.5	
		0.5 mg	0.6	
		0.5 mg	0.8	
Fortaz	**J0713**	500 mg	1	Teligent
Fortaz (Add-V)		500 mg	1	
Fortaz (Frozen)		500 mg	50	
Fortaz Add-V)		500 mg	1	
Fragmin	**J1645**	2500 iu	0.2	Pfizer Inc.
		2500 iu	0.3	
		2500 iu	0.5	
		2500 iu	0.6	

Drug Name	HCPCS	Dose	Pkg Size	Labeler Name
		2500 iu	0.72	
		2500 iu	1	
Furosemide	**J1940**	20 mg	2	Heritage Pharmaceuticals, Inc.
		20 mg	4	Hospira, Inc
		20 mg	10	
Gablofen	**J0475**	10 mg	20	Mallinckrodt
	J0476	50 mcg	1	
Gadavist	**A9585**	0.1 ml	2	Bayer Healthcare Pharmaceuticals Inc.
		0.1 ml	7.5	
		0.1 ml	10	
		0.1 ml	15	
		0.1 ml	30	
		0.1 ml	65	
Gadoxetate Disodium	**A9581**	1 ml	10	
GamaSTAN S/D	**J1460**	1 CC	2	Grifols USA, LLC.
		1 CC	10	
	J1560	10 CC	2	
		10 CC	10	
Gammagard Liquid	**J1569**	500 mg	10	Baxalta Us Inc.
		500 mg	25	
		500 mg	50	
		500 mg	100	
		500 mg	200	
		500 mg	300	
Gammagard S/D	**J1566**	500 mg	1	Baxter Healthcare Corporation
Gammagraft	**Q4111**	1 cm2	2.25	Promethean Lifesciences, Inc.
		1 cm2	7.5	
		1 cm2	18	
		1 cm2	56	
Gammaked	**J1561**	500 mg	10	Kedrion Biopharma, Inc.
		500 mg	50	
		500 mg	100	
		500 mg	200	
Gammaplex	**J1557**	500 mg	100	Bio Products Laboratory
		500 mg	200	
Gamunex-C	**J1561**	500 mg	10	Grifols USA, LLC.
		500 mg	25	
		500 mg	50	
		500 mg	100	
		500 mg	200	
		500 mg	400	

Drug Name	HCPCS	Dose	Pkg Size	Labeler Name
Ganciclovir	**J1570**	500 mg	1	Par Pharmaceutical
Gastrografin	**Q9963**	1 ml	30	Bracco Diagnostics
		1 ml	120	
Gazyva	**J9301**	10 mg	40	Genentech, Inc.
Gel-One	**J7326**	PER DOSE	3	Zimmer Biomet, Inc. (Supplied By Seikagaku Corp.)
Gemcitabine	**J9201**	200 mg	1	Hospira, Inc
		200 mg	5.26	
		200 mg	26.3	
		200 mg	52.6	
Gemcitabine Hcl		200 mg	1	Heritage Pharmaceuticals, Inc.
Gemcitabine Hydrochloride		200 mg	1	
Gemzar		200 mg	1	Eli Lilly And Company
Gengraf	**J7502**	100 mg	30	Abbvie Us, LLC
		100 mg	50	
	J7515	25 mg	30	Abbvie
Gentamicin Sulfate	**J1580**	80 mg	2	Hospira, Inc
		80 mg	20	Fresenius Kabi USA LLC
		80 mg	50	Baxter Healthcare Corporation
		80 mg	100	
Genvisc 850	**J7320**	1 mg	2.5	Orthogenrx Inc.
Geodon	**J3486**	10 mg	1	Pfizer Inc.
Glassia	**J0257**	10 mg	1	Baxalta Us Inc.
GlucaGen	**J1610**	1 mg	1	Bedford Laboratories
GlucaGen Diagnostic Kit		1 mg	1	Boehringer Ingelheim
GlucaGen HypoKit		1 mg	1	Novo Nordisk® Inc.
GlucaGen(R)		1 mg	1	Boehringer Ingelheim
Glucagon Emergency		1 mg	1	Eli Lilly And Company
Glucagon Hydrochloride		1 mg	1	Novo Nordisk® Inc.
Glucagon Hydrochloride Kit		1 mg	1	Fresenius Kabi USA LLC
Grafix Core	**Q4132**	1 cm2	1	Osiris Therapeutics
Grafix Prime	**Q4133**	1 cm2	1	
Graftjacket Std	**Q4107**	1 cm2	1	Kinetic Concepts Incorporated
Graftjacket Xpress	**Q4113**	1 CC	1	
Granisetron Hcl	**J1626**	100 mcg	1	West-Ward Pharmaceuticals Corp
		100 mcg	4	
	Q0166	1 mg	1	Teva Pharmaceuticals USA, Inc.
		1 mg	20	Taro Pharmaceuticals
Granix	**J1447**	1 mcg	0.5	Cephalon Inc.
		1 mcg	0.8	

Drug Name	HCPCS	Dose	Pkg Size	Labeler Name
H.P. Acthar	**J0800**	40 units	5	Mallinckrodt
Halaven	**J9179**	0.1 mg	2	Eisai Inc.
Haldol	**J1630**	5 mg	1	Janssen Pharmaceuticals, Inc.
Haldol Decanoate	**J1631**	50 mg	1	
Haloperidol Decanoate		50 mg	1	Patriot Pharmaceuticals, LLC
		50 mg	5	Amneal Pharmaceuticals, LLC
Haloperidol Lactate	**J1630**	5 mg	1	West-Ward
		5 mg	10	
Hectorol	**J1270**	1 mcg	1	Genzyme Corporation
		1 mcg	2	
Helixate Fs	**J7192**	1 iu	1	Csl Behring
Helixate Fs 3000		1 iu	1	
Hemofil M	**J7190**	1 iu	1	Baxalta Us Inc.
Heparin (Porcine) In D5W	**J1644**	1000 units	250	B. Braun Medical Inc.
		1000 units	500	
Heparin (Porcine) In NaCl		1000 units	250	Hospira, Inc
		1000 units	500	B. Braun Medical Inc.
		1000 units	1000	Baxter Healthcare Corporation
Heparin (Porcine) Lock Flush	**J1642**	10 units	1	Medefil, Inc.
		10 units	3	
		10 units	5	
Heparin Lock Flush		10 units	2	Becton Dickinson & Co.
		10 units	3	
		10 units	5	
		10 units	6	
Heparin Sodium	**J1644**	1000 units	1	Hospira, Inc
Heparin Sodium (Porcine)		1000 units	0.5	
		1000 units	1	Pfizer Inc.
		1000 units	2	
		1000 units	4	Sagent Pharmaceuticals Inc
		1000 units	5	Fresenius Kabi USA LLC
		1000 units	10	Pfizer Inc.
		1000 units	30	
Heparin Sodium Flush	**J1642**	10 units	5	Becton Dickinson & Co.
Heparin Sodium In NaCl	**J1644**	1000 units	1000	Hospira, Inc
Herceptin	**J9355**	10 mg	1	Genentech, Inc.
Hexabrix 320	**Q9967**	1 ml	20	Liebel Flarsheim
		1 ml	50	
		1 ml	100	
		1 ml	200	
Hexabrix 320 mg/ ml, 100 ml Volume		1 ml	100	Guerbet LLC

Drug Name	HCPCS	Dose	Pkg Size	Labeler Name
Hexabrix 320 mg/ ml, 200 ml Volume		1 ml	200	
Hexabrix 320 mg/ ml, 50 ml Volume		1 ml	50	
Hizentra	J1559	100 mg	5	Csl Behring Ag
		100 mg	10	
		100 mg	20	
		100 mg	50	
Humalog	J1815	5 units	3	Eli Lilly And Company
		5 units	10	
	J1817	50 units	3	
		50 units	10	
Humalog Mix 50/50	J1815	5 units	10	
Human Albumin Grifols	P9047	50 ml	50	Grifols
		50 ml	100	
Humate-P Low Diluent	J7187	1 iu	1	Csl Behring Gmbh
Humulin N	J1815	5 units	3	Eli Lilly And Company
		5 units	10	A-S Medication Solutions
	J1817	50 units	10	
Humulin R	J1815	5 units	3	Eli Lilly And Company
		5 units	10	
	J1817	50 units	3	
		50 units	10	
		50 units	20	
Humulin R U-500	J1815	5 units	20	
Hyalgan	J7321	per dose	2	Fidia Pharma USA Inc
Hycamtin	J9351	0.1 mg	1	Novartis Pharmaceuticals Corporation
Hycamtin, Oral	J8705	0.25 mg	1	
Hydralazine Hcl	J0360	20 mg	1	Akorn
Hydromorphone	J1170	4 mg	1	
		4 mg	5	
		4 mg	50	
Hydromorphone Hcl		4 mg	0.5	Hospira, Inc
		4 mg	1	
		4 mg	2	Purdue Pharma Lp
		4 mg	5	Hospira, Inc
		4 mg	20	West-Ward Pharmaceuticals Corp
		4 mg	50	Hospira, Inc
Hydromorphone Hydrochloride		4 mg	1	
		4 mg	5	SICOR Pharmaceuticals, Inc.

Drug Name	HCPCS	Dose	Pkg Size	Labeler Name
		4 mg	50	
Hydroxyzine Hcl	**J3410**	25 mg	1	American Regent
		25 mg	2	
		25 mg	10	
Hylenex	**J3473**	1 USP unit	1	Halozyme Therapeutics, Inc.
HyperRHO S/D	**J2788**	50 mcg	1	Grifols USA, LLC.
	J2790	300 mcg (1500 iu)	1	
Hypertet S/D	**J1670**	250 units	1	
Hyqvia	**J1575**	100 mg	25	Baxalta Us Inc.
		100 mg	50	
		100 mg	100	
		100 mg	200	
		100 mg	300	
Illogic	**J9325**	1 million PFU	1	Amgen USA, Inc.
Ibandronate Sodium	**J1740**	1 mg	3	Sagent Pharmaceuticals Inc
Ibutilide Fumarate	**J1742**	1 mg	10	Mylan Institutional
Idamycin PFS	**J9211**	5 mg	5	Pfizer Inc.
		5 mg	10	
		5 mg	20	
Idarubicin		5 mg	5	SICOR Pharmaceuticals, Inc.
		5 mg	10	
		5 mg	20	
Ifex	**J9208**	1 gm	1	Baxter Healthcare Corporation
Ifosfamide		1 gm	1	Pfizer Inc.
		1 gm	20	Mylan Institutional
		1 gm	60	Pfizer Inc.
Ilaris	**J0638**	1 mg	150	Novartis Pharmaceuticals Corp.
		1 mg	180	Novartis Pharmaceuticals Corporation
Iluvien	**J7313**	0.01 mg	1	Alimera Sciences, Inc.
Imfinzi	**C9492**	10 mg	2.4	AstraZeneca Pharmaceuticals, Lp
		10 mg	10	
Imipenem And Cilastatin	**J0743**	250 mg	1	Hospira, Inc
INFeD	**J1750**	50 mg	2	Watson Pharmaceuticals
Inflectra	**Q5102**	10 mg	1	Pfizer
Infumorph 200	**J2274**	10 mg	20	West-Ward Pharmaceuticals Corp
Infumorph 500		10 mg	20	
Injectafer	**J1439**	1mg	15	American Regent
Intron-A	**J9214**	1 MIL units	1	Schering Corporation

Drug Name	HCPCS	Dose	Pkg Size	Labeler Name
		1 MIL units	2.5	
		1 MIL units	3	
Invanz	**J1335**	500 mg	1	Merck Sharp & Dohme Corp.
Invega Sustenna	**J2426**	1 mg	0.25	Janssen Pharmaceuticals, Inc.
		1 mg	0.5	
		1 mg	0.75	
		1 mg	1	
		1 mg	1.5	
Ipratropium Bromide	**J7644**	1 mg	2.5	Mylan Pharmaceuticals, Inc
Irinotecan Hcl	**J9206**	20 mg	2	West-Ward Pharmaceuticals Corp
		20 mg	5	
		20 mg	25	Hospira, Inc
Isovue-200	**Q9966**	1 ml	50	Bracco Diagnostics
		1 ml	200	
Isovue-250		1 ml	50	
		1 ml	100	
		1 ml	150	
Isovue-250 Multipack		1 ml	200	
Isovue-300	**Q9967**	1 ml	30	
		1 ml	50	
		1 ml	75	
		1 ml	100	
		1 ml	150	
		1 ml	200	
		1 ml	500	
Isovue-300 Multi Pack		1 ml	200	
		1 ml	500	
Isovue-370		1 ml	50	
		1 ml	75	
		1 ml	100	
		1 ml	125	
		1 ml	150	
		1 ml	200	
		1 ml	500	
Isovue-370 Multi Pack		1 ml	200	
		1 ml	500	
Isovue-M-200	**Q9966**	1 ml	10	
		1 ml	20	
Isovue-M-300	**Q9967**	1 ml	15	
Istodax (Romidepsin)	**J9315**	1 mg	1	Celgene Corporation
Ixabepilone	**J9207**	1 mg	1	R-Pharm Us

Drug Name	HCPCS	Dose	Pkg Size	Labeler Name
Ixempra Kit		1 mg	1	
Jetrea	**J7316**	0.125 mg	0.2	Thrombogenics, Inc.
Jevtana	**J9043**	1 mg	1	Sanofi-Aventis
Kadcyla	**J9354**	1 mg	1	Genentech, Inc.
Kalbitor®	**J1290**	1 mg	1	Dyax Corp.
Kcentra	**C9132**	1 iu	1	Csl Behring Gmbh
Kedbumin	**P9046**	20 ml	50	Kedrion Biopharma
	P9047	50 ml	50	
Kenalog	**J3301**	10 mg	1	Bristol-Myers Squibb Company
		10 mg	5	
		10 mg	10	
Kenalog-40		10 mg	5	A-S Medication Solutions
		10 mg	10	
Kengreal	**C9460**	1 mg	1	The Medicines Company
Kepivance	**J2425**	50 mcg	1	Sobi
Kepivance/Palifermin		50 mcg	1	
Ketorolac Tromethamine	**J1885**	15 mg	1	Hospira, Inc
		15 mg	2	
Keytruda	**J9271**	1 mg	4	Merck Sharp & Dohme Corp.
		1mg	50	
Kitabis Pak	**J7682**	300 mg	5	Pari Respiratory Equipment
Koate-DVI	**J7190**	1 iu	1	Kedrion Biopharma, Inc.
Kogenate Fs	**J7192**	1 iu	1	Bayer Healthcare Pharmaceuticals Inc.
Kogenate Fs 3000 Bio-Set		1 iu	1	
Kogenate Fs Bio-Set		1 iu	1	
Kogenate Fs Fixed Poly Bio-Set		1 iu	1	
Krystexxa	**J2507**	1 mg	1	Crealta
Kyprolis	**J9047**	1 mg	1	Amgen USA, Inc.
Lactated Ringers	**J7120**	1000 CC	250	B. Braun Medical Inc.
		1000 CC	500	
		1000 CC	1000	
		1000 CC	3000	
Lanoxin	**J1160**	0.5 mg	1	Covis Pharmaceuticals
Lanoxin Inj		0.5 mg	1	
Lartruvo	**C9485**	10 mg	19	Eli Lilly And Company
		10 mg	50	
Lemtrada	**J0202**	1 mg	1.2	Genzyme Corporation
Leucovorin Calcium	**J0640**	50 mg	1	West-Ward
Leukine (Lyo Pwd)	**J2820**	50 mcg	1	Sanofi-Aventis

Drug Name	HCPCS	Dose	Pkg Size	Labeler Name
Leuprolide Acetate	J9218	1 mg	2.8	Sandoz, Inc.
Leuprolide Acetate Inj		1 mg	1	Sun Pharmaceutical Global Inc.
Levalbuterol	J7612	0.5 mg	0.5	Teva Pharmaceuticals USA, Inc.
	J7614	0.5 mg	3	
Levalbuterol Inhalation Solution Concentrated	J7612	0.5 mg	0.5	Mylan Pharmaceuticals, Inc
Levaquin	J1956	250 mg	50	Sandoz, Inc.
		250 mg	100	
		250 mg	150	
Levetiracetam	J1953	10 mg	5	West-Ward Pharmaceuticals Corp
		10 mg	100	Mylan Institutional
Levetiracetam (Keppra)		10 mg	5	UCB, Inc.
Levofloxacin	J1956	250 mg	20	Akorn
		250 mg	30	
		250 mg	50	West-Ward Pharmaceuticals Corp
		250 mg	100	
		250 mg	150	
Levoleucovorin Calcium	J0641	0.5 mg	1	West-Ward Pharmaceutical Corp.
		0.5 mg	17.5	Sandoz, Inc.
Levsin Injection .5Mg/ ml	J1980	0.25 mg	5	Meda Pharmaceuticals
Levulan Kerastick	J7308	354 mg	1	Dusa Pharmaceuticals
Lidocaine In D5W	J2001	10 mg	250	B. Braun Medical Inc.
		10 mg	500	
Lincocin	J2010	300 mg	2	Pfizer Inc.
		300 mg	10	
Linezolid	J2020	200 mg	300	Hospira, Inc
Lioresal	J0475	10 mg	10	Saol Therapeutics
		10 mg	20	
		10 mg	40	
	J0476	50 mcg	1	
Lorazepam	J2060	2 mg	1	Hospira, Inc
		2 mg	10	
Lovenox	J1650	10 mg	0.3	Sanofi-Aventis
		10 mg	0.4	
		10 mg	0.6	
		10 mg	0.8	
		10 mg	1	
		10 mg	3	

Drug Name	HCPCS	Dose	Pkg Size	Labeler Name
Lucentis	J2778	0.1 mg	0.05	Genentech, Inc.
Lumason	Q9950	1 ml	5	Bracco Diagnostics
Lumizyme	J0221	10 mg	1	Genzyme Corporation
Lupron Depot 3.75Mg	J1950	3.75 mg	1	Abbvie Us, LLC
Lupron Depot 3-Month, 11.25Mg		3.75 mg	1	
Lupron Depot 4-Month, 30Mg	J9217	7.5 mg	1	
Lupron Depot 6-Month, 45Mg		7.5 mg	1	
Lupron Depot 7.5 mg Kit		7.5 mg	1	
Lupron Depot-3 Month 22.5Mg Kit		7.5 mg	1	
Lupron Depot-Ped 11.25Mg	J1950	3.75 mg	1	
Lupron Depot-Ped 15Mg	J9217	7.5 mg	1	
Lupron Depot-Ped 3-Month, 11.25Mg	J1950	3.75 mg	1	
Lupron Depot-Ped 3-Month, 30 mg		3.75 mg	1	
Lupron Depot-Ped 7.5Mg	J9217	7.5 mg	1	
Macugen	J2503	0.3 mg	0.09	Eyetech, Inc.
Magnesium Sulfate	J3475	500 mg	2	Fresenius Kabi USA LLC
		500 mg	10	Hospira, Inc
		500 mg	20	
		500 mg	50	Fresenius Kabi USA LLC
		500 mg	100	Fresenius Kabi USA
		500 mg	500	
		500 mg	1000	
Magnesium Sulfate In 5% Dextrose		500 mg	100	Wg Critical Care
Magnevist 46.9%	A9579	1 ml	5	Bayer Healthcare Pharmaceuticals Inc.
		1 ml	10	
		1 ml	15	
		1 ml	20	
		1 ml	50	
		1 ml	100	
Mannitol	J2150	50 ml	50	Hospira, Inc
Marinol	Q0167	2.5 mg	60	Abbvie Us, LLC
		2.5 mg	100	American Health Packaging
Maxipime	J0692	500 mg	1	Hospira, Inc
Md Gastroview	Q9963	1 ml	30	Liebel Flarsheim
Md-76R		1 ml	50	

Drug Name	HCPCS	Dose	Pkg Size	Labeler Name
		1 ml	100	
		1 ml	200	
Medrol	J7509	4 mg	25	Pfizer Inc.
		4 mg	50	
		4 mg	100	
Medrol (Pak)		4 mg	21	
Melphalan	J9245	50 mg	1	Sagent Pharmaceuticals, Inc.
Meperidine Hcl	J2175	100 mg	1	West-Ward Pharmaceuticals Corp
		100 mg	30	Hospira, Inc
Meropenem	J2185	100 mg	1	B. Braun Medical Inc.
Merrem		100 mg	1	AstraZeneca Pharmaceuticals Lp
Mesna	J9209	200 mg	10	SICOR Pharmaceuticals, Inc.
Mesnex		200 mg	10	Baxter Healthcare Corporation
Metastron	A9600	PER MILLICURIE	4	Ge Healthcare
Methadone Hcl	J1230	10 mg	20	Mylan Institutional
Methocarbamol	J2800	10 ml	10	
Methotrexate	J8610	2.5 mg	20	
		2.5 mg	36	Roxane Laboratories
		2.5 mg	100	
	J9250	5 mg	2	Hospira, Inc
	J9260	50 mg	2	
Methotrexate Powder 1Gm In 50 ml Sd Vial (P.F.)	J9250	5 mg	1	Fresenius Kabi USA LLC
	J9260	50 mg	1	
Methotrexate Sodium	J9250	5 mg	1	
		5 mg	2	SICOR Pharmaceuticals, Inc.
		5 mg	4	Mylan Institutional
		5 mg	8	Pfizer Inc.
		5 mg	10	
		5 mg	40	SICOR Pharmaceuticals, Inc.
	J9260	50 mg	1	Fresenius Kabi USA LLC
		50 mg	2	SICOR Pharmaceuticals, Inc.
		50 mg	4	Mylan Institutional
		50 mg	8	Pfizer Inc.
		50 mg	10	
		50 mg	40	SICOR Pharmaceuticals, Inc.
Methylergonovine Maleate	J2210	0.2 mg	1	American Regent
Methylprednisolone	J7509	4 mg	21	A-S Medication Solutions
		4 mg	25	Greenstone

Drug Name	HCPCS	Dose	Pkg Size	Labeler Name
		4 mg	50	
		4 mg	100	Sandoz, Inc.
Methylprednisolone (Pak)		4 mg	21	
Methylprednisolone Acetate	J1040	80 mg	1	SICOR Pharmaceuticals, Inc.
		80 mg	5	
Methylprednisolone Acetate USP	J1020	20 mg	1	
	J1030	40 mg	1	
		40 mg	5	
		40 mg	10	
Methylprednisolone Sodium Succ	J2920	40 mg	1	Sagent Pharmaceuticals, Inc.
		40 mg	3	Fresenius Kabi USA LLC
	J2930	125 mg	1	Sagent Pharmaceuticals, Inc.
Metoclopramide Hcl	J2765	10 mg	2	Hospira, Inc
Miacalcin	J0630	400 units	2	Novartis Pharmaceuticals Corporation
Micafungin Sodium (Mycamine)	J2248	1 mg	1	Astellas Pharma Us, Inc.
MICRhoGAM	J2788	50 mcg (250 iu)	1	Kedrion Biopharma, Inc.
MICRhoGAM Uf Plus		50 mcg (250 iu)	1	
Midazolam Hcl	J2250	1 mg	1	Hospira, Inc
		1 mg	2	
		1 mg	5	
		1 mg	10	
Milrinone In Dextrose	J2260	5 mg	100	Baxter Healthcare Corporation
		5 mg	200	
Milrinone Lactate		5 mg	10	Hospira, Inc
		5 mg	20	
		5 mg	50	
Mircera	J0887	1 mcg	0.3	Vifor (International) Ltd.
	J0888	1 mcg	0.3	
Mitomycin	J9280	5 mg	1	Accord Healthcare Inc.
Mitoxantrone Hydrochloride	J9293	5 mg	10	SICOR Pharmaceuticals, Inc.
		5 mg	12.5	
		5 mg	15	
Monoclate-P	J7190	1 iu	1	Csl Behring
Mononine	J7193	1 iu	1	
Monovisc	J7327	per dose	1	DePuy Synthes Sales, Inc.
Morphine Sulfate	J2270	10 mg	1	Hospira, Inc
		10 mg	10	

Drug Name	HCPCS	Dose	Pkg Size	Labeler Name
		10 mg	20	
		10 mg	30	
		10 mg	50	
	J2274	10 mg	10	
	J2270	10 mg	30	
Moxifloxacin Hcl	J2280	100 mg	250	Fresenius Kabi USA LLC
Mozobil (Plerixafor)	J2562	1 mg	1.2	Sanofi-Aventis
MultiHance	A9577	1 ml	5	Bracco Diagnostics
		1 ml	10	
		1 ml	15	
		1 ml	20	
MultiHance 5X15 ml Syringe		1 ml	15	
MultiHance Multipack	A9578	1 ml	50	
		1 ml	100	
Mustargen	J9230	10 mg	1	Recordati Rare Diseases
Mycophenolate Mofetil	J7517	250 mg	1	Teva Pharmaceuticals USA, Inc.
		250 mg	100	Strides Pharma Inc.
		250 mg	225	Ascend Laboratories
		250 mg	500	
Mycophenolic Acid	J7518	180 mg	30	American Health Packaging
		180 mg	120	Mylan Pharmaceuticals, Inc
Mycophenolic Acid Dr		180 mg	30	American Health Packaging
		180 mg	100	Mylan Institutional
Myfortic		180 mg	120	Novartis Pharmaceuticals Corporation
Myleran	J8510	2 mg	1	Aspen
Myobloc	J0587	100 units	0.5	Solstice Neurosciences, LLC
		100 units	1	
		100 units	2	
Naglazyme	J1458	1 mg	1	Biomarin Pharmaceutical, Inc.
Nalbuphine Hcl	J2300	10 mg	1	Hospira, Inc
		10 mg	10	
Naloxone Hcl	J2310	1 mg	1	
		1 mg	10	
Naropin	J2795	1 mg	10	Fresenius Kabi USA LLC
		1 mg	20	
		1 mg	30	
		1 mg	100	
		1 mg	200	
		1 mg	20	
		1 mg	30	

Drug Name	HCPCS	Dose	Pkg Size	Labeler Name
Navelbine	J9390	10 mg	1	Pierre Fabre Pharmaceuticals
		10 mg	5	
NebuPent	J2545	300 mg	1	Fresenius Kabi USA LLC
Nembutal	J2515	50 mg	20	Oak
		50 mg	50	
Neoral	J7502	100 mg	30	Novartis Pharmaceuticals Corporation
		100 mg	50	
	J7515	25 mg	30	
Nesacaine	J2400	30 ml	30	Fresenius Kabi USA LLC
Nesacaine-Mpf		30 ml	20	
Netspot	A9587	0.1 mCi	1	Advanced Accelerator Applications
Neulasta	J2505	6 mg	0.6	Amgen USA, Inc.
Neulasta Delivery Kit		6 mg	0.6	
Neumega	J2355	5 mg	1	Pfizer Inc.
Neupogen	J1442	1 mcg	0.5	Amgen USA, Inc.
		1 mcg	0.8	
		1 mcg	1	
		1 mcg	1.6	
Nipent	J9268	10 mg	1	Hospira, Inc
Nova HepaGam B 1 ml	J1571	0.5 ml	1	Cangene Biopharma Inc
Nova HepaGam B 5 ml		0.5 ml	5	
Novaplus Aminophylline	J0280	250 mg	10	Hospira, Inc
Novaplus Fluconazole	J1450	200 mg	200	
Novaplus Zosyn	J2543	1.125 gm	50	Pfizer Inc.
		1.125 gm	100	
Novaplus® Omniscan	A9579	1 ml	10	Ge Healthcare
		1 ml	15	
		1 ml	20	
Novarel	J0725	1000 units	1	Ferring Pharmaceuticals Inc.
Novoeight	J7182	1 iu	1	Novo Nordisk® Inc.
Novolin 70/30	J1815	5 units	10	
	J1817	50 units	10	
Novolin N	J1815	5 units	10	
	J1817	50 units	10	
Novolin R	J1815	5 units	10	
	J1817	50 units	10	
NovoLog	J1815	5 units	10	
	J1817	50 units	10	
NovoLog FlexPen	J1815	5 units	3	
	J1817	50 units	3	

Drug Name	HCPCS	Dose	Pkg Size	Labeler Name
NovoLog Mix 70/30	**J1815**	5 units	10	
	J1817	50 units	10	
NovoLog Mix 70/30 FlexPen	**J1815**	5 units	3	
	J1817	50 units	3	
NovoLog PenFill	**J1815**	5 units	3	
	J1817	50 units	3	
NovoSeven Rt	**J7189**	1 mcg	1	
Nplate	**J2796**	10 mcg	1	Amgen USA, Inc.
Nulojix	**J0485**	1 mg	1	Bristol-Myers Squibb Company
Oasis Wound Matrix	**Q4102**	1 cm2	1	Cook (Smith & Nephew, Inc.)
Ocrevus	**C9494**	1 mg	10	Genentech
Octagam	**J1568**	500 mg	20	Octapharma USA
		500 mg	50	
		500 mg	100	
		500 mg	200	
		500 mg	500	
Octreotide Acetate	**J2354**	25 mcg	1	SICOR Pharmaceuticals, Inc.
		25 mcg	5	
Omidria (Phenylephrine + Ketorolac Irrigation)	**C9447**	4 ml	4	Omeros
Omnipaque	**Q9966**	1 ml	50	Ge Healthcare
	Q9967	1 ml	50	
		1 ml	100	
		1 ml	150	
		1 ml	500	
Omnipaque 140	**Q9965**	1 ml	50	
Omnipaque 180		1 ml	10	
		1 ml	20	
Omnipaque 240	**Q9966**	1 ml	10	
		1 ml	20	
		1 ml	50	
		1 ml	100	
		1 ml	150	
		1 ml	200	
Omnipaque 300	**Q9967**	1 ml	10	
		1 ml	30	
		1 ml	50	
		1 ml	75	
		1 ml	100	
		1 ml	125	
		1 ml	150	

Drug Name	HCPCS	Dose	Pkg Size	Labeler Name
		1 ml	200	
		1 ml	500	
Omnipaque 350		1 ml	50	
		1 ml	75	
		1 ml	100	
		1 ml	125	
		1 ml	150	
		1 ml	200	
		1 ml	500	
Omniscan	**A9579**	1 ml	5	
		1 ml	10	
		1 ml	15	
		1 ml	20	
		1 ml	100	
Oncaspar	**J9266**	1 EA	5	Baxalta Incorporated
Ondansetron	**Q0162**	1 mg	1	Mylan Pharmaceuticals, Inc
		1 mg	10	Glenmark Pharmaceuticals, USA
		1 mg	30	
		1 mg	50	Northstar Rx LLC
Ondansetron Hcl	**J2405**	1 mg	2	Hospira, Inc
		1 mg	20	West-Ward Pharmaceutical Corp.
	Q0162	1 mg	1	Teva Pharmaceuticals USA, Inc.
Ondansetron Odt		1 mg	1	Mylan Pharmaceuticals, Inc
		1 mg	10	American Health Packaging
		1 mg	30	
Onivyde 43Mg/10 ml Per Vial	**J9205**	1 mg	10	Merrimack Pharmaceuticals
Opana	**J2410**	1 mg	1	Endo Pharmaceuticals Inc
Opdivo	**J9299**	1 mg	4	Bristol-Myers Squibb Company
		1 mg	10	
OptiMARK	**A9579**	1 ml	5	Liebel Flarsheim
		1 ml	10	
		1 ml	15	
		1 ml	20	
		1 ml	30	
		1 ml	50	
Optiray 240	**Q9966**	1 ml	50	
		1 ml	100	
		1 ml	125	

Drug Name	HCPCS	Dose	Pkg Size	Labeler Name
		1 ml	200	
Optiray 300	Q9967	1 ml	50	
		1 ml	100	
		1 ml	150	
		1 ml	200	
		1 ml	500	
Optiray 320		1 ml	20	
		1 ml	30	
		1 ml	50	
		1 ml	75	
		1 ml	100	
		1 ml	125	
		1 ml	150	
		1 ml	200	
		1 ml	500	
Optiray 350		1 ml	50	
		1 ml	75	
		1 ml	100	
		1 ml	125	
		1 ml	150	
		1 ml	200	
		1 ml	500	
Optison	Q9956	1 ml	3	Ge Healthcare
Orbactiv	J2407	10 mg	1	The Medicines Company
Orencia	J0129	10 mg	1	Bristol-Myers Squibb Company
		10 mg	0.4	
		10 mg	0.7	
Orencia Clickject		10 mg	1	Bristol-Myers Squibb Co.
Orphenadrine Citrate	J2360	60 mg	2	Watson Pharmaceuticals
Orphenadrine Citrate Injection		60 mg	2	Akorn
Orthovisc	J7324	per dose	2	DePuy Synthes Sales, Inc.
Oxacillin	J2700	250 mg	1	Sagent Pharmaceuticals Inc
Oxacillin Sodium		250 mg	1	Sandoz, Inc.
Oxaliplatin	J9263	0.5 mg	1	Pfizer Inc.
		0.5 mg	10	
		0.5 mg	20	
Oxilan 300	Q9967	1 ml	50	Guerbet LLC
		1 ml	100	
		1 ml	150	
		1 ml	500	

Drug Name	HCPCS	Dose	Pkg Size	Labeler Name
Oxilan 350		1 ml	50	Mallinckrodt
		1 ml	100	Liebel Flarsheim
		1 ml	125	
		1 ml	150	Guerbet LLC
		1 ml	200	
Ozurdex	J7312	0.1 mg	0.7	Allergan Sales, LLC
Paclitaxel	J9267	1 mg	5	Mylan Institutional
		1 mg	16.7	
		1 mg	25	SICOR Pharmaceuticals, Inc.
		1 mg	50	Mylan Institutional
Pamidronate Disodium	J2430	30 mg	1	Sagent Pharmaceuticals Inc
		30 mg	10	Mylan Institutional
Panhematin	J1640	1 mg	1	Recordati Rare Diseases
Panitumumab	J9303	10 mg	5	Amgen USA, Inc.
		10 mg	20	
Paricalcitol	J2501	1 mcg	1	West-Ward Pharmaceuticals Corp
		1 mcg	2	
Penicillin G Pot In Dextrose	J2540	600000 units	50	Baxter Healthcare Corporation
Penicillin G Potassium		600000 units	1	Sandoz, Inc.
Penicillin G Procaine	J2510	Up to 600000 units	1	Pfizer Inc.
		Up to 600000 units	2	
Pentobarbital	J2515	50 mg	20	Sagent Pharmaceutical
Perforomist	J7606	20 mcg	2	Mylan Specialty, L.P.
Perjeta	J9306	1 mg	14	Genentech, Inc.
Pfizerpen-G	J2540	600000 units	1	Pfizer Inc.
Phenergan	J2550	50 mg	1	West-Ward Pharmaceuticals Corp
Phenobarbital Sodium	J2560	120 mg	1	
Phenytoin	J1165	50 mg	2	X-Gen Pharmaceuticals, Inc.
		50 mg	5	
Phenytoin Sodium		50 mg	2	West-Ward Pharmaceuticals Corp
		50 mg	5	
Piperacillin And Tazobactam	J2543	1.125 gm	1	Hospira, Inc
Piperacillin Sodium/ Tazo		1.125 gm	1	
Piperacillin Sodium/ Tazo (Add-Vantage)		1.125 gm	1	
Piperacillin Sodium-Tazobactam Sodium		1.125 gm	1	Pfizer Inc.
		1.125 gm	50	

Drug Name	HCPCS	Dose	Pkg Size	Labeler Name
		1.125 gm	100	
Plasbumin-25	**P9046**	20 ml	20	Talecris
		20 ml	50	
		20 ml	100	
	P9047	50 ml	20	
		50 ml	50	
		50 ml	100	
Plasbumin-5	**P9041**	50 ml	50	
		50 ml	250	
	P9045	250 ml	50	
		250 ml	250	
Polocaine	**J0670**	10 ml	50	Fresenius Kabi USA LLC
Polocaine-Mpf		10 ml	20	
		10 ml	30	
Portrazza	**J9295**	1 mg	50	Eli Lilly And Company
Potassium Chloride	**J3480**	2 MEQ	5	Hospira, Inc
		2 MEQ	10	
		2 MEQ	20	
		2 MEQ	30	Fresenius Kabi USA LLC
		2 MEQ	50	Baxter Healthcare Corporation
		2 MEQ	100	
		2 MEQ	250	B. Braun Medical Inc.
		2 MEQ	1000	
Potassium Chloride/Dextrose		2 MEQ	1000	Baxter Healthcare Corporation
Potassium Chloride/Sodium Chloride		2 MEQ	1000	
Prednisolone	**J7510**	5 mg	60	A-S Medication Solutions
		5 mg	120	Hi-Tech
		5 mg	240	
		5 mg	480	
Prednisone	**J7512**	1 mg	6	A-S Medication Solutions
		1 mg	8	
		1 mg	10	
		1 mg	12	
		1 mg	14	
		1 mg	15	
		1 mg	18	
		1 mg	20	
		1 mg	21	
		1 mg	30	
		1 mg	40	
		1 mg	48	

Drug Name	HCPCS	Dose	Pkg Size	Labeler Name
		1 mg	50	
		1 mg	60	
		1 mg	100	Roxane Laboratories
		1 mg	120	
		1 mg	500	
		1 mg	1000	
Prednisone (Pak)		1 mg	21	A-S Medication Solutions
Prednisone Intensol		1 mg	30	Roxane Laboratories
Premarin	J1410	25 mg	1	Pfizer Inc.
Premierpro Rx Cefoxitin Sodium	J0694	1 gm	1	Fresenius Kabi USA LLC
Prialt	J2278	1 mcg	1	Jazz Pharmaceuticals, Inc.
		1 mcg	5	
		1 mcg	20	
Primaxin Iv	J0743	250 mg	1	Merck Sharp & Dohme Corp.
Privigen	J1459	500 mg	50	Csl Behring Ag
		500 mg	110	
		500 mg	200	
		500 mg	400	
Probuphine System Kit	J0570	74.2 mg	1	Braeburn Pharmaceuticals
Procainamide Hcl	J2690	1 gm	2	Hospira, Inc
		1 gm	10	
Prochlorperazine Edisylate	J0780	10 mg	2	West-Ward Pharmaceutical Corp.
Prochlorperazine Maleate	Q0164	5 mg	6	A-S Medication Solutions
		5 mg	10	
		5 mg	30	
		5 mg	100	Teva Pharmaceuticals USA, Inc.
Procrit	J0885	1000 units	1	Janssen Products, Lp
		1000 units	2	
	Q4081	100 units	1	
		100 units	2	
Profilnine® Sd Fix Sd M2V(1000)	J7194	1 iu	1	Grifols USA, LLC.
Profilnine® Sd Fix Sd M2V(1500)		1 iu	1	
Profilnine® Sd Fix Sd M2V(500)		1 iu	1	
Progesterone	J2675	50 mg	10	West-Ward Pharmaceuticals Corp
Prograf	J7507	1 mg	100	Astellas Pharma Us, Inc.
	J7525	5 mg	1	

Drug Name	HCPCS	Dose	Pkg Size	Labeler Name
ProHance	A9579	1 ml	5	Bracco Diagnostics
		1 ml	10	
		1 ml	15	
		1 ml	20	
ProHance Multipack	A9576	1 ml	50	
ProHance Prefilled Syringes	A9579	1 ml	10	
		1 ml	17	
Prolastin-C	J0256	10 mg	1	Grifols USA, LLC.
Prolia	J0897	1 mg	1	Amgen USA, Inc.
Promethazine	J2550	50 mg	1	West-Ward Pharmaceuticals Corp
Promethazine Hcl		50 mg	1	
	Q0169	12.5 mg	5	A-S Medication Solutions
		12.5 mg	8	
		12.5 mg	10	
		12.5 mg	12	
		12.5 mg	20	
		12.5 mg	30	
		12.5 mg	60	
		12.5 mg	100	Sandoz, Inc.
		12.5 mg	120	A-S Medication Solutions
		12.5 mg	473	Hi-Tech
		12.5 mg	1000	Sandoz, Inc.
Propofol	J2704	10 mg	20	Hospira, Inc
		10 mg	50	
		10 mg	100	
Propranolol	J1800	1 mg	1	West-Ward Pharmaceuticals Corp
Propranolol Hcl		1 mg	1	Fresenius Kabi USA LLC
Protamine Sulfate	J2720	10 mg	5	
		10 mg	25	
Provenge®	Q2043	Per infusion (minimum 50 million cells)	250	Dendreon
Provocholine	J7674	1 mg	1	Methapharm Inc
Pulmicort	J7626	Up to 0.50 mg	2	AstraZeneca Pharmaceuticals Lp
Pulmozyme	J7639	1 mg	2.5	Genentech, Inc.
Pyridoxine Hcl	J3415	100 mg	1	Fresenius Kabi USA LLC
Quadramet	A9604	Up to 150 millicuries	3	Lantheus Medical Imaging, Inc.
Qutenza	J7336	1 cm2	1	Acorda Therapeutics
Radicava	C9493	1 mg	100	Mt Pharma America, Inc.

Drug Name	HCPCS	Dose	Pkg Size	Labeler Name
Ranitidine	J2780	25 mg	2	Zydus Pharmaceuticals USA Inc
		25 mg	6	Teligent
Rapamune	J7520	1 mg	60	Pfizer Inc.
		1 mg	100	
Reclast	J3489	1 mg	100	Novartis Pharmaceuticals Corporation
Recombinate	J7192	1 iu	1	Baxalta Us Inc.
Regadenoson	J2785	0.1 mg	5	Astellas Pharma Us, Inc.
Remicade	J1745	10 mg	1	Janssen Biotech, Inc.
Remodulin	J3285	1 mg	20	united Therapeutics
ReoPro	J0130	10 mg	5	Eli Lilly And Company
Retrovir	J3485	10 mg	20	GlaxoSmithKline
Rheumatrex	J8610	2.5 mg	8	Par Pharmaceutical
		2.5 mg	12	
		2.5 mg	16	
		2.5 mg	20	
		2.5 mg	24	
RhoGAM Ultra-Filtered Plus	J2790	300 mcg (1500 iu)	1	Kedrion Biopharma, Inc.
Rhophylac	J2791	100 units	2	Csl Behring Ag
Rimso-50	J1212	50 ml	50	Mylan Institutional
Risperdal Consta	J2794	0.5 mg	1	Janssen Pharmaceuticals, Inc.
Rituxan	J9310	100 mg	10	Genentech, Inc.
		100 mg	50	
Rixubis	J7200	1 iu	1	Baxalta Us Inc.
Robaxin	J2800	10 ml	10	West-Ward Pharmaceuticals Corp
Ropivacaine	J2795	1 mg	10	Hospira, Inc
		1 mg	20	
		1 mg	30	Sandoz, Inc.
Ropivacaine Hydrochloride		1 mg	10	Hospira, Inc
		1 mg	20	
		1 mg	30	
Ruconest	J0596	10 units	1	Santarus Pharmaceuticals, Inc.
Sandimmune	J7502	100 mg	30	Novartis Pharmaceuticals Corporation
		100 mg	50	
	J7515	25 mg	30	
	J7516	250 mg	5	
Sandostatin	J2354	25 mcg	1	
		25 mcg	5	
Sandostatin Lar Depot	J2353	1 mg	1	

Drug Name	HCPCS	Dose	Pkg Size	Labeler Name
Simponi Aria	J1602	1 mg	4	Janssen Biotech, Inc.
Simulect	J0480	20 mg	1	Novartis Pharmaceuticals Corporation
Sincalide Inj	J2805	5 mcg	1	Bracco Diagnostics
Sinografin	Q9963	1 ml	10	
Sirolimus	J7520	1 mg	30	American Health Packaging
		1 mg	100	Dr. Reddy's Laboratories, Inc.
Sivextro	J3090	1 mg	1	Cubist Pharmaceuticals
Sodium Chloride	J7030	1000 ml	250	B. Braun Medical Inc.
		1000 ml	500	
		1000 ml	1000	
	J7040	500 ml	250	
		500 ml	500	
		500 ml	1000	
	J7050	250 ml	250	
		250 ml	500	
		250 ml	1000	
Sodium Chloride (FDA Ok'd Import)	J7030	1000 ml	250	Baxter Healthcare Corporation
		1000 ml	500	B. Braun Medical Inc.
		1000 ml	1000	Baxter Healthcare Corporation
	J7040	500 ml	250	
		500 ml	500	B. Braun Medical Inc.
		500 ml	1000	Baxter Healthcare Corporation
	J7050	250 ml	250	
		250 ml	500	
		250 ml	1000	
Sodium Ferric Gluconate	J2916	12.5 mg	5	West-Ward Pharmaceuticals Corp
Sodium Ferric Gluconate Complex In Sucrose		12.5 mg	5	Watson Pharmaceuticals
Soliris	J1300	10 mg	1	Alexion Pharmaceuticals
Solu-Cortef	J1720	100 mg	1	Pfizer Inc.
Solu-Cortef 500 mg 4 ml		100 mg	1	
Solu-Medrol	J2920	40 mg	1	
	J2930	125 mg	1	
Somatuline Depot	J1930	1 mg	0.2	Ipsen Biopharmaceuticals, Inc
		1 mg	0.3	
		1 mg	0.5	
Sotalol	C9482	1mg	10	Altathera Pharmaceuticals LLC
Spinraza	C9489	0.1 mg	5	Biogen
Stelara	J3357	1 mg	0.5	Janssen Biotech, Inc.

Drug Name	HCPCS	Dose	Pkg Size	Labeler Name
		1 mg	1	
Stelara (Iv Infusion)	Q9989	1 mg	26	
Streptomycin Sulfate	J3000	1 gm	1	X-Gen Pharmaceuticals, Inc.
Sublimaze	J3010	0.1 mg	2	Akorn
		0.1 mg	5	
		0.1 mg	20	
Supartz	J7321	per dose	2.5	Bioventus LLC
Supprelin La Implant	J9226	50 mg	1	Endo Pharmaceuticals Valera Inc.
Sustol	C9486	0.1 mg	0.4	Heron Therapeutics
Synercid	J2770	500 mg	1	Pfizer Inc.
Synvisc	J7325	1 mg	2	Genzyme Corporation
Synvisc one		1 mg	6	
Tacrolimus	J7507	1 mg	100	Novartis Pharmaceuticals Corporation
Tacrolimus, Oral		1 mg	100	Sandoz, Inc.
Talwin Lactate	J3070	30 mg	1	Hospira, Inc
Taxotere	J9171	1 mg	1	Sanofi-Aventis
		1 mg	4	
Tazicef	J0713	500 mg	1	Hospira, Inc
Tecentriq (Atezolizumab)	C9483	10mg	20	Genentech, Inc.
Teflaro	J0712	10 mg	1	Forest Laboratories
Temodar	J8700	5 mg	1	Schering Corporation
Temodar Iv	J9328	1 mg	1	
Temozolomide	J8700	5 mg	1	Teva Pharmaceuticals USA, Inc.
Temsirolimus	J9330	1 mg	1	Pfizer Inc.
Terbutaline	J3105	1 mg	1	West-Ward Pharmaceuticals Corp
Terbutaline Sulfate		1 mg	1	Fresenius Kabi USA LLC
Testosterone Cypionate	J1071	1 mg	1	Pfizer Inc.
		1 mg	10	
Testosterone Cypionate USP/Nf		1 mg	10	A-S Medication Solutions
Testosterone Enanthate	J3121	1 mg	5	West-Ward Pharmaceuticals Corp
Theophylline In D5W	J2810	40 mg	500	B. Braun Medical Inc.
Theraskin	Q4121	1 cm2	1	Skin And Wound Allograft Institute
		1 cm2	12.9	
		1 cm2	38.71	
Thiamine Hcl	J3411	100 mg	2	Fresenius Kabi USA LLC
Thrombate Iii	J7197	1 iu	1	Grifols Therapeutics, Inc.

Drug Name	HCPCS	Dose	Pkg Size	Labeler Name
Thymoglobulin	J7511	25 mg	1	Genzyme Corporation
Thyrogen	J3240	0.9 mg	1	
Tice BCG	J9031	1 EA	1	Organon USA, Inc.
Tigan	J3250	200 mg	2	Par Sterile Products LLC
		200 mg	20	
Tigecycline	J3243	1 mg	1	Pfizer Inc.
TNKase	J3101	1 mg	1	Genentech, Inc.
TOBI	J7682	300 mg	5	Novartis Pharmaceuticals Corporation
Tobramycin Inhalation		300 mg	5	Teva Pharmaceuticals USA, Inc.
Tobramycin Injection	J3260	80 mg	2	Pfizer Inc.
		80 mg	30	Mylan Institutional
Tobramycin Sulfate		80 mg	1	X-Gen Pharmaceuticals, Inc.
		80 mg	2	Hospira, Inc
		80 mg	30	Akorn
		80 mg	50	Fresenius Kabi USA LLC
Toposar	J9181	10 mg	25	SICOR Pharmaceuticals, Inc.
		10 mg	50	
Topotecan	J9351	0.1 mg	1	Pfizer Inc.
Topotecan Hcl		0.1 mg	1	Sagent Pharmaceuticals Inc
Treanda	J9033	1 mg	0.5	Cephalon Inc.
		1 mg	1	
		1 mg	2	
Trelstar	J3315	3.75 mg	1	Allergan Sales, LLC
Trexall	J8610	2.5 mg	30	Duramed Pharmaceuticals, Inc.
Triamcinolone Acetonide, Preservative Free	J3300	1 mg	1	Alcon Laboratories, Inc.
Trisenox	J9017	1 mg	10	Cephalon Inc.
Tysabri	J2323	1 mg	15	Biogen
Tyvaso	J7686	1.74 mg	2.9	united Therapeutics
Tyvaso (Refill Kit)		1.74 mg	2.9	
Tyvaso (Starter Kit)		1.74 mg	2.9	
Ultravist 240	Q9966	1 ml	100	Bayer Healthcare Pharmaceuticals Inc.
		1 ml	200	
Ultravist 300	Q9967	1 ml	50	
		1 ml	100	
		1 ml	125	
		1 ml	150	
		1 ml	200	
		1 ml	500	

Drug Name	HCPCS	Dose	Pkg Size	Labeler Name
Ultravist 370		1 ml	50	
		1 ml	100	
		1 ml	125	
		1 ml	150	
		1 ml	200	
		1 ml	250	
		1 ml	500	
Unasyn 1.5Gm	J0295	1.5 gm	1	Pfizer Inc.
Unasyn 15Gm		1.5 gm	1	
Unasyn 3Gm		1.5 gm	1	
Valstar	J9357	200 mg	5	Endo Pharmaceuticals Valera Inc.
Vancocin Hcl	J3370	500 mg	200	Baxter Healthcare Corporation
Vancomycin		500 mg	100	
		500 mg	150	
		500 mg	200	
Vancomycin Hcl		500 mg	1	Pfizer Inc.
		500 mg	100	Baxter Healthcare Corporation
		500 mg	150	
Vancomycin Hydrochloride		500 mg	1	Hospira, Inc
Vantas Implant	J9225	50 mg	1	Endo Pharmaceuticals Valera Inc.
Vaprisol	C9488	1 mg	100	Cumberland Pharmaceuticals, Inc.
Velcade	J9041	0.1 mg	1	Millennium Pharmaceuticals
Venofer	J1756	1 mg	2.5	American Regent
		1 mg	5	
		1 mg	10	
Ventavis	Q4074	Up to 20 mcg	1	Actelion Pharmaceuticals U.S, Inc
Vfend Iv	J3465	10 mg	1	Pfizer Inc.
Vibativ	J3095	10 mg	1	Astellas Pharma Us, Inc.
Vinblastine Sulfate	J9360	1 mg	10	Fresenius Kabi USA LLC
Vincristine Sulfate	J9370	1 mg	1	SICOR Pharmaceuticals, Inc.
		1 mg	2	
	J9371	1 mg	1	Spectrum Pharmaceuticals
Vinorelbine Tartrate	J9390	10 mg	1	Mylan Institutional
		10 mg	5	Pfizer Inc.
Visipaque	Q9967	1 ml	50	Ge Healthcare
		1 ml	100	
		1 ml	150	
		1 ml	200	

Drug Name	HCPCS	Dose	Pkg Size	Labeler Name
Visipaque 270	**Q9966**	1 ml	50	
		1 ml	100	
		1 ml	150	
		1 ml	200	
Visipaque 320	**Q9967**	1 ml	50	
		1 ml	100	
		1 ml	150	
		1 ml	200	
		1 ml	500	
Visudyne	**J3396**	0.1 mg	1	Valeant Pharmaceuticals International
Vitamin K1	**J3430**	1 mg	0.5	Hospira, Inc
		1 mg	1	
Vitrase	**J3471**	1 unit	1.2	Bausch & Lomb
Vivitrol	**J2315**	1 mg	1	Alkermes, Inc.
Voraxaze	**C9293**	10 units	1	Btg International
Voriconazole	**J3465**	10 mg	1	Sandoz, Inc.
Vpriv	**J3385**	100 units	1	Shire Us, Inc.
Wilate	**J7183**	1 I.U. VWF:RCO	1	Octapharma USA
WinRho Sdf	**J2792**	100 iu	1.3	Cangene Biopharma Inc
		100 iu	2.2	
		100 iu	4.4	
		100 iu	13	
Xeloda	**J8520**	150 mg	60	Genentech, Inc.
	J8521	500 mg	120	
Xeomin	**J0588**	1 unit	1	Merz Pharmaceuticals, LLC
Xgeva	**J0897**	1 mg	1	Amgen USA, Inc.
Xiaflex (Collagenase Clostridium Histolyticum)	**J0775**	0.01 mg	1	Auxilium Pharmaceuticals
Xofigo	**A9606**	1 mCi	6	Bayer Healthcare Pharmaceuticals Inc.
Xolair	**J2357**	5 mg	1	Genentech, Inc.
Xopenex	**J7612**	0.5 mg	0.5	Akorn
	J7614	0.5 mg	3	Akorn, Inc.
Xyntha	**J7185**	1 iu	1	Pfizer Inc.
Yervoy	**J9228**	1 mg	10	Bristol-Myers Squibb Company
		1 mg	40	
Yondelis	**J9352**	0.1 mg	1	Janssen Products, Lp
Zaltrap	**J9400**	1 mg	4	Sanofi-Aventis
		1 mg	8	
Zanosar	**J9320**	1 gm	1	SICOR Pharmaceuticals, Inc.

Drug Name	HCPCS	Dose	Pkg Size	Labeler Name
Zantac	J2780	25 mg	2	Teligent
		25 mg	40	
Zarxio™ (Filgrastim-Sndz)	Q5101	1 mcg	0.5	Sandoz, Inc.
		1 mcg	0.8	
Zemaira	J0256	10 mg	1	Csl Behring
Zemplar	J2501	1 mcg	1	Abbvie Us, LLC
		1 mcg	2	
Zevalin Y-90	A9543	Up to 40 millicuries	1	Spectrum Pharmaceuticals
Zinacef	J0697	750 mg	1	West-Ward Pharmaceuticals Corp
Zinacef (Frozen)		750 mg	50	Teligent
Zinecard	J1190	250 mg	1	Pfizer Inc.
Zinplava	C9490	10 mg	40	Merck Sharp & Dohme Corp.
Zithromax	J0456	500 mg	1	Pfizer Inc.
Zofran	J2405	1 mg	20	West-Ward Pharmaceuticals Corp
	Q0162	1 mg	1	Novartis Pharmaceuticals Corporation
		1 mg	50	
Zofran Odt		1 mg	1	
Zoladex	J9202	3.6 mg	1	AstraZeneca Pharmaceuticals Lp
Zoledronic Acid	J3489	1 mg	1	Sun Pharmaceutical Global Fze.
		1 mg	5	West-Ward Pharmaceuticals Corp
		1 mg	100	Heritage Pharmaceuticals, Inc.
Zometa		1 mg	5	Novartis Pharmaceuticals Corporation
		1 mg	100	
Zortress	J7527	0.25 mg	60	
Zosyn	J2543	1.125 gm	1	Pfizer Inc.
Zyprexa Relprevv	J2358	1 mg	1	Eli Lilly And Company
Zyvox	J2020	200 mg	100	Pfizer Inc.
		200 mg	300	